ANNUAL REVIEW OF
CELL AND
DEVELOPMENTAL
BIOLOGY

ANNUAL REVIEW OF CELL AND DEVELOPMENTAL BIOLOGY

VOLUME 14, 1998

JAMES A. SPUDICH, *Editor*
Stanford University School of Medicine

JOHN GERHART, *Associate Editor*
University of California, Berkeley

STEVEN L. McKNIGHT, *Associate Editor*
University of Texas

RANDY SCHEKMAN, *Associate Editor*
University of California, Berkeley

http://www.AnnualReviews.org   science@annurev.org   650-493-4400

ANNUAL REVIEWS   4139 EL CAMINO WAY   P.O. BOX 10139   PALO ALTO, CALIFORNIA 94303-0139

ANNUAL REVIEWS
Palo Alto, California, USA

International Standard Serial Number: 1081-0706
International Standard Book Number: 0-8243-3114-1

TYPESET BY TECHBOOKS, FAIRFAX, VA
PRINTED AND BOUND IN THE UNITED STATES OF AMERICA

PREFACE

Biosciences is about to undergo a revolution, which is reflected in the changing nature of reviews in this and other series from Annual Reviews. The next decade will witness an exciting integration of the basic and applied sciences. The new technologies that result from the breaking down of classical barriers between chemistry, physics, engineering, and biology will have an enormous impact on the cell and developmental biology of tomorrow.

This merging of disciplines will have a profound effect, for example, on the way we process and put to use the massive amount of information being generated by the human genome project. Currently, chip technologies with two-dimensional arrays of genetic information are being developed and used to understand expression patterns in cells under a wide variety of conditions—such studies constitute modern genomics. Cell biologists, for example, will be able to determine all the changes in gene expression as a cell enters mitosis and then proceeds through karyokinesis and cytokinesis. Biologists, engineers, physicists, and chemists, working closely together, will create even more powerful approaches to such analyses. Thus, the form that genomics takes will be influenced by new technologies developed by the integration of the basic and applied sciences, and in turn, the genomics effort will have a direct impact on biomedical research and clinical medicine in the very near future. Similarly, other research problems in cell and developmental biology will be affected by the technological innovations to come, and the next decade will be an exciting time.

One of the joys of scientific research is that during any period one feels privileged to be part of new developments that make it possible to do what could not be done before. The next decade will see an explosion of new approaches that arise from interdisciplinary efforts that in the basic and applied sciences. The links between medicine and basic research will become more obvious than ever. The young scientists among you must prepare for this adventure. The Annual Reviews series remain one of the best ways to rapidly assimilate the latest advances in basic and applied research, and I trust you will take advantage of all that the series has to offer.

JAMES A. SPUDICH
EDITOR

Annual Review of Cell and Developmental Biology
Volume 14 (1998)

CONTENTS

SOME RELATED ARTICLES IN OTHER *ANNUAL REVIEWS*

From the *Annual Review of Biochemistry*, Volume 67, 1998:

Transporters of Nucleotide Sugars, ATP, and Nucleotide Sulfate in the Endoplasmic Reticulum and Golgi Apparatus, Carlos B. Hirschberg, Phillips W. Robbins, and Claudia Abeijon

The Molecular Control of Circadian Behavioral Rhythms and Their Entrainment in Drosophila, Michael W. Young

The Caveolae Membrane System, Richard G. W. Anderson

How Cells Respond to Interferons, George R. Stark, Ian M. Kerr, Bryan R. G. Williams, Robert H. Silverman, and Robert D. Schreiber

Nucleocytoplasmic Transport: The Soluble Phase, Iain W. Mattaj and Ludwig Englmeier

Role of Small G Proteins in Yeast Cell Polarization and Wall Biosynthesis, Enrico Cabib, Jana Drgonová, and Thomás Drgon

RNA Localization in Development, Arash Bashirullah, Ramona L. Cooperstock, and Howard D. Lipshitz

The Green Fluorescent Protein, Roger Y. Tsien

Structure and Function in GroEL-Mediated Protein Folding, Paul B. Sigler, Zhaohui Xu, Hays S. Rye, Steven G. Burston, Wayne A. Fenton, and Arthur L. Horwich

Matrix Proteoglycans: From Molecular Design to Cellular Function, Renato V. Iozzo

G Protein-Coupled Receptor Kinases, Julie A. Pitcher, Neil J. Freedman, and Robert J. Lefkowitz

TGF-β Signal Transduction, J. Massagué

Pathologic Conformations of Prion Proteins, Fred E. Cohen and Stanley B. Prusiner

The AMP-Activated/SNF1 Protein Kinase Subfamily: Metabolic Sensors of the Eukaryotic Cell? D. Grahame Hardie, David Carling, and Marian Carlson

From the *Annual Review of Biophysics and Biomolecular Structure*, Volume 27, 1998:

Signaling Complexes: Biophysical Constraints on Intracellular Communication, Dennis Bray

Spatio-Temporal Resolution of Exocytosis from Individual Cells, Eric R. Travis and R. Mark Wightman

Simulation of Prokaryotic Genetic Circuits, Harley H. McAdams and Adam Arkin

Structure, Dynamics, and Function of Chromatin in Vitro, J. Widom

From the *Annual Review of Immunology*, Volume 16, 1998:

Interleukin-1 Receptor Antagonist: Role in Biology, William P. Arend, Mark Malyak, Carla J. Guthridge, and Cem Gabay

Mechanisms of MHC Class I-Restricted Antigen Processing, Eric Pamer and Peter Cresswell

JAKs and STATs: Biological Implications, Warren J. Leonard and John J. O'Shea

BCL-2 Family: Regulators of Cell Death, Debra T. Chao and Stanley J. Korsmeyer

Dimerization as a Regulatory Mechanism in Signal Transduction, Juli D. Klemm, Stuart L. Schreiber, and Gerald R. Crabtree

Divergent Roles for Fc Receptors and Complement in Vivo, Jeffrey V. Ravetch and Raphael A. Clynes

T Cell Memory, R. W. Dutton, L. M. Bradley, and S. L. Swain

Regulation of Immune Responses by TGF-β, John J. Letterio and Anita B. Roberts

The Interleukin-12/Interleukin-12-Receptor System: Role in Normal and Pathologic Immune Responses, Maurice K. Gately, Louis M. Renzetti, Jeanne Magram, Alvin S. Stern, Luciano Adorini, Ueli Gubler, and David H. Presky

The Role of Complement and Complement Receptors in Induction and Regulation of Immunity, Michael C. Carroll

From the *Annual Review of Neuroscience*, Volume 21, 1998:

Local Circuits in Primary Visual Cortex of the Macaque Monkey, Edward M. Callaway

Rab3 and Synaptotagmin: The Yin and Yang of Synaptic Membrane Fusion, Martin Geppert and Thomas C. Südhof

Adhesion Molecules and Inherited Diseases of the Human Nervous System, H. Kamiguchi, M. L. Hlavin, M. Yamasaki, and V. Lemmon

Sense and the Single Neuron: Probing the Physiology of Perception, A. J. Parker and W. T. Newsome

Signal Transduction in the Caenorhabditis Elegans *Nervous System*, Cornelia I. Bargmann and Joshua M. Kaplan

The Ephrins and EPH Receptors in Neural Development, John G. Flanagan and Pierre Vanderhaeghen

Gene Discovery in Drosophila: *New Insights for Learning and Memory*, Josh Dubnau and Tim Tully

From the *Annual Review of Pharmacology and Toxicology*, Volume 38, 1998:

The Mammalian Carboxylesterases: From Molecules to Functions, Tetsuo Satoh and Masakiyo Hosokawa

The Role of Receptor Kinases and Arrestins in G Protein-Coupled Receptor Regulation, Jason G. Krupnick and Jeffrey L. Benovic

Insights from In Vivo Modification of Adrenergic Receptor Gene Expression, Daniel K. Rohrer and Brian K. Kobilka

From the *Annual Review of Plant Physiology and Plant Molecular Biology*, Volume 49, 1998:

Themes in Plant Development, Ian Sussex

Genetic Analysis of Ovule Development, C. S. Gasser, J. Broadhvest, and B. A. Hauser

Protein Targeting to the Thylakoid Membrane, Danny J. Schnell

Elaboration of Body Plan and Phase Change During Development of Acetabularia: How is the Complex Architecture of a Giant Unicell Built? Dina F. Mandoli

Abscisic Acid Signal Transduction, Jeffrey Leung and Jérôme Giraudat

Genetic Control of Flowering Time in Arabidopsis, Maarten Koornneef, Carlos Alonso-Blanco, Anton J. M. Peeters, and Wim Soppe

Brassinosteroids: Essential Regulators of Plant Growth and Development, Steven D. Clouse and Jenneth M. Sasse

Nuclear Control of Plastid and Mitochondrial Development in Higher Plants, P. Leon, A. Arroyo, and S. Mackenzie

For the convenience of readers, a detachable order form/envelope is bound into the back of this volume.

Annu. Rev. Cell Dev. Biol. 1998. 14:1–17

SYSTEMIN: A Polypeptide Signal for Plant Defensive Genes

Clarence A. Ryan and Gregory Pearce

Institute of Biological Chemistry, Washington State University, Pullman, Washington 99164-6340

KEY WORDS: systemic response, herbivore attacks, signal transduction, jasmonic acid

ABSTRACT

Damage to leaves of several plant species by herbivores or by other mechanical wounding induces defense gene activation throughout the plants within hours. An 18-amino acid polypeptide, called systemin, has been isolated from tomato leaves that is a powerful inducer of over 15 defensive genes when supplied to the tomato plants at levels of fmol/plant. Systemin is readily transported from wound sites and is considered to be the primary systemic signal. The polypeptide is processed from a 200-amino acid precursor called prosystemin, analogous to polypeptide hormones in animals. However, the plant prohormone does not possess typical dibasic cleavage sites, nor does it contain a signal sequence or any typical membrane-spanning regions. The signal transduction pathway that mediates systemin signaling involves linolenic acid release from membranes and subsequent conversion to jasmonic acid, a potent activator of defense gene transcription. The pathway exhibits analogies to arachidonic acid/prostaglandin signaling in animals that leads to inflammatory and acute phase responses.

CONTENTS

1

INTRODUCTION

Prior to 1991, polypeptide signals had not been reported as regulators of plant genes or as any other physiological or biochemical process in plants. Plants had been thought to have evolved signals that were unique and unrelated to the signaling molecules of higher animals. Over the past 60 years, five classical plant hormones have been identified and characterized: auxins, gibberellins, ethylene, abscisic acid, and cytokinins (Kende & Zeevart 1997). These small organic compounds regulate growth and developmental processes of plants and are still the center of much of the research in these areas of plant biology. The differences in structures of plant hormones from those of animal hormones had led to the assumption that plants probably evolved an array of regulatory molecules that were totally different from those of animals.

SYSTEMIN

Isolation

The purification of a polypeptide wound signal that regulates proteinase inhibitor synthesis in tomato leaves (Pearce et al 1991) was the culmination of several years of investigation (Ryan 1992). In 1972 it was discovered that tomato and potato plants accumulate a serine proteinase inhibitor protein, called inhibitor I (Inh I), in leaves when wounded by attacking insects (Green & Ryan 1972). Inh I protein was found to accumulate in wounded leaves but also in unwounded leaves that were many centimeters away from wound sites. The inhibitor is a member of the potato Inh I family of proteinase inhibitors and is one of several proteinase inhibitor families now known to exist in plants (Ryan 1990). The inhibitors are defensive proteins that interfere with protein digestion of attacking pests (Ryan 1990, Boulter 1993). Subsequently, a member of the serine proteinase inhibitor II family (Inh II) was found to accumulate in response to wounding along with Inh I (Ryan 1974).

The isolation of the inducing factor was facilitated by the development of a relatively simple assay using young tomato plants. Supplying a few microliters of tomato leaf juice to excised 14-day-old tomato plants through their cut stems for 30 min caused the leaves to accumulate proteinase inhibitor proteins over the next 24 to 48 h (Ryan 1974). This assay indicated that the inducing factor was in the soluble extracts of the leaves and was reasonably stable. Over the next several years the assay was employed to purify several hundred nanograms of the factor from tomato leaves (Pearce et al 1991). The pure substance was found to be an 18-amino acid polypeptide with the sequence AVQSKPPSKRDPPKMQTD. The polypeptide, called systemin, was active at concentrations of fmol/plant when supplied to young excised tomato plants through their cut stems, which ranks it among the most powerful plant gene-activating compounds known. Synthetic systemin was found to be as fully active as the native polypeptide.

Characterization

The polypeptide is highly charged, but has two Pro-Pro motifs that are part of a palindrome, xxQxBPPxBBxPPBxQxx, where B is either Lys or Arg (Pearce et al 1991). An investigation of the structure-activity relationship of systemin was conducted using Ala replacements, as well as sequential deletion of amino acids from the N and C termini (Pearce et al 1993). Substitution of each amino acid of systemin individually with Ala revealed that amino acids at most positions could be replaced with little or moderate change in activity. However, substitution of Pro13 with Ala reduced inducing activity to less than 0.2%, and the change from Thr17 to Ala17 resulted in a totally inactive systemin. This latter analogue was shown to be a powerful antagonist of systemin. Synthetic analogues of systemin with deletions of amino acids from the N terminus exhibit progressively decreased proteinase inhibitor-inducing activities, indicating that the entire 18 amino acids are necessary for full activity. Deletion of the N-terminal Ala reduced activity by 300-fold. Further deletions caused increasing loss of activity, but the tetrapeptide (Met15-Gln16-Thr17-Asp18) retained activity that was about 3×10^5 less than that of systemin (Pearce et al 1993). Deletion of the C-terminal Asp18 from systemin (desAsp-systemin) totally eliminated activity and was an antagonist of systemin in bioassays, but not as effective an antagonist as the Ala17-substituted systemin (Pearce et al 1993). The results of the substitution-deletion experiments indicate that residues near the C terminus of systemin are necessary for activity, possibly involving a phosphorylation at Thr17, and that the N-terminal region of systemin may be important for interacting with a receptor.

A structural study of the systemin polypeptide using proton NMR at both 500 and 600 Mhz in either 90% H_2O/10% D_2O or 99% D_2O, buffered at near neutrality, provided no evidence for persistant common secondary or tertiary structural elements (Russell et al 1992). This study did detect two distinct unassigned molecular conformations at the C terminus. However, NMR measurements at low pH (3.2) allowed the assignment of almost all protons of systemin (Slosarek et al 1995), revealing a Z-like β-sheet structure, similar to many DNA-binding proteins. These structures were suggested to have relevance to the biological function of systemin at neutral pH in binding DNA or a receptor. In a study of systemin structure using circular dichroism in aqueous buffer (Toumadje & Johnson 1995), the four Pro residues of systemin that are present internally as two pairs gave a spectrum with a shape and intensity characteristic of a poly (L-proline) II type, 3_1 structure. Whether this is important to activity is not known, but in Ala substitution experiments (Pearce et al 1993), a substitution of Pro13 with Ala severely decreased systemin activity, suggesting that Pro13 has an important function, perhaps in its secondary or tertiary structure. On the other hand, sequential replacement of Pro6, Pro7, and Pro12 with Ala had only moderate effects on the biological activity of systemin, which indicates that the Pro-Pro motifs may not be important for function.

Transport

Movement of systemin from leaf wounds to distal locations in plants was investigated using autoradiographic and biochemical techniques. Whole-leaf autoradiographic analyses (Narvaez-Vasquez et al 1995) showed that when [14C]systemin was placed on fresh wounds, it was distributed throughout the wounded leaf within 30 min, then transported to the petiole, and finally into the upper leaves within 1 to 2 h of application. Throughout the experiments, intact [14C]systemin could be identified by C18 HPLC in phloem exudates collected from cut stems. The movement of [14C]systemin from wounds was comparable to that of [14C]sucrose, which is phloem-mobile. Light microscopy coupled with autoradiographic techniques (Narvaez-Vasquez et al 1995) demonstrated that within 15 min of application of [3H]systemin to wounds on terminal leaflets, the label was found primarily in the xylem and phloem tissues of leaf veins. Within the next 90 min the label was found in the petiole and main stem, again primarily in the phloem. The data suggest that systemin moves from the wound sites to the vascular system via the apoplasm and xylem, then to the phloem, and finally is transported by the phloem to target cells throughout the plant.

An inhibitor of apoplastic phloem loading in plants, p-chloromercuribenzene sulfonic acid (PCMBS), was shown to be a powerful inhibitor of wound- and systemin-induced activation of proteinase inhibitors in tomato leaves (Narvaez-Vasquez et al 1994). Supplying PCMBS to fresh wounds on leaves of young tomato plants just before, during, or just after supplying [14C]systemin directly to the wounds blocked transport of [14C]systemin out of the leaf and inhibited Inh I and Inh II accumulation in distal leaves. The inhibition could be reversed by the simultaneous application of cysteine, dithiothreitol, or glutathione. The cumulative evidence supports the hypothesis that transport of systemin involves apoplastic phloem loading and subsequent transport.

PROSYSTEMIN

cDNA: Gene and Protein

By screening a primary cDNA library using an oligonucleotide probe corresponding to an amino acid sequence in systemin, a partial cDNA was isolated (McGurl et al 1992), and the gene was subsequently isolated and characterized (McGurl & Ryan 1992). The cDNA and gene structures reveal that systemin is processed from the C-terminal region of a 200-amino acid precursor called prosystemin. The gene coding for prosystemin is composed of 11 exons containing five repeated regions that are a result of several gene duplication-elongation events (McGurl & Ryan 1992). These five imperfect repeats are easily identified in the prosystemin protein. However, systemin is not present in the repeats but is processed from the C-terminal region of prosystemin (residues 179–196) that is not duplicated. The prosystemin protein contains a high percentage of charged amino acids, including 10% aspartic acid, 17% glutamic acid, and 15% lysine. The high percentage of lysine and glutamic acid residues, frequently alternating, is similar to the KEKE motif first identified in a 20S proteosome (Realini et al 1994a) and later in many other proteins (Realini et al 1994b) that is thought to promote protein-protein interactions. No sequences were present at the N terminus or within the prosystemin protein that could be identified as a leader or transit peptide or membrane-spanning domain, implying that synthesis of the protein takes place in the cytoplasm (McGurl & Ryan 1992). There was no indication of processing sites similar to those found in most animal polypeptide hormone precursors, suggesting that the processing sites within prosystemin are probably unique to plants.

No homologues of prosystemin have been found in gene banks, but prosystemin cDNAs have now been isolated from potato, nightshade, and bell pepper (18). Pairwise comparisons of predicted amino acid sequences among them exhibit similarities from 73 to 88%. The deduced systemin polypeptides from the three species are relatively similar, with differences found primarily in the N-terminal half of the molecules. No differences were found among the seven C-terminal amino acids (residues 12–18 of systemin) that include a Pro-Pro motif. Synthetic systemins from potato, nightshade, and bell pepper were active in inducing proteinase inhibitors when assayed in young tomato plants (Constabel et al 1998), but pepper systemin was about an order of magnitude less active than the other systemins. Tomato systemin does not activate defense genes in tobacco leaves, nor could a tomato prosystemin cDNA probe detect a signal in the total RNA from tobacco leaves (P Constabel, L Yip, D Bergey & CA Ryan, unpublished data). A partially pure polypeptide preparation from tobacco leaves has powerful proteinase inhibitor-inducing activity, but a pure polypeptide has not yet been isolated (G Pearce & CA Ryan, unpublished data). If the tobacco polypeptide signal is related to systemin, then significant amino acid sequence differences must be present, and if this is the case, it is anticipated that even larger differences in the sequences of various prosystemins and systemins among plant genera and families will be found. The occurrence of systemins in families other than the Solanacae is not known, but systemic wound induction of proteinase inhibitors, with kinetics and other characteristics similar to tomato, has been reported in members of diverse plant families (Brown & Ryan 1984, Rohrmeier & Lehle 1993, Bradshaw et al 1989, Saarikoski et al 1996).

Low levels of prosystemin mRNA were found in unwounded tomato leaves, but levels in both wounded and distal unwounded leaves increased in response to severe wounding (McGurl et al 1992). The increased levels of prosystemin mRNA following wounding appear to result from a mechanism by which prosystemin protein is amplified following insect attack to release more systemin if the insect attack persists.

The central role of prosystemin in signaling the defense response was demonstrated by transforming tomato plants with a gene consisting of the CaMV promoter and a prosystemin cDNA in its antisense orientation (McGurl et al 1992). The transformed plants expressed high levels of the antisense prosystemin message and a severely depressed systemic wound induction of proteinase inhibitors. The resistance of the transgenic plants toward *Manduca sexta* larvae herbivory was compromised compared with that of wild-type plants, demonstrating that prosystemin plays a crucial role in the inducible defense response of tomatoes against an insect pest.

Localization of Prosystemin Synthesis

The tissue-specific expression of the prosystemin gene was investigated using a gene with 2.2 kb of the promoter region of the prosystemin gene fused with the open reading frame of the β-glucuronidase (GUS) gene (Jacinto et al 1997). Tomato plants transformed with the gene exhibited low levels of GUS activity that increased in response to wounding and treatment with methyl jasmonate. Histochemical staining showed that wound-inducible GUS activity was associated with the cells of the vascular bundles of leaf main veins, petiolules, petioles, and stems. The increase in GUS activity in response to methyl jasmonate correlated with wound-inducible increases in prosystemin mRNA. The localization of prosystemin mRNA in the phloem parenchyma and paraveinal mesophyll cells surrounding the xylem was confirmed by in situ hybridization using fluorescence microscopy (G Birkenmeier, CA Ryan, unpublished data). Additionally, tissue printing (Jacinto et al 1997, Delano-Freier 1997), using prosystemin antibodies prepared by expressing the prosystemin protein in *Escherichia coli*, confirmed that the prosystemin protein was wound inducible in the vascular bundles of petiolules, petioles, and stems of wild-type plants.

Thus prosystemin appears to be synthesized within the vascular bundles where wounding would release systemin in the vicinity of the phloem for transport to other parts of the plant.

A chimeric gene comprised of the constitutive CaMV promoter and the prosystemin cDNA was constructed to produce transformed tomato plants that would overexpress the prosystemin protein (McGurl et al 1994). The transformants were expected to respond faster and stronger to wounding as a result of the higher levels of constitutive prosystemin protein. Unexpectedly, the plants overexpressing the gene exhibited a constitutive synthesis and accumulation of proteinase inhibitors in cells throughout the plants, as if they were in a permanently wounded state in the absence of wounding. Young tomato plants exhibited levels of proteinase inhibitors equivalent to wounded plants, whereas older plants that had grown for several weeks accumulated over 1 mg proteinase inhibitors per gram leaf tissue, an extraordinarily high level of the inhibitors. It was proposed that the expression of the prosystemin transgene in tissues other than the vascular tissue may have caused a continual, abnormal processing of prosystemin and activation of the defense genes. Grafting wild-type plants onto rootstalks of the transgenic plants resulted in the wild-type scions producing proteinase Inh I and Inh II, as if they were severely wounded. Grafting wild-type scions onto wild-type rootstalks did not result in the induction of proteinase inhibitors in leaves of the scions. These experiments indicate that the wound signal, presumably systemin, is transported from the transgenic rootstalks to the upper wild-type leaves (McGurl et al 1994), demonstrating that propagation of a wound signal does not require wounding or the generation of electrical or hydraulic signals to achieve systemic signaling.

Electrophoretic analysis of the leaf proteins of the transgenic plants expressing the prosystemin gene revealed the accumulation of not only the proteinase inhibitors but many other proteins as well (Bergey et al 1996). Several of the proteins were isolated from SDS-PAGE gels, partially sequenced, and identified from data banks as wound-inducible proteins from potato or tomato leaves (Walker-Simmons & Ryan 1979, Hildemann et al 1992, Pautot et al 1993, Bolter 1993). Some novel proteins were also identified. Oligonucleotide probes synthesized using PCR methodology were used to screen a cDNA library prepared from RNA from the leaves of the transgenic plants. Over 15 genes have now been identified in the transgenic plants that are upregulated in the leaves of the wild-type tomato plants in response to wounding or systemin (Bergey et al 1996).

The protein products of these wound-inducible genes are shown in Figure 1. The genes can be classified into four categories: (*a*) defensive genes that are proteinase inhibitors and polyphenol oxidase, all directed toward the reduction of protein digestion in insects' guts (Ryan 1990, Boulter 1993); (*b*) signal

Defensive Proteins	Signal Pathway Components
Inhibitor I	Systemin
Inhibitor II	Calmodulin
Cystatin	Lipoxygenase
Aspartic Protease Inhibitor	Allene Oxide Synthase
Polyphenol Oxidase	
Proteinases	**Others--Functions Unknown**
Leucine Aminopeptidase	Polygalacturonase Catalytic Subunit
Carboxypeptidase	Polygalacturonase β-Subunit
Aspartic Proteinase	Threonine Deaminase
Ubiquitin	Nucleotide Diphosphate Kinase
Ubiquitin-like Protein	Acyl CoA Binding Protein

Figure 1   Proteins in leaves of tomato plants that are induced systemically by wounding and systemin.

pathway components; (*c*) proteinases; and (*d*) enzymes with unknown roles in plant defense. In addition to the proteins that accumulate in the transgenic plants, several proteins were identified that either had decreased or had disappeared from the SDS-PAGE gels, when compared with unwounded wild-type plants (Bergey et al 1996). These proteins have not been isolated nor identified.

SYSTEMIN SIGNALING PATHWAY

Octadecanoid Pathway

The signaling pathway for the activation of defensive genes by systemin is mediated by lipid-derived intermediates (Farmer & Ryan 1992). Systemin activates an intracellular cascade that results in the release of linolenic acid (LA) from membranes, with the LA subsequently converted to phytodienoic acid (PDA) and jasmonic acid (JA) (Vick & Zimmerman 1984), both powerful inducers of defensive genes in plants (Doares et al 1995, Weiler 1997). Ethylene and the jasmonates are required for gene activation by the pathway (O'Donnell et al 1996). The pathway from LA to JA, called the octadecanoid pathway (Vick & Zimmerman 1984), also mediates the activation of defensive genes by carbohydrate signals generated from plant and fungal pathogen cell walls during pathogen attacks (Farmer & Ryan 1992, Gundlach et al 1992). The octadecanoid pathway appears to be a general signaling pathway for many plant processes involved in defense, stress, and development (Weiler 1997). Other than systemin and elicitors, the primary signals that regulate the pathway are unknown. Whether the lipid-derived signal that activates gene expression is PDA, JA, or a derivative(s) has not been determined.

The role of the octadecanoid pathway in mediating systemin signaling has been confirmed in several ways. Systemin causes an increase in JA in leaves of tomato plants (Doares et al 1995b, Howe et al 1996, Conconi et al 1996), and inhibitors of the octadecanoid pathway, such as diethyldithiocarbamate (Farmer et al 1994) and salicylic acid (Pena-Cortes et al 1993, Doares et al 1995a), inhibit systemin activation of defensive genes. The most convincing evidence has come from a mutant tomato line deficient in a component of the octadecanoid pathway (Lightner et al 1993, Howe et al 1996). This mutant, called *defenseless 1* (*def 1*), produces only very small amounts of defensive proteins when wounded and is nearly unresponsive to systemin. When the mutant plants are subjected to attacks by tobacco hornworm larvae, the plants are literally defenseless compared with the wild-type plants; the mutants were stripped of their foliage while the leaves of wild-type plants were only partially consumed by the larvae.

Kinetic analysis of the synthesis of wound-inducible genes of tomato suggest that the genes involved in the signaling pathway are expressed much earlier than the defensive genes. Prosystemin mRNA (McGurl et al 1994), lipoxygenase mRNA (Heitz et al 1997), and allene oxide synthase mRNA (G Howe & CA Ryan, unpublished data), all components of the signaling pathway, exhibit similar kinetics, with levels increasing in both wounded and unwounded leaves within 0.5 h following wounding. The mRNA levels maximize at 2 to 3 h and decrease thereafter. This is in contrast to the accumulation of proteinase inhibitor mRNAs (Graham et al 1986), which show no constitutive accumulation in tomato leaves and begin to accumulate within 3 to 4 h following wounding, peaking 5 to 8 h later. The difference in the timing of synthesis of signaling and defensive genes may be due to their localization in the leaves. Jacinto et al (1997) have shown that prosystemin synthesis is primarily associated with cells of the vascular bundle, whereas Narvaez-Vasquez et al (1993) have shown that defensive proteinase inhibitor proteins accumulate primarily in palisade and mesophyll cells. The early activation of the signal pathway genes may reflect their localization in cells near the phloem. Systemin might signal the amplification of signaling pathway enzymes in these cells very early. The subsequent transport of signals from the vascular bundles to the surrounding cells would then activate the defensive genes in palisade and mesophyll cells, which would explain their delayed synthesis. Further studies of the in situ and immunological localization of both the signaling and defensive mRNAs and proteins should resolve this matter.

Effects of ABA and Auxin

The systemin signaling pathway is influenced by plant hormones such as abscisic acid (ABA) and indole acetic acid (auxin). Plants deficient in ABA do not produce proteinase inhibitors in response to wounding, in contrast to their wild-type parent plants (Pena-Cortes et al 1989). In a series of reports (Pena-Cortes et al 1989, 1991, 1996; Sanchez-Serrano et al 1991) ABA has been hypothe-sized to be an integral part of the signaling pathway, and ABA-deficient mutants were reported to be incapable of producing proteinase Inh II mRNA in response to systemin. However, recent evidence (Birkenmeier & Ryan 1998) indicates that ABA does not play a direct role in the signaling pathway but enhances the systemin-induced response that occurs in leaves of both wild-type and ABA-deficient tomato plants, with the enhancement being more pronounced in the ABA mutants.

Auxin has been reported to depress the wound response (Kernan & Thornburg 1989), but its effect on systemin-mediated induction of defense genes has not been studied.

Membrane-Mediated Responses

The putative systemin receptor has not been identified. In binding studies of ra-diolabeled systemin with purified tomato leaf plasma membranes, no significant binding of systemin to the membranes could be detected (S Doares & CA Ryan, unpublished data). A derivative of systemin, in which Ser8 was replaced with a Cys and biotinylated, was used to identify systemin-binding proteins present in purified tomato plasma membranes (Schaller & Ryan 1994, 1995). Both the Cys8 substitution and the biotinylated derivative were nearly as active as native systemin in inducing proteinase inhibitors in excised tomato plants. When bi-otinylated systemin was mixed with purified tomato leaf plasma membranes and crosslinked, it selectively bound to a 50-kDa protein in the membranes. How-ever, the binding protein resembled proteinases of the Kex2p-like prohormone convertases (Seidah et al 1994) rather than a receptor. When the biotinylated systemin was simultaneously labeled at Met15 with [^{35}S]methionine, the biotin, but not the radioactivity, was bound to the membrane protein (Schaller & Ryan 1994), indicating that at least four, and as many as eight C-terminal residues could have been cleaved from systemin during the interaction with the protein. Within the systemin amino acid sequence is a dibasic cleavage site similar to that of a furin-like enzyme (Seidah et al 1994), and an antibody against a Kex2p-like protease from *Drosophila* inhibited binding of the biotinylated systemin to the membrane protein. The authors (Schaller & Ryan 1994) suggest that a systemin-binding protein may be a proteinase involved in a cleavage of systemin as a matu-ration step, facilitating systemin activity or its degradation. This hypothesis was supported with experiments in which the Lys14-Met15 peptide bond in systemin was shown to be stabilized by replacing Lys14 with Ala14, with subsequent N-methylation of the Ala14 (Schaller 1998). This analogue exhibited an increase in its biological activity when compared with that of systemin. Systemin is inactivated by *Lycopersicon peruvianum* suspension cultures (Schaller 1998, Felix & Boller 1995), but N-methylated Ala14-systemin exhibited prolonged stability when added to the cultures (Schaller 1998). Isolation of peptides generated by the interaction with the cultured cells indicates that an initial cleavage of the polypeptide occurs at the peptide bond C-terminal to Lys14. The cleavage apparently is involved in the in vivo inactivation of systemin.

The addition of systemin to *L. peruvianum* cell cultures caused an alkalinization of the medium accompanied by an increased efflux of K^+, an induction of 1-aminocyclopropane-1-carboxylate synthase (ACC) and phenylalanine ammonia lyase (PAL) activities. These responses are often observed in cell cultures of many species of plants when challenged with pathogens or elicitors. Ala17-systemin, the powerful antagonist of systemin, was a weak inducer of ACC synthase when added to the cultured cells, but antagonized the induction of the enzyme by systemin. Ala17-systemin did not antagonize the inducing activities of other elicitors, indicating that its antagonism is specific for systemin. ACC is a key enzyme in the biosynthesis of ethylene, which was also shown to increase in response to systemin. This response agrees with recent data showing that JA activated ethylene biosynthesis which, together with JA, activated proteinase inhibitor genes in tomato leaves (Weiler 1997). PAL mRNA and protein had previously been shown to be synthesized in response to JA in cell cultures of *Glycine max* (O'Donnell et al 1996), but the possible role of ethylene in these studies was not examined.

Systemin-induced changes in membrane potentials of leaf cells of *Lycopersicon esculentum* var. Moneymaker were examined using a standard electrophysiological cell impalement technique (Moyen & Johannes 1996). The plasma membrane of tomato mesophyll cells was shown to be transiently depolarized by systemin with a lag period of 30 s to 4 min, whereas the pH of the medium increased. This was followed by a sustained alkalinization of the medium over a period of up to 18 h. Fusicoccin, which causes a hyperpolarization of membranes and is an antagonist of proteinase inhibitor synthesis in tomato plants, attenuated the depolarization and transient H^+ efflux, supporting the suggestion that ion transport is involved with the initial stages of systemin-induced defense gene activation.

Systemin and the Oxidative Burst

Tomato (*L. esculentum*) cell cultures do not exhibit an oxidative burst when exposed to either systemin or Ala17-systemin, but they potentiate the burst caused by oligogalacturonides (MJ Stennis, S Chandra, CA Ryan, PS Low, in review). The oxidative burst is a rapid response of plant cells when exposed to pathogens or elicitors of defense responses, depending upon the compatibility of the host-plant pathogen interaction (Low & Marida 1996, Doke et al 1996). Oligogalacturonides are among the elicitors that cause the oxidative burst (Legendre et al 1993, Moyen & Johannes 1996). Neither systemin nor

Ala17-systemin modified the oligogalacturonide-induced oxidative burst of tomato cells when added to the culture medium within a few minutes of each other. However, pre-exposure of the cells to systemin for 6 to 12 h led to a progressive enhancement of the oligogalacturonide-induced oxidative burst. The burst, occurring 12 h after adding systemin to the cells, was more than 16-fold higher than the burst caused by the oligogalacturonides alone. Preincubation of cells with Ala17-systemin did not enhance the oxidative burst caused by oligogalacturonides. The enhancement caused by systemin, which was shown to involve protein synthesis, was suggested to be a part of the defense response of plants that enhances the plants ability to potentiate defense against pathogens in addition to defending against herbivores.

Analogies to the Inflammatory Response of Animals

The signaling pathway mediated by systemin has been likened to the inflammatory response of macrophages and mast cells of animals in response to pathogens and parasites (Stevens 1995, Bergey et al 1996). In the inflammatory response, a polypeptide cytokine, TNF-α, activates the release of arachidonic acid (AA) (20 carbons and 4 double bonds) from animal cells, leading to prostaglandin synthesis, fever, and the inflammatory response (Lin et al 1993, Malaviya et al 1996). In tomato leaves, phytodienoic acid and JA, which are derived from LA (18 carbons and 3 double bonds) in response to herbivore attacks, are analogues of animal prostaglandins (Samuelsson et al 1978). Ca^{2+}, MAP kinases, and phospholipase A_2 are important in the release of arachidonic acid from animal cell membranes (Samuelsson et al 1978), and the phosphorylation of phospholipase A_2 by the kinase has been proposed to lead to its activation. MAP kinases have recently been shown to be activated in plants by wounding (Usami et al 1991, Seo et al 1995, Adam et al 1997, Stratmann & Ryan 1997). A MAP kinase activated by systemin (Stratmann & Ryan 1997) was shown to function between the perception of the primary signal and the *DEF 1* gene product of the *def 1* mutant plants mentioned above (Schaller & Ryan 1994). An involvement of Ca^{2+} and calmodulin in the response of tomato plants to wounding and systemin has been demonstrated (DR Bergey, CA Ryan, unpublished data), as well as changes in free C18 fatty acids and lipid composition (Conconi et al 1996, Lee et al 1997; J Narvaez-Vasquez, CA Ryan, unpublished data). The data suggest that a rapidly propagating systemic signal, such as an electric or hydraulic signal, may initiate or prime the signaling process, followed by the slower but sustained migrating signal, systemin.

This signaling pathway in plants also exhibits some general similarities to the wound-mediated acute-phase response (APR) of animals (Haumann & Gauldie 1994, Steel & Whitehead 1994) (Figure 2). In animals, immediately following

PLANTS

ANIMALS

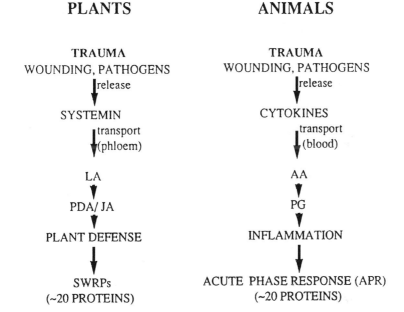

Figure 2 Comparison of some features of trauma responses in plants and animals. Wound-signaling pathways leading to the synthesis of systemic wound response proteins (SWRPs) in plants and acute phase response proteins (APRs) in animals. LA, linolenic acid; PDA, phytodienoic acid; JA, jasmonic acid; AA, arachidonic acid; PG, prostaglandins.

a severe physical trauma (wounding, surgery, UV) or a bacterial, viral, or parasitic infection, a program is initiated that leads to a wide range of complex physiological changes. Fever, various changes in vascular permeability, and biosynthetic and anabolic profiles are noted in many organs. The response is orchestrated by several inflammatory mediators of which TNF-α is a key player. Over 25 genes are known to be activated during the APR, which lasts only a few days (Steel & Whitehead 1994). In both wounded plants and animals, the down-regulation of several proteins has been observed (Steel & Whitehead 1994, Bergey et al 1996). The overall strategies of the APR and the plant wound responses are to activate several classes of genes, including proteinases and proteinase inhibitors, for defense and wound healing.

The plant response so far appears to be primarily for defense against intruders, and wound-healing genes have not been identified. However, the plant defense system has been studied for only a short time compared with the APR, and the full extent of its response is likely to be much more complex. The relationship between systemin and wounding to signaling pathways for defense against pathogens is not known, although crosstalk between the induced defense response, mediated by systemin, and the pathogen-induced response, mediated by salicylic acid, has been suggested (Doares et al 1995a).

FUTURE PROSPECTS

Although considerable knowledge about systemin and prosystemin has been obtained, much research remains to be done. The details of how prosystemin is synthesized, compartmentalized, processed, and transported are not known. The systemin receptor remains elusive, and how the intracellular signal transduction mechanism involves the MAP kinase, Ca^{2+}/calmodulin, and the activation of the phospholipase remain obscure, despite apparent similarities to the animal inflammatory response.

The extent of the occurrence of prosystemin throughout the plant kingdom must be determined, and how it fits into complex defense responses that have evolved in different ecological niches. It is anticipated that such studies will be fundamentally important in the future for the application of this knowledge to biotechnology and agriculture.

Recently, other polypeptide signals of plant origins have been reported that regulate cell division. One polypeptide, identified as the gene product of the *ENOD 40* gene, is an early nodulation gene expressed in soybean plants associated with the initial steps of nitrogen fixation (van de Sande et al 1996). *ENOD 40* codes for a small 12-amino acid polypeptide that is synthesized in root cells in response to bacterial lipochitooligosaccharides. The polypeptide appears to be involved in the early steps that condition the cell for cell division and nodulation.

Two small sulfated polypeptides of four and five amino acids, respectively, have recently been shown to be components of conditioned media that is necessary for prolific growth of cultured asparagus cells (Matsubayashi & Sakagami 1996) and rice cells (Matsubayashi & Sakagami 1997). The sulfated polypeptides may have a role in cell division in plants as well. Additionally, indirect evidence supporting possible roles of polypeptides as important signals in plant processes comes from the recent identification of genes that encode putative polypeptide receptors (Braun & Walker 1996, Beacraft et al 1996, Torii et al 1996) containing leucine-rich repeats (LRRs) that resemble animal polypeptide receptors. Thus it appears that polypeptide hormones and/or factors are playing major roles in plant responses, and that more of these regulatory polypeptides will surely be revealed as we delve deeper into the processes of growth, development, and stress in plants.

Literature Cited

Adam AL, Pike S, Hoyos ME, Stone JM, Walker JC, Novacky A. 1997. Rapid and transient activation of a myelin basic protein kinase in tobacco leaves treated with harpin from *Erwinia amylovora*. *Plant Physiol.* 115:853–61

Beacraft PW, Stinard PS, McCarty DR. 1996. CRINKLY4: a TNRF-like receptor kinase involved in maize epidermal differentiation. *Science* 273:1406–9

Bergey D, Howe G, Ryan CA. 1996. Polypeptide signaling for plant defensive genes exhibits analogies to defense signaling in animals. *Proc. Natl. Acad. Sci. USA* 93:12053–58

Birkenmeier G, Ryan CA. 1998. Wound signaling in tomato plants: evidence that abscisic acid is not a primary signal for defence gene activation. *Plant Physiol.* In press

Bolter CJ. 1993. Methyl jasmonate induces papain inhibitor(s) in tomato leaves. *Plant Physiol.* 103:1347–53

Boulter D. 1993. Insect pest control by copying nature using genetically engineered crops. *Phytochemistry* 34:1453–66

Bradshaw HD Jr, Hillick JB, Parsons TJ, Clarke HRG, Gordon MP. 1989. Systemically wound-responsive genes in poplar trees encode proteins similar to sweet potato sporamins and legume Kunitz trypsin inhibitors. *Plant Mol. Biol.* 14:51–59

Braun DM, Walker JC. 1996. Plant transmembrane receptors: new pieces in the signaling puzzle. *Trends Biol. Sci.* 21:70–73

Brown WE, Ryan CA. 1984. Isolation and characterization of a wound-induced trypsin inhibitor from alfalfa leaves. *Biochemistry* 23:3418–22

Conconi A, Miquel M, Ryan CA. 1996. Changes in the intracellular lipid composition and free fatty acids of tomato leaves in response to wounding. *Plant Physiol.* 111:797–803

Constabel CP, Yip L, Ryan CA. 1998. Prosystemin from potato, black nightshade, and bell pepper: primary structures and biological acivities of the predicted systemins. *Plant Mol. Biol.* 34:55–62

Delano-Freier J. 1997. *Expression of the prosystemin cDNA in E. coli: isolation, characterization and in situ localization of the prosystemin protein*. PhD thesis. Washington State Univ. 150 pp.

Doares S, Narvaez-Vasquez J, Conconi A, Ryan CA. 1995a. Salicylic acid inhibits synthesis of proteinase inhibitors in tomato leaves induced by systemin and jasmonic acid. *Plant. Physiol.* 108:1741–46

Doares S, Syrovets T, Weiler EW, Ryan CA. 1995b. Oligouronides and chitosan utilize the octadecanoid pathway to activate plant defensive genes. *Proc. Natl. Acad. Sci. USA* 92:4095–98

Doke, N, Miura Y, Sanchez LM, Park H-J, Noritake T, et al. 1996. The oxidative burst protects plants against pathogen attack: mechanism and role as an emergency signal for plant bio-defence: a review. *Gene* 179:45–51

Farmer EE, Caldelari D, Walker-Simmons M, Ryan CA. 1994. Diethyldithiocarbamic acid (DIECA) inhibits the octadecanoid signaling pathway for the wound-induction of proteinase inhibitors in tomato leaves. *Plant Physiol.* 106:337–42

Farmer EE, Ryan CA. 1992. Octadecanoid jasmonate precursors activate the synthesis of wound-inducible proteinase inhibitors. *Plant Cell* 4:129–34

Felix G, Boller T. 1995. Systemin induces rapid ion fluxes and ethylene biosynthesis in *Lycopersicon peruvianum* cells. *Plant J.* 7:381–89

Graham JS, Hall G, Pearce G, Ryan CA. 1986. Regulation of synthesis of proteinase inhibitors I and II mRNAs in leaves of wounded tomato plants. *Planta* 169:399–405

Green TR, Ryan CA. 1972. Wound-induced proteinase inhibitor in plant leaves: a possible defense mechanism against insects. *Science* 175:776–77

Gundlach H, Muller MJ, Kutchan TM, Zenk MH. 1992. Jasmonic acid is a signal transducer in elicitor-induced plant cell cultures. *Proc. Natl. Acad. Sci. USA* 89:2389–93

Haumann H, Gauldie J. 1994. The acute phase response. *Immunol. Today* 15:75–80

Heitz T, Bergey D. Ryan CA. 1997. A gene encoding a chloroplast lipoxygenase is transiently induced by wounding, systemin, and methyl jasmonate in tomato leaves. *Plant Physiol.* 114:1805–9

Hildemann T, Ebneth M, Pena-Cortes H, Sanchez-Serrano JJ, Wilmitzer L, Prat S. 1992. General roles of abscisic and jasmonic acids in gene activation as a result of mechanical wounding. *Plant Cell* 4:1157–70

Howe G, Lightner J, Browse J, Ryan CA. 1996. Characterization of a tomato wound response mutant blocked in the octadecanoid defense signaling pathway. *Plant Cell* 8:2067–77

Jacinto T, McGurl B, Franceschi V, Delano-Freier J, Ryan CA. 1997. Tomato prosystemin confers wound-inducible, vascular bundle-specific expression of the β-glucuronidase gene in transgenic tomato and tobacco plants. *Planta* 203:406–11

Kende H, Zeevart JAD. 1997. The five "Classical" hormones. *Plant Cell* 9:1197–10

Kernan A, Thornburg RW. 1989. Auxin levels regulate the expression of a wound-inducible proteinase inhibitor II-chloramphenicol acetyl transferase gene fusion in vitro and in vivo. *Plant Physiol.* 91:73–77

Lee L, Suh S, Kim S, Crain RC, Dwak JM, et al. 1997. Systemic elevation of phosphatidic acid and lysophospholipid levels in wounded plants. *Plant J.* 12:547–56

Legendre L, Rueter S, Heinsten PF, Low PS. 1993. Characterization of the oligogalacturonide-induced oxidative burst in cultured soybean (*Glycine max*) cells. *Plant Physiol.* 102:233–40

Lightner J, Browse J, Ryan CA. 1993. Isolation of signalling mutants of tomato (*Lycopersicum esculentum*). *Mol. Gen. Genet.* 241:595–601

Lin LL, Wartmann M, Lin AY, Knopf JL, Seth A, Davis RJ. 1993. cPLA$_2$ is phosphorylated and activated by MAP kinase. *Cell* 72:269–78

Low PS, Merida JR. 1996. The oxidative burst in plant defense: function and signal transduction. *Physiol. Plant* 96:533–42

Malaviya R, Ikeda T, Ross E, Abraham SN. 1996. Mast cell modulation of neutrophil influx and bacterial clearance at sites of infection through TFN-α. *Nature* 381:77–79

Matsubayashi Y, Sakagami Y. 1996. Phytosulfokines, sulfated peptides that induce the proliferation of single mesophyll cells of *Asparagus officinalis. Proc. Natl. Acad. Sci. USA* 93:7623–27

Matsubayshi Y, Takagi L, Sakagami Y. 1997. Phytosulfokine-a, a sulfated pentapeptide, stimulates the proliferation of rice cells by means of specific high- and low-affinity binding sites. *Proc. Natl. Acad. Sci. USA.* 94:13357–62

McGurl B, Orozco-Cardenas, M, Pearce G, Ryan CA. 1994. Overexpression of a CaMV-prosystemin gene in transgenic tomato plants generates a systemic signal that induces proteinase inhibitor synthesis. *Proc. Natl. Acad. Sci. USA* 91:9799–802

McGurl B, Pearce G, Orozco-Cardenas M, Ryan CA. 1992. Structure, expression, and antisense inhibition of the systemin precursor gene. *Science* 255:1570–73

McGurl B, Ryan CA. 1992. The organization of the prosystemin gene. *Plant Mol. Biol.* 20:405–9

Moyen C, Johannes E. 1996. Systemin transiently depolarizes the tomato mesophyll cell membrane and antagonizes fusicoccin-induced extracellular acidification of mesophyll tissue. *Plant Cell Environ.* 19:464–70

Narvaez-Vasquez J, Franceschi V, Ryan CA. 1993. Proteinase inhibitor synthesis in tomato plants: evidence for extracellular deposition in roots through the secretory pathway. *Planta* 189:257–66

Narvaez-Vasquez J, Orozco-Cardenas ML, Ryan CA. 1994. Sulfhydryl reagents modulate systemic signaling for wound-induced and systemin-induced proteinase inhibitor synthesis. *Plant Physiol.* 105:725–30

Narvaez-Vasquez J, Pearce G, Orozco-Cardenas ML, Franceschi VR, Ryan CA. 1995. Autoradiographic and biochemical evidence for the systemic translocation of systemin in tomato plants. *Planta* 195:593–600

O'Donnell PJ, Calvert C, Atzorn R, Wasternack C, Leyser HMO, Bowles DJ. 1996. Ethylene as a signal mediating the wound response of tomato plants. *Science* 274:1914–17

Pautot V, Holzer FM, Reisch B, Walling LL. 1993. Leucine aminopeptidase: an inducible component of the defense response in *Lycopersicon esculentum* (tomato). *Proc. Natl. Acad Sci. USA* 90:9906–10

Pearce G, Johnson S, Ryan CA. 1993. Structure-activity of deleted and substituted systemin, an eighteen amino acid polypeptide inducer of plant defensive genes. *J. Biol. Chem.* 268:212–16

Pearce G, Strydom D, Johnson S, Ryan CA. 1991. A polypeptide from tomato leaves activates the expression of proteinase inhibitor genes. *Science* 253:895–87

Pena-Cortes H, Albrecht T, Prat S, Weiler EW, Wilmitzer L. 1993. Aspirin prevents wound-induced gene expression in tomato leaves by blocking jasmonic acid biosynthesis. *Planta* 191:123–28

Pena-Cortes H, Prat S, Axtorn R, Wasternack C, Willmitzer L. 1996. Abscisic acid-deficient plants do not accumulate proteinase inhibitor II following systemin treatment. *Planta* 198:447–51

Pena-Cortes H, Sanchez-Serrano JJ, Mertens R, Willmitzer L, Prat S. 1989. Abscisic acid is involved in the wound-induced expression of the proteinase inhibitor II gene in potato and tomato. *Proc. Natl. Acad. Sci. USA* 86:9851–55

Pena-Cortes H, Willmitzer L, Sanchez-Serrano JJ. 1991. Abscisic acid mediates wound induction but not developmental-specific expression of the proteinase inhibitor gene family. *Plant Cell* 3:963–72

Realini C, Dubiel W, Pratt G, Ferrell K, Rechsteiner M. 1994a. Molecular cloning and expression of a γ-interferon-inducible activator of the multicatalytic protease. *J. Biol. Chem.* 32:20727–32

Realini C, Rogers SW, Rechsteiner M. 1994b. Proposed roles in protein-protein association and presentation of peptides by MHC Class I receptors. *FEBS Lett.* 348:109–13

Rohrmeier T, Lehle L. 1993. *WIPl*, a wound-inducible gene from maize with homology to Bowman-Birk proteinase inhibitors. *Plant Mol. Biol.* 22:783–92

Russell DJ, Pearce G, Ryan CA, Satterlee JD. 1992. Proton NMR assignments of systemin. *J. Protein Chem.* 11:265–74

Ryan CA. 1974. Assay and biochemical properties of the proteinase inhibitor inducing factor, a wound hormone. *Plant Physiol.* 54: 328–32

Ryan CA. 1990. Proteinase inhibitors in plants: genes for improving defenses against insects and pathogens. *Annu. Rev. Phytopathol.* 28:425–49

Ryan CA. 1992. The search for the proteinase inhibitor inducing factor, PIIF. *Plant Mol. Biol.* 19:123–34

Saarikoski P, Clapham D, von Arnold S. 1996. A wound-inducible gene from *Salix viminalis* coding for a trypsin inhibitor. *Plant Mol. Biol.* 31:465–78

Samuelsson B, Goldyne E, Granström M, Hamberg S, Hammarström S, Malmsten C. 1978. Prostaglandins and thromboxanes. *Annu. Rev. Biochem.* 47:997–1029

Sanchez-Serrano JJ, Amati S, Egneth M, Hildmann T, Mertens R, et al. 1991. The involvement of ABA in wound responses in plants. In *Abscisic Acid Physiology and Biochemistry*, ed. WJ Davies, HG Jones, pp. 201–16. Oxford: BIOS Sci.

Schaller A. 1998. Action of proteolysis-resistant systemin analogues in wound signalling. *Phytochemistry* 47:605–9

Schaller A, Ryan CA. 1994. Identification of a 50 kDa systemin-binding protein in tomato plasma membranes having Kex2p-like properties. *Proc. Natl. Acad. Sci. USA* 91:11802–6

Schaller A, Ryan CA. 1995. Systemin-A polypeptide signal in plants. *BioEssays* 18:27–33

Seidah NG, Chretien M, Day, R. 1994. The family of subtilisin/kexin-like pro-protein and pro-hormone convertases: divergent or shared functions. *Biochimie* 76:197–209

Seo S, Okamoto M, Seto H, Ishisuka K, Sano H, Ohashi Y. 1995. Tobacco MAP kinase: a possible mediator in wound signal transduction pathways. *Science* 270:1988–92

Slosarek G, Kalbitzer HR, Mucha P, Rekowski P, Kupryszewski G. 1995. Mechanism of the activation of proteinase inhibitor synthesis by systemin involves β-sheet structure, a specific DNA-binding protein domain. *J. Struct. Biol.* 115:30–36

Steel DM, Whitehead AS. 1994. The major acute phase reactants: c-reactive protein, serum amyloid P component and serum amyloid A protein. *Immunol. Today* 15:81–88

Stevens DL. 1995. Could non-steroidal anti-inflammatory drugs (NSAIDs) enhance the progression of bacterial infections to toxic shock syndrome? *Clin. Infect. Dis.* 21:977

Stratmann JW, Ryan CA. 1997. Myelin basic protein kinase activity in tomato leaves is induced systemically by wounding and increases in response to systemin and oligosaccharide elicitors. *Proc. Natl. Acad. Sci. USA* 94:11085–89

Torii KU, Mitsukawa N, Oolumi T, Mastuura Y, Yoioyama, et al. 1996. The *Arabidopsis* *ERECTA* gene encodes a putative receptor protein kinase with extracellular leucine rich repeats. *Plant Cell* 8:735–46

Toumadje A, Johnson WC Jr. 1995. Systemin has the characteristics of a poly(L-proline) II type helix. *J. Am. Chem. Soc.* 117:7023–24

Usami S, Banno H, Ito Y, Nishihama R, Machida Y. 1991. Cutting activates a 46-kilodalton protein kinase in plants. *Proc. Natl. Acad. Sci. USA* 92:8660–64

van der Sande K, Pawlowski K, Czaja I, Wienke U, Schell J, et al. 1996. A peptide encoded by ENOD40 of legumes and a nonlegume modifies phytohormone response. *Science* 273:370–73

Vick BA, Zimmerman DC. 1984. Biosynthesis of jasmonic acid by several plant species. *Plant Physiol.* 75:458–61

Walker-Simmons M, Ryan CA. 1979. Carboxypeptidase from tomato leaves: isolation and properties of the enzyme from leaves of wounded tomato plants (*Lycopersicum esculentum* var. Bonny Best). *Phytochemistry* 19:43–47

Weiler EW. 1997. Octadecanoid-mediated signal transduction in higher plants. *Naturwissenschaften* 84:340–49

Annu. Rev. Cell Dev. Biol. 1998. 14:19–57

UBIQUITIN AND THE CONTROL OF PROTEIN FATE IN THE SECRETORY AND ENDOCYTIC PATHWAYS[1]

Juan S. Bonifacino

Cell Biology and Metabolism Branch, National Institute of Child Health and Human Development, National Institutes of Health, Bethesda, Maryland 20892-5430; e-mail: juan@helix.nih.gov

Allan M. Weissman

Laboratory of Immune Cell Biology, Division of Basic Sciences, National Cancer Institute, National Institutes of Health, Bethesda, Maryland 20892-1152; e-mail: amw@nih.gov

KEY WORDS: proteasomes, ER degradation, quality control, endocytosis, lysosomes, adaptors

ABSTRACT

The modification of proteins by chains of ubiquitin has long been known to mediate targeting of cytosolic and nuclear proteins for degradation by proteasomes. In this article, we discuss recent developments that reveal the involvement of ubiquitin in the degradation of proteins retained within the endoplasmic reticulum (ER) and in the internalization of plasma membrane proteins. Both luminal and transmembrane proteins retained in the ER are now known to be retrotranslocated into the cytosol in a process that involves ER chaperones and components of the protein import machinery. Once exposed to the cytosolic milieu, retro-translocated proteins are degraded by the proteasome, in most cases following polyubiquitination. There is growing evidence that both the ubiquitin-conjugating machinery and proteasomes may be associated with the cytosolic face of the ER membrane and that they could be functionally coupled to the process of retro-translocation. The ubiquitination of plasma membrane proteins, on the other hand, mediates internalization of the proteins, which in most cases is followed by

---

[1]The US Government has the right to retain a nonexclusive, royalty-free license in and to any copyright covering this paper.

lysosomal/vacuolar degradation. There is, however, a well-documented case of a plasma membrane protein (the c-Met receptor) for which ubiquitination results in proteasomal degradation. These recent findings imply that ubiquitin plays more diverse roles in the regulation of the fate of cellular proteins than originally anticipated.

CONTENTS

INTRODUCTION

The ability to degrade proteins is an essential function of all eukaryotic cells. The two main proteolytic systems within eukaryotic cells are lysosomes and proteasomes. Lysosomes are membrane-bound organelles that contain an assortment of acidic hydrolases, including many proteolytic enzymes (Bohley & Seglen 1992). Lysosomes degrade macromolecules taken up from the extracellular medium and plasma membrane receptors down-regulated in response to ligand binding. They are also responsible for the turnover of most organellar proteins of the endocytic and late [post-endoplasmic reticulum (ER)] secretory pathways.

Proteasomes are multi-protein complexes found in the cytosol and the nucleus (reviewed in Coux et al 1996). Despite this localization, proteasomes do not digest cellular proteins indiscriminately, but rather participate in the regulated breakdown of proteins that have been altered so as to be susceptible to degradation. As is discussed below, the most well-established means of targeting proteins to proteasomes is by their modification with chains of ubiquitin.

A simplistic view of cellular protein degradation thus would have the route of degradation determined in a topologically restricted manner, with lysosomes serving as the site for degradation of luminal and transmembrane proteins of the endocytic and secretory pathways, and proteasomes being responsible for ubiquitin-dependent degradation of cytosolic and nuclear proteins. However, recent developments indicate that the mechanisms involved in targeting proteins for degradation are substantially more complex than originally anticipated. In this review, we discuss observations in both yeast and mammalian cells that establish previously unappreciated roles for the ubiquitin-conjugating system in protein degradation from the ER and in the targeting of plasma membrane proteins for endocytosis and eventual degradation in lysosomes.

OVERVIEW OF THE UBIQUITIN-PROTEASOME DEGRADATION SYSTEM

Ubiquitin is a 76-amino acid polypeptide expressed in all eukaryotic cells and highly conserved from yeast to humans (reviewed in Wilkinson 1995). The covalent modification of proteins with chains of ubiquitin constitutes a potent targeting signal leading to recognition and destruction by the 26S proteasomes. The first physiological ubiquitination substrate was characterized in 1987 (Shanklin et al 1987); there are now at least 60 known substrates that include transcription factors, cell cycle regulators, kinases, phosphatases, tumor suppressors, and, as is described in detail below, a number of different transmembrane proteins. Importantly, for many of the substrates identified, ubiquitination occurs in a regulated manner, playing important roles in cellular processes for which regulation of protein levels are crucial (reviewed in Weissman 1997, Hershko & Ciechanover 1998).

Ubiquitination is an essential cellular process effected by a multi-enzyme cascade involving classes of enzymes known as E1s (ubiquitin-activating enzymes), E2s (ubiquitin-conjugating enzymes or Ubcs), and E3s (ubiquitin-protein ligases) (reviewed in Hochstrasser 1996, Weissman 1997, Hershko & Ciechanover 1998). A general scheme for ubiquitination is depicted in Figure 1. E1 activates ubiquitin in an ATP-dependent manner, with the formation of a thiol-ester linkage between the carboxy terminus of ubiquitin and E1. Sequential, transient thiol-ester bonds are then generated between the carboxy terminus of ubiquitin and specific cysteines of E2 and E3 enzymes. This "bucket brigade" of thiol-ester bonds culminates in the formation of an isopeptide linkage ‘

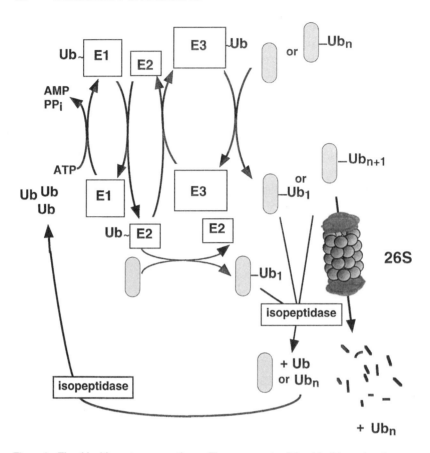

Figure 1   The ubiquitin-proteasome pathway. The components of the ubiquitin-conjugating system are shown schematically. Substrate is indicated by *shaded* object. Thiol-ester bond formation (∼) between Ub and E3 is based on studies of HECT family E3s and may not universally apply. While E2s clearly can carry out mono-ubiquitination in the absence of E3s, it may be that in certain instances E2s can function in the polyubiquitination of substrates unassisted by E3s. The term isopeptidase is used to refer to any protein that cleaves linkages between the carboxy terminus of ubiquitin and the ϵ-amino group of a lysine residue. De-ubiquitinating enzymes therefore are members of the isopeptidase family.

between the activated carboxy terminus of ubiquitin and the ϵ-amino group of a lysine on a target protein or within another ubiquitin chain (usually K48 of ubiquitin), resulting in the generation of chains of ubiquitin generally referred to as either polyubiquitin or multiubiquitin (Figure 1). Although E1 serves a general purpose within the cell, specificity in substrate recognition lies largely at the level of E3s, with an additional degree of combinatorial specificity likely resulting from specific E2-E3 interaction. There is also evidence that E2s, either singly or in pairs, function to at least mono-ubiquitinate proteins in the absence of E3s. Additionally, it should be noted that while some E3s form transient thiol-ester bonds with ubiquitin, there are other E3 activities where this may not occur and in which E3s serve primarily to bring E2s and substrates into proximity (reviewed in Weissman 1997, Hershko & Ciechanover 1998).

Two forms of E1 are distinguishable by SDS-PAGE: These are likely generated from use of alternative translation start sites in the E1 mRNA (Handley-Gearhart et al 1994a, Stephen et al 1996). The importance of E1, and of ubiquitination in general, is underscored by the cell cycle arrest exhibited by mammalian cells that express a temperature-sensitive E1 (Kulka et al 1988, Handley-Gearhart et al 1994b, Sudha et al 1995). This cell cycle arrest may be due to the now well-established role of the ubiquitin-conjugating system in degradation of cyclins and other molecules crucial to normal cell cycle progression (Weissman 1997, Hershko & Ciechanover 1998). In contrast to the paucity of distinct E1s, *Saccharomyces cerevisiae* expresses 12 distinct E2 enzymes, each of which is the product of a different gene; at least 17 E2s have been described in humans. E2s are characterized by a conserved 14–16-kDa core domain with amino- and carboxy-terminal extensions that provide substrate specificity or may allow for E3-independent ubiquitination (reviewed in Jentsch 1992, Hochstrasser 1996, Haas & Siepmann 1997). Despite the similarity among the various E2s, in multiple instances loss of a single E2 produces discernible phenotypes (Muralidhar & Thomas 1993, Harbers et al 1996, Roest et al 1996, Zhen et al 1996). E2s of particular relevance to this review are the core 16-kDa *S. cerevisiae* E2s—Ubc4p and Ubc5p—that are implicated in a number of cellular functions, and *S. cerevisiae* Ubc6p and Ubc7p. Ubc6p is unique among E2s in having a carboxy-terminal hydrophobic tail that allows for posttranslational anchoring to the ER membrane (Sommer & Jentsch 1993, Yang et al 1997). Ubc7p is a soluble E2 that interacts functionally with Ubc6p and is recruited to the ER membrane by interactions with a newly described membrane-anchored protein, Cue1p (Chen et al 1993, Biederer et al 1996, 1997).

As already noted, E2s may directly donate ubiquitin to proteins. However, in most cases, the modification of proteins requires E3 activity (Weissman 1997, Hershko & Ciechanover 1998). Despite the clear importance of E3s, the characterization of this class of enzyme is in its infancy. The first E3 described at a molecular level was the *S. cerevisiae* enzyme responsible for the amino-terminal-dependent ubiquitination of proteins, a process canonized by Varshavsky and co-workers in the "N-end rule" (Varshavsky 1996). This E3 is known as Ubr1p; functionally related mammalian proteins, for which amino acid sequence is not yet available, have been termed E3α and E3β (Hershko & Ciechanover 1998).

Much of our knowledge of E3 enzymes has emerged from studies on p53 ubiquitination and degradation. This tumor suppressor is rapidly degraded in cells expressing isotypes of the human papilloma virus (HPV) E6 protein from strains of this virus that predispose to malignant transformation (Scheffner et al 1990). Work from Howley and co-workers led to the discovery that E6 proteins from these strains (HPV16 and HPV18) serve as adaptors between p53 and a normal cellular protein known as E6-AP (E6-associated protein), allowing for the ubiquitination of p53 by E6-AP (Scheffner et al 1993). This led to the realization that the deduced amino acid sequences of a number of partially characterized cDNAs share carboxy-terminal homology with E6-AP, in a region implicated in the E3 activity of E6-AP (Huibregtse et al 1995). For this reason, these proteins have been termed HECT (homology to E6-AP carboxy terminus) proteins. It is now clear that several of these related proteins are enzymatically active E3s and, as will become evident, at least one member of this family plays a crucial role in the ubiquitination and the subsequent fate of plasma membrane proteins. There is also emerging evidence that a number of other structurally unrelated proteins, either singly or in combination, act as E3s. A recent example is the complex of Skp1p, Cdc53p, and Cdc4p, which has E3 activity in the ubiquitination of the Cdk inhibitor Sic1 (Feldman et al 1997). As proteins with E3 activity are identified, what it actually means to be an E3 will need to be re-evaluated (discussed in Weissman 1997).

The formation of K48-linked polyubiquitin chains on proteins constitutes a potent targeting signal for degradation in 26S proteasomes. These polyubiquitin chains are generated by isopeptide linkages between the ϵ-amino group of K48 of a ubiquitin moiety and the carboxy terminus of a newly added member of the chain. These K48-linked chains can be extensive in length (20 or more). It is generally accepted that a single ubiquitin on a protein, or single ubiquitins on multiple distinct lysines, are not sufficient to serve as a proteasomal targeting signal. The minimal chain length required for proteasome targeting has not been established with certainty, but appears to be no more than a chain of four ubiquitin moieties (Deveraux et al 1994, 1995). The extent to which polyubiquitin chains, linked through lysine residues other than K48, are generated in vivo or serve as proteasomal targeting signals remains an open issue.

The proteolytic component of the eukaryotic 26S proteasome is a 20S multicatalytic structure with trypsin-, chymotrypsin-, and postglutamyl hydrolase-like activities (reviewed in Coux et al 1996). This 20S structure consists of four stacks of seven subunits arranged in a barrel-like configuration with a hollow core (Lowe et al 1995, Groll et al 1997). Formation of the 26S proteasome occurs as a result of the addition of one or two multi-subunit 19S caps to ends of the 20S structure. These caps are notable for several features. First, at least one subunit capable of binding polyubiquitin chains has been discerned (S5a in human, MBP1 in *Arabidopsis thaliana*) (Deveraux et al 1994, 1995). Initial enthusiasm that S5a represents the unique ubiquitin recognition element has been tempered by the observation that yeast cells deficient in the homologue of this subunit are viable, despite the clearly essential roles of ubiquitination and proteasomal degradation in *S. cerevisiae* (Coux et al 1996). Thus there may be other, yet to be determined, recognition elements for ubiquitinated proteins. Second, Doa4p, a subunit of the 19S cap in *S. cerevisiae*, has been shown to cleave polyubiquitin chains from residual peptides that remain proteasome associated after digestion of proteins (Papa & Hochstrasser 1993). Third, the 19S structure includes multiple subunits with ATPase activity. Although the range of activities of these subunits has not been exhaustively analyzed, they may be responsible for the unfolding of proteins as they are fed into the multi-catalytic proteasome core (reviewed in Coux et al 1996). Finally, other recognition elements exist within the 19S structure. In particular, the 19S cap recognizes the protein antizyme in a ubiquitin-independent manner. Antizyme complexes with ornithine decarboxylase, thereby targeting the latter for ubiquitin-independent proteasomal degradation (Bercovich et al 1989, Murakami et al 1992, Elias et al 1995, Li et al 1996).

Proteasomes are not static, fixed structures, but rather are subject to dynamic alterations in composition. For example, treatment of cells with γ-interferon results in increased incorporation of three subunits into the 20S multi-catalytic complex and the reciprocal loss of three other subunits. These alterations facilitate generation of peptides that, when transported into the ER, are efficiently loaded onto and presented at the cell surface by major histocompatibility complex (MHC) encoded class I molecules. Exposure to γ-interferon also results in the replacement of the 19S cap with the 11S regulator or PA28. This alternative proteasome component is not known to have a ubiquitin recognition element, but results in a particle believed to have enhanced overall activity, facilitating the generation of peptides appropriate for presentation by MHC class I molecules (reviewed in Coux et al 1996, Rock 1996, Weissman 1997).

Although the addition of polyubiquitin chains is a potent targeting signal for degradation in the 26S proteasome, it is also evident that ubiquitination is reversible and that a number of not fully characterized, de-ubiquitinating enzymes exist free in the cytosol (Zhu et al 1996, 1997; reviewed in Hochstrasser 1996, Wilkinson 1997). Underscoring this significance of de-ubiquitination is the recurrent observation that when proteasome function is inhibited, primarily non-ubiquitinated forms of proteins accumulate.

DEGRADATION OF ER-RETAINED PROTEINS BY THE UBIQUITIN-PROTEASOME SYSTEM

As mentioned above, most physiological substrates for proteasomal degradation identified to date are cytosolic or nuclear proteins (Coux et al 1996,

Weissman 1997). A major development in the past three years has been the realization that many proteins retained in the ER are translocated back into the cytosol and subsequently degraded by proteasomes. This discovery has shed light into the long-known but, until recently, poorly understood phenomenon of protein degradation from the ER (Bonifacino & Klausner 1994, Brodsky & McCracken 1997). Among the ER-retained proteins targeted for proteasomal degradation are abnormal newly synthesized proteins (e.g. mutant proteins or unassembled subunits of multi-protein complexes) and ER resident proteins, the levels of which are controlled by regulated proteolysis (e.g. HMG-CoA reductase) (Table 1). Although the final effectors of the degradation of these proteins are well-known components of the ubiquitin-proteasome machinery, the molecular mechanisms involved in translocating the proteins from the ER back to the cytosol are only now beginning to be unraveled. In the following sections, we review recent progress in the understanding of this process.

Import of Nascent Proteins into the ER

In order to understand how ER-retained proteins are targeted to the ubiquitin-proteasome system for degradation, it is first necessary to describe how proteins are initially imported into the ER. The vast majority of proteins destined for secretion into the extracellular space or for residence within compartments of the secretory pathway enter this pathway when they are co- or post-translationally translocated from the cytosol into the ER (reviewed by Corsi & Schekman 1996, Rapoport et al 1996). Both co- and post-translational passage of polypeptide chains through the ER membrane are mediated by the translocon, a cylindrical protein complex with a central pore. The basic structure of the translocon has been conserved throughout evolution; it consists of a complex (referred to as the Sec61p complex) of three integral membrane proteins named Sec61p, Sbh1p, and Sss1p in yeast, which correspond to Sec61α, Sec61β, and Sec61γ, respectively, in mammals (Corsi & Schekman 1996, Rapoport et al 1996). Sec61p/Sec61α is a multi-spanning membrane protein that constitutes the main protein translocation channel. An additional complex known as the Sec63p complex, composed of Sec62p, Sec63p, Sec71p, and Sec72p, is required for post-translational protein translocation. This complex is thought to bind newly synthesized proteins on the cytosolic side of the membrane and to transfer them to the Sec61p complex. Finally, there is evidence for the existence of a third complex composed of Ssh1p, Sbh2p, and Sss1p subunits that may be involved in the co-translational translocation of some proteins (Finke et al 1996). The ER luminal chaperone Kar2p (known as BiP in higher eukaryotes) binds to the luminal, DnaJ-like domain of Sec63p and, in an ATP-dependent manner, aids in the translocation process (Corsi & Schekman 1996, Rapoport et al 1996). Newly synthesized polypeptides containing hydrophobic transmembrane domains are

Table 1 Proteins retained in the ER that are degraded by the proteasome

Protein	Cause of ER retention-degradation	Evidence of ubiquitin involvement	References
α_1-antitrypsin	Mutant		(Qu et al 1996, Werner et al 1996)
α-GL-PLAP chimera	Mutation of GPI addition site		(Oda et al 1996)
Antithrombin	Mutant		(Tokunaga et al 1997)
ApoB	Limited availability of lipids	+	(Yeung et al 1996, Benoist & Grand-Perret 1997, Fisher et al 1997, Wu et al 1997)
CD4	Induced by HIV-1 Env and Vpu proteins		(Fujita et al 1997)
CFTR	Mutant, normal	+	(Jensen et al 1995, Ward et al 1995)
CPY (yeast)	Mutant	+	(Hiller et al 1996, Plemper et al 1997)
Cytochrome P-450s	Chemical damage, oxidation	+	(Tierney et al 1992, Roberts 1997, Yang & Cederbaum 1997)
HMG-CoA reductase (yeast)	Induced by mevalonate or its metabolites		(Hampton & Rine 1994, Hampton et al 1996)
MHC class I heavy chains	Induced by HCMV US11/ US2 proteins or by DTT treatment, unassembled		(Wiertz et al 1996a,b, Hughes et al 1997)
p185c-erb B-2	Induced by geldanamycin		(Mimnaugh et al 1996)
Presenilin-2	Expressed in transfected cells	+	(Kim et al 1997)
Pro-α-factor (yeast)	Unglycosylated		(McCracken & Brodsky 1996, Werner et al 1996, Pilon et al 1997)
Proteinase A (yeast)	Mutant	+	(Hiller et al 1996)
Sec61p translocon subunit (yeast)	Mutant	+	(Biederer et al 1996)
Sss1p translocon subunit (yeast)	Mutation in associated Sec61p	+	(Biederer et al 1996)
TCR-α chain	Unassembled, differentiation-controlled in normal thymocytes	+	(Huppa & Ploegh 1997, Yu et al 1997, Yang et al 1998)
TCR-CD3-δ chain	Unassembled, differentiation-controlled in normal thymocytes	+	(Yang et al 1998, Bonifacino & Klausner 1994)
Tropoelastin	Brefeldin A-induced		(Davis & Mecham 1996)
Tyrosinase	Normal, increased in amelanotic melanomas	+	(Halaban et al 1997)

integrated into the ER membrane, whereas soluble polypeptides are delivered into the lumen of the ER.

Protein Modifications and Quality Control in the ER

As nascent polypeptide chains emerge in the ER lumen, they are subjected to a series of posttranslational modifications including signal peptide cleavage, addition of N-linked oligosaccharide chains, disulfide-bond formation, addition of glycosyl-phosphatidylinositol anchors, folding, and assembly into oligomeric complexes. These maturation events are effected by the concerted action of ER-resident enzymes and molecular chaperones. Properly modified proteins then move to sites of vesicle budding and are transported to the Golgi complex. For most proteins, this intricate set of reactions is completed with astonishing efficiency. When proteins fail to undergo some of these modifications, however, they are generally retained in the ER (Hammond & Helenius 1995). Some ER-retained proteins are quite stable and, in the most extreme cases, accumulate in distended regions of the ER [e.g. Russell bodies containing abnormal immunoglobulins in myeloma cells (Valetti et al 1991)]. Other ER-retained proteins undergo rapid degradation from the ER (Bonifacino & Klausner 1994, Brodsky & McCracken 1997). The ability to discriminate between properly modified (i.e. normal) and improperly modified (i.e. abnormal) proteins, and the ensuing retention in the ER and degradation of abnormal proteins, have been referred to as the quality control function of the ER (Hammond & Helenius 1995). Quality control mechanisms are thought to serve an important physiological role by preventing the deployment of abnormal proteins at sites where they could potentially interfere with vital cellular functions.

Non-Lysosomal Nature of the Degradation of Proteins Retained in the ER

Over the past 10 years, numerous proteins have been shown to undergo degradation soon after translocation into the ER (for a comprehensive list, see Bonifacino & Klausner 1994). This phenomenon has been documented in a wide range of eukaryotic organisms, from yeast to humans, suggesting that it is the result of general, evolutionarily conserved processes. Early studies established some of the general characteristics of these processes (reviewed by Bonifacino & Klausner 1994, Brodsky & McCracken 1997). First, degradation from the ER was found to be highly selective, such that some proteins retained in the ER were rapidly degraded whereas others were not. Second, degradation was insensitive to inhibitors of lysosomal degradation in mammalian cells and unaffected by mutations of genes required for vacuolar degradation in yeast. Third, the proteins were last detected in the ER prior to degradation. Finally, degradation was not inhibited by blocking transport out of the ER-Golgi system with pharmacological inhibitors such as brefeldin A in mammalian cells or by mutation of genes involved in ER to Golgi transport in yeast (e.g. *SEC12, SEC17, SEC18,* or *SEC23*). The intriguing implication of these findings was that lysosomes, the main site of protein degradation within the secretory and endocytic pathways, were not involved in the degradation of proteins retained in the ER. Owing to these properties, the phenomenon became known as degradation from the ER, ER-associated degradation, or, simply, ER degradation.

Involvement of the Ubiquitin-Proteasome Pathway in the Degradation of Proteins Retained in the ER

The mechanisms involved in the degradation of proteins retained in the ER remained obscure for several years. One of the possibilities was that proteins were degraded by ER-resident proteases. However, despite some reports of proteolytic activities associated with ER fractions, efforts to identify specific ER proteases capable of complete, yet selective, protein degradation were unsuccessful. A major conceptual breakthrough occurred in 1993, when Sommer & Jentsch demonstrated that a defect in protein translocation into the ER caused by a mutation that destabilizes the Sec61p component of the translocon could be suppressed by mutation of the ubiquitin-conjugating enzyme Ubc6p (Sommer & Jentsch 1993). This observation suggested, for the first time, a connection between the degradation of an abnormal protein from the ER and the ubiquitin system. Then, in 1995, two groups reported that peptide aldehyde proteasome inhibitors (Rock et al 1994) and the structurally unrelated proteasome inhibitor lactacystin (Fenteany et al 1994) prevented degradation of both normal and mutant forms of the cystic fibrosis transmembrane conductance regulator (CFTR) in the ER (Jensen et al 1995, Ward et al 1995). This observation provided the first piece of evidence implicating proteasomes in the destruction of ER-retained proteins.

Additional experiments (Ward et al 1995) demonstrated that the proteasomal degradation of the CFTR required polyubiquitination of the protein. Treatment with proteasomal inhibitors, for instance, resulted in the accumulation of high molecular weight CFTR species that were recognized by anti-ubiquitin antibodies on immunoblot analyses (Ward et al 1995). Moreover, expression of a dominant-negative ubiquitin mutant (K48R), which prevents formation of polyubiquitin chains (Chau et al 1989), blocked degradation of both the normal and mutant forms of the CFTR (Ward et al 1995). In addition, decreased conjugation of ubiquitin and decreased degradation of the CFTR were observed in cells that carry a temperature-sensitive mutation of the ubiquitin-activating enzyme E1 at the nonpermissive temperature (Ward et al 1995). These observations firmly established a role for the ubiquitin-proteasome pathway in the degradation of the CFTR retained in the ER and raised the possibility that other ER-retained proteins could be degraded by the same pathway. This is now known to be the case, as many other proteins retained in the ER have been shown to be polyubiquitinated and degraded by a process sensitive to proteasome inhibitors (Table 1).

Export of Degradation Substrates from the ER to the Cytosol

The CFTR and other polytopic membrane proteins such as HMG-CoA reductase degraded from the ER have sizable portions of their polypeptide chains exposed to the cytosol and are thus directly accessible to the ubiquitin-proteasome degradative machinery. In contrast, many other ER-retained proteins degraded by this pathway (Table 1) either have short cytosolic tails [e.g. the T-cell antigen receptor (TCR) α chain] or are completely sequestered within the ER lumen (e.g. α_1-antitrypsin mutants). This topology poses a problem of access because components of the ubiquitin-proteasome pathway are cytosolic. Obviously, such proteins must be transported back into the cytosol to be degraded by proteasomes.

The ER membrane is permeable to nascent polypeptide chains by virtue of the translocon (see above), as well as to peptides transported into the ER by an ABC-type transporter, TAP (Hill & Ploegh 1995). In both cases, however, the direction of the polypeptide flow is from the cytosol to the ER lumen. Although there was evidence for the release of partially translocated nascent chains from ER membranes in in vitro translation-translocation assays (Garcia et al 1988, Ooi & Weiss 1992) and for the release of a glycosylated tripeptide from the ER lumen in permeabilized yeast cells (Römisch & Schekman 1992), it was not known until recently whether these processes also occurred in live cells. Studies by Wiertz et al (1996a,b) demonstrated that this was indeed the case for MHC class I heavy chains synthesized in the presence of either the US2 or US11 proteins of human cytomegalovirus (HCMV). MHC class I molecules are complexes of a glycosylated type I integral membrane heavy chain bound to peptide and a soluble luminal protein, $\beta2$-microglobulin. US2 and US11 were found to cause dislocation of newly synthesized MHC class I heavy chains from the ER membrane to the cytosol in vivo, leading to their rapid destruction by a pathway sensitive to proteasome inhibitors. Fully folded and assembled MHC class I heavy chains could also be dislocated and targeted for proteasomal destruction in the absence of viral gene products by treatment of cells with dithiothreitol, a reducing agent that induces misfolding of proteins in the ER.

Like translocation of nascent chains into the ER, dislocation into the cytosol was expected to involve a proteinaceous channel that allows transfer of the polypeptide chains across the lipid bilayer. The work of Wiertz et al (1996b) showed that MHC class I heavy chains targeted for cytosolic destruction were transiently associated with the Sec61p complex, suggesting that dislocation is mediated by the translocon. Thus the release of ER proteins for cytosolic destruction seems to represent a reversal of the process by which nascent polypeptide chains are initially inserted into and translocated across the ER membrane.

Permeabilized Cell Systems and Yeast Genetic Approaches to Study Degradation of ER-Retained Proteins

In addition to the use of proteasome inhibitors, other approaches contributing to the explanation of the mechanism of degradation from the ER were the reconstitution of the degradative process in permeabilized cells and the use of yeast genetic methodologies. McCracken, Brodsky, and colleagues (McCracken & Brodsky 1996, Werner et al 1996) developed a permeabilized yeast cell system that recapitulated some of the properties of the degradation process in vivo. In this system, newly synthesized, unglycosylated yeast prepro-α-factor, a soluble luminal protein, was released from the ER into the incubation medium and underwent degradation in a cytosol- and ATP-dependent fashion. The system proved particularly informative when used in combination with mutant yeast strains as sources of permeabilized cells or cytosol. Thus it was possible to establish that the ER-chaperone Cne1p/calnexin and the proteasome subunits Pre1p and Pre2p are involved in this process (McCracken & Brodsky 1996, Werner et al 1996).

Other yeast proteins such as HMG-CoA reductase and mutant forms of carboxypeptidase Y and proteinase A are also degraded from the ER (Hampton et al 1996, Hiller et al 1996). The availability of various yeast degradation substrates allowed the development of assays to examine the involvement of known gene products in the process, as well as to screen for novel components of the pathway. Among the known proteins that have thus been implicated in the process are ER chaperones (Cne1p/calnexin and Kar2p/BiP), the catalytic subunits of signal peptidase (Sec11p and Spc3p), components of the translocon (Sec61p and Sec63p), ubiquitin-conjugating enzymes (Ubc6p and Ubc7p), and subunits of the proteasome (Cim3p, Cim5p, Hrd2p, Pre1p, Pre2p, and Pre4p) (Table 2). One of the novel components identified through yeast genetic screens is Der1p, a small multi-spanning membrane protein localized to the ER (Knop et al 1996). Another novel component, Der3p/Hrd1p, has five putative transmembrane spans and a large carboxy-terminal domain oriented toward the ER lumen (Hampton et al 1996, Bordallo et al 1998). Finally, a third novel component of the pathway is Hrd3p, which is predicted to be a type I integral membrane protein with a large amino-terminal luminal domain (Hampton et al 1996) (Table 2). The functions of these latter three proteins, Der1p, Der3p/Hrd1p, and Hrd3p, have not been established.

An Integrated View of the Mechanism of Protein Degradation from the ER

The studies described above have begun to delineate the steps of the pathway by which ER-retained proteins are targeted for degradation by the proteasome. A hypothetical depiction of the pathway is shown in Figure 2. In this scheme, misfolded, unassembled or aberrantly modified proteins are recognized by ER chaperones such as Cne1p/calnexin or Kar2p/BiP or by other components of the protein processing or transport machineries (step 1, substrate recognition and targeting to the translocon). The translocon is then opened and reprogrammed

Table 2   Yeast mutants defective in degradation of proteins retained in the ER

Mutant	Protein	Probable role in ER degradation	References
cim3/sug1	Cim3p, subunit of the 19S proteasome particle	Substrate recognition in the cytosol and targeting to the 20S proteasome particle	(Hiller et al 1996)
cim5	Cim5p, subunit of the 19S proteasome particle	Substrate recognition in the cytosol and targeting to the 20S proteasome particle	(Hiller et al 1996)
cne1	Cne1p/calnexin, ER integral membrane chaperone	Substrate recognition in the ER? Targeting to the translocon?	(McCracken & Brodsky 1996)
cue1	Cue1p, cytosolically disposed, membrane-anchored protein localized to the ER	Binds Ubc7p	(Biederer et al 1997)
der1	Der1p, small hydrophobic protein localized to the ER membrane, four potential transmembrane spans	Substrate recognition in the ER? Targeting to the translocon? Retrotranslocation?	(Knop et al 1996)
der2/ubc7	Der2p/Ubc7p, ubiquitin-conjugating enzyme, interacts with Ubc6p, recruited to the ER membrane by Cue1p	Substrate ubiquitination	(Biederer et al 1996, Hiller et al 1996)
der3/hrd1	Der3p/Hrd1p, multi-spanning ER integral membrane protein with a luminally oriented domain containing a RING-H2 finger motif	Substrate recognition in the ER? Targeting to the translocon? Retrotranslocation?	(Hampton et al 1996, Bordallo et al 1998)
hrd2	Hrd2p, p97 component of the 19S proteasome particle, also known as TRAP-2	Substrate recognition in the cytosol and targeting to the 20S proteasome particle	(Hampton et al 1996)
hrd3	Hrd3p, luminally disposed ER integral membrane protein	Substrate recognition in the ER? Targeting to the translocon? Retrotranslocation?	(Hampton et al 1996)
kar2	Kar2p/BiP, ER luminal chaperone	Substrate unfolding in the ER? Retrotranslocation?	(Plemper et al 1997)

(Continued)

Table 2   *(Continued)*

Mutant	Protein	Probable role in ER degradation	References
pre1	Pre1p, component of the 20S proteasome particle responsible for its chymotrypsin-like activity	Proteolysis	(Biederer et al 1996, 1997, Hiller et al 1996, Werner et al 1996)
pre2	Pre2p, component of the 20S proteasome particle	Proteolysis	(Hiller et al 1996)
pre4	Pre1p, component of the 20S proteasome particle	Proteolysis	(Hiller et al 1996)
spc3	Spc3p, catalytic subunit of signal peptidase	Endoproteolytic cleavage in the ER lumen	(Fang et al 1997)
sec11	Sec11p, catalytic subunit of signal peptidase	Endoproteolytic cleavage in the ER lumen	(Mullins et al 1995)
sec61	Sec61p, pore-forming subunit of the translocon	Retrotranslocation	(Pilon et al 1997, Plemper et al 1997)
sec63	Sec63p, translocon subunit	Retrotranslocation	(Plemper et al 1997)
ubc6	Ubc6p, ubiquitin-conjugating enzyme anchored to the cytosolic face of the ER membrane, interacts with Ubc7p	Substrate ubiquitination	(Biederer et al 1996, Hiller et al 1996)

for retrotranslocation. Next the polypeptide chains are unfolded and forced through the translocon (step 2, retrotranslocation). Proteins such as Der1p, Der3p/Hrd1p, and Hrd3p can be involved in either of the two previous steps. Cytosolic chaperones (e.g. members of the Hsp70 and DnaJ families) can supply the force needed to drive the polypeptide chains through the channel. The retrotranslocated polypeptide chains either are released into the cytosol as soluble proteins or remain adhered to the cytosolic face of the ER membrane. N-linked oligosaccharides are removed from the polypeptides by a cytosolic N-glycanase, and the proteins are polyubiquitinated (step 3, release into the cytosol, deglycosylation, and polyubiquitination); the order of these three events has not been established. Polyubiquitinated proteins bind to the proteasome and are degraded to peptides; peptides are further broken down by cytosolic exopeptidases (step 4, proteasomal degradation). The entire process is likely to consume a large amount of energy because unfolding, retrotranslocation, ubiquitination, and proteasomal degradation are known (or expected) to be ATP

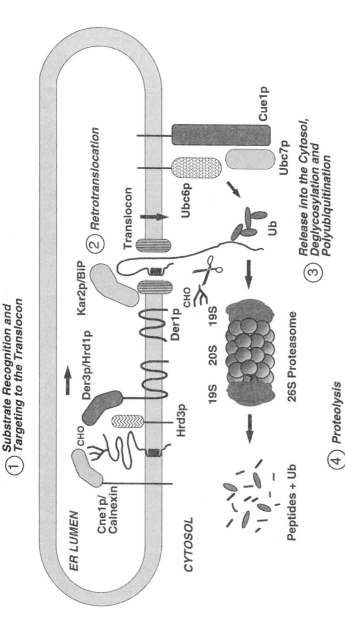

Figure 2   Schematic representation of the degradation of an ER-retained protein. See section "An Integrated View of the Mechanism of Protein Degradation from the ER" for description of the steps.

dependent. The steps of the process are discussed in more detail in the next four sections.

Recognition of Protein Substrates and Targeting to the Translocon

Quality control mechanisms are likely to involve sensing of the maturation state of newly synthesized proteins, a role probably played by the same proteins responsible for protein processing. For example, Kar2p/BiP has been shown to recognize specific sequences in folding or assembly intermediates (reviewed by Gething & Sambrook 1992). Similarly, Cne1p/calnexin binds monoglucosylated N-linked oligosaccharides that are intermediates in the processing of glycoproteins in the ER (Hammond & Helenius 1995). Thus whereas dynamic association with these ER chaperones may mediate folding and oligomerization of nascent proteins, failure to dissociate may promote interaction with the translocon, eventually leading to ejection of the proteins into the cytosol (see Knittler et al 1995). Analyses of yeast mutant strains have demonstrated that Kar2p and Cne1p are indeed required for the degradation of certain substrates by the ubiquitin-proteasome pathway (McCracken & Brodsky 1996, Plemper et al 1997).

In addition to misfolding, other features appear to predispose proteins for degradation from the ER. It is now clear that quality control mechanisms are capable of monitoring the trimming status of N-linked oligosaccharide chains and deciding the fate of a protein on this basis. For example, inhibition of ER mannosidases, which trim mannose residues from high-mannose, N-linked oligosaccharide chains, prevents degradation of unassembled TCR-CD3-δ chains of the T-cell antigen receptor (Yang et al 1998). This suggests that the ER may contain mannose-binding lectins that mediate recognition for degradation. Another feature known to destabilize proteins in the ER is the presence of short or unusually hydrophilic transmembrane domains, as is the case for the TCR-α and TCR-β chains (Bonifacino & Klausner 1994). When not assembled with other subunits of the complex, such transmembrane domains may remain associated with the translocon or with other transmembrane proteins in the ER, resulting in their rapid clearance from the ER. The reduced hydrophobicity of these transmembrane domains may also facilitate slippage of these proteins into the cytosol.

Certain viral gene products may target specific classes of proteins for degradation. For example, the HCMV US2 and US11 proteins are predicted to be transmembrane proteins with luminal domains that bind MHC class I heavy chains and transmembrane domains that might interact with the translocation machinery (Wiertz et al 1996a,b). The Vpu protein of human immunodeficiency virus-1 is another example of a viral protein that functions as a specific recognition/targeting molecule, in this case for the CD4 co-receptor (Fujita et al 1997). ER proteins such as HMG-CoA reductase that are subject to metabolic control may interact with specific regulatory molecules that bring them to the translocation apparatus in response to metabolic stimuli. Finally, two of the transmembrane proteins newly identified through yeast genetic screens, Der3p/Hrd1p and Hrd3p, are predicted to have large luminal domains; these domains could participate in interactions with luminal substrates either before or during retrotranslocation.

Preparation of some proteins for retrotranslocation may entail limited proteolysis in the ER lumen. Signal peptidase has been shown to cause discrete fragmentation of certain abnormal proteins retained in the ER, prior to their complete degradation (Mullins et al 1995, Fang et al 1997). Interestingly, mutations in Sec11p and Spc3p, the subunits of signal peptidase required for catalytic activity, prevent both the fragmentation and the eventual destruction of chimeric proteins (Mullins et al 1995, Fang et al 1997), suggesting that signal-peptidase-mediated fragmentation may be an obligatory step in the targeting of those proteins for degradation in the cytosol. Indeed, cooperation between luminal cleavages performed by signal peptidase and degradation in the cytosol by the 26S proteosome has been suggested for the removal of mutant Sec61p from the yeast ER (Biederer et al 1996).

Retrotranslocation

MHC class I heavy chains targeted for destruction in the cytosol were shown to associate transiently with the mammalian Sec61p complex by co-precipitation with antibodies to its Sec61β or Sec61γ subunits (yeast Sbh1p and Sss1p, respectively) (Wiertz et al 1996b). In yeast cells, unglycosylated prepro-α-factor targeted for degradation was found to associate with Sec61p (the equivalent of mammalian Sec61α) (Pilon et al 1997). Taken together, these data suggest that the three basic subunits of the translocon are components of the complex involved in retrotranslocation. Strong support for these correlations comes from observations that some mutants in Sec61p are defective in retrotranslocation, thus implying that this protein is essential for export from the ER to the cytosol (Pilon et al 1997, Plemper et al 1997). In contrast, retrotranslocation is not affected by deletion of the gene encoding Sbh1p, indicating that other subunits of the translocon are not required for retrotranslocation even though they may interact with the translocating polypeptide chain (Plemper et al 1997). The degradation of mutant carboxypeptidase Y in yeast was not affected by mutations in Sec62p, Sec71p, Sec72p, Ssh1p, and Sbh2, all components of the protein import machinery (Plemper et al 1997). Mutations in Sec63p result in stabilization of mutant carboxypeptidase Y (Plemper et al 1997); however, other mutations in Sec63p that affect protein import have no effect in retrotranslocation of unglycosylated prepro-α-factor (Pilon et al 1997). A possible explanation for these differences is that Sec63p may be necessary for export of some, but not all, substrates.

By analogy with the Sec63p complex, which adapts the Sec61p complex for post-translational import into the ER (Corsi & Schekman 1996, Rapoport et al 1996), there is likely a set of proteins that program the Sec61p complex for export from the ER. Perhaps this is one role played by the transmembrane proteins Der1p, Der3p/Hrd1p, and Hrd3p. Kar2p may promote retrotranslocation by effecting unfolding of the polypeptide chains. It is also likely that cytosolic chaperones such as hsc70 might bind to the polypeptides as they emerge on the cytosolic side of the membrane (Yang et al 1993).

Release into the Cytosol, Deglycosylation, and Polyubiquitination

Upon inhibition of proteasomal degradation, some retrotranslocated proteins are released as soluble proteins into the cytosol. These include luminal proteins such as unglycosylated yeast prepro-α-factor (McCracken & Brodsky 1996) and transmembrane proteins such as MHC class I heavy chains (Wiertz et al 1996a,b) and TCR-α chains transiently overexpressed in non-T cells (Huppa & Ploegh 1997, Yu et al 1997). Other proteins such as yeast carboxypeptidase Y (Hiller et al 1996) and a fraction of the transmembrane TCR-α in non-T cells adhere to the cytosolic face of the ER membrane (Huppa & Ploegh 1997, Yu et al 1997). For MHC class I heavy chains and TCR-α (Wiertz et al 1996a,b; Hughes et al 1997, Huppa & Ploegh 1997, Yu et al 1997), retrotranslocation is accompanied by the removal of N-linked oligosaccharides. Since the translocation pore is thought to be sufficiently wide to allow passage of complete N-linked oligosaccharides moieties attached to the polypeptide chains, and a cytosolic peptide:N-glycanase has been described (Suzuki et al 1994), it is likely that this deglycosylation occurs upon exposure to the cytosolic milieu.

Studies carried out in T lymphocytes on the TCR-CD3-δ chain have revealed another possible topology for proteins protected from degradation by inhibition of proteasome function. When the proteasome is inhibited, undegraded TCR-CD3-δ actually retains its normal transmembrane topology and remains dimerized with TCR-CD3-ϵ, which, unlike TCR-CD3-δ, is not normally targeted for degradation (Yang et al 1998). Along the same vein, when analyzed in its native context in T cells, TCR-α was found to undergo only partial retrotranslocation when proteasome function was inhibited, with the majority of the protein mass remaining sequestered within the ER lumen (Yang et al 1998). These observations suggest that the proteolytic activity of the proteasome is required for complete extraction of TCR-CD3-δ and TCR-α from the ER. Since both of these subunits are polyubiquitinated while still bound to the ER membrane (Yang et al 1998), it may be that polyubiquitination provides the physical link necessary for proteasome-dependent removal from ER membranes. Interestingly, TCR-α

lacks cytosolic lysine residues but has a number of luminal lysine residues, as well as one in the transmembrane domain (Chien et al 1984). Therefore, for this TCR subunit, initiation of retrotranslocation must precede polyubiquitination.

It is apparent that many, though apparently not all, proteins retrotranslocated into the cytosol become polyubiquitinated (Table 1). Biochemical and genetic analyses of the CFTR (Ward et al 1995), Sec61p and Sss1p (Biederer et al 1996) and mutant carboxypeptidase Y (Hiller et al 1996), have all demonstrated that polyubiquitination is required for degradation by the proteasome. Given that polyubiquitination is a prerequisite for the proteasomal degradation of many cytosolic and nuclear proteins, we anticipate that this will similarly be the case for other ER-retained proteins.

Attachment of polyubiquitin chains to degradation substrates is probably mediated by the ubiquitin-conjugating enzymes Ubc6p or Ubc7p, as mutation of genes encoding either of these enzymes in yeast prevents or retards degradation of proteins retained in the ER (Biederer et al 1996, Hiller et al 1996). Ubc6p is unique among ubiquitin-conjugating enzymes in that it is anchored to the ER and nuclear membranes by a carboxy-terminal hydrophobic tail, with its catalytic domain facing the cytosol (Sommer & Jentsch 1993, Yang et al 1997). The localization of Ubc6p to the ER may allow it to have immediate access to the retrotranslocated proteins, thus effecting rapid polyubiquitination of the proteins, perhaps while polypeptide chains are in the process of emerging from the translocon. Ubc7p is a soluble, cytosolic protein that is recruited to the ER membrane by interaction with a protein called Cue1p (Biederer et al 1997). Mutations in Cue1p abolish degradation of ER-retained proteins and, interestingly, prevent retrotranslocation as well, providing further evidence that ubiquitination and retrotranslocation are linked. The localization of Ubc6p and Ubc7p to the ER membrane raises the possibility that other components of the ubiquitin-proteasome pathway may be similarly associated with this membrane.

Western blot analyses of MHC class I heavy chains retrotranslocated by the US2 and US11 proteins have failed to reveal polyubiquitination when the proteasome is inhibited (Wiertz et al 1996a,b). Thus this protein may be an example of a group of proteins for which polyubiquitination is not required for targeting to the proteasome, as has been previously shown for the cytosolic protein ornithine decarboxylase (Murakami et al 1992). However, it is also possible that polyubiquitination of MHC class I heavy chains may not have been detected owing to either rapid deubiquitination by cytosolic deubiquitinating enzymes or to the quality of the antiubiquitin antibodies used for detection.

Proteasomal Degradation

Analyses of yeast mutants have implicated both the 19S and 20S particles of the 26S proteasome in the degradation of proteins released from the ER.

The involvement of the 19S particle in degradation was first suggested by the observation that a yeast gene involved in the regulated turnover of HMG-CoA reductase, HRD2, encodes a 109-kDa protein homologous to a component of the human 19S particle referred to as p97/TRAP-2 (Hampton et al 1996). Mutations in two additional subunits of the yeast 19S particle, Cim3p/Sug1p and Cim5p, also reduce the rate of degradation of ER-retained proteins (Hiller et al 1996). The 20S particle of eukaryotic proteasomes contains several catalytic subunits that hydrolyze peptide bonds with distinct site specificities (see above). The Pre1p subunit is responsible, at least in part, for the chymotryptic activity of the proteasome. Mutations in Pre1p alone, or in combination with mutations in two other proteasomal subunits, Pre2p or Pre4p, cause a marked decrease in the rate of degradation of ER-retained proteins (Biederer et al 1996, Hiller et al 1996, Werner et al 1996). Peptides produced by the proteasome escape from the central proteolytic channel through gaps between the proteasome subunits and are degraded by cytosolic exopeptidases.

Upon homogenization of cells, proteasomes are recovered mostly in the cytosolic fraction (Palmer et al 1996), suggesting that they exist free in solution. However, a subpopulation of proteasomes are bound to the cytosolic face of ER membranes (Rivett et al 1992, Palmer et al 1996). These membrane-bound proteasomes could be interacting with the Sec61p complex or with other proteins involved in retrotranslocation. Alternatively, proteasomes could be interacting directly with the lipid bilayer. In support of this notion, it has been demonstrated that proteasomes bind to lipid monolayers with the proteasome channel oriented perpendicular to the monolayer (Newman et al 1996). Membrane-bound proteasomes would be ideally disposed to degrade proteins as they emerge from the translocation apparatus. An attractive possibility, discussed above, is that proteasomes may even contribute to the extraction of ubiquitinated proteins from the ER membrane. Membrane-bound proteasomes could also be engaged in degradation of the cytosolic domains of integral membrane proteins prior to their extraction from the ER membrane. Evidence for this comes from in vitro experiments in which the 20S proteasome was found to degrade a cytosolically disposed segment of cytochrome P-450, leaving a fragment of the protein attached to the ER membrane (Roberts 1997).

Physiological Role of the Process of Protein Degradation from the ER

How essential is the ability to degrade proteins from the ER? Apparently, yeast cells can do very well without it. For instance, yeast cells bearing null mutations in the *HRD3, HRD1/DER3*, and *DER1* genes are viable and exhibit normal rates of growth in liquid culture (Hampton et al 1996, Knop et al 1996, Bordallo et al 1998). It remains to be determined, however, whether this pathway is required for growth of yeast cells under conditions of stress. In mammalian cells, accumulation of undegraded abnormal proteins in the ER could potentially lead to cytopathic effects and cell death. This has been suggested as the underlying cause for liver disease in human patients, wherein abnormal forms of α_1-antitrypsin are synthesized (Amara et al 1992). In addition, the degradation of proteins from the ER is an integral part of mechanisms that regulate protein expression during development (e.g. the TCR complex) and under certain metabolic conditions (e.g. HMG-CoA reductase and apolipoprotein B) (reviewed by Bonifacino & Klausner 1994). It is thus likely that the ability to degrade proteins from the ER is essential in higher eukaryotes.

Another potentially important role for the degradation of ER-retained proteins in mammals is the production of antigenic peptides for presentation by MHC class I molecules. For instance, it has recently been demonstrated that dedifferentiation of melanoma cells causes tyrosinase, a type I integral membrane protein, to be retained in the ER and degraded by the ubiquitin-proteasome pathway (Halaban et al 1997). Interestingly, tyrosinase peptides produced in this way appear to be imported back into the ER and presented to the immune system by MHC class I molecules (Skipper et al 1996). It will now be of interest to determine whether other antigenic peptides derived from endogenous integral membrane or luminal proteins are also generated by this pathway.

UBIQUITINATION OF PLASMA MEMBRANE PROTEINS

In addition to the degradation of ER-retained proteins, ubiquitination has recently been implicated in the internalization and degradation of plasma membrane proteins. The first hints of a role for ubiquitin in the regulation of plasma membrane proteins were obtained in the mid-1980s, when several cell surface receptors, including the platelet-derived growth factor β-receptor (PDGFRβ) (Yarden et al 1986) and growth hormone receptor (GHR) (Leung et al 1987), were found to contain covalently attached ubiquitin chains. Also at that time, it was reported that the leukocyte homing receptor (Mel-14) was modified with ubiquitin on its intraluminal domain during its processing through the secretory pathway; the significance of this finding remains unclear (Siegelman et al 1986, St. John et al 1986). These initial observations occurred at a time when ubiquitination had been studied primarily as an in vitro process, and its role in general protein turnover was not fully appreciated. Beginning in 1992, studies involving multi-subunit receptors of the immune system and growth factor receptors revealed that ubiquitination of a number of cell surface receptors that signal through tyrosine kinase activation occurs in response to binding of ligands (Table 3).

Table 3 Transmembrane cell surface mammalian and yeast proteins that are subject to ubiquitination

Transmembrane protein	Characteristics (see below)	References
TCR	b,d,i	(Cenciarelli et al 1992, 1996, Hou et al 1994)
FcεRI	b,j	(Paolini & Kinet 1993)
PDGFRβ	b,d	(Mori et al 1992, 1993)
c-kit	b,d,i	(Miyazawa et al 1994, AM Weissman unpublished data)
GHR	b,f	(Strous et al 1996, 1997)
EGFR	b,d	(Galcheva-Gargova et al 1995)
c-Met	b,g	(Jeffers et al 1997)
Fibroblast growth factor receptor	b	(Mori et al 1995a)
Colony stimulating factor 1 receptor	b	(Mori et al 1995a)
Insulin receptor	a,g,k	(Sepp-Lorenzino et al 1995)
Insulin-like growth factor receptor	a,g,k	(Sepp-Lorenzino et al 1995)
p185c-erbB-2	g,k	(Mimnaugh et al 1996)
Mel-14	l	(Siegelman et al 1986, St. John et al 1986)
ErbB-4	m	(Vecchi & Carpenter 1997)
Ste2p	b,e,f,h	(Hicke & Riezman 1996, Hicke et al 1998, Terrell et al 1998)
Ste6p	f	(Kolling & Hollenberg 1994, Kolling & Losko 1997)
Pdr5p	f	(Egner & Kuchler 1996)
Fur4p	c,f,h	(Galan & Haguenauer-Tsapis 1997, Galan et al 1996, Hein et al 1995, Marchal et al 1998)
Ste3p	b,f	(Roth & Davis 1996)
Gap1p	f,h	(Hein et al 1995, Springael & André 1998)

a, Ubiquitination not directly demonstrated; b, ligand-dependent ubiquitination; c, ubiquitin linkage analyzed; d, associated with tyrosine phosphorylation; e, associated with serine/threonine phosphorylation; f, ubiquitination associated with endocytosis; g, ubiquitination associated with proteasomal degradation; h, Rsp5 implicated; i, degraded primarily in lysosomes; ubiquitination not directly implicated; j, reversible ubiquitination; k, in response to benzoquinone ansamycins (herbimycin A, geldenamycin); l, luminal ubiquitination, significance unclear; m, ubiquitin-proteasome-mediated degradation of an intracellular cleavage product.

Ligand-Dependent Ubiquitination

One of the first plasma membrane receptors shown to be ubiquitinated upon ligand binding was the TCR (Cenciarelli et al 1992). These receptors are multi-subunit structures consisting of six distinct transmembrane polypeptides that, when appropriately assembled in the ER, are transported to the plasma membrane as an octameric complex ($\alpha\beta\gamma\delta\epsilon_2\zeta_2$) (reviewed in Weissman 1994,

Ashwell & Weissman 1995). The earliest requisite event in the pathway leading to T cell activation in response to TCR engagement is the activation of protein tyrosine kinases; these include Src family kinases and ZAP-70. Multiple TCR subunits were found to be ubiquitinated on cytosolic lysines in response to receptor occupancy (Cenciarelli et al 1992), and multiple lysine residues on the TCR-ζ subunit (which has nine intracytoplasmic lysines) were substrates for ubiquitination. Notably, lysines introduced into positions where they did not normally exist were similarly modified (Hou et al 1994). The high-affinity receptor for IgE (FcϵRI), like the TCR receptor, is a multi-subunit receptor ($\alpha\beta\gamma_2$) (Blank et al 1989). As with the TCR, the β and γ subunits of FcϵRI are rapidly ubiquitinated on ligation, and this ubiquitination is reversed when ligand is disengaged (Paolini & Kinet 1993).

In response to ligation, the PDGFRβ dimerizes with proximal sequelae that include activation of tyrosine kinase activity and autophosphorylation; this is followed by internalization and lysosomal degradation. Interestingly, PDGFRβ ligation also results in the appearance of high-molecular-weight ubiquitinated forms that are stabilized at 4°C (Mori et al 1992). Notably, a truncation of the carboxy terminus of this protein that substantially diminished detection of ubiquitinated forms had minimal effects on ligand-induced internalization (Mori et al 1993). Similar to PDGFRβ, the stem cell factor receptor, c-kit, undergoes ligand-induced ubiquitination (Miyazawa et al 1994). A number of other growth factor receptors have also been shown to be ubiquitinated in response to ligand (see Table 3).

Common to mammalian receptors that have been shown to undergo ligand-induced ubiquitination is a relationship between tyrosine kinase activation and ubiquitination. For the TCR, receptor occupancy in the absence of receptor-mediated activation of tyrosine kinases does not result in ubiquitination (Cenciarelli et al 1996). Inhibition of tyrosine phosphatase activity with resultant enhancement of receptor tyrosine phosphorylation correlates with increased levels of ubiquitinated forms for the TCR (Cenciarelli et al 1996). Similarly, for the PDGFRβ, mutations that destroy tyrosine kinase activity result in a loss of ligand-mediated ubiquitination (Mori et al 1993).

A key question regarding ligand-induced ubiquitination of plasma membrane receptors is whether this modification plays a role in receptor down-regulation by targeting to 26S proteasomes. For the TCR, the most effective agents in blocking degradation of the cell surface receptors are the lysosome inhibitors monensin and ammonium chloride (AM Weissman, unpublished observations). Proteasome inhibitors have minimal effects on occupancy-induced receptor degradation, and ubiquitinated forms do not accumulate to significant levels when T cells are treated with these reagents. We have obtained similar results with c-kit (AM Weissman, unpublished observations). For the PDGFRβ, proteasomes have been alluded to as a means of degradation; however, the inhibition of degradation achieved with proteasome inhibitors is only partial (<20%), and the capacity of neither monensin nor ammonium chloride to inhibit ligand-mediated degradation has been assessed (Mori et al 1995b,c). Thus despite the fact that the TCR, c-kit, and PDGFRβ are all subject to ligand-mediated ubiquitination, for none is there convincing evidence that proteasomes play a major role in ligand-mediated degradation.

Observations made with the tyrosine-kinase-containing receptor c-Met clearly demonstrate at least one instance where a close relationship does exist between ubiquitination of a plasma membrane receptor and proteasomal degradation (Jeffers et al 1997). c-Met is composed of a 50-kDa extracellular α subunit and a 140-kDa membrane-spanning β subunit. On ligand binding, the β subunit is ubiquitinated and degraded in a proteasome-dependent manner. When proteasomes are inhibited, a 55-kDa intracellular cleavage product of the β subunit, which is normally labile and is generated as part of a shedding process, is also protected. These data suggest that for this receptor not only is ligand-mediated degradation a ubiquitin-proteasome-dependent process, but that the same pathway serves to degrade an intracytoplasmic fragment of this protein that has been freed from its normal physical and regulatory constraints. For the tyrosine kinase receptor ErbB-4, there is also evidence for ubiquitin-proteasome-dependent degradation of a proteolytic fragment; however, in this case ubiquitination is not implicated in the degradation of intact receptors (Vecchi & Carpenter 1997).

A Novel Role for Ubiquitination in Internalization

Although c-Met clearly exhibits proteasome-dependent degradation, in other instances such a relationship has not been established. If not for proteasomal degradation, what then is the role of ubiquitination of plasma membrane receptors? In considering this, we should bear in mind that ubiquitination represents a significant modification, each ubiquitin moiety adding 76 amino acids to a protein. If added to multiple lysines, it is hard to envisage that protein-protein interactions would not be markedly affected. Thus it is unlikely that ubiquitination of cell surface receptors is without functional consequences. One exciting clue to an alternative role for ubiquitination comes from a series of recent studies of yeast membrane proteins, demonstrating that for several receptors and transporters, ubiquitination is a targeting signal for endocytosis and subsequent degradation in vacuoles.

Ste2p is a G protein–coupled receptor that binds the yeast pheromone, α-factor. This receptor, like other G protein–coupled receptors, has seven membrane-spanning segments and a carboxy-terminal cytosolic tail that is subject to regulatory serine phosphorylation. In response to α-factor, Ste2p is rapidly internalized and degraded. Hicke & Riezman (1996) have demonstrated that Ste2 accumulates in high-molecular-weight ubiquitinated forms at the cell surface in response to α-factor in endocytosis-deficient cells (*end4*). Three E2 enzymes, Ubc1p, Ubc4p, and Ubc5p, appear to be essential for viability in *S. cerevisiae* (Jentsch 1992). *ubc1ubc4* and *ubc4ubc5* mutants exhibited profound defects on Ste2p internalization that were not due to the general cellular consequences of these mutations (Hicke & Riezman 1996). These cells also exhibited a substantial reduction in α-factor-induced ubiquitinated forms. Ste2p degradation was also dramatically diminished in cells defective in vacuolar protease function (*pep4prb1*) but not in proteasome mutants (*pre1pre2* and *yta5*). These results establish a link between ligand-induced ubiquitination, endocytosis, and eventual targeting for vacuolar degradation. There are also additional data suggesting a role for ubiquitination in the relatively slow ligand-independent constitutive endocytosis of Ste2p (Hicke et al 1998).

Further insights into the relationship between ligand-mediated ubiquitination and endocytosis have been derived from an analysis of the carboxy-terminal tail of Ste2p, where evaluation of a region previously identified as crucial for endocytosis (SINNDAKSS, amino acids 333–339) led to the determination that this region is also required for ubiquitination (Hicke & Riezman 1996). When the cytoplasmic tail of Ste2p was truncated at amino acid 345, constitutive endocytosis and ubiquitination occurred in response to α-factor. However, when this was accompanied by mutation of the three S residues within the SINNDAKSS sequence to A, or of the K to R, both processes were largely curtailed; further analysis demonstrated that K337 is, at least within the context of the truncated receptor, a site of ubiquitination (Hicke & Riezman 1996). The finding that mutation of serine residues has effects on ubiquitination is reminiscent of findings in mammalian systems with IκBα (Alkalay et al 1995, Li et al 1995, Chen et al 1996) and of more recent studies with β-catenin, where serine phosphorylation plays important roles in ubiquitination (Orford et al 1997). It has recently been established that loss of a casein kinase I-like activity required for phosphorylation of the cytoplasmic tail also results in failure of Ste2p to undergo both ubiquitination and internalization (Hicke et al 1998).

The yeast **a**-factor receptor, Ste3p, like Ste2p, is a seven transmembrane segment G protein–coupled receptor. As with Ste2p, this protein undergoes both constitutive and ligand-induced internalization; however, it is distinguished from Ste2p by its rapid rate of constitutive internalization ($t_{1/2} = 20$ min). Ste3p undergoes constitutive mono- and di-ubiquitination, as well as phosphorylation (Roth & Davis 1996). Analysis of cells mutant for Ubc4p and Ubc5p or for ubiquitin has provided convincing evidence that constitutive Ste3p internalization is ubiquitin dependent. When endocytosis is blocked, increased levels of ubiquitinated species are detected, indicating that ubiquitination precedes endocytosis. Because of its rapid constitutive turnover, evaluation of ligand-mediated endocytosis of wild-type Ste3p is problematic. To circumvent this, a truncated form of Ste3p, defective in constitutive endocytosis, was evaluated for ligand-dependent internalization. As with constitutive internalization, a-factor-dependent internalization is also ubiquitin dependent.

Ste6p is a member of the ABC family of transporters, responsible for secretion of the yeast mating pheromone a-factor. This transporter also accumulates at the plasma membrane in a ubiquitinated form in endocytosis-deficient mutants (Kolling & Hollenberg 1994). Consistent with a regulatory role for ubiquitination, the half-life of this protein was increased two- to threefold in *ubc4ubc5* double mutants. As with Ste2p, the half-life of this protein was most markedly increased in a strain in which vacuolar function was compromised (*pep4*). It was subsequently determined that the 117-amino acid linker joining the two halves of this ABC family transporter is important for ubiquitination and protein turnover. This linker region, known as the D-box, contains a sequence, DAKTI, reminiscent of the last five amino acids of the Ste2p SINNDAKSS sequence. As with Ste2p, removal of the region containing the DAKTI motif correlates with decreased ubiquitination and diminished endocytosis. Receptors bearing a lysine-to-arginine mutation within this sequence were modestly impaired in constitutive turnover but still capable of being substrates for ubiquitination (Kolling & Losko 1997). Thus the importance of this region is not due to the lysine residue serving as a potential site for ubiquitination. Transfer of the entire D-box to a heterologous stable membrane protein, Pma1p, resulted in endocytosis and a marked decrease in half-life, which correlated with Pma1p ubiquitination. However, transfer of a more limited region containing the DAKTI sequence did not effect such a change in stability. These results suggest that while the DAKTI region is important, it is by itself not sufficient to confer susceptibility to ubiquitination and endocytosis.

There are several other examples where a relationship between ubiquitination and endocytosis/vacuolar degradation of yeast multi-spanning membrane transporters has been established. These include the uracil permease (Fur4p) (Galan et al 1996), the yeast multidrug transporter (Pdr5p) (Egner & Kuchler 1996), and the general amino acid permease (Gap1p) (Springael & André 1998). For all of these, ubiquitinated species accumulate in mutants defective in internalization. Fur4p contains a destruction box (Galan et al 1994) similar to that found in the mitotic cyclins (Glotzer et al 1991). A point mutation within this region stabilizes this transporter from degradation (Galan et al 1994). In addition, Fur4p contains a PEST sequence near its amino terminus. PEST sequences rich in proline, glutamic acid, serine, and threonine are found in a number of soluble proteins that are rapidly degraded (Mansur & Androphy 1993). Mutation of serines to alanines within this region results in decreased ubiquitination and degradation of Fur4p. The possibility that the significance of these sites is due to their being sites of phosphorylation is supported by the observation that mutations of these serines to glutamic acid, which mimics the charge of a phosphate residue, substantially restores turnover and ubiquitination to Fur4p (Marchal et al 1998).

The findings obtained with yeast receptors and transporters are leading to an expanded view of the role of ubiquitination in cellular function. It is now evident that ubiquitination is not just a targeting signal for proteasomal degradation but that it also plays an important role in targeting of plasma membrane proteins for ligand-dependent and constitutive internalization. How do the findings obtained in yeast relate to observations made in mammalian cells? In fact, they provide potential explanations for earlier observations where correlations were found between cellular E1 activity and stress-induced lysosomal degradation of proteins (Gropper et al 1991) and with maturation of autophagocytic vesicles (Lenk et al 1992). A role in trafficking within the endosomal/lysosomal system in mammalian cells may also help account for the abnormal accumulation of ubiquitinated species found in intraluminal inclusions in neurodegenerative disorders (Mayer et al 1991). To date, studies directly implicating ubiquitination in endocytosis and lysosomal degradation in mammalian systems have been limited to an analysis of the GHR in cells expressing a temperature-sensitive E1 (Strous et al 1996). In this analysis, GHR endocytosis was dependent on an intact ubiquitin-conjugating system, and GHRs were found to be degraded in lysosomes. Although this study established a correlation, no evidence has yet been provided demonstrating that it is the ubiquitination of GHR itself that is required for endocytosis.

Ubiquitin Linkages and Endocytosis

It is generally accepted that formation of polyubiquitin chains is required for targeting to and degradation by proteasomes. Studies on the TCR (Cenciarelli et al 1992) and FcεRI (Paolini & Kinet 1993) have demonstrated that receptors may have a low valency of ubiquitin molecules attached. These findings, together with the known existence of multiple ubiquitination sites on TCR-ζ (Hou et al 1994), raise the possibility that these plasma membrane receptors are subject primarily to multiple mono-ubiquitinations. More recent studies on yeast proteins have added to our knowledge of ubiquitination linkages at the plasma membrane, and for several of these proteins, the predominant ubiquitinated forms appear to exhibit relatively few ubiquitins per protein (Roth & Davis 1996, Galan & Haguenauer-Tsapis 1997), compared with the high-molecular-weight smear often seen with proteins targeted for proteasomal degradation. In the case of Ste2p, truncated forms with only a single ubiquitination site exhibit a low valency of ubiquitination, which is apparently sufficient for internalization (Hicke & Riezman 1996).

Genetic evidence suggests that mono-ubiquitination is sufficient for ligand-induced endocytosis of Ste2p (Terrell et al 1998). When ubiquitin is added to proteins or when polyubiquitin chains are generated, the carboxy terminus of ubiquitin condenses with the ϵ-amino group of a lysine through an isopeptide bond, and the amino terminus of ubiquitin itself is free. However, a chimeric molecule consisting of truncated Ste2p in tandem with ubiquitin in which the amino terminus of ubiquitin is contiguous with Ste2p supports internalization of Ste2p in the absence of any other ubiquitination events (Terrell et al 1998). These somewhat counterintuitive findings suggest that if there is a specific recognition event occurring at the plasma membrane involving ubiquitin, the structure recognized is substantially different from the polyubiquitin signal that leads to proteasomal degradation.

The nature of the linkage required for endocytosis of uracil permease (Fur4p) has also been explored, in this case by making use of a mutant yeast strain deficient in a proteasome-associated ubiquitin isopeptidase (Doa4p) (Papa & Hochstrasser 1993). This isopeptidase is responsible for the removal of ubiquitin chains from residual proteasome-associated peptides. When this enzyme is inactive, the levels of free ubiquitin available for conjugation are markedly reduced. In *doa4* cells, ubiquitination and endocytosis of Fur4p were rescued by overexpression of wild-type ubiquitin and also by expression of a mutant ubiquitin gene in which K48 was mutated (the classic site for polyubiquitin chain formation) but only partially rescued by a K63 mutant (Galan & Haguenauer-Tsapis 1997). These iconoclastic observations raise the possibility that for ubiquitination of Fur4p, K63 is a critical residue for ubiquitin chain addition.

Enzymes Implicated in Ubiquitination at the Plasma Membrane

As already discussed, ubiquitination is thought to involve the sequential action of three classes of enzymes. The E2s implicated in degradation from the ER, Ubc6p and Ubc7p, possess features that allow them to associate either directly or indirectly with the ER membrane. These characteristics may facilitate a role for these E2s in the ubiquitination of proteins undergoing retrotranslocation from the ER, perhaps even without an accompanying E3. In contrast, Ubc4p and Ubc5p, which are implicated in plasma membrane protein ubiquitination, are core E2s that lack characteristics predisposing them to being concentrated at the plasma membrane. Thus in modeling ubiquitination of transporters and receptors, it is reasonable to suspect the existence of E3-like molecules that can associate with the plasma membrane, and in fact there is accumulating evidence for the involvement of such proteins in ubiquitination at the plasma membrane.

Studies on yeast uracil permease (Fur4p) (Hein et al 1995, Galan et al 1996), Gap1p (Hein et al 1995), and Ste2p (L Hicke, personal communication) have all revealed that an essential gene, *NPI1*, is involved in their endocytosis/degradation and that this gene encodes an E3 termed Rsp5 (Huibregtse et al 1995). Rsp5 is highly homologous to the fission yeast E3, Pub1 (Nefsky & Beach 1996) and to a mammalian HECT domain E3, Nedd-4 (Hatakeyama et al 1997, Kumar et al 1997), as well as to two other recently characterized human cDNAs that encode polypeptides containing HECT domains (Pirozzi et al 1997) (see below). All these proteins are characterized by multiple copies within their amino-terminal half of a tryptophan-based region known as a WW or Rsp5 domain (reviewed in Hofmann & Bucher 1995, Sudol et al 1995). WW domains associate with proline-rich regions (PXY) on proteins that are similar but not identical to regions recognized by SH3 domains. Additionally, Rsp5, Pub1, Nedd-4, and one of the human homologues all share an amino-terminal Ca^{2+}-dependent-lipid (CaL) binding domain first described for protein kinase C isoforms (Coussens et al 1986). Nedd-4 has been shown to translocate to the plasma membrane in response to increased intracellular Ca^{2+}, in a fashion dependent on this amino-terminal motif (Staub et al 1997). Although not yet directly implicated in ubiquitination at the plasma membrane, Nedd-4 is a binding partner for subunits of the amiloride-sensitive sodium channel in a yeast two-hybrid screen through a WW/PXY interaction (Staub et al 1996). The significance of this interaction has been verified by co-immunoprecipitation in mammalian cells. Notably, the Nedd-4 binding sites within the sodium channel subunits are deleted in Liddle's syndrome, an inherited form of hypertension characterized by failure to down-regulate these plasma membrane proteins (Hansson et al 1995, Tamura et al 1996).

Adaptor Molecules at the Plasma Membrane

A working model for ubiquitination of plasma membrane proteins is one in which proteins containing WW domains ubiquitinate a number of membrane and other cellular proteins, with specificity conferred by the relative affinity of different WW domains for cognate PXY motifs. However, unlike the amiloride-sensitive sodium channel, the primary amino acid sequence of a number of plasma membrane proteins that undergo ubiquitination, including Fur4p, and Ste2p, do not themselves encode PXY motifs. This suggests several possibilities: one is that there are other families of E3s involved in ubiquitination at the plasma membrane; alternatively there may be other, as yet to be discerned, interaction motifs contained within WW domain-containing E3s. Another possibility is that these E3s do not in all cases interact directly with plasma membrane proteins, but rather they are brought into proximity of receptors by adaptor molecules. One candidate likely to fulfill such an adaptor role in mammalian cells is epidermal growth factor receptor (EGFR) -associated protein clone 15 (Eps15). This 100-kDa protein was first identified as a substrate for EGFR tyrosine kinase activity. Eps15 is a component of clathrin-coated pits, where it is localized to rims. Eps15 also interacts with the ear of α-adaptin, a component of the AP-2 clathrin adaptor complex (Benmerah et al 1995, 1996, Tebar et al 1996, Wendland et al 1996, van Delft et al 1997b). Interestingly, Eps15 is a substrate for mono-ubiquitination in response to EGFR ligation (van Delft et al 1997a) and contains within its carboxy terminus a proline-rich region with potential WW domain interaction sites. The yeast homologue of Eps15 is a protein known as Pan1p, which is essential both for receptor-mediated endocytosis and for internalization of lipids (Wendland et al 1996, Tang et al 1997). One can envisage that Pan1p/Eps15 recruits WW domain-containing E3s to the plasma membrane where they are brought into proximity of transmembrane proteins predisposed to ubiquitination.

PERSPECTIVES

The ubiquitin-conjugating system, once largely a subject of in vitro analysis, and more recently implicated in the proteasomal degradation of an increasingly long list of cytosolic and nuclear regulatory proteins, is now taking center stage in our evolving understanding of the means by which the fates of ER luminal proteins and of transmembrane proteins in the ER and beyond are controlled. The remarkable observations that have been made in the past few years are leading inexorably to the acceptance of the notion of bidirectional movement of proteins into and out of the ER. They also suggest previously unappreciated roles for translocons, chaperones, and oligosaccharides in the degradation of proteins from the ER and open exciting new vistas with links to clinical disorders

A major question that remains to be addressed is the overall significance of ubiquitination and proteasomes in extraction of proteins from the ER. In some cases, such as in the degradation of MHC class I molecules (Wiertz et al 1996a,b, Hughes et al 1997) and carboxypeptidase Y (Hiller et al 1996), ubiquitination is implicated either not at all, or only after proteins have been functionally denatured by removal from the ER membrane. In these instances, proteasomes basically serve to discard what has become cytosolic junk. In other cases, such as in the degradation of a temperature-sensitive mutant form of Sec61p, the ubiquitin-conjugating system is implicated in determining the fate of the protein while still in its native lipid environment (Biederer et al 1996). In the case of the degradation of some TCR subunits from the ER, not only does ubiquitination occur while still ER-membrane associated, but as a consequence, proteasomes may be given the opportunity to provide the driving force for their removal from ER membranes (Yang et al 1998). It is clear that there are multiple variations on these themes. In some instances, ubiquitination might even be indirectly facilitating degradation from the ER in *trans*, as has been suggested for calnexin in the degradation of α_1-antitrypsin (Qu et al 1996). It would thus appear that the same chaperones that potentiate protein folding and oligomerization also serve to target proteins for degradation. If this is indeed the case, how do chaperones decide whether to move a protein onward or participate in its expulsion into the cytosol? Is this strictly a stochastic process, or are there specific recognition sites that determine the fate of nascent proteins? In the next few years, we can look forward to the identification of additional components involved in this process and to the development of a more integrated view of the mechanism and regulation of this important pathway.

On the cell surface, it is now clear that ubiquitination is unequivocally linked to endocytosis and subsequent lysosomal degradation of plasma membrane transporters and receptors. At first glance, it would appear that ubiquitination of lysosomally degraded plasma membrane proteins also serves as a degradation signal. However, it should be emphasized that, to date, ubiquitination has been implicated in internalization and only indirectly in lysosomal/vacuolar degradation. An obvious unaddressed question is how ubiquitin mediates endocytosis. A likely possibility is that ubiquitin binds to some component of the internalization machinery such as clathrin or the AP-2 adaptor complex in mammalian cells or the actin cytoskeleton in yeast cells (Marks et al 1997, Riezman et al 1996). Unlike yeast receptors and transporters, which tend to be delivered to the vacuole after internalization, a number of mammalian receptors undergo cycles of constitutive endocytosis and recycling or ligand-induced internalization, dissociation from ligand, and re-expression at the cell surface. Another important issue that needs to be addressed is the extent to which cycling of receptors correlates with rounds of ubiquitination and de-ubiquitination.

Although ubiquitination of plasma membrane proteins usually results in internalization, which in some cases is followed by lysosomal degradation, there is at least one example where ligand-mediated ubiquitination apparently targets a plasma membrane receptor (c-Met) for proteasomal degradation (Jeffers et al 1997). There are several examples of pharmacologically induced degradation of tyrosine kinase-containing plasma membrane receptors where ubiquitination and proteasomal degradation have been implicated (see Table 3). Having only just now addressed the topological conundrum of proteasomal degradation from the ER by invoking the involvement of the ER protein import machinery, we are once again faced with explaining how transmembrane proteins are targeted for proteasomal degradation, but this time either from the plasma membrane or from within the endocytic pathway. Stay tuned and watch as this story unfolds.

ACKNOWLEDGMENTS

We thank Drs. Bruno André, Rosine Haguenauer-Tsapis, Linda Hicke, Ron Kopito, Howard Riezman, Thomas Sommer, Jean-Yves Springael, and Dieter Wolf for generously sharing results prior to publication and Dr. Chris Mullins for critical review of the manuscript.

Visit the *Annual Reviews home page* at
http://www.AnnualReviews.org

Literature Cited

Alkalay I, Yaron A, Hatzubai A, Orian A, Ciechanover A, Ben-Neriah Y. 1995. Stimulation-dependent IκBα phosphorylation marks the NFκB inhibitor for degradation via the ubiquitin-proteasome pathway. *Proc. Natl. Acad. Sci. USA* 92:10599–603

Amara JF, Cheng SH, Smith AE. 1992. Intracellular protein trafficking defects in human disease. *Trends Cell Biol.* 2:145–49

Ashwell JD, Weissman AM. 1995. T cell antigen receptor genes, gene products and co-receptors. In *Clinical Immunology: Principles and Practice*, ed. RR Rich, TA Fleisher, BD Schwartz, WT Shearer, W Strober, p. 69. St. Louis, MO: Mosby-Year Book

Benmerah A, Begue B, Dautry-Varsat A, Cerf-Bensussan N. 1996. The ear of α-adaptin interacts with the COOH-terminal domain of the Eps 15 protein. *J. Biol. Chem.* 271:12111–16

Benmerah A, Gagnon J, Begue B, Megarbane B, Dautry-Varsat A, Cerf-Bensussan N. 1995. The tyrosine kinase substrate eps15 is constitutively associated with the plasma membrane adaptor AP-2. *J. Cell Biol.* 131:1831–38

Benoist F, Grand-Perret T. 1997. Co-translational degradation of apolipoprotein B100 by the proteasome is prevented by microsomal triglyceride transfer protein. Synchronized translation studies on HepG2 cells treated with an inhibitor of microsomal triglyceride transfer protein. *J. Biol. Chem.* 272:20435–42

Bercovich Z, Rosenberg-Hasson Y, Ciechanover A, Kahana C. 1989. Degradation of ornithine decarboxylase in reticulocyte lysate is ATP-dependent but ubiquitin-independent. *J. Biol. Chem.* 264:15949–52

Biederer T, Volkwein C, Sommer T. 1996. Degradation of subunits of the Sec61p complex, an integral component of the ER membrane, by the ubiquitin-proteasome pathway. *EMBO J.* 15:2069–76

Biederer T, Volkwein C, Sommer T. 1997. Role of Cue1p in ubiquitination and degradation at the ER surface. *Science* 278:1806–9

Blank U, Ra C, White K, Metzger H, Kinet J-P. 1989. Complete structure and expression in transfected cells of high affinity IgE receptor. *Nature* 337:187–89

Bohley P, Seglen PO. 1992. Proteases and proteolysis in the lysosome. *Experientia* 48:151–57

Bonifacino JS, Klausner RD. 1994. Degradation of proteins retained in the endoplasmic reticulum. In *Cellular Proteolytic Systems*, ed. A Ciechanover, AL Schwartz, p. 137. New York: Wiley-Liss

Bordallo J, Plemper RK, Finger A, Wolf DH. 1998. Der3p/Hrd1p is required for endoplasmic reticulum-associated degradation of misfolded lumenal and integral membrane proteins. *Mol. Biol. Cell* 9:209–22

Brodsky JL, McCracken AA. 1997. ER-associated and proteasome-mediated protein degradation: How two topologically restricted events came together. *Trends. Cell Biol.* 7:151–56

Cenciarelli C, Hou D, Hsu K-C, Rellahan BL, Wiest DL, et al. 1992. Activation-induced ubiquitination of the T cell antigen receptor. *Science* 257:795–97

Cenciarelli C, Wilhelm Jr. KJ, Guo A, Weissman AM. 1996. T cell antigen receptor ubiquitination is a consequence of receptor-mediated tyrosine kinase activation. *J. Biol. Chem.* 271:8709–13

Chau V, Tobias JW, Bachmair A, Marriott D, Ecker DJ, et al. 1989. A multiubiquitin chain is confined to specific lysine in a targeted short-lived protein. *Science* 243:1576–83

Chen P, Johnson P, Sommer T, Jentsch S, Hochstrasser M. 1993. Multiple ubiquitin-conjugating enzymes participate in the in vivo degradation of the yeast MAT alpha 2 repressor. *Cell* 74:357–69

Chen ZJ, Parent L, Maniatis T. 1996. Site-specific phosphorylation of IκBα by a novel ubiquitination-dependent protein kinase activity. *Cell* 84:853–62

Chien Y, Becker DM, Lindsten T, Okamura M, Cohen DI, Davis MM. 1984. A third type of murine T-cell receptor gene. *Nature* 312:31–35

Corsi AK, Schekman R. 1996. Mechanism of polypeptide translocation into the endoplasmic reticulum. *J. Biol. Chem.* 271:30299–302

Coussens L, Parker PJ, Rhee L, Yang-Feng TL, Chen E, et al. 1986. Multiple, distinct forms of bovine and human protein kinase C suggest diversity in cellular signaling pathways. *Science* 233:859–66

Coux O, Tanaka K, Goldberg AL. 1996. Structure and function of the 20S and 26S proteasomes. *Annu. Rev. Biochem.* 65:801–47

Davis EC, Mecham RP. 1996. Selective degradation of accumulated secretory proteins in the endoplasmic reticulum. A possible clearance pathway for abnormal tropoelastin. *J. Biol. Chem.* 271:3787–94

Deveraux Q, Ustrell V, Pickart C, Rechsteiner M. 1994. A 26S protease subunit that binds ubiquitin conjugates. *J. Biol. Chem.* 269:7059–61

Deveraux Q, van Nocker S, Mahaffey D, Vierstra R, Rechsteiner M. 1995. Inhibition of ubiquitin-mediated proteolysis by the *Arabidopsis* 26S protease subunit S5a. *J. Biol. Chem.* 270:29660–63

Egner R, Kuchler K. 1996. The yeast multidrug transporter Pdr5 of the plasma membrane is ubiquitinated prior to endocytosis and degradation in the vacuole. *FEBS Lett.* 378:177–81

Elias S, Bercovich B, Kahana C, Coffino P, Fischer M, et al. 1995. Degradation of ornithine decarboxylase by the mammalian and yeast 26S proteasome complexes requires all the components of the protease. *Eur. J. Biochem.* 229:276–83

Fang H, Mullins C, Green N. 1997. In addition to *SEC11*, a newly identified gene, *SPC3*, is essential for signal peptidase activity in the yeast endoplasmic reticulum. *J. Biol. Chem.* 272:13152–58

Feldman RMR, Correll CC, Kaplan KB, Deshaies RJ. 1997. A complex of Cdc4p, Skp1p, and Cdc53p/Cullin catalyzes ubiquitination of the phosphorylated CDK inhibitor Sic1p. *Cell* 91:221–30

Fenteany G, Standaert RF, Reichard GA, Corey EJ, Schreiber SL. 1994. A β-lactone related to lactacystin induces neurite outgrowth in a neuroblastoma cell line and inhibits cell cycle progression in an osteosarcoma cell line. *Proc. Natl. Acad. Sci. USA* 91:3358–62

Finke K, Plath K, Panzner S, Prehn S, Rapoport TA, et al. 1996. A second trimeric complex containing homologs of the Sec61p complex functions in protein transport across the ER membrane of *S. cerevisiae*. *EMBO J.* 15:1482–94

Fisher EA, Zhou M, Mitchell DM, Wu X, Omura S, et al. 1997. The degradation of apolipoprotein B100 is mediated by the ubiquitin-proteasome pathway and involves heat shock protein 70. *J. Biol. Chem.* 272:20427–34

Fujita K, Omura S, Silver J. 1997. Rapid degradation of CD4 in cells expressing human immunodeficiency virus type 1 Env and Vpu is blocked by proteasome inhibitors. *J. Gen. Virol.* 78:619–25

Galan J, Haguenauer-Tsapis R. 1997. Ubiquitin lys63 is involved in ubiquitination of a yeast plasma membrane protein. *EMBO J.* 16:5847–54

Galan JM, Moreau V, Andre B, Volland C, Haguenauer-Tsapis R. 1996. Ubiquitination mediated by the Npi1p/Rsp5p ubiquitin-protein ligase is required for endocytosis of the yeast uracil permease. *J. Biol. Chem.* 271:10946–52

Galan JM, Volland C, Urban-Grimal D, Haguenauer-Tsapis R. 1994. The yeast plasma membrane uracil permease is stabilized against stress induced degradation by a point mutation in a cyclin-like "destruction box." *Biochem. Biophys. Res. Commun.* 201:769–75

Galcheva-Gargova Z, Theroux SJ, Davis RJ. 1995. The epidermal growth factor receptor is covalently linked to ubiquitin. *Oncogene* 11:2649–55

Garcia PD, Ou JH, Rutter WJ, Walter P. 1988. Targeting of the hepatitis B virus precore protein to the endoplasmic reticulum membrane: after signal peptide cleavage translocation can be aborted and the product released into the cytoplasm. *J. Cell Biol.* 106:1093–104

Gething MJ, Sambrook J. 1992. Protein folding in the cell. *Nature* 355:33–45

Glotzer M, Murray AW, Kirschner MW. 1991. Cyclin is degraded by the ubiquitin pathway. *Nature* 349:132–38

Groll M, Ditzel L, Lowe J, Stock D, Bochtler M, et al. 1997. Structure of 20S proteasome from yeast at 2.4 Å resolution. *Nature* 386:463–71

Gropper R, Brandt RA, Elias S, Bearer CF, Mayer A, et al. 1991. The ubiquitin-activating enzyme, E1, is required for stress-induced lysosomal degradation of cellular proteins. *J. Biol. Chem.* 266:3602–10

Haas AL, Siepmann TJ. 1997. Pathways of ubiquitin conjugation. *FASEB J.* 11:1257–68

Halaban R, Cheng E, Zhang Y, Moellmann G, Hanlon D, et al. 1997. Aberrant retention of tyrosinase in the endoplasmic reticulum mediates accelerated degradation of the enzyme and contributes to the dedifferentiated phenotype of amelanotic melanoma cells. *Proc. Natl. Acad. Sci. USA* 94:6210–15

Hammond C, Helenius A. 1995. Quality control in the secretory pathway. *Curr. Opin. Cell. Biol.* 7:523–29

Hampton RY, Gardner RG, Rine J. 1996. Role of 26S proteasome and HRD genes in the degradation of 3-hydroxy-3-methylglutaryl-CoA reductase, an integral endoplasmic reticulum membrane protein. *Mol. Biol. Cell* 7:2029–44

Hampton RY, Rine J. 1994. Regulated degradation of HMG-CoA reductase, an integral membrane protein of the endoplasmic reticulum, in yeast. *J. Cell Biol.* 125:299–312

Handley-Gearhart PM, Stephen AG, Trausch-Azar JS, Ciechanover A, Schwartz AL. 1994a. Human ubiquitin-activating enzyme, E1. Indication of potential nuclear and cytoplasmic subpopulations using epitope-tagged cDNA constructs. *J. Biol. Chem.* 269:33171–78

Handley-Gearhart PM, Trausch-Azar JS, Ciechanover A, Schwartz AL. 1994b. Rescue of the complex temperature-sensitive phenotype of Chinese hamster ovary E36ts20 cells by expression of the human ubiquitin-activating enzyme cDNA. *Biochem. J.* 304:1015–20

Hansson JH, Schild L, Lu Y, Wilson TA, Gautschi I, et al. 1995. A de novo missense mutation of the β subunit of the epithelial sodium channel causes hypertension and Liddle syndrome, identifying a proline-rich segment critical for regulation of channel activity. *Proc. Natl. Acad. Sci. USA* 92:11495–99

Harbers K, Müller U, Grams A, Li E, Jaenisch R, Franz T. 1996. Provirus integration into a gene encoding a ubiquitin-conjugating enzyme results in a placental defect and embryonic lethality. *Proc. Natl. Acad. Sci. USA* 93:12412–17

Hatakeyama S, Jensen JP, Weissman AM. 1997. Subcellular localization and ubiquitin-conjugating enzyme (E2) interactions of mammalian HECT family ubiquitin protein ligases. *J. Biol. Chem.* 272:15085–92

Hein C, Springael JY, Volland C, Haguenauer-Tsapis R, André B. 1995. *NPI1*, an essential yeast gene involved in induced degradation of Gap1 and Fur4 permeases, encodes the Rsp5 ubiquitin-protein ligase. *Mol. Microbiol.* 18:77–87

Hershko A, Ciechanover A. 1998. The ubiquitin system. *Annu. Rev. Biochem.* 67:In press

Hicke L, Zanolari B, Riezman H. 1998. Cytoplasmic tail phosphorylation and ubiquitination are required sequentially to trigger internalization of the α-factor receptor. *J. Cell Biol.* 141:349–58

Hicke L, Riezman H. 1996. Ubiquitination of a yeast plasma membrane receptor signals its ligand-stimulated endocytosis. *Cell* 84:277–87

Hill A, Ploegh H. 1995. Getting the inside out: the transporter associated with antigen processing (TAP) and the presentation of viral antigen. *Proc. Natl. Acad. Sci. USA* 92:341–43

Hiller MM, Finger A, Schweiger M, Wolf DH. 1996. ER degradation of a misfolded luminal protein by the cytosolic ubiquitin-proteasome pathway. *Science* 273:1725–28

Hochstrasser M. 1996. Ubiquitin-dependent protein degradation. *Annu. Rev. Genet.* 30:405–40

Hofmann K, Bucher P. 1995. The rsp5-domain is shared by proteins of diverse functions. *FEBS Lett.* 358:153–57

Hou D, Cenciarelli C, Jensen JP, Nguyen HB, Weissman AM. 1994. Activation-dependent ubiquitination a T cell antigen receptor subunit on multiple intracellular lysines. *J. Biol. Chem.* 269:14244–47

Hughes EA, Hammond C, Cresswell P. 1997. Misfolded major histocompatibility complex class I heavy chains are translocated into the cytoplasm and degraded by the proteasome. *Proc. Natl. Acad. Sci. USA* 94:1896–901

Huibregtse JM, Scheffner M, Beaudenon S, Howley PM. 1995. A family of proteins structurally and functionally related to the E6-AP ubiquitin-protein ligase. *Proc. Natl. Acad. Sci. USA* 92:2563–67

Huppa JB, Ploegh HL. 1997. The α chain of the T cell antigen receptor is degraded in the cytosol. *Immunity* 7:113–22

Jeffers M, Taylor GA, Weidner KM, Omura S, Vande Woude GF. 1997. Degradation of the Met tyrosine kinase receptor by the ubiquitin-proteasome pathway. *Mol. Cell. Biol.* 17:799–808

Jensen TJ, Loo MA, Pind S, Williams DB, Goldberg AL, Riordan JR. 1995. Multiple proteolytic systems, including the proteasome, contribute to CFTR processing. *Cell* 83:129–35

Jentsch S. 1992. The ubiquitin-conjugation system. *Annu. Rev. Genet.* 26:179–207

Kim TW, Pettingell WH, Hallmark OG, Moir RD, Wasco W, Tanzi RE. 1997. Endoproteolytic cleavage and proteasomal degradation of presenilin 2 in transfected cells. *J. Biol. Chem.* 272:11006–10

Knittler MR, Dinks S, Hass IG. 1995. Molecular chaperones involved in protein degradation in the endoplasmic reticulum: quantitative interaction of the heat shock cognate protein BIP with partially folded immunoglobulin light chains that are degraded in the endoplasmic reticulum. *Proc. Natl. Acad. Sci. USA* 92:1764–68

Knop M, Finger A, Braun T, Hellmuth K, Wolf DH. 1996. Der1, a novel protein specifically required for endoplasmic reticulum degradation in yeast. *EMBO J.* 15:753–63

Kolling R, Hollenberg CP. 1994. The ABC-transporter Ste6 accumulates in the plasma membrane in a ubiquitinated form in endocytosis mutants. *EMBO J.* 13:3261–71

Kolling R, Losko S. 1997. The linker region of the ABC-transporter Ste6 mediates ubiquitination and fast turnover of the protein. *EMBO J.* 16:2251–61

Kulka RG, Raboy B, Schuster R, Parag HA, Diamond G, et al. 1988. A Chinese hamster cell cycle mutant arrested at G2 phase has a temperature-sensitive ubiquitin-activating enzyme, E1. *J. Biol. Chem.* 263:15726–31

Kumar S, Harvey KF, Kinoshita M, Copeland NG, Noda M, Jenkins NA. 1997. cDNA cloning, expression analysis, and mapping of the mouse *Nedd4* gene. *Genomics* 40:435–43

Lenk SE, Dunn WAJ, Trausch JS, Ciechanover A, Schwartz AL. 1992. Ubiquitin-activating enzyme, E1, is associated with maturation of autophagic vacuoles. *J. Cell Biol.* 118:301–8

Leung DW, Spencer SA, Cachianes G, Hammonds RG, Collins C, et al. 1987. Growth hormone receptor and serum binding protein: purification, cloning and expression. *Nature* 330:537–43

Li CC, Dai RM, Longo DL. 1995. Inactivation of NFκB inhibitor IκBα: ubiquitin-dependent proteolysis and its degradation product. *Biochem. Biophys. Res. Commun.* 215:292–301

Li X, Stebbins B, Hoffman L, Pratt G, Rechsteiner M, Coffino P. 1996. The N terminus of antizyme promotes degradation of heterologous proteins. *J. Biol. Chem.* 271:4441–46

Lowe J, Stock D, Jap B, Zwickl P, Baumeister W, Huber R. 1995. Crystal structure of the 20S proteasome from the archaeon *T. acidophilum* at 3.4 Å resolution. *Science* 268:533–39

Mansur CP, Androphy EJ. 1993. Cellular transformation by papillomavirus oncoproteins. *Biochim. Biophys. Acta* 1155:323–45

Marchal C, Haguenauer-Tsapis R, Urban-Grimal D. 1998. A PEST-like sequence mediates phosphorylation and efficient ubiquitination of yeast uracil permease. *Mol. Cell. Biol.* 18:314–21

Marks MS, Ohno H, Kirchhausen T, Bonifacino JS. 1997. Protein sorting by tyrosine-based signals: adapting to the Ys and wherefores. *Trends Cell Biol.* 7:124–28

Mayer RJ, Arnold J, Laszlo L, Landon M, Lowe J. 1991. Ubiquitin in health and disease. *Biochim. Biophys. Acta* 1089:141–57

McCracken AA, Brodsky JL. 1996. Assembly of ER-associated protein degradation in vitro: dependence on cytosol, calnexin and ATP. *J. Cell Biol.* 132:291–98

Mimnaugh EG, Chavany C, Neckers L. 1996. Polyubiquitination and proteasomal degradation of the p185c-erbB-2 receptor protein-tyrosine kinase induced by geldanamycin. *J. Biol. Chem.* 271:22796–801

Miyazawa K, Toyama K, Gotoh A, Hendrie PC, Mantel C, Broxmeyer HE. 1994. Ligand-dependent polyubiquitination of c-kit gene product: a possible mechanism of receptor down modulation in M07e cells. *Blood* 83:137–45

Mori S, Claesson-Welsh L, Okuyama Y, Saito Y. 1995a. Ligand-induced polyubiquitination of receptor tyrosine kinases. *Biochem. Biophys. Res. Commun.* 213:32–39

Mori S, Heldin C-H, Claesson-Welsh L. 1992. Ligand-induced polyubiquitination of the platelet-derived growth factor β-receptor. *J. Biol. Chem.* 267:6429–34

Mori S, Heldin CH, Claesson-Welsh L. 1993. Ligand-induced ubiquitination of the platelet-derived growth factor β-receptor plays a negative regulatory role in its mitogenic signaling. *J. Biol. Chem.* 268:577–83

Mori S, Kanaki H, Tanaka K, Morisaki N, Saito Y. 1995b. Ligand-activated platelet-derived growth factor β-receptor is degraded through proteasome-dependent proteolytic pathway. *Biochem. Biophys. Res. Commun.* 217:224–29

Mori S, Tanaka K, Omura S, Saito Y. 1995c. Degradation process of ligand-stimulated platelet-derived growth factor β-receptor involves ubiquitin-proteasome proteolytic pathway. *J. Biol. Chem.* 270:29447–52

Mullins C, Lu Y, Campbell A, Fang H, Green N. 1995. A mutation affecting signal peptidase inhibits degradation of an abnormal membrane protein in *Saccharomyces cerevisiae*. *J. Biol. Chem.* 270:17139–47

Murakami Y, Matsufuji S, Kameji T, Hayashi S, Igarashi K, et al. 1992. Ornithine decarboxylase is degraded by the 26S proteasome without ubiquitination. *Nature* 360:597–99

Muralidhar MG, Thomas JB. 1993. The *Drosophila bendless* gene encodes a neural protein related to ubiquitin-conjugating enzymes. *Neuron* 11:253–66

Nefsky B, Beach D. 1996. Pub1 acts as an E6-AP-like protein ubiquitin ligase in the degradation of cdc25. *EMBO J.* 15:1301–12

Newman RH, Whitehead P, Lally J, Coffer A, Freemont P. 1996. 20S human proteasomes bind with a specific orientation to lipid monolayers in vitro. *Biochim. Biophys. Acta* 1281:111–16

Oda K, Ikehara Y, Omura S. 1996. Lactacystin, an inhibitor of the proteasome, blocks the degradation of a mutant precursor of glycosylphosphatidylinositol-linked protein in a pre-Golgi compartment. *Biochem. Biophys. Res. Commun.* 219:800–5

Ooi CE, Weiss J. 1992. Bidirectional movement of a nascent polypeptide across microsomal membranes reveals requirements for vectorial translocation of proteins. *Cell* 71:87–96

Orford K, Crockett C, Jensen JP, Weissman AM, Byers SW. 1997. Serine phosphorylation-regulated ubiquitination and degradation of β-catenin. *J. Biol. Chem.* 272:24735–38

Palmer A, Rivett AJ, Thomson S, Hendil KB, Butcher GW, et al. 1996. Subpopulations of proteasomes in rat liver nuclei, microsomes and cytosol. *Biochem. J.* 316:(Pt 2):401–7

Paolini R, Kinet JP. 1993. Cell surface control of the multiubiquitination and deubiquitination of high-affinity immunoglobulin E receptors. *EMBO J.* 12:779–86

Papa FR, Hochstrasser M. 1993. The yeast *DOA4* gene encodes a deubiquitinating enzyme related to a product of the human tre-2 oncogene. *Nature* 366:313–19

Pilon M, Schekman R, Römisch K. 1997. Sec61p mediates export of a misfolded secretory protein from the endoplasmic reticulum to the cytosol for degradation. *EMBO J.* 16:4540–48

Pirozzi G, McConnell SJ, Uveges AJ, Carter JM, Sparks AB, et al. 1997. Identification of novel human WW domain-containing proteins by cloning of ligand targets. *J. Biol. Chem.* 272:14611–16

Plemper RK, Böhmler S, Bordallo J, Sommer T, Wolf DH. 1997. Mutant analysis links the translocon and BiP to retrograde protein transport for ER degradation. *Nature* 388:891–95

Qu D, Teckman JH, Omura S, Perlmutter DH. 1996. Degradation of a mutant secretory protein, α_1-antitrypsin Z, in the endoplasmic reticulum requires proteasome activity. *J. Biol. Chem.* 271:22791–95

Rapoport TA, Jungnickel B, Kutay U. 1996. Protein transport across the eukaryotic endoplasmic reticulum and bacterial inner membranes. *Annu. Rev. Biochem.* 65:271–303

Riezman H, Munn A, Geli MI, Hicke L. 1996. Actin-, myosin- and ubiquitin-dependent endocytosis. *Experientia* 52:1033–41

Rivett AJ, Palmer A, Knecht E. 1992. Electron microscopic localization of the multicatalytic proteinase complex in rat liver and in cultured cells. *J. Histochem. Cytochem.* 40:1165–72

Roberts BJ. 1997. Evidence of proteasome-mediated cytochrome P-450 degradation. *J. Biol. Chem.* 272:9771–78

Rock KL. 1996. A new foreign policy: MHC class I molecules monitor the outside world.

Immunol. Today 17:131–37

Rock KL, Gramm C, Rothstein L, Clark K, Stein R, et al. 1994. Inhibitors of the proteasome block the degradation of most cell proteins and the generation of peptides presented on MHC class I molecules. *Cell* 78:761–71

Roest HP, van Klaveren J, de Wit J, van Gurp CG, Koken MH, et al. 1996. Inactivation of the HR6B ubiquitin-conjugating DNA repair enzyme in mice causes male sterility associated with chromatin modification. *Cell* 86:799–810

Römisch K, Schekman R. 1992. Distinct processes mediate glycoprotein and glycopeptide export from the endoplasmic reticulum in *Saccharomyces cerevisiae*. *Proc. Natl. Acad. Sci. USA* 89:7227–31

Roth AF, Davis NG. 1996. Ubiquitination of the yeast α-factor receptor. *J. Cell Biol.* 134:661–74

Scheffner M, Huibregtse JM, Vierstra RD, Howley PM. 1993. The HPV-16 E6 and E6-AP complex functions as a ubiquitin-protein ligase in the ubiquitination of p53. *Cell* 75:495–505

Scheffner M, Werness BA, Huibregtse JM, Levine AJ, Howley PM. 1990. The E6 oncoprotein encoded by human papillomavirus types 16 and 18 promotes the degradation of p53. *Cell* 63:1129–36

Sepp-Lorenzino L, Ma Z, Lebwohl DE, Vinitsky A, Rosen N. 1995. Herbimycin A induces the 20S proteasome- and ubiquitin-dependent degradation of receptor tyrosine kinases. *J. Biol. Chem.* 270:16580–87

Shanklin J, Jabben M, Vierstra RD. 1987. Red light-induced formation of ubiquitin-phytochrome conjugates: identification of possible intermediates of phytochrome degradation. *Proc. Natl. Acad. Sci. USA* 84:359–63

Siegelman M, Bond MW, Gallatin WM, St. John T, Smith HT, et al. 1986. Cell surface molecule associated with lymphocyte homing is a ubiquitinated branched-chain glycoprotein. *Science* 231:823–29

Skipper JC, Hendrickson RC, Gulden PH, Brichard V, Van Pel A, et al. 1996. An HLA-A2-restricted tyrosinase antigen on melanoma cells results from posttranslational modification and suggests a novel pathway for processing of membrane proteins. *J. Exp. Med.* 183:527–34

Sommer T, Jentsch S. 1993. A protein translocation defect linked to ubiquitin conjugation at the endoplasmic reticulum. *Nature* 365:176–79

Springael J-Y, André B. 1998. Nitrogen regulated ubiquitination of the Gap1 permease of *Saccharomyces cerevisiae*. *Mol. Biol. Cell.* 9:In press

St. John T, Gallatin WM, Siegelman M, Smith

HT, Fried VA, Weissman IL. 1986. Expression cloning of a lymphocyte homing receptor cDNA: ubiquitin is the reactive species. *Science* 231:845–50

Staub O, Dho S, Henry P, Correa J, Ishikawa T, et al. 1996. WW domains of Nedd4 bind to the proline-rich PY motifs in the epithelial Na$^+$ channel deleted in Liddle's syndrome. *EMBO J.* 15:2371–80

Staub O, Yeger H, Plant PJ, Kim H, Ernst SA, Rotin D. 1997. Immunolocalization of the ubiquitin-protein ligase Nedd4 in tissues expressing the epithelial Na$^+$ channel (ENaC). *Am. J. Physiol.* 272:C1871–80

Stephen AG, Trausch-Azar JS, Ciechanover A, Schwartz AL. 1996. The ubiquitin-activating enzyme E1 is phosphorylated and localized to the nucleus in a cell cycle-dependent manner. *J. Biol. Chem.* 271:15608–14

Strous GJ, van Kerkhof P, Govers R, Ciechanover A, Schwartz AL. 1996. The ubiquitin conjugation system is required for ligand-induced endocytosis and degradation of the growth hormone receptor. *EMBO J.* 15:3806–12

Strous GJ, van Kerkhof P, Govers R, Rotwein P, Schwartz AL. 1997. Growth hormone-induced signal tranduction depends on an intact ubiquitin system. *J. Biol. Chem.* 272:40–43

Sudha T, Tsuji H, Sameshima M, Matsuda Y, Kaneda S, et al. 1995. Abnormal integrity of the nucleolus associated with cell cycle arrest owing to the temperature-sensitive ubiquitin-activating enzyme E1. *Chromosome Res.* 3:115–23

Sudol M, Chen HI, Bougeret C, Einbond A, Bork P. 1995. Characterization of a novel protein-binding module—the WW domain. *FEBS Lett.* 369:67–71

Suzuki T, Seko A, Kitajima K, Inoue Y, Inoue S. 1994. Purification and enzymatic properties of peptide:N-glycanase from C3H mouse-derived L-929 fibroblast cells. Possible widespread occurrence of post-translational remodification of proteins by N-deglycosylation. *J. Biol. Chem.* 269:17611–18

Tamura H, Schild L, Enomoto N, Matsui N, Marumo F, Rossier BC. 1996. Liddle disease caused by a missense mutation of β subunit of the epithelial sodium channel gene. *J. Clin. Invest.* 97:1780–84

Tang HY, Munn A, Cai M. 1997. EH domain proteins Pan1p and End3p are components of a complex that plays a dual role in organization of the cortical actin cytoskeleton and endocytosis in *Saccharomyces cerevisiae*. *Mol. Cell. Biol.* 17:4294–304

Tebar F, Sorkina T, Sorkin A, Ericsson M, Kirchhausen T. 1996. Eps15 is a component of clathrin-coated pits and vesicles and is located at the rim of coated pits. *J. Biol. Chem.* 271:28727–30

Terrell J, Shih S, Dunn R, Hicke L. 1998. A function for monoubiquitination in the internalization of a G protein-coupled receptor. *Mol. Cell* 1:193–202

Tierney DJ, Haas AL, Koop DR. 1992. Degradation of cytochrome P450 2E1: selective loss after labilization of the enzyme. *Arch. Biochem. Biophys.* 293:9–16

Tokunaga F, Shirotani H, Hara K, Kozuki D, Omura S, Koide T. 1997. Intracellular degradation of secretion defect-type mutants of antithrombin is inhibited by proteasomal inhibitors. *FEBS Lett.* 412:65–69

Valetti C, Grossi CE, Milstein Z, Sitia R. 1991. Russell bodies: a general response of secretory cells to synthesis of a mutant immunoglobulin which can neither exit from, nor be degraded in, the endoplasmic reticulum. *J. Cell Biol.* 115:983–94

van Delft S, Govers R, Strous GJ, Verkleij AJ, van Bergen en Henegouwen PM. 1997a. Epidermal growth factor induces ubiquitination of Eps15. *J. Biol. Chem.* 272:14013–16

van Delft S, Schumacher C, Hage W, Verkleij AJ, van Bergen en Henegouwen PM. 1997b. Association and colocalization of Eps15 with adaptor protein-2 and clathrin. *J. Cell Biol.* 136:811–21

Varshavsky A. 1996. The N-end rule: functions, mysteries, uses. *Proc. Natl. Acad. Sci. USA* 93:12142–49

Vecchi M, Carpenter G. 1997. Constitutive proteolysis of the ErbB-4 receptor tyrosine kinase by a unique, sequential mechanism. *J. Cell Biol.* 139:995–1003

Ward CL, Omura S, Kopito RR. 1995. Degradation of CFTR by the ubiquitin-proteasome pathway. *Cell* 83:121–27

Weissman AM. 1994. The T-cell antigen receptor: a multisubunit signaling complex. *Chem. Immunol.* 59:1–18

Weissman AM. 1997. Regulating protein degradation by ubiquitination. *Immunol. Today* 18:189–98

Wendland B, McCaffery JM, Xiao Q, Emr SD. 1996. A novel fluorescence-activated cell sorter-based screen for yeast endocytosis mutants identifies a yeast homologue of mammalian eps15. *J. Cell Biol.* 135:1485–500

Werner ED, Brodsky JL, McCracken AA. 1996. Proteasome-dependent endoplasmic reticulum-associated protein degradation: an unconventional route to a familiar fate. *Proc. Natl. Acad. Sci. USA* 93:13797–801

Wiertz EJ, Jones TR, Sun L, Bogyo M, Geuze HJ, Ploegh HL. 1996a. The human cytomegalovirus US11 gene product dislocates MHC class I heavy chains from the endoplasmic reticulum to the cytosol. *Cell* 84:769–79

Wiertz EJ, Tortorella D, Bogyo M, Yu J, Mothes W, et al. 1996b. Sec61-mediated transfer of a membrane protein from the endoplasmic reticulum to the proteasome for destruction. *Nature* 384:432–38

Wilkinson KD. 1995. Roles of ubiquitinylation in proteolysis and cellular regulation. *Annu. Rev. Nutr.* 15:161–89

Wilkinson KD. 1997. Regulation of ubiquitin-dependent processes by deubiquitinating enzymes. *FASEB J.* 11:1245–56

Wu X, Sakata N, Lele KM, Zhou M, Jiang H, Ginsberg HN. 1997. A two-site model for ApoB degradation in HepG2 cells. *J. Biol. Chem.* 272:11575–80

Yang M, Ellenberg J, Bonifacino JS, Weissman AM. 1997. The transmembrane domain of a carboxy-terminal anchored protein determines localization to the endoplasmic reticulum. *J. Biol. Chem.* 272:1970–75

Yang M, Omura S, Bonifacino JS, Weissman AM. 1998. Novel aspects of degradation of TCR subunits from the ER in T cells: importance of oligosaccharide processing, ubiquitination, and proteasome-dependent removal from ER membranes. *J. Exp. Med.* 187:1835–46

Yang MX, Cederbaum AI. 1997. Characterization of cytochrome P4502E1 turnover in transfected HepG2 cells expressing human CYP2E1. *Arch. Biochem. Biophys.* 341:25–33

Yang Y, Janich S, Cohn JA, Wilson JM. 1993. The common variant of cystic fibrosis transmembrane conductance regulator is recognized by hsp70 and degraded in a pre-Golgi nonlysosomal compartment. *Proc. Natl. Acad. Sci. USA* 90:9480–84

Yarden Y, Escobedo JA, Kuang WJ, Yang-Feng TL, Daniel TO, et al. 1986. Structure of the receptor for platelet-derived growth factor helps define a family of closely related growth factor receptors. *Nature* 323:226–32

Yeung SJ, Chen SH, Chan L. 1996. Ubiquitin-proteasome pathway mediates intracellular degradation of apolipoprotein B. *Biochemistry* 35:13843–48

Yu H, Kaung G, Kobayashi S, Kopito RR. 1997. Cytosolic degradation of T-cell receptor α chains by the proteasome. *J. Biol. Chem.* 272:20800–4

Zhen M, Schein JE, Baillie DL, Candido PM. 1996. An essential ubiquitin-conjugating enzyme with tissue and develpmental specificity in the nematode *Caenorhabditis elegans*. *EMBO J.* 15:3229–37

Zhu Y, Carroll M, Papa FR, Hochstrasser M, D'Andrea AD. 1996. DUB-1, a deubiquitinating enzyme with growth-suppressing activity. *Proc. Natl. Acad. Sci. USA* 93:3275–79

Zhu Y, Lambert K, Corless C, Copeland NG, Gilbert DJ, et al. 1997. DUB-2 is a member of a novel family of cytokine-inducible deubiquitinating enzymes. *J. Biol. Chem.* 272:51–57

Annu. Rev. Cell Dev. Biol. 1998. 14:59–88

MECHANISMS OF WNT SIGNALING IN DEVELOPMENT

Andreas Wodarz
Institut für Genetik, Universität Düsseldorf, Universitätsstrasse 1, 40225 Düsseldorf, Germany; e-mail: wodarz@uni-duesseldorf.de

Roel Nusse
Howard Hughes Medical Institute and Department of Developmental Biology, Stanford University, Stanford, CA 94305-5428; e-mail: rnusse@cmgm.stanford.edu

KEY WORDS: Wnt, wingless, frizzled, catenin, signal transduction

ABSTRACT

Wnt genes encode a large family of secreted, cysteine-rich proteins that play key roles as intercellular signaling molecules in development. Genetic studies in *Drosophila* and *Caenorhabditis elegans*, ectopic gene expression in *Xenopus*, and gene knockouts in the mouse have demonstrated the involvement of Wnts in processes as diverse as segmentation, CNS patterning, and control of asymmetric cell divisions. The transduction of Wnt signals between cells proceeds in a complex series of events including post-translational modification and secretion of Wnts, binding to transmembrane receptors, activation of cytoplasmic effectors, and, finally, transcriptional regulation of target genes. Over the past two years our understanding of Wnt signaling has been substantially improved by the identification of Frizzled proteins as cell surface receptors for Wnts and by the finding that β-catenin, a component downstream of the receptor, can translocate to the nucleus and function as a transcriptional activator. Here we review recent data that have started to unravel the mechanisms of Wnt signaling.

CONTENTS

59

1081-0706/98/1115-0059$08.00

INTRODUCTION

Together with other families of secreted factors such as FGF, TGF-beta, and Hedgehog proteins, Wnt proteins are implicated in a wide variety of biological processes. The first Wnt gene, mouse Wnt-1, was discovered in 1982 as a proto-oncogene activated by integration of mouse mammary tumor virus in mammary tumors (Nusse & Varmus 1982). Consequently, the potential involvement of Wnt genes in cancer was the main area of research in the 1980s (reviewed by Nusse & Varmus 1992). With the molecular identification of the *Drosophila* segment polarity gene *wingless* (*wg*) as the orthologue of Wnt-1 (Cabrera et al 1987, Rijsewijk et al 1987) and the phenotypic analysis of Wnt-1 mutations in the mouse (McMahon & Bradley 1990, Thomas & Capecchi 1990), it became clear that Wnt genes are important regulators of many developmental decisions (reviewed in Nusse & Varmus 1992, Parr & McMahon 1994, Cadigan & Nusse 1997) (Table 1). At this moment, close to 100 Wnt genes have been isolated from species ranging from human to the nematode *Caenorhabditis elegans* (a comprehensive and regularly updated list of Wnt genes can be viewed on the Wnt homepage at http://www.stanford.edu/~rnusse/wntwindow.html). All these genes encode proteins with a signal sequence and a nearly invariant pattern of 23 cysteines. Presumably, all Wnt proteins are secreted from cells and act through cell surface receptors either on the producing or on adjacent cells to determine cell fate or other differentiation parameters.

Table 1 Phenotypes of Wnt mutations in mouse, *Drosophila*, and *C. elegans*[a]

Gene	Organism	Phenotype
Wnt-1	Mouse	Loss of midbrain and cerebellum
Wnt-2	Mouse	Placental defects
Wnt-3A	Mouse	Lack of caudal somites and tailbud
Wnt-4	Mouse	Kidney defects
Wnt-7A	Mouse	Ventralization of limbs
wingless	*Drosophila*	Segment polarity, limb development, many others
Dwnt-2	*Drosophila*	Muscle defects, testis development
lin-44	*C. elegans*	Defects in asymmetric cell divisions
mom-2	*C. elegans*	Defects in endoderm induction and spindle orientation

[a]A fully referenced version of this table can be found on the Wnt homepage: http://www.stanford.edu/~rnusse/wntwindow.html

GENETIC ANALYSIS OF WINGLESS/WNT SIGNALING IN *DROSOPHILA* AND *CAENORHABDITIS ELEGANS*

Drosophila

The *Drosophila wg* gene is one of the best-characterized Wnt family members. The function of *wg* as a segment polarity gene was uncovered in a genetic screen for zygotic lethal mutations that affect larval cuticle pattern (Nüsslein-Volhard & Wieschaus 1980). In the *Drosophila* embryo, *wg* is required for formation of parasegment boundaries and for maintenance of *engrailed* (*en*) expression in adjacent cells. The epidermis of *wg* mutant embryos shows only rudimentary segmentation, which is reflected in an abnormal cuticle pattern. While the ventral cuticle of a wild-type larva displays denticle belts alternating with naked regions, the cuticle of a *wg* larva is completely covered with denticles. Embryos mutant for the genes *porcupine* (*porc*), *dishevelled* (*dsh*), *armadillo* (*arm*), and *pangolin* (*pan*) show a very similar phenotype. By contrast, mutations in *zeste-white 3* (*zw3*) show the opposite phenotype, a naked cuticle (reviewed by Klingensmith & Nusse 1994, Perrimon 1994). Analysis of double mutants indicates that these genes cooperate in a pathway to transduce the Wg signal (Noordermeer et al 1994, Peifer et al 1994, Siegfried et al 1994, Brunner et al 1997, van de Wetering et al 1997) (Figure 1).

C. elegans

Wnt genes have recently been implicated in early *C. elegans* embryogenesis as well. In the *C. elegans* embryo, the EMS cell undergoes an unequal division to generate the MS cell, which gives rise to mesoderm, and the E cell, which is the founder cell of the complete gut lineage. An inductive signal from P2 to EMS is required at the four-cell stage for this unequal division to occur. In

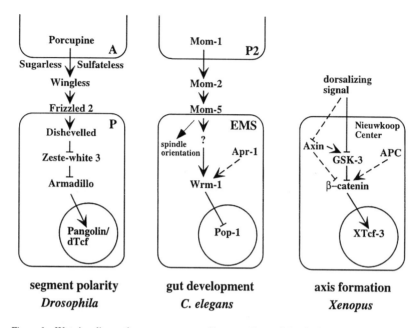

Figure 1 Wnt signaling pathways are conserved between *Drosophila, C. elegans,* and vertebrates. In *Drosophila,* anterior epidermal cells (*A*) express Wg and signal to adjacent posterior cells (*P*). This signal is required for establishment of parasegment boundaries and for maintenance of *engrailed* expression in posterior cells. In *C. elegans* a very similar pathway is used to induce the asymmetric division of the EMS cell. Note that only the first three components of this pathway, *mom-1, mom-2,* and *mom-5* are also involved in orientation of mitotic spindles during development. Formation of the primary body axis in *Xenopus* depends on a Wnt pathway comprising GSK3, β-catenin, and XTcf-3. Although overexpression of various Wnts and of Dsh leads to duplication of the body axis, they do not appear to be required for formation of the primary axis. Instead, the Wnt pathway may be triggered at the level of GSK3 by a hypothetical dorsalizing signal. Whether axin, APC, and its *C. elegans* counterpart *apr-1* are integral components of a common Wnt signaling pathway remains to be shown.

the absence of signal, EMS divides symmetrically and gives rise to two MS-like daughters that form mesoderm but no gut. In a screen for mutants that interrupt signaling from P2 to EMS, five genes called *mom1-5* were identified. Molecular analysis of three revealed that they encode proteins similar to *porc* (*mom-1*), Wnt (*mom-2*), and *frizzled* (*fz*), a Wnt receptor (*mom-5*; Rocheleau et al 1997, Thorpe et al 1997). Mutation of *pop-1,* an HMG box protein similar to *pan,* has the opposite effect of *mom* mutations: Both EMS daughters adopt the E fate and produce exclusively gut (Lin et al 1995). These results indicate that a Wnt signaling cascade mediates induction of EMS by P2 (reviewed in Han 1997; see Figure 1).

ASSAYS FOR WNT SIGNALING

Axis Duplication in Xenopus

Among the various ways to test for function of Wnt signaling components, injection of RNA into *Xenopus* embryos is perhaps the most convenient and informative. These tests are based on the observation that injection of Wnt-1 mRNA into ventral blastomeres of early *Xenopus* embryos leads to duplication of the body axis (McMahon & Moon 1989). This property of Wnt-1 is shared with many, but not all, members of the Wnt family (Table 2). The apparent functional differences between Wnts have led to the hypothesis that Wnts can be divided into two distinct classes that might employ different signal transduction mechanisms; members of the Xwnt-8 class (among them Wnt-1) are active in the axis duplication assay, whereas members of the Xwnt-5A class are not. Instead, overexpression of members of the Xwnt-5A class affects morphogenetic movements and may antagonize members of the Xwnt-8 class (Moon et al 1993, Du et al 1995, Torres et al 1996, Moon et al 1997a). Experiments in zebrafish indicate that Xwnt-5A may signal through a pathway involving phosphatidylinositol, G proteins, and release of intracellular calcium (Slusarski et al 1997a,b). However, the inability of Xwnt-5A to induce a secondary axis can be overcome by coinjection of human Frizzled 5, suggesting that the availability of a specific receptor rather than a fundamental difference in its signal transduction

Table 2 Axis duplication and cell transformation by different Wnts[a]

Gene	Axis duplication in *Xenopus*	Transformation of C57 or RAC cells
Wnt-1	yes	yes
Wnt-2	yes	yes
Wnt-3A	yes	yes
Wnt-4	no	no
Wnt-5A	no	no
Wnt-5B	nd	yes
Wnt-6	nd	no
Wnt-7A	nd	yes
Wnt-7B	nd	yes
Wnt-8A	yes	nd
Wnt-8B	yes	nd
Wnt-11	yes/no[b]	yes

[a]A fully referenced version of this table can be found on the Wnt homepage: http://www.stanford.edu/~rnusse/wnt-window.html

[b]See references on the Wnt homepage.

mechanism determines whether a particular Wnt can induce a secondary axis (He et al 1997).

Duplication of the embryonic axis can not only be induced by Wnts but also by overexpression of downstream components of Wnt signaling. Overexpression of Dsh, β-catenin (the vertebrate homologue of Arm), and dominant-negative glycogen synthase kinase 3 (GSK3, the vertebrate homologue of Zw3) all lead to an ectopic axis (Dominguez et al 1995, Guger & Gumbiner 1995, He et al 1995, Sokol et al 1995). These results provide strong evidence that components of Wnt signaling are structurally and functionally conserved between *Drosophila*, *C. elegans*, and vertebrates (Figure 1).

WNT SIGNALING AND FORMATION OF THE PRIMARY BODY AXIS IN XENOPUS Despite the ability of injected Wnts to induce a secondary axis, it is not clear whether an endogenous Wnt protein is involved in the establishment of the primary body axis in *Xenopus*. So far there is no Wnt gene known to be expressed at the expected place and time during embryogenesis. Moreover, injection of a dominant-negative form of Xwnt-8 can block induction of a secondary axis by Wnts but does not block formation of the primary axis (Hoppler et al 1996). The same is true for a dominant-negative form of Dsh (Sokol 1996). By contrast, overexpression of wild-type GSK3, dominant-negative Xtcf-3 (an HMG box protein similar to Pan and Pop-1), depletion of β-catenin by antisense RNA injection, or overexpression of cadherins leads to ventralization (Heasman et al 1994, Dominguez et al 1995, He et al 1995, Molenaar et al 1996). It has been suggested that the Wnt signaling cascade may be triggered downstream of Dsh by an unknown dorsalizing signal unrelated to Wnts, possibly a stimulus provided by rotation of the egg cortex after fertilization (Moon et al 1997a).

Tissue Culture Assays for Wingless/Wnt Signaling

MAMMALIAN TISSUE CULTURE   Although the genetic and developmental systems described above are invaluable for the identification of new components of Wnt signaling and for establishment of their epistatic relationship, their usefulness for biochemical analysis of the signaling mechanism is somewhat limited. Therefore, many laboratories have used cultured cells to study Wnt signaling. This approach has been hampered by a major problem: Most Wnts including Wnt-1 are difficult to obtain in a soluble, biologically active form and tend to stick to the extracellular matrix (Bradley & Brown 1990, Smolich et al 1993). Due to these limitations, most studies used cells transfected with Wnt cDNAs instead of soluble Wnt protein preparations to study effects of Wnts on cell morphology, proliferation, transformation, or gene expression.

When assayed for their ability to transform mammary epithelial cells, two functional classes of Wnts can be distinguished: Members of one class, including Wnt-1, Wnt-3A, and Wnt-7A, readily transform cells at high frequency, whereas members of the other class, Wnt-4, Wnt-5A, and Wnt-6, do not (Wong et al 1994) (Table 2). Interestingly, the two functional classes defined by this assay are similar to the functional classes defined by the axis duplication assay in *Xenopus* (Du et al 1995) (Table 2).

DROSOPHILA TISSUE CULTURE   In contrast to mammalian Wnts, Wg produced in transfected *Drosophila* Schneider S2 cells is secreted into the medium and is biologically active when added to Wg-responsive cells (van Leeuwen et al 1994). The assay used for Wg activity is derived from the observation that in the *Drosophila* embryo, Arm protein accumulates in the cytoplasm of cells that are exposed to Wg (Riggleman et al 1990, Peifer et al 1994). A *Drosophila* imaginal disc cell line, cl-8, shows the same response upon incubation with Wg-conditioned medium (van Leeuwen et al 1994). Overexpression of Dsh or dominant-negative Zw3 also leads to Arm accumulation (Yanagawa et al 1995, 1997). By contrast, S2 cells do not show increased Arm levels after exposure to Wg although they respond to overexpression of Dsh, which led to the suggestion that S2 cells lack a functional Wg receptor (Yanagawa et al 1995).

WNT SIGNALING UPSTREAM OF THE RECEPTOR

A Role for Porcupine in Post-Translational Modification and Secretion of Wnts

Drosophila embryos mutant for the gene *porc* show a phenotype similar to that of *wg* mutants (van den Heuvel et al 1993, Kadowaki et al 1996). Clones of *porc* mutant cells display non-cell-autonomous effects, similar to *wg* clones, indicating that Porc is required in the cell that produces the signal rather than in the receiving cell (Kadowaki et al 1996). In *porc* embryos, Wg protein is confined to the narrow stripe of cells where the *wg* gene is transcribed, instead of spreading to adjacent cells as in wild-type embryos (van den Heuvel et al 1989, 1993). Several mutations in *wg* itself also cause retention of mutant Wg protein, indicating that changes of the protein structure can lead to misfolding and impair secretion (van den Heuvel et al 1993, Bejsovec & Wieschaus 1995, Hays et al 1997).

Molecular cloning of *porc* revealed that it encodes a multi-transmembrane protein predominantly found in the endoplasmic reticulum, consistent with a role in processing of Wg (Kadowaki et al 1996). Biochemical studies in cultured cells revealed increased N-linked glycosylation of Wg after coexpression with Porc (Kadowaki et al 1996). Glycosylation appears to be a common modification of Wnts and may be important for folding, secretion, and biological activity (Smolich et al 1993).

In *C. elegans*, the *porc* homologue *mom-1* is required in the P2 cell for signaling to the EMS cell by *mom-2* (a Wnt) (Rocheleau et al 1997, Thorpe et al 1997). Apart from this example, it is not known whether *porc* is essential for every Wnt protein to become secreted, mainly because there are few reagents to study the distribution of Wnt proteins in vivo.

Another ER-resident protein, the molecular chaperone BiP, associates with Wnt-1 (Kitajewski et al 1992). Although the functional significance of this interaction has not been tested, it is likely that BiP assists in proper folding of Wnts.

Proteoglycans Facilitate Wnt Signaling

The *Drosophila sugarless* (*sgl*) gene encodes UDP-glucose dehydrogenase, a key enzyme required for synthesis of proteoglycans. Mutants of *sgl* show a larval phenotype similar to *wg* (Binari et al 1997, Häcker et al 1997, Haerry et al 1997). Phenocopies of *sgl* can be generated by injection of heparinase, which selectively degrades heparin-like glycosaminoglycans, but not by chondroitinase, which degrades chondroitin sulfate, hyaluronic acid, and dermatan sulfate. Conversely, injection of heparan sulfate is sufficient to rescue the *sgl* mutant phenotype (Binari et al 1997). Mutations in *sulfateless* (*sfl*), a gene encoding heparan sulfate *N*-deacetylase/*N*-sulfotransferase, another enzyme required for heparan sulfate biosynthesis, also cause a *wg*-like phenotype, underpinning the importance of proteoglycans for Wg signaling (X Lin & N Perrimon, personal communication).

Sulfated glycosaminoglycans also affect Wg signaling in tissue culture. Treatment of cl-8 cells with heparinase, heparitinase, chondroitin ABC lyase, or perchlorate leads to reduced Wg-induced accumulation of Arm. This effect can be reversed by addition of chondroitin sulfate or heparin. Heparin binds to Wnt-1 (Bradley & Brown 1990) and Wg, and addition of heparin to Wg-conditioned medium leads to increased Wg activity (Reichsman et al 1996). However, heparin has also been reported to inhibit the activity of Wnt-1 in a cell transformation assay (Jue et al 1992). In *Xenopus* animal caps, removal of heparan sulfate proteoglycans blocks mesoderm induction by Xwnt-8, again suggesting that proteoglycans are important for the function of Wnts (Itoh & Sokol 1994).

Little is known about the role of proteoglycans in Wnt signaling. In analogy to FGF signaling, proteoglycans may be low-affinity coreceptors for Wnts, which would serve to increase the local concentration of ligand available for binding to high-affinity receptors. Alternatively, proteoglycans in the ECM may crosslink Wnts to induce clustering of Wnt receptors in the plasma membrane. In the absence of soluble, sufficiently pure, biologically active preparations of Wnts, this issue will be difficult to address.

INTERACTIONS BETWEEN WNTS AND PROTEINS OF THE FRIZZLED FAMILY

Frizzleds Are Receptors for Wnts

For many years a big question mark in models about Wnt signaling has been the nature of Wnt receptors. Recently, however, good evidence has emerged that seven-pass transmembrane proteins of the Frizzled family are involved in Wnt signaling: (*a*) Studies on tissue polarity in *Drosophila* reveal genetic interactions between *dsh* and *frizzled* (*fz*). Both genes act in a signaling pathway that controls correct orientation of hairs, bristles, and ommatidia in the epidermis and eyes of the adult fly (Adler 1992, Wong & Adler 1993, Krasnow et al 1995, Strutt et al 1997) (Figure 2). (*b*) Certain asymmetric cell divisions in *C. elegans* depend on the genes *lin-44* and *lin-17*. *lin-44* encodes a Wnt protein (Herman et al 1995), and *lin-17* encodes a Fz-like transmembrane protein, which led to the hypothesis that both proteins might interact in a ligand-receptor relationship (Sawa et al 1996).

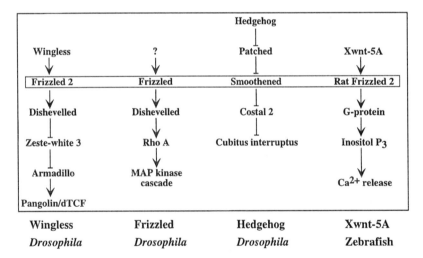

Figure 2   Frizzled receptors participate in different signaling pathways. Four examples are shown here. *Drosophila* Frizzled 2 functions in the classical Wg pathway, as shown in Figure 1. Frizzled is part of a pathway regulating planar polarity in the adult epidermis and in the eye of *Drosophila*. Downstream of Dsh, this pathway appears to be distinct from the Wg pathway. Whether Wg or another Wnt ligand is involved in planar polarity is unknown. Smoothened is a component of the Hedgehog signaling cascade and forms a complex with the Hedgehog receptor, Patched. Whether Smoothened has a ligand of its own is unknown. Rat Frizzled 2 cooperates with Xwnt-5A to activate a G protein–dependent pathway when overexpressed in zebrafish embryos. It is not known whether the interaction between rat Frizzled 2 and G proteins is direct.

This issue has been directly addressed in tissue culture. Transfection of Dfz2, a member of the Fz family, from *Drosophila* into S2 cells (S2Dfz2) confers responsiveness to Wg to these cells. Like cl-8 cells, S2Dfz2 cells accumulate Arm when incubated with Wg-conditioned medium. Moreover, S2Dfz2 cells and human 293 cells transfected with Dfz2 bind Wg on their cell surfaces, whereas untransfected cells of both cell lines do not (Bhanot et al 1996).

Cadigan et al (1998) also showed that a dominant-negative form of the *Dfz2* gene blocks signaling by *wg* in the *Drosophila* imaginal disc and that overexpression of this receptor causes phenotypes similar to those brought about by ectopic *wg*, in a *wg*-dependent way.

Additional evidence for Frizzleds as Wnt receptors comes from studies in *Xenopus*. Coinjection of rat Frizzled 1 and Xwnt-8 into frog embryos results in recruitment of Xwnt-8 to the plasma membrane and in increased expression of Xwnt-8 target genes, compared with injection of Xwnt-8 alone (Yang-Snyder et al 1996). Also, as mentioned above, coinjection of rat Frizzled 5 and Xwnt-5A leads to axis duplication, whereas injection of either rat Frizzled 5 or Xwnt-5A does not (He et al 1997).

Genetic Analysis of Frizzled-Wnt Interactions

DROSOPHILA   Genetic data on the requirement for Frizzleds in Wnt signaling are limited in *Drosophila*. Loss-of-function mutants of the original *fz* are viable and show misorientation of hairs and bristles in the adult epidermis (Vinson & Adler 1987). Rotation of ommatidia in the eye imaginal disc is also defective in *fz* mutants, resulting in a rough eye phenotype (Zheng et al 1995). Clones of *fz* mutant cells induced in wing imaginal discs show an interesting feature termed directional nonautonomy, which describes the fact that cells within the clone, as well as wild-type cells located outside the clone, have misoriented wing hairs. Those "shadows" are found in a distal direction (Vinson & Adler 1987), which led to the suggestion that Fz is required for not only reception of a polarity signal but also for generation or propagation of a signal. This signal, whose nature remains to be determined, would spread in a proximal-distal direction across the wing imaginal disc (Adler 1992).

Although a physiological ligand for Fz has not been identified, it is anticipated that this ligand may be a Wnt. It has been suggested that there is a gradient of Fz activity across the wing that is caused by a graded distribution of the ligand and that hair polarity follows the slope of that gradient. Support for this notion comes from the observation that creation of an artificial gradient of Fz expression with the high point at the distal tip of the wing leads to polarity reversal (Adler et al 1997).

Interestingly, some alleles of *fz* do not show directional nonautonomy in clones and instead behave strictly cell autonomously. Molecular analysis of four

Frizzleds   FRPs

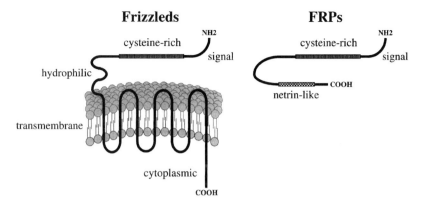

Figure 3 Structure of Frizzleds and FRPs. Frizzled receptors are characterized by an N-terminal signal peptide, a cysteine-rich ligand-binding domain (CRD) followed by a hydrophilic linker, seven transmembrane regions, and a cytoplasmic tail. FRPs are secreted proteins with a CRD similar to Frizzleds. In addition, they contain a region with similarity to netrins, secreted proteins involved in axon guidance.

of these alleles revealed that they all change the same proline residue in the first cytoplasmic loop (Jones et al 1996) (Figure 3). Because cell-autonomous and nonautonomous functions can be separated genetically, it has been speculated that *fz* interacts with at least two different effectors; one responsible for polarization of the cytoskeleton (cell-autonomous function) and the other one for relaying the signal to adjacent cells (nonautonomous function; Jones et al 1996).

In tissue culture, Fz binds Wg (Bhanot et al 1996). Whether Wg functions in tissue polarity is difficult to test because of the widespread effects of Wg on pattern formation. Nonetheless, ectopic expression of Wg in the eye imaginal disc leads to tissue polarity phenotypes (Tomlinson et al 1997). Conversely, overexpression of Fz in the embryonic epidermis causes phenotypes similar to those resulting from modest overexpression of Wg, which has been taken as evidence for Fz's involvement in Wg signaling (Tomlinson et al 1997).

Mutations in a second Fz gene, *Dfz2*, have not been isolated in *Drosophila*. Nonetheless, zygotic removal of Dfz2 by means of a large deficiency generated by chromosomal translocations does not block Wg signaling because the cytoplasmic increase of Armadillo protein in response to Wg is normal (HA Müller & E Wieschaus, personal communication). These results can be explained in several ways: *fz* and *Dfz2* act redundantly, and removal of both genes may be necessary to impair Wg signaling. Alternatively, maternally provided Dfz2 may be sufficient for Wg signaling during embryogenesis so that only removal of both maternal and zygotic expression would yield a phenotype. A third possibility would be the existence of additional Fz genes in *Drosophila*.

Besides *fz* and *Dfz2*, a third family member, *smoothened* (*smo*), has been identified in *Drosophila* (Alcedo et al 1996, van den Heuvel & Ingham 1996). Genetic analysis indicates that *smo* is required for Hedgehog (Hh) signaling rather than for Wg signaling (Figure 2). These findings, together with the predicted protein structure of Smo, led to the suggestion that Smo is an Hh receptor, implicating direct protein-protein interaction between Smo and Hh (Alcedo et al 1996, van den Heuvel & Ingham 1996). This hypothesis has been questioned by the finding that Hh and a vertebrate homologue, Sonic Hedgehog, can bind to Patched (Ptc), a multi-transmembrane protein, whereas no direct binding to Smo was detected (Chen & Struhl 1996, Marigo et al 1996, Stone et al 1996). However, Ptc can form a complex with Smo, suggesting that Hh activates Smo indirectly via Ptc (Chen & Struhl 1996, Stone et al 1996) (Figure 2).

C. ELEGANS   In the worm, more genetic data are available for fz/Wnt interactions. The genes *lin-44* (a Wnt) and *lin-17* (an Fz) interact genetically in the control of certain asymmetric cell divisions. In *lin-44* mutants, the polarity of two asymmetric daughter cells is reversed, whereas in *lin-17* mutants, polarity is lost, resulting in two symmetric daughter cells (Herman et al 1995, Sawa et al 1996). *lin-44/lin-17* double mutants also produce symmetric daughter cells, indicating that *lin-17* acts downstream of *lin-44*. The fact that the phenotypes of *lin-44* and *lin-17* are not identical has led to the hypothesis that Lin-17 acts as a receptor for two signals coming from different directions—one Lin-44 and the other an unknown ligand X, possibly another Wnt (Sawa et al 1996).

Mutants in *mom-5*, a second Fz-like gene from *C. elegans*, also show some unexpected features. *mom-5* interacts with *mom-2* (a Wnt) to specify the gut precursor cell E, which is generated in the asymmetric division of EMS (Rocheleau et al 1997, Thorpe et al 1997; see above). The penetrance of the gutless phenotype of *mom-5* is low, ≈5%. Mutations in *mom-2* have a much higher penetrance, ≈40%. Surprisingly, the double mutant *mom-2/mom-5* shows a penetrance of only 8%, so the low penetrance of the *mom-5* phenotype is epistatic over the high penetrance *mom-2* phenotype, which is not compatible with the model that the receptor Mom-5 is simply activated by its ligand Mom-2 to specify the E fate. One explanation for these data would be that Mom-5 constitutively represses specification of E fate in the absence of the ligand Mom-2 and that this repression can be overcome by binding of Mom-2 (Rocheleau et al 1997).

In contrast to the low penetrance of endoderm defects in *mom-5* and *mom-2/mom-5* double mutant embryos, *mom-1* (Porc-like), *mom-2*, and *mom-5* mutants show a fully penetrant defect in orientation of the mitotic spindle in the ABar cell. This kind of defect is not observed in mutants for *apr-1* (APC), *wrm-1* (β-catenin), and *pop-1* (HMG box protein), indicating a branching of the Wnt pathway downstream of *mom-5* (Rocheleau et al 1997, Thorpe et al 1997) (Figure 1). Interestingly, the function of *mom-1, mom-2,* and *mom-5* in spindle orientation may not require transcriptional regulation of Wnt target genes, since inhibition of the large subunit of RNA polymerase or α-amanitin treatment of embryos does not affect spindle orientation until the 26-cell stage (Rocheleau et al 1997 and references therein).

Together, these data indicate that Frizzled receptors can participate in several distinct signal transduction pathways (Figure 2). Moreover, there is evidence that an individual Frizzled can have more than one physiological ligand and, vice versa, that a Wnt may bind to more than one Frizzled. Regulation of Frizzleds may occur within the plane of the plasma membrane by association with other transmembrane proteins such as Ptc. In addition, Frizzleds may possess constitutive activity, allowing both activation and repression of downstream signaling components, depending on availability of ligand(s).

Structure of Frizzled Proteins

All members of the Fz family are characterized by the following features (beginning at the N terminus): a putative signal sequence, followed by a sequence of 120 amino acids (aa) containing 10 highly conserved cysteine residues (CRD), a highly divergent region of 40–100 aa predicted to form a flexible linker, seven transmembrane segments separated by short extracellular and cytoplasmic loops, and a cytoplasmic tail (Vinson et al 1989, Wang et al 1996) (Figure 3). The CRD appears to be the ligand-binding site of Frizzleds. Expression of the CRD of Dfz2 anchored in the membrane by a glycosyl-phosphatidylinositol (GPI) anchor is sufficient to provide binding sites for Wg on the surface of cells (Cadigan et al 1998). By contrast, expression of a mouse Fz4 construct lacking the CRD, but containing the signal sequence and all seven transmembrane domains, does not confer binding of Wg (Bhanot et al 1996).

The Wg-binding assay provides a means to test the specificity of ligand-receptor interactions. Several Fz proteins from human, mouse, and *Drosophila* have been tested for their ability to allow cell surface binding of Wg. Many of the Frizzleds tested, including the original Fz from *Drosophila*, do confer Wg binding, whereas others, e.g. mouse Fz3 and Fz6 and Smoothened, do not (Bhanot et al 1996, Nusse et al 1997, YK Wang et al 1997; Table 3). Although this assay does not provide measurement of binding affinities between Wg and different Frizzleds, it indicates that there is considerable promiscuity in the interaction of Wnts with their receptors.

The overall structure of Frizzleds resembles that of G protein-coupled receptors, which also have seven transmembrane regions. However, this similarity is mostly restricted to the membrane topology of both protein families, and there is little sequence identity between them. Nonetheless, expression of Xwnt-5A

Table 3 Interaction of Wnts with Frizzleds[a]

Frizzled Gene	Organism	Interaction with	Type of Interaction
Mfz3	Mouse	Not with Wg	Binding
Mfz4	Mouse	Wg	Binding
Mfz6	Mouse	Not with Wg	Binding
Mfz7	Mouse	Wg	Binding
Mfz8	Mouse	Wg	Binding
Hfz5	Human	Wg	Binding
		Xwnt-5A	Axis duplication in *Xenopus*
FZD3	Human	Wg	Binding
Rfz1	Rat	Xwnt-8	Recruitment to plasma membrane
Rfz2	Rat	Xwnt-5A	Activation of Ca^{2+}-signaling in zebrafish
Fz	*Drosophila*	Wg	Binding
Dfz2	*Drosophila*	Wg	Binding
Smo	*Drosophila*	Not with Wg	Binding
Lin-17	*C. elegans*	Lin-44	Genetic
		Egl-20	Genetic
Mom-5	*C. elegans*	Mom-2	Genetic

[a]A fully referenced version of this table can be found on the Wnt homepage: http://www.stanford.edu/~rnusse/wntwindow.html

in zebrafish embryos causes release of calcium from intracellular stores in a G protein-dependent fashion, whereas Xwnt-8 does not (Slusarski et al 1997a,b) (Figure 2). Expression of rat Frizzled 2 has a similar effect, whereas rat Frizzled 1 is inactive in this assay. Coinjection of Xwnt-5A and rat Frizzled 2 causes a more than additive increase in calcium release, indicating that both proteins may operate in a common pathway. Calcium release in response to Xwnt-5A or rat Frizzled 2 can be blocked by several inhibitors of G proteins, as well as by agents interfering with phosphatidylinositol signaling (Slusarski et al 1997a). While these data argue for an involvement of phosphatidylinositol and G proteins in Xwnt-5A signaling (Figure 2), it remains to be shown if they function as integral components of the pathway. Based on the available data (Slusarski et al 1997a,b), activation of G protein signaling by Xwnt-5A could also be a secondary effect.

Two downstream components of the Wnt-Fz pathway, Axin and Dishevelled, contain domains that are found in proteins involved in G protein signaling (Figure 4; see below). Thus the question whether G proteins play a role in Wnt signaling remains open and needs closer examination.

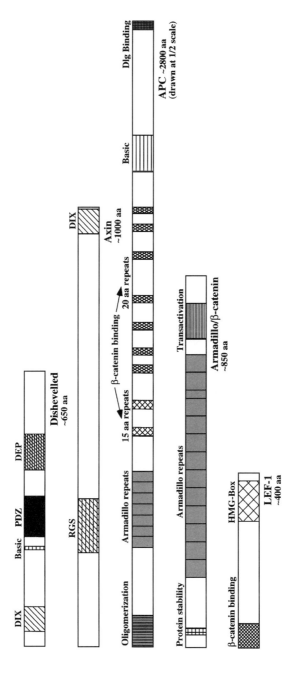

Figure 4 Components of Wnt signaling downstream of the receptor. Protein domains identified either by sequence similarity to other proteins or by functional assays are highlighted. For further explanations, see the respective paragraphs in the text.

The C terminus of many, but not all, Frizzleds has the sequence S/TXV, which has been described as a potential binding site for PDZ domains (Songyang et al 1997). Dsh is an obvious candidate for binding to the C terminus of Frizzleds because genetically it is most proximal to the receptor and contains a PDZ domain. However, attempts to show such a direct interaction have been unsuccesful (Nusse et al 1997). Moreover, the PDZ domain of Dsh lacks crucial amino acid residues predicted to interact with the S/TXV motif and therefore probably binds to a different sequence motif (Doyle et al 1996). The functional importance of the C terminus of Frizzleds is also questioned by an in vivo experiment in *C. elegans*: A Lin-17-GFP fusion protein lacking the 8 most C-terminal residues of Lin-17 rescues the *lin-17* mutant phenotype (Sawa et al 1996).

Frizzled/Wnt Interactions: How Many Pathways Are There?

One of the most important questions arising from the data summarized above is the following: How can individual Wnts elicit specific biological responses that are distinct from the effects of other members of the Wnt family? One way to achieve specificity is provided by restricting the expression pattern of different Wnts to discrete, nonoverlapping regions of the organism. This is often the case, but there are many examples for overlapping expression patterns of Wnts. The next level to discern between Wnts may be the specificity of ligand-receptor interactions. While the experiments described above reveal that not every Wnt can bind to every Frizzled, they also show that there is a high degree of promiscuity in Wnt/Frizzled interactions. However, many Frizzleds show highly specific expression patterns themselves (Bhanot et al 1996, Wang et al 1996), which further restricts the number of potential ligand-receptor interactions in any given tissue.

Once a Wnt has bound to a suitable Frizzled receptor, what happens next? Several scenarios are possible:

1 Every Wnt/Frizzled interaction leads to activation of the same downstream signaling cassette, comprising Dsh, GSK3, β-catenin, and HMG box proteins.

2 There are different signaling pathways downstream of Frizzleds, but each member of the Frizzled family can couple to only one of these pathways. If an individual Frizzled can bind different Wnts, binding of any one will activate the same pathway.

3 There are different signaling pathways downstream of Frizzleds, and a given Frizzled can couple to several of these pathways. Which pathway is activated depends on the Wnt ligand bound to the receptor.

4 There are different signaling pathways downstream of Frizzleds, but only some can be triggered by Wnts, while others are ligand independent or are triggered by ligands unrelated to Wnts.

This list can of course be extended, and the true situation may not be reflected correctly by any of these statements. Fortunately, we now have an increasing number of experimental tools to study these questions in various systems.

FRPs Are Structurally Related to the CRD of Frizzleds and Act as Secreted Antagonists of Wnts

Recently, a family of secreted proteins containing a CRD similar to that of Frizzleds has been identified in vertebrates (Hoang et al 1996, Finch et al 1997, Leyns et al 1997, Mayr et al 1997, Rattner et al 1997, S Wang et al 1997). In addition to the CRD, these frizzled-related proteins (FRPs) contain a C-terminal region with similarity to netrins, secreted proteins involved in axon guidance (Leyns et al 1997, S Wang et al 1997) (Figure 3). Some evidence has been obtained that FRPs can bind Wnts directly and that the CRD is necessary and sufficient for this interaction (Leyns et al 1997, Lin et al 1997, Rattner et al 1997, S Wang et al 1997) (Table 4). Coinjection of different FRP mRNAs together with Xwnt-8 mRNA into ventral blastomeres in *Xenopus* blocks axis duplication by Xwnt-8 (Finch et al 1997, Leyns et al 1997, Mayr et al 1997, S Wang et al 1997). In the case of Frzb-1 (also called FRP-3 or Fritz), this inhibition is also observed when Frzb-1 and Xwnt-8 are injected into different blastomeres, consistent with Frzb-1's being a secreted, diffusible antagonist of

Table 4 Interaction of Wnts with FRPs[a]

FRP Gene	Organism	Interaction with	Type of Interaction
FRP-1	Human	Wg, Wnt-1, Xwnt-8	Inhibition of axis duplication in frogs
FRP-2 (SDF-5)	Mouse	Wg	Binding
FRP-3 (Frzb-1)	Mouse	Wg, Xwnt-8	Binding, inhibition of axis duplication in frogs
	Xenopus	Xwnt-8, Wnt-1	Binding, coimmuno-precipitation, inhibition of axis duplication in frogs
	Bovine	Wnt-1, Wnt-5A	Coimmuno-precipitation, inhibition of Wnt-1-induced accumulation of β-catenin in cells, no effect on Wnt-5A in frog assay
Sizzled	*Xenopus*	Xwnt-8	Antagonism to Xwnt-8 in several frog assays

[a]A fully referenced version of this table can be found on the Wnt homepage: http://www.stanford.edu/~rnusse/wntwindow.html

Xwnt-8 (Leyns et al 1997, Mayr et al 1997, S Wang et al 1997). A similar conclusion was drawn from tissue culture experiments with mammalian cells, where Frzb-1 inhibits Wnt-1-mediated accumulation of β-catenin (Lin et al 1997). Interestingly, although Frzb-1 can also bind to Wnt-5A, as shown by coimmunoprecipitation, it does not block the activity of Wnt-5A in a *Xenopus* assay (Lin et al 1997) (Table 4).

Although a function for FRPs during normal development has not been rigorously shown owing to the absence of mutants, Frzb-1 shows an intriguing expression pattern during *Xenopus* embryogenesis. Expression is restricted to the region of the Spemann organizer and thus is complementary to the pattern of Xwnt-8, which is expressed in the ventral marginal zone (Leyns et al 1997, S Wang et al 1997). Because Xwnt-8 appears to specify ventrolateral mesoderm, it is tempting to speculate that Frzb-1 expression in the Spemann organizer specifies dorsal cell fates by antagonizing Xwnt-8 (Christian & Moon 1993, Hoppler et al 1996, Leyns et al 1997, Moon et al 1997b, S Wang et al 1997).

Are Frizzleds the Only Receptors for Wnts?

Based on genetic interaction studies in *Drosophila*, it has been speculated that Notch (N), a transmembrane protein involved in many developmental processes, might be a receptor for Wg (Couso & Martinez-Arias 1994, Hing et al 1994). However, in the complete absence of N, Wg signaling appears unaffected in the embryo (Cadigan & Nusse 1996). In the wing imaginal disc, the effect of N on Wg signaling may be indirect. Removal of N by means of a temperature-sensitive mutation or in clones leads to loss of Wg expression, providing an explanation for the genetic interaction between these two genes. Nonetheless, clones of N mutant cells show a normal response to Wg produced by wild-type cells adjacent to the clone (Rulifson & Blair 1995). Transfection of S2 cells with N does not lead to significant cell surface binding of Wg and does not confer responsiveness to Wg (Bhanot et al 1996). Taken together, these data do not support a direct role for N in reception of the Wg signal.

WNT SIGNALING DOWNSTREAM OF THE RECEPTOR

Dishevelled

Genetic analysis in *Drosophila* reveals an absolute requirement for *dsh* in reception of the Wg signal (Klingensmith et al 1994, Theisen et al 1994). *dsh* acts cell autonomously and has been placed genetically between *wg* and *zw3* in the Wg signaling cascade (Klingensmith et al 1994, Noordermeer et al 1994, Siegfried et al 1994, Theisen et al 1994) (Figure 1). *dsh* is also part of a tissue polarity signaling pathway, where it is required cell autonomously downstream of *fz* and upstream of *rhoA* (Theisen et al 1994, Krasnow et al 1995, Strutt et al 1997) (Figure 2). Furthermore, Dsh has been reported to suppress N signaling when overexpressed and to directly bind to the cytoplasmic domain of N in a yeast two-hybrid assay (Axelrod et al 1996).

Knockout mice lacking *dvl-1*, a mouse homologue of *dsh*, do not have any obvious anatomical abnormalities and are viable and fertile. However, on closer examination, these animals show abnormal social behavior and several neurological defects (Lijam et al 1997). Similar defects are commonly seen in human patients suffering from certain neurological disorders. The some-what surprising lack of gross morphological defects in the *dvl-1* knockout mice may be explained by a redundant function provided by at least two other *dsh* homologues in the mouse.

dsh encodes a ubiquitously expressed cytoplasmic protein containing four domains that are highly conserved among all known Dsh homologues, ranging from *C. elegans* to human (Figure 4). At the N terminus, Dsh contains a stretch of 50 aa similar to a region in axin, a protein implicated in Wnt signaling in vertebrates (Zeng et al 1997) (Figure 4). The three other conserved regions are a short basic domain, a centrally located PDZ domain, and a more C-terminal DEP-domain, which is also found in several proteins interacting with protein kinase C (PKC) (Klingensmith et al 1994, Theisen et al 1994, Ponting & Bork 1996). The function of Dsh is unknown, but the presence of two domains im-plicated in protein-protein interactions suggests that Dsh may be an adaptor protein required for assembly of a signaling complex, analogous to Grb-2 in the Ras pathway.

Dsh is a phosphoprotein that becomes more highly phosphorylated on ser-ine and threonine residues when Wg signaling is activated. Moreover, the most highly phosphorylated form of Dsh is enriched in the membrane frac-tion, suggesting that Wg signaling leads to recruitment of Dsh to a membrane compartment. Overexpression of Dsh in the absence of Wg also leads to hyper-phosphorylation and to accumulation of Arm and thus mimics activation of Wg signaling (Yanagawa et al 1995). The latter conclusion has also been confirmed in vivo (Axelrod et al 1996, Cadigan & Nusse 1996).

Affinity purification of a complex containing Dsh and several associated proteins revealed the association of Dsh with casein kinase 2 (CK2), a serine-threonine-specific protein kinase. CK2 efficiently phosphorylates Dsh in vitro and in vivo, but the functional significance of this phosphorylation is not clear (Willert et al 1997).

Frizzled expression can affect the phosphorylation status of Dsh (Willert et al 1997) and alter its subcellular localization. In *Xenopus*, overexpressed

Xdsh-GFP is localized in the cytoplasm in a punctate pattern. By contrast, overexpression of Xdsh-GFP together with Rat Frizzled 1 results in relocalization of Xdsh-GFP to the plasma membrane (Yang-Snyder et al 1996).

Zeste-White 3/Glycogen Synthase Kinase 3

Mutations in *zeste-white 3* (*zw3*), a gene encoding the *Drosophila* homologue of vertebrate glycogen synthase kinase 3 (GSK3), a serine-threonine protein kinase, have the opposite phenotypes of the mutations in *wg, dsh*, and *arm* (Siegfried et al 1992). By genetic epistasis analysis, *zw3* has been placed between *dsh* and *arm* in the Wg signaling pathway (Peifer et al 1994, Siegfried et al 1994) (Figure 1). The consensus model is that *zw3* acts as a constitutive repressor of the signaling activity of Arm, further implying that Wg signaling leads to repression of this constitutive activity of Zw3, thus allowing activation of Arm.

Results consistent with this model were obtained after injection of RNAs encoding wild-type and dominant-negative forms of GSK3 into *Xenopus* embryos, supporting the view that GSK3 is an integral component of Wnt signaling in vertebrates (Dominguez et al 1995, He et al 1995) (Figure 1).

These findings raise two major questions: (*a*) What is the mechanism for suppression of Zw3/GSK3 activity by Wg/Wnt, and (*b*) what are the targets for Zw3/GSK3 activity responsible for suppressing the signaling activity of Arm/β-catenin?

In cultured mouse 10T1/2 fibroblast cells, the enzymatic activity of GSK3 is inhibited by incubation of cells with Wg-conditioned medium (Cook et al 1996). Several inhibitors of established signal transduction pathways were tested for their ability to block Wg-induced inhibition of GSK3 activity. Treatment of cells with wortmannin, an inhibitor of insulin-mediated repression of GSK3 activity, had no effect on inhibition by Wg. By contrast, treatment of cells with different inhibitors of PKC blocked the effect of Wg on GSK3, indicating an involvement of PKC signaling in Wg-mediated inhibition of GSK3 (Cook et al 1996). Because Dsh is required for transduction of the Wg signal and contains a potential PKC-binding site in its DEP domain, there is increasing evidence for PKC playing a role in Wg signaling. Interestingly, several PKC isoforms can inhibit GSK3-β by direct phosphorylation in vitro (Goode et al 1992).

Axin

A novel and unexpected player in Wnt signaling has emerged from studying a classical mouse mutation, *fused* (now called *axin*). Mutations in this gene, which encodes a protein with sequence similarity to the conserved N-terminal region of Dsh and to regulators of G protein signaling (RGS) proteins result in axial duplications in mouse embryos (Zeng et al 1997). Ectopic expression of wild-type axin in dorsal blastomeres of *Xenopus* embryos causes ventralization, indicating an inhibitory function of axin in normal axis formation. Conversely, ventral injection of RNA encoding a mutant axin lacking the RGS domain leads to axis duplication, suggesting that this mutant is a dominant-negative form of axin. Coinjection of *axin* RNA together with RNAs encoding components of Wnt signaling revealed that axin acts downstream of Xwnt-8, Dsh, and GSK3 and upstream of β-catenin (Zeng et al 1997; Figure 1). Indeed, it was recently shown that the axin protein can bind to GSK3 and to β-catenin directly, promoting phosphorylation of β-catenin in this complex (Ikeda et al 1998, Sakanaka et al 1998). Loss of axin would therefore lead to lack of GSK3-mediated β-catenin phosphorylation, up-regulation of β-catenin activity, and axis duplication, which is the phenotype of the mouse-fused mutation, the gene encoding axin.

Beside the fact that deletion of the RGS domain creates a dominant-negative protein, the role of this domain for regulation or function of axin is unclear. Whether the RGS domain of axin can bind to G_α subunits of heterotrimeric G proteins is unknown. Nonetheless, together with the similarity of Frizzleds to G protein-coupled receptors, the presence of this domain in axin provides an additional hint to the potential involvement of G proteins in Wnt signaling.

A Role for Zw3/GSK3 and APC in Regulation of Arm/β-Catenin Turnover

As discussed above, Zw3/GSK3 acts as a constitutive inhibitor of the signaling activity of Arm/β-catenin. Zw3/GSK3 appears to shorten the half life of Arm/β-catenin by promoting phosphorylation of several sites in the N-terminal portion of Arm/β-catenin (Munemitsu et al 1996, Yost et al 1996, Pai et al 1997). Although these sites fit the consensus for phosphorylation by Zw3/GSK3, Arm/β-catenin appears to be a poor substrate for Zw3/GSK3 (Stambolic et al 1996, Pai et al 1997). However, phosphorylation of β-catenin by GSK3 is promoted in the ternary complex between these two proteins and axin (Ikeda et al 1998, Sakanaka et al 1998).

How does phosphorylation affect the stability of Arm/β-catenin? A common pathway for regulated degradation of short-lived proteins involves ubiquitination of the protein, followed by degradation in the proteasome. In line with this mechanism, β-catenin is ubiquitinated, and its turnover is slowed after incubation of cells with specific proteasome inhibitors. Ubiquitination is reduced in Wnt-1 transfected cells, resulting in stabilization of β-catenin (Aberle et al 1997). The potential GSK3 phosphorylation sites mentioned above are required for ubiquitination to occur, providing an explanation for the observed stabilization of mutant β-catenin lacking these sites (Aberle et al 1997).

Moreover, mutations in the *Drosophila* gene *slimb*, which encodes an F-box WD40-repeat protein, reveal that this gene negatively regulates wg signaling (Jiang & Struhl 1998). These F-box proteins have been shown to target other proteins for degradation by the ubiquitin/proteasome pathway, and in the case of wg signaling, the target of *slimb* could be the Arm protein (Jiang & Struhl 1998).

The turnover of Arm/β-catenin can be regulated not only by Zw3/GSK3, but also by the adenomatous polyposis coli (APC) protein (Figure 4). APC can bind to Arm/β-catenin and promotes its degradation in tissue culture (Rubinfeld et al 1993, Su et al 1993, Munemitsu et al 1995). Loss of APC function is observed in the majority of human colon cancers and leads to elevated β-catenin levels (Korinek et al 1997, Morin et al 1997, Rubinfeld et al 1997). Mutations in β-catenin that lead to stabilization of the protein are also frequently found in colon cancers and melanomas, suggesting that the main function of APC as a tumor suppressor is the control of β-catenin levels (Morin et al 1997, Rubinfeld et al 1997). In this function APC may be regulated by GSK3, because APC, GSK3, axin, and β-catenin can associate in a complex. APC is a good substrate for GSK3 in vitro and association of β-catenin with APC appears to depend on phosphorylation of APC by GSK3 (Rubinfeld et al 1996; reviewed in Barth et al 1997, Cavallo et al 1997, Willert & Nusse 1998).

WHAT IS THE ROLE OF APC IN WNT SIGNALING?   Despite the impressive amount of data implicating APC in β-catenin regulation, its role in Wnt signaling is not firmly established: (*a*) Mutation of a *Drosophila* homologue of APC does not interfere with Wg signaling (Hayashi et al 1997). (*b*) Based on its role in promoting degradation of β-catenin, APC would be predicted to act antagonistically to Wnts or β-catenin. Exactly the opposite has been found in *Xenopus* and *C. elegans*. Injection of RNAs encoding various forms of APC capable of promoting degradation of β-catenin in tissue culture into *Xenopus* embryos leads to axis duplication, as does injection of Xwnt-8 or β-catenin (Vleminckx et al 1997). Axis duplication by APC requires β-catenin, but it is not correlated with downregulation of β-catenin, indicating that APC and β-catenin may signal together in a complex (Vleminckx et al 1997). In *C. elegans*, inhibition of *apr-1*, an APC-related gene, by RNA interference has a phenotype similar to that of mutants in *mom-2* (Wnt) or *wrm-1* (β-catenin) (Rocheleau et al 1997). Together, these data indicate that APC may have additional functions in Wnt signaling independent of its role in downregulation of β-catenin (reviewed in Barth et al 1997, Cavallo et al 1997, Willert & Nusse 1998).

Wnt Signaling Regulates Transcription of Target Genes Through a Complex of Arm/β-Catenin with HMG-Box Proteins

Significant progress has been made in understanding how Wnt signals are transduced into the nucleus to alter cell fate and transcription of target genes. The most downstream component of Wnt signaling identified by genetics was Arm/β-catenin, a cadherin-associated protein required for assembly of adherens junctions (Noordermeer et al 1994, Peifer et al 1994, Siegfried et al 1994) (Figure 4). Studies in *Drosophila* reveal that Wg signaling leads to post-transcriptional stabilization of Arm in the cytoplasm of embryonic and cultured cells (Riggleman et al 1990, Peifer et al 1994, van Leeuwen et al 1994). Similar observations were made for β-catenin in Wnt-1-transfected mammalian cells (Hinck et al 1994). Upon closer examination it became clear that Wg/Wnt signaling predominantly stabilizes a soluble, cytoplasmic form of Arm/β-catenin that is not associated with cadherins (Peifer et al 1994, Papkoff et al 1996; A Wodarz, DB Stewart, WJ Nelson & R Nusse, unpublished data). Genetically, the functions of Arm in Wg signaling and in cadherin-mediated cell adhesion can be separated, arguing that they are, to some extent, independent of each other (Orsulic & Peifer 1996, Sanson et al 1996). These findings led to the conclusion that the non-cadherin bound form of Arm/β-catenin, stabilized by Wg/Wnt signaling, is crucial for transduction of the signal to the nucleus.

According to recent data, the stabilized form of β-catenin forms a complex with the HMG-box transcription factor LEF-1 and acts as a transcriptional activator in the nucleus (Behrens et al 1996, Huber et al 1996). This rather unexpected finding has been corroborated by the identification of the LEF-1 homologue *pan/dTCF* as a segment polarity gene in *Drosophila*, which acts downstream of *arm* in Wg signaling (Brunner et al 1997, van de Wetering et al 1997). In *Xenopus*, injection of RNA encoding a dominant-negative form of the LEF-1 homolog *XTcf-3* blocks axis duplication by β-catenin and leads to ventralization, indicating that *XTcf-3* acts downstream of β-catenin and is essential for formation of the endogenous axis (Molenaar et al 1996).

All these findings imply a function of Arm/β-catenin in the nucleus, which is supported by in situ analysis of Arm/β-catenin protein localization in *Drosophila* and *Xenopus* embryos and in cultured cells (Funayama et al 1995, Behrens et al 1996, Huber et al 1996, Molenaar et al 1996, Orsulic & Peifer 1996, Schneider et al 1996, Larabell et al 1997, Miller & Moon 1997).

In conclusion, Wg/Wnt signaling stabilizes uncomplexed Arm/β-catenin in the cytoplasm, which can then translocate to the nucleus to associate with transcription factors of the HMG-box protein family to directly regulate transcription of Wg/Wnt target genes.

However, HMG-box proteins do not always act synergistically with Wnts: The *pop-1* gene encodes a HMG-box protein participating in a Wnt cascade that regulates the asymmetric division of the EMS cell in *C. elegans*. Mutation of this gene leads to the opposite phenotype of those phenotypes produced by mutations in *mom-2* (Wnt) or *wrm-1* (β-catenin) (Lin et al 1995, Rocheleau et al 1997, Thorpe et al 1997) (Figure 1). Constitutive repression of a target gene promoter in the absence of nuclear β-catenin has also been demonstrated for XTcf-3 (Brannon et al 1997). Thus, HMG-box proteins appear to have the intrinsic ability to either activate or repress transcription of target genes, a decision that may be regulated by interaction with Arm/β-catenin.

For further information the reader is referred to several recent reviews (Barth et al 1997, Cavallo et al 1997, Nusse 1997, Willert & Nusse 1998).

TARGET GENES OF WNT SIGNALING

In most models, the main function of Wnt signaling is the regulation of cell fate decisions by altering the transcriptional program of target cells in an instructive fashion. Consistent with these models, mutation of Wnt genes or inappropriate expression of Wnts usually leads to cell fate changes, which are reflected by altered gene expression. Not surprisingly, many genes directly or indirectly regulated by Wnts are transcription factors or secreted signaling molecules that are likely to be key players in a hierarchy of regulatory genes. Among the best studied examples of such genes are members of the homeobox family of genes, e.g. *engrailed* (*en*) and *ultrabithorax* (*ubx*). For two of these genes, *ubx* and *siamois*, the latter a gene expressed in the Nieuwkoop center in the *Xenopus* embryo, there is evidence for direct transcriptional activation by binding of a complex consisting of Arm/β-catenin and HMG-box proteins to specific sites in the target gene promoter (Brannon et al 1997, Riese et al 1997). Both studies found that transcriptional activation by Wnt signaling alone is not sufficient to explain the normal expression pattern of the target gene. Additional inputs from other sources of patterning information appear to be integrated at the level of the target gene promoter, giving rise to the final transcriptional pattern. Such a combinatorial mechanism of gene activation may explain how Wnt signaling can regulate a large number of different target genes and participate in apparently unrelated processes depending on the cellular context in which signaling takes place. One example for tissue-specific differences in target gene regulation is the effect of Wg on expression of *achaete* (*ac*), a proneural gene. In the wing imaginal disc, Wg activates *ac* expression (Couso et al 1994), whereas in the eye imaginal disc, Wg acts as a repressor of *ac* (Cadigan & Nusse 1996). Cooperation with other signaling pathways at the level of target gene promoters may also explain why ubiquitous expression of Wg does not lead to ubiquitous expression of Wg target genes (Noordermeer et al 1992, Sampedro et al 1993, Baylies et al 1995).

Do Wnts Act as Morphogens?

One of the most interesting questions in pattern formation has been whether secreted signaling molecules such as Wnts can form gradients and activate target genes in a concentration-dependent manner. In the case of Wg, ample evidence indicates that this is indeed the case (Zecca et al 1996, Neumann & Cohen 1997). In the wing imaginal disc, expression of the Wg target genes *neuralized* (*neur*), *Distalless* (*Dll*), and *vestigial* (*vg*) depends on the distance from Wg-expressing cells and is abolished or strongly reduced in clones of *dsh* or *arm* mutant cells, even at a distance of more than 10 cell diameters away from the stripe of Wg at the wing margin. Furthermore, ectopic expression of Wg, but not of Dsh or constitutively active Arm, leads to non-autonomous activation of Wg target genes (Zecca et al 1996, Neumann & Cohen 1997). These results indicate that Wg can move over a considerable distance and argue against the existence of a signal relay mechanism to explain the long-range action of Wg. In the *Drosophila* wing imaginal disc, the stability and distribution of the Wg protein appears to be regulated by the concentration of one of its putative receptors, *Dfz2*. Because *Dfz2* expression itself is subject to transcriptional downregulation by *wg*, the *wg* gene controls the shape of its own morphogen gradient in a negative feed-back loop (Cadigan et al 1998).

PERSPECTIVE

Despite the impressive amount of novel data that have substantially improved our understanding of Wnt signaling, many gaps remain to be filled before we will get a glimpse of the complete picture. Open questions include: (*a*) What determines the specificity of interactions between Wnts and Frizzled receptors? (*b*) How do Frizzleds activate downstream signaling components? (*c*) What is the function of Dsh? (*d*) What is the relationship between Wnt signaling and tissue polarity signaling? (*e*) Is there a role for G proteins and PKC in Wnt signaling? (*f*) How do Wnts affect cell polarity and cell adhesion? (*g*) What is the role of Wnt signaling in cancer?

Given the multitude of experimental systems being used to study Wnt signaling, answers to remaining questions will undoubtedly come from many different directions, at an accelerated pace.

ACKNOWLEDGMENTS

We thank N Perrimon, X Lin, HA Müller, E Wieschaus, and RT Moon for communication of results prior to publication.

Visit the *Annual Reviews home page* at
http://www.AnnualReviews.org

Literature Cited

Aberle H, Bauer A, Stappert J, Kispert A, Kemler R. 1997. beta-Catenin is a target for the ubiquitin-proteasome pathway. *EMBO J.* 16:3797–804

Adler PN. 1992. The genetic control of tissue polarity in *Drosophila. BioEssays* 14:735–41

Adler PN, Krasnow RE, Liu J. 1997. Tissue polarity points from cells that have higher Frizzled levels towards cells that have lower Frizzled levels. *Curr. Biol.* 7:940–49

Alcedo J, Ayzenzon M, Von Ohlen T, Noll M, Hooper JE. 1996. The Drosophila smoothened gene encodes a seven-pass membrane protein, a putative receptor for the hedgehog signal. *Cell* 86:221–32

Axelrod JD, Matsuno K, Artavanis-Tsakonas S, Perrimon N. 1996. Interaction between Wingless and Notch signaling pathways mediated by dishevelled. *Science* 271:1826–32

Barth AI, Näthke IS, Nelson WJ. 1997. Cadherins, catenins and APC protein: interplay between cytoskeletal complexes and signaling pathways. *Curr. Opin. Cell Biol.* 9:683–90

Baylies MK, Martinez-Arias A, Bate M. 1995. *wingless* is required for the formation of a subset of muscle founder cells during *Drosophila* embryogenesis. *Development* 121:3829–37

Behrens J, von Kries J, Kühl M, Bruhn L, Wedlich D, et al. 1996. Functional interaction of beta-catenin with the transcription factor LEF-1. *Nature* 382:638–42

Bejsovec A, Wieschaus E. 1995. Signaling activities of the *Drosophila wingless* gene are separately mutable and appear to be transduced at the cell surface. *Genetics* 139:309–20

Bhanot P, Brink M, Harryman Samos C, Hsieh JC, Wang Y, et al. 1996. A new member of the frizzled family from *Drosophila* functions as a Wingless receptor. *Nature* 382:225–30

Binari RC, Staveley BE, Johnson WA, Godavarti R, Sasisekharan R, Manoukian AS. 1997. Genetic evidence that heparin-like glycosaminoglycans are involved in wingless signaling. *Development* 124:2623–32

Bradley RS, Brown AM. 1990. The proto-oncogene int-1 encodes a secreted protein associated with the extracellular matrix. *EMBO J.* 9:1569–75

Brannon M, Gomperts M, Sumoy L, Moon RT, Kimelman D. 1997. A beta-catenin/XTcf-3 complex binds to the siamois promoter to regulate dorsal axis specification in *Xenopus*. *Genes Dev.* 11:2359–70

Brunner E, Peter O, Schweizer L, Basler K. 1997. *pangolin* encodes a Lef-1 homologue that acts downstream of Armadillo to transduce the Wingless signal in *Drosophila*. *Nature* 385:829–33

Cabrera CV, Alonso MC, Johnston P, Phillips RG, Lawrence PA. 1987. Phenocopies induced with antisense RNA identify the *wingless* gene. *Cell* 50:659–63

Cadigan KM, Nusse R. 1996. *wingless* signaling in the *Drosophila* eye and embryonic epidermis. *Development* 122:2801–12

Cadigan K, Fish M, Rulifson E, Nusse R. 1998. Wingless repression of Drosophila frizzled2 expression shapes the *wingless* morphogen

gradient in the wing. *Cell*. In press

Cadigan KM, Nusse R. 1997. Wnt signaling: a common theme in animal development. *Genes Dev.* 11:3286–305

Cavallo R, Rubenstein D, Peifer M. 1997. Armadillo and dTCF: a marriage made in the nucleus. *Curr. Opin. Genet. Dev.* 7:459–66

Chen Y, Struhl G. 1996. Dual roles for patched in sequestering and transducing Hedgehog. *Cell* 87:553–63

Christian JL, Moon RT. 1993. Interactions between Xwnt-8 and Spemann organizer signaling pathways generate dorsoventral pattern in the embryonic mesoderm of *Xenopus*. *Genes Dev.* 7:13–28

Cook D, Fry MJ, Hughes K, Sumathipala R, Woodgett JR, Dale TC. 1996. Wingless inactivates glycogen synthase kinase-3 via an intracellular signalling pathway which involves a protein kinase C. *EMBO J.* 15:4526–36

Couso JP, Bishop SA, Martinez-Arias A. 1994. The *wingless* signalling pathway and the patterning of the wing margin in *Drosophila*. *Development* 120:621–36

Couso JP, Martinez-Arias A. 1994. Notch is required for wingless signaling in the epidermis of *Drosophila*. *Cell* 79:259–72

Dominguez I, Itoh K, Sokol SY. 1995. Role of glycogen synthase kinase 3 beta as a negative regulator of dorsoventral axis formation in *Xenopus* embryos. *Proc. Natl. Acad. Sci. USA* 92:8498–502

Doyle DA, Lee A, Lewis J, Kim E, Sheng M, MacKinnon R. 1996. Crystal structures of a complexed and peptide-free membrane protein-binding domain: molecular basis of peptide recognition by PDZ. *Cell* 85:1067–76

Du SJ, Purcell SM, Christian JL, McGrew LL, Moon RT. 1995. Identification of distinct classes and functional domains of Wnts through expression of wild-type and chimeric proteins in *Xenopus* embryos. *Mol. Cell. Biol.* 15:2625–34

Finch PW, He X, Kelley MJ, Uren A, Schaudies RP, et al. 1997. Purification and molecular cloning of a secreted, Frizzled-related antagonist of Wnt action. *Proc. Natl. Acad. Sci. USA* 94:6770–75

Funayama N, Fagotto F, McCrea P, Gumbiner BM. 1995. Embryonic axis induction by the armadillo repeat domain of beta-catenin: evidence for intracellular signaling. *J. Cell Biol.* 128:959–68

Goode N, Hughes K, Woodgett JR, Parker PJ. 1992. Differential regulation of glycogen synthase kinase-3 beta by protein kinase C isotypes. *J. Biol. Chem.* 267:16878–82

Guger KA, Gumbiner BM. 1995. beta-Catenin has Wnt-like activity and mimics the Nieuwkoop signaling center in *Xenopus* dorsal-ventral patterning. *Dev. Biol.* 172:115–25

Häcker U, Lin X, Perrimon N. 1997. The *Drosophila sugarless* gene modulates Wingless signaling and encodes an enzyme involved in polysaccharide biosynthesis. *Development* 124:3565–73

Haerry TE, Heslip TR, Marsh JL, O'Connor MB. 1997. Defects in glucuronate biosynthesis disrupt Wingless signaling in *Drosophila*. *Development* 124:3055–64

Han M. 1997. Gut reaction to Wnt signaling in worms. *Cell* 90:581–84

Hayashi S, Rubinfeld B, Souza B, Polakis P, Wieschaus E, Levine AJ. 1997. A *Drosophila* homolog of the tumor suppressor gene *adenomatous polyposis coli* down-regulates beta-catenin but its zygotic expression is not essential for the regulation of Armadillo. *Proc. Natl. Acad. Sci. USA* 94:242–47

Hays R, Gibori GB, Bejsovec A. 1997. Wingless signaling generates pattern through two distinct mechanisms. *Development* 124:3727–36

He X, Saint JJ, Wang Y, Nathans J, Dawid I, Varmus H. 1997. A member of the Frizzled protein family mediating axis induction by Wnt-5A. *Science* 275:1652–54

He X, Saint JJ, Woodgett JR, Varmus HE, Dawid IB. 1995. Glycogen synthase kinase-3 and dorsoventral patterning in *Xenopus* embryos. *Nature* 374:617–22

Heasman J, Crawford A, Goldstone K, Garner HP, Gumbiner BM, et al. 1994. Overexpression of cadherins and underexpression of beta-catenin inhibit dorsal mesoderm induction in early Xenopus embryos. *Cell* 79:791–803

Herman MA, Vassilieva LL, Horvitz HR, Shaw JE, Herman RK. 1995. The C. elegans gene lin-44, which controls the polarity of certain asymmetric cell divisions, encodes a Wnt protein and acts cell nonautonomously. *Cell* 83:101–10

Hinck L, Nelson WJ, Papkoff J. 1994. Wnt-1 modulates cell-cell adhesion in mammalian cells by stabilizing beta-catenin binding to the cell adhesion protein cadherin. *J. Cell Biol.* 124:729–41

Hing HK, Sun X, Artavanis-Tsakonas S. 1994. Modulation of wingless signaling by Notch in *Drosophila*. *Mech. Dev.* 47:261–68

Hoang B, Moos MJ, Vukicevic S, Luyten FP. 1996. Primary structure and tissue distribution of FRZB, a novel protein related to *Drosophila* frizzled, suggest a role in skeletal morphogenesis. *J. Biol. Chem.* 271:26131–37

Hoppler S, Brown JD, Moon RT. 1996. Expression of a dominant-negative Wnt blocks induction of MyoD in *Xenopus* embryos. *Genes Dev.* 10:2805–17

Huber O, Korn R, McLaughlin J, Ohsugi M,

Herrmann BG, Kemler R. 1996. Nuclear localization of beta-catenin by interaction with transcription factor LEF-1. *Mech. Dev.* 59:3–10

Ikeda S, Kishida S, Yamamoto H, Murai H, Koyama S, Kikuchi A. 1998. Axin, a negative regulator of the Wnt signaling pathway, forms a complex with GSK-3beta and beta-catenin and promotes GSK-3beta-dependent phosphorylation of beta-catenin. *EMBO J.* 17:1371–84

Itoh K, Sokol SY. 1994. Heparan sulfate proteoglycans are required for mesoderm formation in *Xenopus* embryos. *Development* 120:2703–11

Jiang J, Struhl G. 1998. Regulation of the Hedgehog and Wingless signalling pathways by the F-box/WD40-repeat protein Slimb. *Nature* 391:493–96

Jones KH, Liu J, Adler PN. 1996. Molecular analysis of EMS-induced frizzled mutations in *Drosophila melanogaster*. *Genetics* 142:205–15

Jue SF, Bradley RS, Rudnicki JA, Varmus HE, Brown AM. 1992. The mouse *Wnt-1* gene can act via a paracrine mechanism in transformation of mammary epithelial cells. *Mol. Cell. Biol.* 12:321–8

Kadowaki T, Wilder E, Klingensmith J, Zachary K, Perrimon N. 1996. The segment polarity gene *porcupine* encodes a putative multitransmembrane protein involved in Wingless processing. *Genes Dev.* 10:3116–28

Kitajewski J, Mason JO, Varmus HE. 1992. Interaction of Wnt-1 proteins with the binding protein BiP. *Mol. Cell. Biol.* 12:784–90

Klingensmith J, Nusse R. 1994. Signaling by *wingless* in *Drosophila*. *Dev. Biol.* 166:396–414

Klingensmith J, Nusse R, Perrimon N. 1994. The *Drosophila* segment polarity gene *dishevelled* encodes a novel protein required for response to the wingless signal. *Genes Dev.* 8:118–30

Korinek V, Barker N, Morin PJ, van Wichen D, de Weger R, et al. 1997. Constitutive transcriptional activation by a beta-catenin-Tcf complex in APC−/− colon carcinoma. *Science* 275:1784–87

Krasnow RE, Wong LL, Adler PN. 1995. Dishevelled is a component of the frizzled signaling pathway in *Drosophila*. *Development* 121:4095–102

Larabell CA, Torres M, Rowning BA, Yost C, Miller JR, et al. 1997. Establishment of the dorso-ventral axis in *Xenopus* embryos is presaged by early asymmetries in beta-catenin that are modulated by the Wnt signaling pathway. *J. Cell Biol.* 136:1123–36

Leyns L, Bouwmeester T, Kim SH, Piccolo S, De Robertis E. 1997. Frzb-1 is a secreted antagonist of Wnt signaling expressed in the Spemann organizer. *Cell* 88:747–56

Lijam N, Paylor R, McDonald MP, Crawley JN, Deng CX, et al. 1997. Social interaction and sensorimotor gating abnormalities in mice lacking Dvl1. *Cell* 90:895–905

Lin K, Wang S, Julius MA, Kitajewski J, Moos MJ, Luyten FP. 1997. The cysteine-rich frizzled domain of Frzb-1 is required and sufficient for modulation of Wnt signaling. *Proc. Natl. Acad. Sci. USA* 94:11196–200

Lin R, Thompson S, Priess JR. 1995. pop-1 encodes an HMG box protein required for the specification of a mesoderm precursor in early C. elegans embryos. *Cell* 83:599–609

Marigo V, Davey RA, Zuo Y, Cunningham JM, Tabin CJ. 1996. Biochemical evidence that patched is the Hedgehog receptor. *Nature* 384:176–79

Mayr T, Deutsch U, Kuhl M, Drexler HC, Lottspeich F, et al. 1997. Fritz: a secreted frizzled-related protein that inhibits Wnt activity. *Mech. Dev.* 63:109–25

McMahon AP, Bradley A. 1990. The Wnt-1 (int-1) proto-oncogene is required for development of a large region of the mouse brain. *Cell* 62:1073–85

McMahon AP, Moon RT. 1989. Ectopic expression of the proto-oncogene int-1 in Xenopus embryos leads to duplication of the embryonic axis. *Cell* 58:1075–84

Miller JR, Moon RT. 1997. Analysis of the signaling activities of localization mutants of beta-catenin during axis specification in *Xenopus. J. Cell Biol.* 139:229–43

Molenaar M, van de Wetering M, Oosterwegel M, Petersen-Maduro J, Godsave S, et al. 1996. XTcf-3 transcription factor mediates beta-catenin-induced axis formation in Xenopus embryos. *Cell* 86:391–99

Moon RT, Brown JD, Torres M. 1997a. WNTs modulate cell fate and behavior during vertebrate development. *Trends Genet.* 13:157–62

Moon RT, Brown JD, Yang-Snyder J, Miller JR. 1997b. Structurally related receptors and antagonists compete for secreted Wnt ligands. *Cell* 88:725–28

Moon RT, Campbell RM, Christian JL, McGrew LL, Shih J, Fraser S. 1993. Xwnt-5A: a maternal Wnt that affects morphogenetic movements after overexpression in embryos of *Xenopus laevis. Development* 119:97–111

Morin PJ, Sparks AB, Korinek V, Barker N, Clevers H, et al. 1997. Activation of beta-catenin-Tcf signaling in colon cancer by mutations in beta-catenin or APC. *Science* 275:1787–90

Munemitsu S, Albert I, Rubinfeld B, Polakis P. 1996. Deletion of an amino-terminal sequence stabilizes beta-catenin in vivo and promotes hyperphosphorylation of the ade-

nomatous polyposis coli tumor suppressor protein. *Mol. Cell. Biol.* 16:4088–94

Munemitsu S, Albert I, Souza B, Rubinfeld B, Polakis P. 1995. Regulation of intracellular beta-catenin levels by the adenomatous polyposis coli (APC) tumor-suppressor protein. *Proc. Natl. Acad. Sci. USA* 92:3046–50

Neumann CJ, Cohen SM. 1997. Long-range action of Wingless organizes the dorsal-ventral axis of the *Drosophila* wing. *Development* 124:871–80

Noordermeer J, Johnston P, Rijsewijk F, Nusse R, Lawrence PA. 1992. The consequences of ubiquitous expression of the wingless gene in the *Drosophila* embryo. *Development* 116:711–19

Noordermeer J, Klingensmith J, Perrimon N, Nusse R. 1994. Dishevelled and armadillo act in the wingless signalling pathway in *Drosophila. Nature* 367:80–83

Nusse R. 1997. A versatile transcriptional effector of Wingless signaling. *Cell* 89:321–23

Nusse R, Harryman Samos C, Brink M, Willert K, Cadigan KM, et al. 1997. Cell culture and whole animal approaches to understanding signaling by Wnt proteins in *Drosophila. Cold Spring Harbor Symp. Quant. Biol.* LXII:185–90

Nusse R, Varmus HE. 1982. Many tumors induced by the mouse mammary tumor virus contain a provirus integrated in the same region of the host genome. *Cell* 31:99–109

Nusse R, Varmus HE. 1992. Wnt genes. *Cell* 69:1073–87

Nüsslein-Volhard C, Wieschaus E. 1980. Mutations affecting segment number and polarity in *Drosophila. Nature* 287:795–801

Orsulic S, Peifer M. 1996. An in vivo structure-function study of Armadillo, the beta-catenin homologue, reveals both separate and overlapping regions of the protein required for cell adhesion and for Wingless signaling. *J. Cell Biol.* 134:1283–300

Pai LM, Orsulic S, Bejsovec A, Peifer M. 1997. Negative regulation of Armadillo, a Wingless effector in *Drosophila. Development* 124:2255–66

Papkoff J, Rubinfeld B, Schryver B, Polakis P. 1996. Wnt-1 regulates free pools of catenins and stabilizes APC-catenin complexes. *Mol. Cell. Biol.* 16:2128–34

Parr BA, McMahon AP. 1994. Wnt genes and vertebrate development. *Curr. Opin. Genet. Dev.* 4:523–28

Peifer M, Sweeton D, Casey M, Wieschaus E. 1994. Wingless signal and Zeste-white 3 kinase trigger opposing changes in the intracellular distribution of Armadillo. *Development* 120:369–80

Perrimon N. 1994. The genetic basis of

patterned baldness in *Drosophila*. *Cell* 76: 781–84

Ponting CP, Bork P. 1996. Pleckstrin's repeat performance: a novel domain in G-protein signaling? *Trends Biochem. Sci.* 21:245–46

Rattner A, Hsieh JC, Smallwood PM, Gilbert DJ, Copeland NG, et al. 1997. A family of secreted proteins contains homology to the cysteine-rich ligand-binding domain of frizzled receptors. *Proc. Natl. Acad. Sci. USA* 94:2859–63

Reichsman F, Smith L, Cumberledge S. 1996. Glycosaminoglycans can modulate extracellular localization of the wingless protein and promote signal transduction. *J. Cell Biol.* 135:819–27

Riese J, Yu X, Munnerlyn A, Eresh S, Hsu SC, et al. 1997. LEF-1, a nuclear factor coordinating signaling inputs from wingless and decapentaplegic. *Cell* 88:777–87

Riggleman B, Schedl P, Wieschaus E. 1990. Spatial expression of the Drosophila segment polarity gene armadillo is posttranscriptionally regulated by wingless. *Cell* 63:549–60

Rijsewijk F, Schuermann M, Wagenaar E, Parren P, Weigel D, Nusse R. 1987. The Drosophila homolog of the mouse mammary oncogene int-1 is identical to the segment polarity gene wingless. *Cell* 50:649–57

Rocheleau CE, Downs WD, Lin R, Wittmann C, Bei Y, et al. 1997. Wnt signaling and an APC-related gene specify endoderm in early C. elegans embryos. *Cell* 90:707–16

Rubinfeld B, Albert I, Porfiri E, Fiol C, Munemitsu S, Polakis P. 1996. Binding of GSK3beta to the APC-beta-catenin complex and regulation of complex assembly. *Science* 272:1023–26

Rubinfeld B, Robbins P, El GM, Albert I, Porfiri E, Polakis P. 1997. Stabilization of beta-catenin by genetic defects in melanoma cell lines. *Science* 275:1790–92

Rubinfeld B, Souza B, Albert I, Müller O, Chamberlain SH, et al. 1993. Association of the APC gene product with beta-catenin. *Science* 262:1731–34

Rulifson EJ, Blair SS. 1995. Notch regulates wingless expression and is not required for reception of the paracrine wingless signal during wing margin neurogenesis in *Drosophila*. *Development* 121:2813–24

Sakanaka C, Weiss JB, Williams LT. 1998. Bridging of beta-catenin and glycogen synthase kinase-3beta by axin and inhibition of beta-catenin-mediated transcription. *Proc. Natl. Acad. Sci. USA* 95:3020–23

Sampedro J, Johnston P, Lawrence PA. 1993. A role for wingless in the segmental gradient of *Drosophila*. *Development* 117:677–87

Sanson B, White P, Vincent JP. 1996. Uncoupling cadherin-based adhesion from wingless signalling in *Drosophila*. *Nature* 383:627–30

Sawa H, Lobel L, Horvitz HR. 1996. The *Caenorhabditis elegans* gene *lin-17*, which is required for certain asymmetric cell divisions, encodes a putative seven-transmembrane protein similar to the *Drosophila* frizzled protein. *Genes Dev.* 10:2189–97

Schneider S, Steinbeisser H, Warga RM, Hausen P. 1996. Beta-catenin translocation into nuclei demarcates the dorsalizing centers in frog and fish embryos. *Mech. Dev.* 57:191–98

Siegfried E, Chou TB, Perrimon N. 1992. wingless signaling acts through zeste-white 3, the Drosophila homolog of glycogen synthase kinase-3, to regulate engrailed and establish cell fate. *Cell* 71:1167–79

Siegfried E, Wilder EL, Perrimon N. 1994. Components of wingless signalling in *Drosophila*. *Nature* 367:76–80

Slusarski DC, Corces VG, Moon RT. 1997a. Interaction of Wnt and a Frizzled homologue triggers G-protein-linked phosphatidylinositol signalling. *Nature* 390:410–13

Slusarski DC, Yang-Snyder J, Busa WB, Moon RT. 1997b. Modulation of embryonic intracellular Ca^{2+} signaling by Wnt-5A. *Dev. Biol.* 182:114–20

Smolich BD, McMahon JA, McMahon AP, Papkoff J. 1993. Wnt family proteins are secreted and associated with the cell surface. *Mol. Biol. Cell* 4:1267–75

Sokol SY. 1996. Analysis of Disheveled signalling pathways during *Xenopus* development. *Curr. Biol.* 6:1456–67

Sokol SY, Klingensmith J, Perrimon N, Itoh K. 1995. Dorsalizing and neuralizing properties of Xdsh, a maternally expressed Xenopus homolog of dishevelled. *Development* 121:1637–47

Songyang Z, Fanning AS, Fu C, Xu J, Marfatia SM, et al. 1997. Recognition of unique carboxyl-terminal motifs by distinct PDZ domains. *Science* 275:73–77

Stambolic V, Ruel L, Woodgett JR. 1996. Lithium inhibits glycogen synthase kinase-3 activity and mimics wingless signalling in intact cells. *Curr. Biol.* 6:1664–68

Stone DM, Hynes M, Armanini M, Swanson TA, Gu Q, et al. 1996. The tumour-suppressor gene patched encodes a candidate receptor for Sonic hedgehog. *Nature* 384:129–34

Strutt DI, Weber U, Mlodzik M. 1997. The role of RhoA in tissue polarity and Frizzled signalling. *Nature* 387:292–95

Su LK, Vogelstein B, Kinzler KW. 1993. Association of the APC tumor suppressor protein with catenins. *Science* 262:1734–77

Theisen H, Purcell J, Bennett M, Kansagara D, Syed A, Marsh JL. 1994. *dishevelled* is required during *wingless* signaling to establish both cell polarity and cell identity. *Development* 120:347–60

Thomas KR, Capecchi MR. 1990. Targeted disruption of the murine int-1 proto-oncogene resulting in severe abnormalities in midbrain and cerebellar development. *Nature* 346:847–50

Thorpe CJ, Schlesinger A, Carter JC, Bowerman B. 1997. Wnt signaling polarizes an early C. elegans blastomere to distinguish endoderm from mesoderm. *Cell* 90:695–705

Tomlinson A, Strapps WR, Heemskerk J. 1997. Linking Frizzled and Wnt signaling in *Drosophila* development. *Development* 124:4515–21

Torres MA, Yang-Snyder J, Purcell SM, DeMarais AA, McGrew LL, Moon RT. 1996. Activities of the Wnt-1 class of secreted signaling factors are antagonized by the Wnt-5A class and by a dominant negative cadherin in early *Xenopus* development. *J. Cell Biol.* 133:1123–37

van den Heuvel M, Harryman Samos C, Klingensmith J, Perrimon N, Nusse R. 1993. Mutations in the segment polarity genes wingless and porcupine impair secretion of the wingless protein. *EMBO J.* 12:5293–302

van den Heuvel M, Ingham PW. 1996. *smoothened* encodes a receptor-like serpentine protein required for *hedgehog* signalling. *Nature* 382:547–51

van den Heuvel M, Nusse R, Johnston P, Lawrence PA. 1989. Distribution of the wingless gene product in Drosophila embryos: a protein involved in cell-cell communication. *Cell* 59:739–49

van de Wetering M, Cavallo R, Dooijes D, van Beest M, van Es J, et al. 1997. Armadillo coactivates transcription driven by the product of the Drosophila segment polarity gene dTCF. *Cell* 88:789–99

van Leeuwen F, Harryman Samos C, Nusse R. 1994. Biological activity of soluble wingless protein in cultured *Drosophila* imaginal disc cells. *Nature* 368:342–44

Vinson CR, Adler PN. 1987. Directional non-cell autonomy and the transmission of polarity information by the frizzled gene of *Drosophila*. *Nature* 329:549–51

Vinson CR, Conover S, Adler PN. 1989. A *Drosophila* tissue polarity locus encodes a protein containing seven potential transmembrane domains. *Nature* 338:263–64

Vleminckx K, Wong E, Guger K, Rubinfeld B, Polakis P, Gumbiner BM. 1997. Adenomatous polyposis coli tumor suppressor protein has signaling activity in *Xenopus laevis* embryos resulting in the induction of an ectopic dorsoanterior axis. *J. Cell Biol.* 136:411–20

Wang S, Krinks M, Lin K, Luyten FP, Moos MJ. 1997. Frzb, a secreted protein expressed in the Spemann organizer, binds and inhibits Wnt-8. *Cell* 88:757–66

Wang Y, Macke JP, Abella BS, Andreasson K, Worley P, et al. 1996. A large family of putative transmembrane receptors homologous to the product of the *Drosophila* tissue polarity gene *frizzled*. *J. Biol. Chem.* 271:4468–76

Wang YK, Harryman Samos C, Peoples R, Perez JL, Nusse R, Francke U. 1997. A novel human homologue of the *Drosophila frizzled* wnt receptor gene binds wingless protein and is in the Williams syndrome deletion at 7q11.23. *Hum. Mol. Genet.* 6:465–72

Willert K, Brink M, Wodarz A, Varmus H, Nusse R. 1997. Casein kinase 2 associates with and phosphorylates dishevelled. *EMBO J.* 16:3089–96

Willert K, Nusse R. 1998. β-catenin: a key mediator of Wnt signaling. *Curr. Opin. Genet. Dev.* 8:95–102

Wong GT, Gavin BJ, McMahon AP. 1994. Differential transformation of mammary epithelial cells by Wnt genes. *Mol. Cell. Biol.* 14:6278–86

Wong LL, Adler PN. 1993. Tissue polarity genes of *Drosophila* regulate the subcellular location for prehair initiation in pupal wing cells. *J. Cell Biol.* 123:209–21

Yanagawa S, van Leeuwen F, Wodarz A, Klingensmith J, Nusse R. 1995. The dishevelled protein is modified by wingless signaling in *Drosophila*. *Genes Dev.* 9:1087–97

Yanagawa S, Lee J-S, Haruna T, Oda H, Uemura T, et al. 1997. Accumulation of Armadillo induced by Wingless, Dishevelled, and dominant-negative Zeste-white 3 leads to elevated DE-cadherin in *Drosophila* clone 8 wing disc cells. *J. Biol. Chem.* 272:25243–51

Yang-Snyder J, Miller JR, Brown JD, Lai CJ, Moon RT. 1996. A frizzled homolog functions in a vertebrate Wnt signaling pathway. *Curr. Biol.* 6:1302–6

Yost C, Torres M, Miller JR, Huang E, Kimelman D, Moon RT. 1996. The axis-inducing activity, stability, and subcellular distribution of beta-catenin is regulated in *Xenopus* embryos by glycogen synthase kinase 3. *Genes Dev.* 10:1443–54

Zecca M, Basler K, Struhl G. 1996. Direct and long-range action of a wingless morphogen gradient. *Cell* 87:833–44

Zeng L, Fagotto F, Zhang T, Hsu W, Vasicek TJ, et al. 1997. The mouse Fused locus encodes Axin, an inhibitor of the Wnt signaling pathway that regulates embryonic axis formation. *Cell* 90:181–92

Zheng L, Zhang J, Carthew RW. 1995. frizzled regulates mirror-symmetric pattern formation in the *Drosophila* eye. *Development* 121:3045–55

Annu. Rev. Cell Dev. Biol. 1998. 14:89–109

THE TIGHT JUNCTION: Morphology to Molecules

Bruce R. Stevenson
Department of Cell Biology and Anatomy, University of Alberta, Edmonton, Alberta, Canada, T6G 2H7; e-mail: bruce.stevenson@ualberta.ca

Brigitte H. Keon
Department of Cell Biology, Harvard Medical School, Boston, Massachusetts 02115; e-mail: bkeon@warren.med.harvard.edu

KEY WORDS: epithelium, intercellular junctions, MAGUK protein family, paracellular pathway, tumor suppressor

---

ABSTRACT

The tight junction forms a regulated barrier in the paracellular pathway between epithelial and endothelial cells. This intercellular junction also demarcates the compositionally distinct apical and basolateral membranes. While the existence of a paracellular barrier in epithelia was hypothesized by physiologists over a century ago, the molecular characterization of the tight junction is a relatively new and rapidly expanding area of research. It is now recognized that the tight junction is comprised of at least nine peripheral and one integral membrane proteins. This complex includes members of a protein family related to tumor suppression and signal transduction, a rab protein, and a Ras target protein. The characteristics of, interactions between, and potential physiological roles of these proteins at the tight junction are discussed.

CONTENTS

1081-0706/98/1115-0089$08.00

INTRODUCTION

The tight junction (zonula occludens) serves two primary functions in epithelia and endothelia. It forms a regulated barrier in the spaces between cells (the paracellular space), restricting the movement of molecules as small as ions across cell sheets. The tight junction also acts as a boundary within the plasma membrane itself, separating the compositionally unique apical and basolateral cell surface domains. The field of tight junction biology extends back 35 years. Although physiologists suspected the presence of a paracellular permeability barrier over a century ago (Bonnet 1895), Farquhar & Palade provided the seminal description of the tight junction as a distinct morphological entity in 1963. Moreover, they furnished direct evidence that this intercellular junction serves as a barrier to the paracellular movement of proteins. Combined, these observations created the foundation for the exploration of tight junction molecular biology (Farquhar & Palade 1963).

Significant steps have been made in the molecular analysis of the tight junction since the electron microscopy (EM) observations of Farquhar & Palade. These include the characterization of zonula occludens-1 (ZO-1), the first protein specifically localized to the tight junction (Stevenson et al 1986); the cloning of ZO-1 and the recognition that it belongs to a family of proteins that may function in tumor suppression (Itoh et al 1993, Willott et al 1993); and the discovery of a transmembrane protein termed occludin that almost certainly plays a direct role in the paracellular permeability barrier (Furuse et al 1993). Ten proteins have now been specifically localized to the tight junction (Table 1), and actin is strongly implicated in the regulation of junction permeability. Study of these molecules and how they interact is now proceeding at a rapid pace, with the assumption that this basic characterization will facilitate understanding tight junction physiology. Interest in these studies has been heightened by the findings that some tight junction molecules are likely to be involved in signal transduction. The aim of this chapter is to present an overview of the proteins involved in the tight junction: how we got to our current understanding, what we know at this moment, and where we are likely to be headed in the immediate future. Through this approach we hope to supplement and expand on several other recent reviews (Anderson & Van Itallie 1995, Howarth & Stevenson 1996, Anderson 1996, Tsukita et al 1996, Yap et al 1998).

MOLECULAR BIOLOGY OF THE TIGHT JUNCTION

Initial Approaches to Understanding Tight Junction Composition

MORPHOLOGY   EM observation of thin sections reveals the tight junction as a series of discrete contacts between the plasma membranes of adjacent cells

Table 1 Tight junction proteins

Protein	Reference	Species/chromosome	GenBank accession #
ZO-1	Stevenson et al 1986		
	Willott et al 1993	Human/15q13[A]	L14837
	Itoh et al 1993	Mouse	D14340
ZO-2	Gumbiner et al 1991		
	Jesaitis & Goodenough 1994	Canine	L27152
	Duclos et al 1994	Human X104/9q13-q21	L27476
	Beatch et al 1996		
ZO-3	Haskins et al 1998	Canine	AF023617
Occludin	Furuse et al 1996	Chick	D21837
	Ando-Akatsuka 1996	Mouse	U49185
		Canine	U49221
		Human	U49184
		Rat-kangaroo	U49183
Cingulin	Citi et al 1988	NA[a]	—
7H6	Zhong et al 1993	NA	—
Rab3b	Weber et al 1994	Human	M28214
			J04941
Symplekin	Keon et al 1996	Human/19q13.3	U49240
	Ueki et al 1997		U88726
AF-6	Prasad et al 1993	Human 6q27	U02478
	Yamamoto et al 1997		
19B1	Merzdorf & Goodenough 1997	NA	—

[a]NA, Not applicable.

(Figure 1; Farquhar & Palade 1963). Fibrillar material, including actin filaments, is seen associated with the cytoplasmic surface of the junctional membrane (Farquhar & Palade 1963, Hirokawa & Tilney 1982, Madara 1987). In freeze-fracture EM, the tight junction appears as a series of branching and anastomosing fibrils lying within the plane of the membrane. These fibrils correspond to the sites of membrane contact (Staehelin et al 1969, Goodenough & Revel 1970). As predicted by the fluid-mosaic model of membrane structure (Singer & Nicolson 1972), the fibrils appear to be capable of dynamic rearrangement within the membrane bilayer (Hull & Staehelin 1976).

A large body of work has characterized the intricacies of both the membrane contacts and fibrils (see Stevenson et al 1988 for review). A controversial interpretation of these data suggests that the points of junctional membrane-membrane contact are sites of partial bilayer fusion and that the intramembrane fibrils are composed of inverted cylindrical lipid micelles (Kachar & Reese

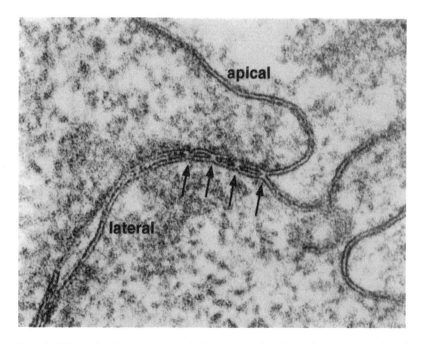

Figure 1 Thin section electron micrograph showing the points of membrane contact at the tight junction (*arrows*). The tight junction stands at the interface of the apical and lateral epithelial cell plasma membranes (micrograph provided by M Farquhar & G Palade).

1982). While the common belief has always been that the intramembrane particles and fibrils visible in freeze-fracture are composed of protein, it is difficult to prove unequivocally or disprove the lipid hypothesis. However, experiments examining the movement of lipid probes between the cell surfaces of adjacent epithelial cells (van Meer et al 1986), combined with the insolubility of the fibrils themselves in various detergents (Stevenson & Goodenough 1984), argue that the membranes are not fused at contact sites and that their fibrils are composed, at least in part, of proteins. This latter point has been substantiated by the subsequent localization of an intramembrane protein directly to the fibrils (Furuse et al 1996). Although it is likely that specific lipids are important in tight junction structure and physiology, this area remains relatively less explored than the ongoing study of tight junction proteins.

CELL FRACTIONATION   The elucidation of the molecular composition of desmosomes (Skerrow & Matoltsy 1974) and gap junctions (Bennedetti & Emmelot 1968, Goodenough & Stoeckenius 1972) was initially approached through purification of these intercellular junctions by cell fractionation and differential detergent solubilization. Attempts to apply such techniques to the tight junction were largely unsuccessful, due in part to the relative instability of the tight junction to various fractionation treatments. Moreover, the absence of a reliable marker protein meant that all fractions had to be assayed by morphological techniques, a time-consuming approach. However, fractions enriched in the area of the lateral epithelial cell surface containing both tight and adherens junctions were obtained (Stevenson & Goodenough 1984, Tsukita & Tsukita 1989). These fractions were not only useful in the further dissection of the adherens junction, they also provided a reasonable immunogen for a monoclonal antibody approach to identifying tight junction components.

Tight Junction Proteins

ZO-1   Application of monoclonal antibody techniques resulted in the identification of the first tight junction protein, ZO-1, a phosphoprotein having a species-dependent relative mass between 210 and 225 K (Stevenson et al 1986, Anderson et al 1988). ZO-1 is a peripheral membrane protein specifically enriched at the points of tight junction membrane contact in polarized epithelial and endothelial cells. Interestingly, ZO-1 is also found at the cytoplasmic undercoat of adherens junctions in non-epithelial cells (Itoh et al 1991, 1993, Howarth et al 1992, Jesaitis & Goodenough 1994). Using a calcium concentration modulation paradigm to control tight junction formation in epithelial cells, Rajasekaran et al (1996) showed that ZO-1 associates initially with adherens junction components prior to final localization at the tight junction. It has also been reported that ZO-1 accumulates in the nucleus under certain experimental and physiological conditions characterized by dynamic rearrangement of cell-cell contacts (Gottardi et al 1996). These results suggest that ZO-1 may serve multiple roles within the cell. Biochemical analyses have revealed that ZO-1 is phosphorylated at serine residues under steady state conditions (Anderson et al 1988) and becomes tyrosine phosphorylated in response to certain extracellular stimuli (Kurihara et al 1995, Staddon et al 1995, Takeda & Tsukita 1995, Van Itallie et al 1995). In vitro binding studies have shown that a serine kinase is capable of binding to and phosphorylating ZO-1 (Balda et al 1996a). The exact physiological meaning of these phosphorylation events is not yet clear (see Molecular Interactions and Assembly below).

Molecular cloning and analysis of a partial ZO-1 cDNA resulted in the identification of two isoforms of ZO-1 which, as a result of alternative RNA splicing, differ by an internal 80–amino acid domain designated motif α (Willott et al 1992; Figure 2). Data suggest that the two isoforms have functionally distinct roles in the assembly and regulation of the tight junction. Immunohistochemical experiments employing isoform-specific antibodies have revealed a correlation between the presence of each isoform and junctional "plasticity" (Balda &

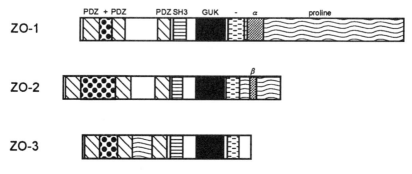

Figure 2   Schematic diagram showing the domain arrangement of the three MAGUK family members found at the tight junction. PDZ, *diagonal stripes*; SH3, *horizontal stripes*; GUK, *black*; basic domain, *dots* (+); acidic domain, *horizontal dashes* (−); proline-rich, *wavy horizontal lines*; alternative splices, α (ZO-1) and β (ZO-2) (reproduced from *J. Cell Biol.* 1998, 141:206 by copyright permission of the Rockefeller Univ. Press).

Anderson 1993): ZO-1α⁻ was found in endothelial cell tight junctions and in the specialized junctions of podocytes and Sertoli cells, whereas ZO-1α⁺ was determined to be present in all other epithelia. A recent study of tight junctions of the blood-testis barrier demonstrated distinct temporal and spatial expression patterns of ZO-1 isoforms in Sertoli cells during development (Pelletier et al 1997). Similarly, ZO-1 isoforms exhibit differential expression and assembly characteristics during mouse preimplantation embryo development (Sheth et al 1997).

The MAGUK protein family   Full-length cDNA sequence analysis indicates that ZO-1 belongs to a family of diverse proteins that have in common a core group of protein-protein interaction domains and localization at the cytoplasmic surface of the plasma membrane (Tsukita et al 1993, Willott et al 1993). All members of the family contain a tripartite protein domain mosaic consisting of one or more PDZ (P̲SD-95/SAP90, d̲iscs-large, Z̲O-1) domains, a *src* homology 3 (SH3) domain, and a region homologous to guanylate kinase (GUK), arranged in conserved sequential order. The m̲embrane a̲ssociation and presence of the GUK domain have resulted in naming this group of proteins the MAGUK family. This family is rapidly growing, and its members have diverse phylogeny, attesting to the evolutionary conservation and functional importance of the characteristic domains (for reviews see Kim 1995, Anderson 1996, Fanning et al 1996, Ponting et al 1997). In addition to ZO-1, the identification of two other members of this family at the tight junction (see ZO-2 and ZO-3 below; Figure 2) supports the hypothesis that the characteristic MAGUK domains function in the formation of a molecular lattice at the tight junction.

All MAGUKs contain at least one PDZ domain, an 80–90 amino acid motif containing GLGF repeats. These domains were originally identified in the postsynaptic density protein PSD-95 (Cho et al 1992), also referred to as

SAP90 (Kistner et al 1993). Homologous domains were subsequently identified in the lethal(1)discs-large-1 (*dlg*) tumor suppressor gene product (*dlg*-A) of *Drosophila* (Woods & Bryant 1991), nitric oxide synthase (Bredt et al 1991), and ZO-1 (Willott et al 1993). PDZ domains are being identified in an increasing number and variety of proteins within and outside of the MAGUK family. Although diverse in nature, these proteins share some common functional characteristics. Many signaling molecules, such as *dlg*-A, the invasion-inducing Tiam-1 protein, protein tyrosine phosphatases, and protein kinases, contain PDZ domains. In addition, most PDZ domain-containing proteins appear to associate with the cytoskeleton at the inner surface of the plasma membrane. Here they are believed to play roles in junction assembly and regulation, channel clustering, and/or signal transduction (Ponting & Phillips 1995, Fanning & Anderson 1996, Ponting et al 1997).

PDZ domains have been shown to mediate reversible and regulated protein-protein interactions by at least two mechanisms: dimerization with other PDZ domains (Brenman et al 1996), or recognition of specific amino acid sequence motifs at the C termini of integral membrane proteins (Marfatia et al 1994, Grootjans et al 1997, Kim et al 1995, 1998). PDZ domains also appear to interact with cytosolic proteins such as the adenomatous polyposis coli (APC) tumor suppressor protein via the C-terminal motif (Matsumine et al 1996). Mutational analysis and oriented peptide library approaches have defined consensus C-terminal amino acid–binding motifs (Saras & Heldin 1996, Kornau et al 1995, 1997, Songyang et al 1997). Although some PDZ-containing proteins preferentially bind ligands containing aromatic or hydrophobic residues at the three terminal positions, others preferentially bind the consensus motif E-(S/T)-X-(V/I). These residues are compatible with the predicted ligand-binding amino acids of PDZ domains identified by crystal structure analysis (Cabral et al 1996, Doyle et al 1996). Interestingly, those PDZ domain amino acids predicted to be important in binding are conserved in the tight junction MAGUKs, suggesting that these proteins are capable of interacting with hydrophobic C termini of other proteins.

All MAGUK proteins contain a single SH3 domain, a conserved 50–70 amino acid motif first identified among the *src* family of nonreceptor protein tyrosine kinases (Mayer et al 1993, Pawson et al 1993). Similar to the PDZ domain, SH3 domain-containing proteins are being identified at a rapid rate and include cytoskeletal-related proteins and signal transduction molecules (Bar-Sagi et al 1993, Bork et al 1997, Kuriyan & Cowburn 1997). SH3 domains function as protein-protein interaction modules that, in general, bind the proline amino acid motif PXXP. Binding specificity among various SH3 domains is conferred by interactions of specific spatially conserved amino acid residues on either side of the PXXP motif (Ren et al 1993, Alexandropoulos et al 1995, Sparks et al 1996). For example, the *src* SH3 domain binds preferentially to the consensus sequence RPLPXXP, in which the arginine residue is essential. For binding to other SH3 domains, the arginine residue at this position is dispensable (Alexandropoulos et al 1995).

The third component of the MAGUK mosaic is the GUK domain. Yeast guanylate kinase catalyzes the conversion of GMP to GDP at the expense of ATP, and the amino acids shown to be important in nucleotide binding and catalysis have been identified (Stehle & Schulz 1990). These amino acids are differentially conserved within the MAGUK protein family. In particular, the GUK domains of the tight junction MAGUK family members are missing several of the key residues and are not predicted to be enzymatically active. However, the recent identification of novel proteins that interact with MAGUK proteins via their GUK domains indicates that this region is also involved in protein-protein interactions (Satoh et al 1997, Takeuchi et al 1997).

The accessibility of the *Drosophila* system to genetic studies has provided insights into the functions of invertebrate MAGUK proteins and individual domains. The conservation of these domains in the vertebrate MAGUKs permits speculation of similar functions in the tight junction homologues. The founding member of the MAGUK family is the *Drosophila* tumor suppressor *dlg*-A (Woods & Bryant 1991). *dlg*-A is a component of the *Drosophila* septate junction, believed to be the functional equivalent of the vertebrate tight junction. Mutations in *dlg*, resulting in loss of the PDZ3, SH3, and GUK domains, cause neoplastic overgrowth of larval imaginal disc epithelial cells, loss of septate junctions, redistribution of adherens junctions, and loss of apical-basal polarity (Woods & Bryant 1991, Woods et al 1996). While loss of function mutations in other genes result in imaginal disc overgrowth, none of these mutations affects the integrity of the septate and adherens junctions (Woods et al 1997). *dlg*-A is also localized to synapses in *Drosophila*, and similar mutations in the MAGUK domains result in the formation of brain tumors and disruption of normal neuromuscular junction structure (Lahey et al 1994). The *Drosophila dlg*-A deletion mutation studies of Hough et al (1997) have provided further information on MAGUK domain function. These data indicate a role for the PDZ2, PDZ3, and SH3 domains in the establishment of an organized epithelium. Although all three domains appear to be indispensable for growth control, the SH3 domain also plays a critical role in the regulation of epithelial structure. Finally, the *Drosophila tamou* gene product (TamA), more closely related to ZO-1 than is *dlg*-A, also localizes to septate junctions (Takahisa et al 1996). Partial mutations in the *tamou* gene result in an extra-bristle phenotype. By an uncharacterized mechanism, the *tam* mutation causes down-regulation in the transcription of the repressor gene *extramacrochaetae* (*emc*), resulting in abnormal cell growth and the formation of extra bristle cells in the fly wing. Of particular interest is the observation that ZO-1 is capable of rescuing this phenotype. Taken together, these *Drosophila* mutational studies led to the speculation that ZO-1 also functions as a tumor suppressor and/or signaling molecule. Although the ability of ZO-1 to enter the nucleus under certain physiological conditions (Gottardi et al 1996) supports this idea, direct evidence for this hypothesis has not been obtained to date.

ZO-2   Two additional tight junction-associated members of the MAGUK family have been identified as proteins that co-immunoprecipitate with ZO-1 under conditions designed to preserve protein-protein interactions. The first of these to be characterized, ZO-2, is a M_r 160 K phosphoprotein peripherally associated with the cytoplasmic surface of the tight junction (Gumbiner et al 1991, Jesaitis & Goodenough 1994). ZO-2 shares strong sequence homology with ZO-1, especially within the conserved MAGUK domains, but is restricted in its cellular distribution to the tight junction (Jesaitis & Goodenough 1994, Beatch et al 1996). Similar to ZO-1, ZO-2 contains three PDZ domains, an SH3 domain, and a GUK domain (Figure 2). Unique from other MAGUK proteins but similar to ZO-1, ZO-2 contains a basic region between PDZ1 and PDZ2 that is rich in arginine residues, and acidic and proline-rich domains C-terminal to the GUK domain. Although the amino acid sequences of ZO-1 and ZO-2 are 51% identical overall, the bulk of the identity occurs within the MAGUK domains. Only 25% identity is displayed in the respective C-terminal portions, suggesting that these regions may be functionally distinct. Similar to ZO-1, ZO-2 contains at least one alternatively spliced domain of 36 amino acids, termed the β motif, within the C-terminal region (Beatch et al 1996). Differences in expression or localization patterns for the two isoforms have not been determined. Database searches revealed that a human cDNA (clone X104), which had been isolated and cloned in an effort to delineate the Friedreich ataxia gene locus (Duclos et al 1994), is the human homologue of canine ZO-2. The amino acid sequences between canine ZO-2 and human X104 are 87% identical overall and show 92–100% identity within the MAGUK domains (Beatch et al 1996). The gene encoding human ZO-2 is not related to the Friedreich ataxia gene mutations.

ZO-3   A third MAGUK family member localizing to the tight junction recently has been identified and designated ZO-3 (Haskins et al 1998). ZO-3 was first described as an unknown polypeptide of M_r 130 K (p130) that co-immunoprecipitated with the ZO-1/ZO-2 complex (Balda et al 1993, Jesaitis & Goodenough 1994). ZO-3 is present in ZO-1 immunoprecipitates in much smaller amounts relative to ZO-1 and ZO-2. Whether this represents limited extractability of the protein, affinity differences, or quantitative in vivo expression differences is not known. ZO-3 shares strong sequence homology with both ZO-1 and ZO-2, especially within the MAGUK portions of the molecules.

Similar to ZO-1 and ZO-2, ZO-3 contains three PDZ domains, an arginine-rich basic region between PDZ1 and 2, an SH3 domain, and a GUK domain followed by an acidic domain (Figure 2). In contrast to the proline-rich region located at the C-terminal regions of ZO-1 and ZO-2, ZO-3 contains a unique proline-rich region between PDZ2 and 3. RT-PCR analyses of ZO-3 gave no indication of ZO-3 isoforms resulting from alternative-splicing events. Although ZO-1, ZO-2, and ZO-3 share high sequence homology within the common MAGUK regions, indicating their functional importance, linker and C-terminal regions are less well conserved. Among the three MAGUK tight junction proteins, ZO-1 and ZO-2 are more closely related to each other than either is to ZO-3.

OCCLUDIN   Occludin is the only known integral membrane component of the tight junction. It is a $M_r \approx 65$ K phosphoprotein identified by screening monoclonal antibodies raised against adherens and tight junction-containing membrane fractions from chicken liver (Furuse et al 1993). Subsequently, occludin cDNAs were isolated from four mammalian species: human, mouse, canine, and rat kangaroo (Ando-Akatsuka et al 1996). Sequence analysis shows that occludin is a unique protein containing four transmembrane domains, with both N and C termini oriented into the cytoplasm (Figure 3). The first extracellular loop contains $\approx 60\%$ tyrosine and glycine residues, and this distinct amino acid content is suggested to play a role in cell-cell coupling (Ando-Akatsuka et al 1996). Exogenous expression of occludin in occludin-deficient fibroblasts increases cell-cell adhesion, and this adhesive function is inhibited by synthetic peptides corresponding to the first extracellular domain (Van Itallie & Anderson 1997). The second extracellular loop of occludin has been implicated in the

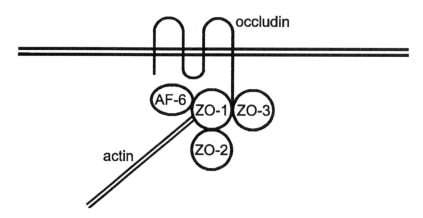

Figure 3   Schematic diagram showing the known binding interactions of tight junction proteins.

formation of the paracellular barrier itself. Treatment of epithelial cells in vitro with a synthetic peptide corresponding to this domain reversibly alters junctional permeability, whereas peptides corresponding to the first extracellular domain had no effect in the same assays (Wong & Gumbiner 1997). Combined, these data suggest that the first loop functions in adhesion, presumably via homotypic interactions between occludin molecules on adjacent cells, whereas the second extracellular domain may be more directly related to a presumptive paracellular channel.

The role of the C-terminal 255 amino acids of occludin in tight junction physiology has been examined in some detail. This region of the molecule directly interacts with both ZO-1 (Furuse et al 1994) and ZO-3 (Haskins et al 1998). Epithelial cell lines expressing exogenous full-length occludin or C-terminal deletion constructs have been assayed for changes in paracellular permeability. These studies have recently been reviewed in detail (Yap et al 1998). In brief, exogenous expression of both full-length and C-terminal truncated chicken occludin in canine-derived MDCK cells causes an increase in transepithelial electrical resistance, believed to reflect a decrease in tight junction ionic permeability. However, transepithelial flux of nontransported solutes, thought to directly measure paracellular permeability, also increases in these cells (Balda et al 1996b, McCarthy et al 1996). The basis of this paradox remains unknown, although several possible explanations have been put forth (Yap et al 1998). In another system, *Xenopus* embryos injected with mRNAs corresponding to C-terminal truncations of occludin show an increase in the ability of a biotinylating reagent to penetrate tight junctions (Chen et al 1997). Although it is clear that occludin functions in paracellular permeability, the precise nature of that role remains to be determined.

Additional interesting observations have been made in the MDCK cell occludin transfection experiments. Expression of C-terminal truncated occludin in MDCK cells causes both the mutant and endogenous forms of occludin, which co-polymerize in *Xenopus* embryos (Chen et al 1997), to acquire a discontinuous distribution along sites of cell-cell contact. However, ZO-1 retains a continuous linear localization, and the morphology of the tight junction, as assessed by both thin section and freeze-fracture EM, was unchanged (Balda et al 1996b). These observations, together with the measured increase in transepithelial resistance, led to the suggestion that transmembrane elements other than occludin participate in the tight junction barrier (Balda et al 1996b). Such an element or elements remains to be identified.

CINGULIN   Cingulin was identified through monoclonal antibody techniques (Citi et al 1988) and has been characterized by biochemical and immunolocalization approaches (Citi et al 1989). Cingulin is a M_r 140 K phosphoprotein specifically present at the cytoplasmic surface of the tight junction in epithelial and endothelial cells. ImmunoEM demonstrates that cingulin is more distant from the junctional membrane than is ZO-1 (Stevenson et al 1989). Nevertheless, the presence of cingulin at the membrane correlates with a functional tight junction (Citi et al 1994). The expression of cingulin during development has been studied in *Xenopus* embryos (Cardellini et al 1997), where maternally expressed protein is present at sites of cell-cell contact as early as the 2-cell stage. A preliminary report of a partial cDNA indicates that cingulin shares structural homology with coiled-coiled cytoskeletal proteins, having sequence homology with the myosin rod, paramyosin, and other proteins (Citi et al 1990). These results are intriguing in light of the observations that actin filaments may act in the regulation of tight junction physiology; however, further analysis of the role of cingulin at the tight junction is contingent upon the generation of a full-length cDNA.

7H6   7H6 was identified by screening monoclonal antibodies raised against bile canaliculi-enriched membrane fractions from rat liver (Zhong et al 1993). The 7H6 antibody recognizes an M_r 155–175 K polypeptide on immunoblots. By immunohistochemistry and immunoEM, the 7H6 antigen has been distinguished from other known tight junction components by its restricted expression in polarized epithelia and its absence from tight junctions of endothelia. The presence of 7H6 at the tight junction directly correlates with the paracellular barrier function of epithelia (Zhong et al 1994).

RAB3B   The rab family of monomeric GTPases are found at specific membrane domains where they regulate membrane trafficking events (Goud et al 1990, Chavrier et al 1991). Rab3B is a 25-kDa isoform preferentially expressed in cultured epithelial cells and native epithelia. Immunohistochemistry and immunoEM reveal that this protein is associated with the cytoplasmic surface of the tight junction (Weber et al 1994). Rab3B is highly similar to a brain-specific rab3 isoform found at the presynaptic membrane (Fischer von Mollard et al 1991). A second rab protein, rab13, has been localized to the apical region of the lateral membranes of epithelial cells (Zahraoui et al 1994), although the explicit localization of this molecule to the tight junction by immunoEM has not been published. The presence of at least one rab protein at the tight junction suggests that membrane trafficking may function in junctional assembly, maintenance, and/or regulation.

SYMPLEKIN   Symplekin was identified as a M_r 150 K protein by a monoclonal antibody raised against lateral membrane junctional components. By immunohistochemistry and immunoEM the protein has been specifically localized to the cytoplasmic surface of the tight junction in polarized epithelia and Sertoli cells of the testis (Keon et al 1996). Similar to 7H6, symplekin is not detected at tight junctions of endothelial cells. In addition to its localization at the tight junction, symplekin appears to be an ubiquitous component of the nucleoplasm in both epithelial and non-epithelial cells. Molecular cloning of symplekin resulted in the isolation of a 3.7-kb cDNA containing a translation initiation codon preceded by a semi-conserved Kozak (1989) sequence. Subsequently, a longer cDNA was isolated during exon trapping experiments performed in an effort to identify a tumor suppressor gene involved in human gliomas (Ueki et al 1997). This cDNA contains an additional 302 base pairs at the 5' end of the molecule, including a well-conserved Kozak consensus sequence and an initiation site that is in-frame with that of the originally identified cDNA. Although symplekin has since been excluded as a candidate for the glioma genetic defect, the study provided the more likely full-length cDNA as well as the chromosomal location of the symplekin gene.

AF-6   The AF-6 protein was originally described as the fusion partner of the acute lymphoblastic leukemia-1 (ALL-1) protein (Prasad et al 1993). AF-6 is a M_r 180–195 K polypeptide that contains a Ras-binding domain, a PDZ domain, and a myosinV-like domain. More recently, AF-6 has been localized to the tight junction by immunofluorescence and immunoEM (Yamamoto et al 1997). In vitro binding analyses demonstrate that the Ras-binding domain of AF-6 interacts directly with ZO-1. Moreover, activated Ras inhibits this interaction. In non-epithelial cells, AF-6 colocalizes with ZO-1 at adherens junctions, and overexpression of activated Ras in Rat1 fibroblasts perturbs cell-cell contacts and decreases the amount of both AF-6 and ZO-1 at the cell surface. These results suggest that Ras-induced disruption of cell-cell interactions may be mediated in part through the AF-6/ZO-1 complex.

19B1   Working with cell fractionation and monoclonal antibody techniques in a *Xenopus* system, Merzdorf & Goodenough (1997) identified a M_r 210 K protein that specifically localizes to the tight junction. Data from immunoblot analyses and double-label immunoEM experiments indicate that the 19B1 antigen is distinct from ZO-1.

ACTIN   Actin, although not exclusively localized to the tight junction, was actually the first protein shown by morphological techniques to be associated with the junctional membrane (Hirokawa & Tilney 1982, Madara 1987). In addition, several lines of investigation suggest that actin functions in the regulation of tight junction permeability. These investigations include treatment of epithelial cells with agents that disrupt the actin cytoskeleton, resulting in alterations in junction architecture and flux through the paracellular space (Bentzel et al 1976, Montesano et al 1976, Meza et al 1980, Madara et al 1986), and manipulations that alter junctional permeability, causing perturbations in actin filament arrangement (Madara 1983, Madara & Pappenheimer 1987).

Molecular Interactions and Assembly

The identification and characterization of multiple tight junction proteins raises questions about how these molecules interact and how they are assembled to form a functional unit at the tight junction. Immunoprecipitation experiments indicate that ZO-1, ZO-2, and ZO-3 exist in a relatively stable complex (Gumbiner et al 1991, Balda et al 1993, Jesaitis & Goodenough 1994, Haskins et al 1998). Interestingly, this complex has been isolated from epithelial cells lacking established tight junctions (Balda et al 1993, Stuart & Nigam 1995), suggesting that ZO-1, ZO-2, and ZO-3 assemble into a preformed aggregate prior to their arrival at the tight junction. What are the direct interactions within this complex, and how does this cluster of proteins relate to occludin, the only known transmembrane element?

In vitro affinity-binding experiments using recombinant proteins have shown that ZO-3 directly interacts with ZO-1 but not ZO-2 (Haskins et al 1998), and preliminary evidence indicates that ZO-2 binds directly to ZO-1 (E Wittchen & BR Stevenson, unpublished data), likely through the PDZ2 domain of ZO-1 (AS Fanning & JM Anderson, personal communication). These data substantiate the earlier co-immunoprecipitation of the ZO-1/ZO-2/ZO-3 complex (Gumbiner et al 1991, Balda et al 1993, Jesaitis & Goodenough 1994, Haskins et al 1998). It is also known that ZO-1 interacts directly with AF-6 (Yamamoto et al 1997), and it has been demonstrated that the C-terminal, cytoplasmic tail of occludin directly interacts with ZO-1 (Furuse et al 1994) and ZO-3 (Haskins et al 1998). Whether these interactions are mutually exclusive, competitive, or independent of one another awaits determination of the specific binding sites involved. Recent studies have determined that the GUK domain of ZO-1 is required for binding to occludin (AS Fanning & JM Anderson, personal communication). The relationship of occludin to ZO-2 remains unknown.

The molecular linkage through which actin acts to control tight junction permeability is now beginning to be understood. Initial evidence suggested that ZO-1 interacts with actin: ZO-1 colocalizes with disrupted actin aggregates in epithelial cells treated with cytochalasin D (Stevenson & Begg 1994), and ZO-1 in non-epithelial cells invariably codistributes with actin filaments (Itoh et al 1991, Howarth et al 1992, Howarth & Stevenson 1995). These results are consistent with the observations that other MAGUK family members bind protein 4.1, a key element of the actin cytoskeletal system (Marfatia et al 1994, Lue et al 1994). More recently it has been documented that ZO-1, specifically the C-terminal half of the protein, can be cosedimented from whole cell lysates with actin filaments (Itoh et al 1997; AS Fanning & JM Anderson, personal communication), although these experiments do not rule out the possibility that other unidentified proteins mediate the interaction between actin and ZO-1. Additional evidence that the modulation of tight junction barrier properties occurs through an actin/ZO-1/occludin linkage comes from the observation that exogenous expression of either the N-terminal (containing the occludin binding domain) or C-terminal (actin binding) halves of ZO-1 in stably trans-fected MDCK cells results in an apparent decrease in paracellular permeability (AS Fanning & JM Anderson, personal communication). The participation of other junctional proteins in this linkage remains to be determined.

How does this complex of proteins at the tight junction assemble? Do in-dividual proteins join the array at the junction itself, or does a complex or subcomplex form elsewhere in the cell? Information in this area is limited. Initial experiments looking at which domains of occludin are responsible for targeting of the protein to the tight junction have produced enigmatic results. The C-terminal 150 amino acids are highly conserved among species and con-tain a sequence consistent with an α-helical coiled-coil (Ando-Akatsuka et al 1996). This region has been shown to bind directly to both ZO-1 (Furuse et al 1994) and ZO-3 (Haskins et al 1998). This same domain was also shown to be necessary for proper localization of occludin to the tight junction in MDBK cells (Furuse et al 1994). However, Chen et al (1997), working with *Xenopus* embryos, showed that occludin constructs missing the cytoplasmic C terminus localized correctly to the junction. This latter group also provided immunopre-cipitation results indicating that the C-terminal deletion constructs oligomerized with endogenous occludin, leading to the hypothesis that the association be-tween mutant and endogenous forms leads to proper targeting of the molecule (Chen et al 1997). In related experiments, colocalization of occludin with one splice isoform of ZO-1 has been observed in the perinuclear region of devel-oping mouse embryos, suggesting the formation of an intracellular complex of at least these two proteins, which is then transported to the junction (Sheth et al 1997). In contrast, E-cadherin–deficient embryos showed a normal distri-bution of occludin at the membrane, whereas ZO-1 and actin localization was disrupted (Ohsugi et al 1997).

A wide range of investigations has indicated that phosphorylation events are involved in tight junction assembly. For example, Balda et al (1993) showed that protein kinase C is likely to play a key role in this process, although the level of phosphorylation of ZO-1, ZO-2, and ZO-3 did not change during tight junction assembly induced by a protein kinase C agonist. In separate experiments, ZO-1 phosphorylation levels did appear to correlate with the localization of this pro-tein in epithelial cells (Howarth et al 1994). The localization of occludin to the tight junction, as well as an increase in the resistance of this protein to non-ionic detergent extraction, corresponds with an increase in occludin phosphorylation levels (Sakakibara et al 1997, Wong 1997). While these results are interesting, it is obvious that much more work is needed to understand the direct relationship between protein phosphorylation and junctional assembly, and how the overall assembly of junctional components is orchestrated.

SUMMARY AND FUTURE DIRECTIONS

We are now a little over a decade into the molecular characterization of the tight junction. We have a list of ten proteins found at the junction (Table 1), plus actin, which appears to play a central role in the regulation of tight junction physiology. Three of the junctional molecules, ZO-1, ZO-2, and ZO-3, are members of a growing family of proteins that are potentially involved in tumor suppression and signal transduction. The presence of rab3B and the Ras target protein AF-6 lends further credence to the notion that important signaling events are taking place at the cytoplasmic surface of the tight junction. Furthermore, we are now acquiring information on transmembrane and extracellular events through the characterization of occludin.

Combining these elements permits us to construct a working model of the molecular architecture of the tight junction (Figure 3). Although this model shows all the known interactions among junctional molecules, it more accurately depicts how much we have to learn about this structure. How does the remainder of the molecules not shown in this diagram fit into the picture and what are the interactions among these components? Which protein domains are responsible for binding interactions? How is this complex of proteins assembled at the membrane, and by what mechanism does the complex disassemble during, for example, carcinogenesis? How do interactions among junctional elements lead to modulation of junctional barrier properties, both paracellular and within the plasma membrane? Or, put another way, how do the paracellular channel and membrane barrier functions of the tight junction correlate with the molecular components? Are there other junctional molecules yet to be identified? Recent evidence suggests that additional transmembrane proteins are present, and it seems likely that other peripheral membrane components will be discovered as well. What signaling events are occurring at the tight junction, and how are these events communicated throughout the rest of the cell? Although great progress has been made in our understanding of the molecular biology of the tight junction, the field remains crowded with exciting questions for future research.

ACKNOWLEDGMENTS

We thank Yan-Hua Chen, Daniel Goodenough, Zoia Muresan, Sandra Ryeom, Tom White, Erika Wittchen, and Alpha Yap for their helpful comments on the manuscript, and Alan Fanning and Jim Anderson for discussing unpublished data. We also thank Marilyn Farquhar and George Palade for providing the image in Figure 1. BRS is a Senior Scholar of the Alberta Heritage Foundation for Medical Research supported by operating grants from the Medical Research Council of Canada and Kidney Foundation of Canada. BHK is supported by NIH grant GM18974 to Daniel Goodenough.

> Visit the *Annual Reviews home page* at
> http://www.AnnualReviews.org

Literature Cited

Alexandropoulous K, Cheng G, Baltimore D. 1995. Proline-rich sequences that bind to Src homology 3 domains with individual specificities. *Proc. Natl. Acad. Sci. USA* 92:3110–14

Anderson JM 1996. Cell signalling: MAGUK magic. *Curr. Biol.* 6:382–84

Anderson JM, Stevenson BR, Jesaitis LA, Goodenough DA, Mooseker MS. 1988. Characterization of ZO-1, a protein component of the tight junction from mouse liver and Madin-Darby canine kidney cells. *J. Cell Biol.* 106:1141–49

Anderson JM, Van Itallie CM. 1995. Tight junctions and the molecular basis for regulation of paracellular permeability. *Am. J. Physiol.* 269:G467–75

Ando-Akatsuka Y, Saitou M, Hirase T, Kishi M, Sakakibara A, et al. 1996. Interspecies diversity of the occludin sequence: cDNA cloning of human, mouse, dog, and rat-kangaroo homologues. *J. Cell Biol.* 133:43–47

Balda MS, Anderson JM. 1993. Two classes of tight junctions revealed by ZO-1 isoforms. *Am. J. Physiol.* 264:C918–24

Balda MS, Anderson JM, Matter K. 1996a. The SH3 domain of the tight junction protein ZO-1 binds to a serine protein kinase that phosphorylates a region C-terminal to this domain. *FEBS Lett.* 399:326–32

Balda MS, Gonzalez-Mariscal L, Matter K, Cereijido M, Anderson JM. 1993. Assembly of the tight junction: the role of diacylglycerol. *J. Cell Biol.* 123:293–302

Balda MS, Whitney JA, Flores C, Gonzalez S, Cereijido M, Matter K. 1996b. Functional dissociation of paracellular permeability and transepithelial electrical resistance and disruption of the apical-basolateral intramembrane diffusion barrier by expression of a mutant tight junction membrane protein. *J. Cell Biol.* 134:1031–49

Bar-Sagi D, Rotin D, Batzer A, Mandiyan V, Schlessinger J. 1993. SH3 domains direct

cellular localization of signaling molecules. *Cell* 74:83–91

Beatch M, Jesaitis LA, Gallin JA, Goodenough DA, Stevenson BA. 1996. The tight junction protein ZO-2 contains three PDZ (PSD-95/Discs-large/ZO-1) domains and an alternatively spliced region. *J. Biol. Chem.* 271: 25723–26

Benedetti EL, Emmelot P. 1968. Hexagonal array of subunits in tight junctions separated from isolated rat liver plasma membranes. *J. Cell Biol.* 38:15–24

Bentzel CJ, Hainau B, Edelman A, Anagnostopoulos T, Benedetti EL. 1976. Effect of plant cytokinins on microfilaments and tight junction permeability. *Nature* 264:666–68

Bonnet. 1895. Uber die schlussleisten der epithelien. *Deut. Med. Wochenschr.* 21:58–77

Bork P, Schultz J, Ponting CP. 1997. Cytoplasmic signalling domains: the next generation. *Trends Biochem. Sci.* 22:296–98

Bredt DS, Glatt CE, Hwang PM, Fotuhi M, Dawson TM, Snyder SH. 1991. Nitric oxide synthase protein and mRNA are discretely localized in neuronal populations of the mammalian CNS together with NADPH diaphorase. *Neuron* 7:615–24

Brenman JE, Chao DS, Gee SH, McGee AW, Craven SE, et al. 1996. Interaction of nitric oxide synthase with the postsynaptic density protein PSD-95 and α1-syntrophin mediated by PDZ domains. *Cell* 84:757–67

Cabral JHM, Petosa C, Sutcliffe MJ, Raza S, Byron O, Poy F, et al. 1996. Crystal structure of a PDZ domain. *Nature* 382:649–52

Cardellini P, Davanzo G, Citi S. 1997. Tight junctions in early amphibian development: detection of junctional cingulin from the 2-cell stage and its localization at the boundary of distinct membrane domains in dividing blastomeres in low calcium. *Dev. Dynam.* 207:104–13

Chavrier P, Gorvel JP, Stelzer E, Simons K,

Gruenberg J, Zerial M. 1991. Hypervariable C-terminal domain of rab proteins acts as targeting signal. *Nature* 353:769–72

Chen YH, Merzdorf C, Paul DL, Goodenough DA. 1997. COOH terminus of occludin is required for tight junction barrier function in early *Xenopus* embryos. *J. Cell Biol.* 138:891–99

Cho K-O, Hunt CA, Kennedy MB. 1992. The rat brain postsynaptic density fraction contains a homolog of the *Drosophila* discs-large tumor suppressor protein. *Neuron* 9:929–42

Citi S, Kendrick-Jones J, Shore D. 1990. Cloning of cingulin cDNA: evidence for a tight junction protein with a coiled-coil structure. *J. Cell Biol.* 111:409a (Abstr.)

Citi S, Sabanay H, Jakes R, Geiger B, Kendrick-Jones J. 1988. Cingulin, a new peripheral component of tight junctions. *Nature* 333:272–76

Citi S, Sabanay H, Kendrick-Jones J, Geiger B. 1989. Cingulin: characterization and localization. *J. Cell Sci.* 93:107–22

Citi S, Volberg T, Bershadsky AD, Denisenko N, Geiger B. 1994. Cytoskeletal involvement in the modulation of cell-cell junctions by the protein kinase inhibitor H-7. *J. Cell Sci.* 107:683–92

Doyle DA, Lee A, Lewis J, Kim E, Sheng M, et al. 1996. Crystal structures of a complexed and peptide-free membrane protein-binding domain—molecular basis of peptide recognition by PDZ. *Cell* 85:1067–76

Duclos F, Rodius F, Wrogemann W, Mandel J-L, Koenig M. 1994. The Friedreich ataxia region: characterization of two novel genes and reduction of the critical region to 300 kb. *Hum. Mol. Genet.* 3:909–14

Fanning AS, Anderson JM. 1996. Protein-protein interactions: PDZ domain networks. *Curr. Biol.* 6:1385–88

Fanning AS, Lapierre L, Brecher AR, Van Itallie CM, Anderson JM. 1996. Protein interactions in the tight junction: the role of MAGUK proteins in regulating tight junction organization and function. In *Current Topics in Membranes*, ed. WJ Nelson, 43:211–35. New York: Academic

Farquhar MG, Palade GE. 1963. Junctional complexes in various epithelia. *J. Cell Biol.* 17:375–412

Fischer von Mollard G, Sudhof TC, Jahn R. 1991. A small GTP-binding protein dissociates from synaptic vesicles during exocytosis. *Nature* 349:79–81

Furuse M, Fujimoto K, Sato N, Hirase T, Tsukita S. 1996. Overexpression of occludin, a tight junction-associated integral membrane protein, induces the formation of intracellular multilamellar bodies bearing tight junction-like structure. *J. Cell Sci.* 109:429–35

Furuse M, Hirase T, Itoh M, Nagafuchi A, Yonemura S, et al. 1993. Occludin: a novel integral membrane protein localizing at tight junctions. *J. Cell Biol.* 123:1777–88

Furuse M, Itoh M, Hirase T, Nagafuchi A, Yonemura S, et al. 1994. Direct association of occludin with ZO-1 and its possible involvement in the localization of occludin at tight junctions. *J. Cell Biol.* 127:1617–26

Goodenough DA, Revel JP. 1970. A fine structural analysis of intercellular junctions in the mouse liver. *J. Cell Biol.* 45:272–90

Goodenough DA, Stoeckenius W. 1972. The isolation of mouse hepatocyte gap junctions. Preliminary chemical characterization and X-ray diffraction. *J. Cell Biol.* 54:646–56

Goud B, Zahraoui A, Tavitian A, Saraste J. 1990. Small GTP-binding protein associated with Golgi cisternae. *Nature* 345:553–56

Gottardi CJ, Arpin M, Fanning AS, Louvard D. 1996. The junction-associated protein, zonula occludens-1, localizes to the nucleus before the maturation and during the remodeling of cell-cell contacts. *Proc. Natl. Acad. Sci. USA* 93:10779–84

Grootjans JJ, Zimmermann P, Reekmans G, Smets A, Degeest G, et al. 1997. Syntenin, a PDZ protein that binds syndecan cytoplasmic domains. *Proc. Natl. Acad. Sci. USA* 94:13683–88

Gumbiner B, Lowenkopf T, Apatira D. 1991. Identification of a 160-kDa polypeptide that binds to the tight junction protein ZO-1. *Proc. Natl. Acad. Sci. USA* 88:3460–64

Haskins J, Gu L, Wittchen E, Hibbard J, Stevenson BR. 1998. ZO-3, a novel member of the MAGUK protein family found at the tight junction, interacts with ZO-1 and occludin. *J. Cell Biol.* 141:199–208

Hirokawa N, Tilney LG. 1982. Interactions between actin filaments and between actin filaments and membranes in quick-frozen and deeply etched hair cells of the chick ear. *J. Cell Biol.* 95:249–61

Hough CD, Woods DF, Park S, Bryant PJ. 1997. Organizing a functional junctional complex requires specific domains of the *Drosophila* MAGUK discs large. *Genes Dev.* 11:3242–53

Howarth AG, Hughes MR, Stevenson BR. 1992. Detection of the tight junction-associated protein ZO-1 in astrocytes and other nonepithelial cell types. *Am. J. Physiol.* 262:C461–69

Howarth AG, Singer KL, Stevenson BR. 1994. Analysis of the distribution and phosphorylation state of ZO-1 in MDCK and nonepithelial cells. *J. Membr. Biol.* 137:261–70

Howarth AG, Stevenson BR. 1995. Molecular environment of ZO-1 in epithelial and non-epithelial cells. *Cell Motil. Cytoskelet.* 31:323–32

Howarth AG, Stevenson BR. 1996. The molecular composition of the tight junction. *Adv. Struc. Biol.* 4:25–39

Hull BE, Staehelin LA. 1976. Functional significance of the variations in the geometrical organization of tight junction networks. *J. Cell Biol.* 68:688–704

Itoh M, Nagafuchi A, Moroi S, Tsukita S. 1997. Involvement of ZO-1 in cadherin-based cell adhesion through its direct binding to α catenin and actin filaments. *J. Cell Biol.* 138:181–92

Itoh M, Nagafuchi A, Yonemura S, Kitani-Yasuda T, Tsukita S, Tsukita S. 1993. The 220-kD protein colocalizing with cadherins in non-epithelial cells is identical to ZO-1, a tight junction-associated protein in epithelial cells: cDNA cloning and immunoelectron microscopy. *J. Cell Biol.* 121:491–502

Itoh M, Yonemura S, Nagafuchi A, Tsukita S. 1991. A 220-kD undercoat-constitutive protein: its specific localization at cadherin-based cell-cell adhesion sites. *J. Cell Biol.* 115:1449–62

Jesaitis LA, Goodenough DA. 1994. Molecular characterization and tissue distribution of ZO-2, a tight junction protein homologous to ZO-1 and the *Drosophila* discs-large tumor suppressor protein. *J. Cell Biol.* 124:949–61

Kachar B, Reese TS. 1982. Evidence for the lipidic nature of tight junction strands. *Nature* 296:464–66

Keon BH, Schafer S, Kuhn C, Grund C, Franke WW. 1996. Symplekin, a novel type of tight junction plaque protein. *J. Cell Biol.* 134:1003–18

Kim E, Demarco SJ, Marfatia SM, Chishti AH, Sheng M, Strehler EE. 1998. Plasma membrane Ca^{2+} ATPase isoform 4b binds to membrane-associated guanylate kinase (MAGUK) proteins via their PDZ (PSD-95/dlg/ZO-1) domains. *J. Biol. Chem.* 273:1591–95

Kim E, Niethammer M, Rothschild A, Jan YN, Sheng M. 1995. Clustering of shaker-type K^+ channels by interaction with a family of membrane-associated guanylate kinases. *Nature* 378:85–88

Kim SK. 1995. Tight junctions, membrane-associated guanylate kinases and cell signaling. *Curr. Opin. Cell Biol.* 7:641–49

Kistner U, Wenzel BM, Veh RW, Cases-Langhoff C, Garner AM, et al. 1993. SAP90, a rat presynaptic protein related to the product of the *Drosophila* tumor suppressor gene *dlg-A*. *J. Biol. Chem.* 268:4580–83

Kornau HC, Schenker LT, Kennedy MB, Seeburg PH. 1995. Domain interaction between NMDA receptor subunits and the postsynaptic density protein PSD-95. *Science* 269:1737–40

Kornau HC, Seeburg PH, Kennedy MB. 1997. Interaction of ion channels and receptors with PDZ domain proteins. *Curr. Opin. Neurobiol.* 7:368–73

Kozak M. 1989. The scanning model for translation: an update. *J. Cell Biol.* 108:229–41

Kurihara H, Anderson JM, Farquhar MG. 1995. Increased Tyr phosphorylation of ZO-1 during modification of tight junctions between glomerular foot processes. *Am. J. Physiol.* 37:F514–24

Kuriyan J, Cowburn D. 1997. Modular peptide recognition domains in eukaryotic signaling. *Annu. Rev. Biophys. Biomol. Struct.* 26:259–88

Lahey T, Gorczyca M, Jia XX, Budnik V. 1994. The *Drosophila* tumor suppressor gene *dlg* is required for normal synaptic bouton structure. *Neuron* 13:823–35

Lue RA, Marfatia SM, Branton D, Chishti AH. 1994. Cloning and characterization of hdlg: the human homologue of the *Drosophila* discs large tumor suppressor binds to protein 4.1. *Proc. Natl. Acad. Sci. USA* 91:9818–22

Madara JL. 1983. Increases in guinea pig small intestinal transepithelial resistance induced by osmotic loads are accompanied by rapid alterations in absorptive-cell tight-junction structure. *J. Cell Biol.* 97:125–36

Madara JL. 1987. Intestinal absorptive cell tight junctions are linked to the cytoskeleton. *Am. J. Physiol.* 253:C171–75

Madara JL, Barenberg D, Carlson S. 1986. Effects of cytochalasin D on occluding junctions of intestinal absorptive cells: further evidence that the cytoskeleton may influence paracellular permeability and junctional charge selectivity. *J. Cell Biol.* 102:2125–36

Madara JL, Pappenheimer JR. 1987. Structural basis for physiological regulation of paracellular pathways in intestinal epithelia. *J. Membr. Biol.* 100:149–64

Marfatia SM, Lue RA, Branton D, Chishti AH. 1994. In vitro binding studies suggest a membrane-associated complex between erythroid p55, protein 4.1, and glycophorin C. *J. Biol. Chem.* 269:8631–34

Matsumine A, Ogai A, Senda T, Okumura N, Satoh K, et al. 1996. Binding of APC to the human homolog of the *Drosophila* discs large tumor suppressor protein. *Science* 272:1020–23

Mayer BJ, Ren R, Clark KL, Baltimore D. 1993. A putative modular domain present in diverse signaling proteins. *Cell* 73:629–30

McCarthy KM, Skare IB, Stankewich MC, Furuse M, Tsukita S, et al. 1996. Occludin is a functional component of the tight junction. *J. Cell Sci.* 109:2287–98

Merzdorf CS, Goodenough DA. 1997. Localization of a novel 210 kDa protein in *Xenopus* tight junctions. *J. Cell Sci.* 110:1005–12

Meza I, Ibarra G, Sabanero M, Martinez-Palomo A, Cereijido M. 1980. Occluding junctions and cytoskeletal components in a cultured transporting epithelium. *J. Cell Biol.* 87: 746–54

Montesano R, Gabbiani G, Perrelet A, Orci L. 1976. In vivo induction of tight junction proliferation in rat liver. *J. Cell Biol.* 68:793–98

Ohsugi M, Larue L, Schwarz H, Kemler R. 1997. Cell-junctional and cytoskeletal organization in mouse blastocysts lacking E-cadherin. *Dev. Biol.* 185:261–71

Pawson T, Olivier P, Rozakis-Adcock M, McGlade J, Henkemeyer M. 1993. Proteins with SH2 and SH3 domains couple receptor tyrosine kinases to intracellular signalling pathways. *Philos. Trans. R. Soc. London Ser. B* 340:279–85

Pelletier RM, Okawara Y, Vitale ML, Anderson JM. 1997. Differential distribution of the tight-junction-associated protein ZO-1 isoforms $\alpha(+)$ and $\alpha(-)$ in guinea pig sertoli cells: a possible association with f-actin and g-actin. *Biol. Reprod.* 57:367–76

Ponting CP, Phillips C. 1995. DHR domains in syntrophins, neuronal NO synthases and other intracellular proteins. *Trends Biochem. Sci.* 20:102–03

Ponting CP, Phillips C, Davies KE, Blake DJ. 1997. PDZ domains: targeting signalling molecules to sub-membranous sites. *BioEssays* 19:469–79

Prasad R, Gu Y, Alder H, Nakamura T, Canaani O, et al. 1993. Cloning of the ALL-1 fusion partner, the AF-6 gene, involved in acute myeloid leukemias with the t(6;11) chromosome translocation. *Cancer Res.* 53:5624–28

Rajasekaran AK, Hojo M, Huima T, Rodriguez-Boulan E. 1996. Catenins and zonula occludens-1 form a complex during early stages in the assembly of tight junctions. *J. Cell Biol.* 132:451–63

Ren R, Mayer BJ, Chichetti P, Baltimore D. 1993. Identification of a ten-amino acid proline-rich SH3 binding site. *Science* 259: 1157–61

Sakakibara A, Furuse M, Saitou M, Tsukita S. 1997. Possible involvement of phosphorylation of occludin in tight junction formation. *J. Cell Biol.* 137:1393–401

Saras J, Heldin CH. 1996. PDZ domains bind carboxy-terminal sequences of target proteins. *Trends Biochem. Sci.* 21:455–58

Satoh K, Yanai H, Senda T, Kohu K, Nakamura T, et al. 1997. DAP-1, a novel protein that interacts with the guanylate kinase-like domains of hDLG and PSD-95. *Genes Cells* 2:415–24

Sheth B, Fesenko I, Collins JE, Moran B, Wild AE, et al. 1997. Tight junction assembly during mouse blastocyst formation is regulated by late expression of ZO-1 $\alpha(+)$ isoform. *Development* 124:2027–37

Singer SJ, Nicolson GL. 1972. The fluid mosaic model of the structure of cell membranes. *Science* 175:720–31

Skerrow CJ, Matoltsy AG. 1974. Chemical characterization of isolated epidermal desmosomes. *J. Cell Biol.* 63:524–30

Songyang Z, Fanning AS, Fu C, Xu J, Marfatia SM, et al. 1997. Recognition of unique carboxyl-terminal motifs by distinct PDZ domains. *Science* 275:73–77

Sparks AB, Rider JE, Hoffman NG, Fowlkes DM, Quillam LA, Kay BK. 1996. Distinct ligand preferences of Src homology 3 domains from Src, Yes, Abl, Cortactin, p53bp2, PLCγ, Crk, and Grb2. *Proc. Natl. Acad. Sci. USA* 93:1540–44

Staddon JM, Herrenknecht K, Smales C, Rubin LL. 1995. Evidence that tyrosine phosphorylation may increase tight junction permeability. *J. Cell Sci.* 108:609–19

Staehelin LA, Mukherjee TM, Williams AW. 1969. Freeze-etch appearance of the tight junctions in the epithelium of small and large intestine of mice. *Protoplasma* 67:165–84

Stehle T, Schulz GE. 1990. Three-dimensional structure of the complex of guanylate kinase from yeast with its substrate GMP. *J. Mol. Biol.* 211:249–54

Stevenson BR, Anderson JM, Bullivant S. 1988. The epithelial tight junction: structure, function and preliminary biochemical characterization. *Mol. Cell. Biochem.* 83:129–45

Stevenson BR, Begg DA. 1994. Concentration-dependent effects of cytochalasin D on tight junctions and actin filaments in MDCK epithelial cells. *J. Cell Sci.* 107:367–75

Stevenson BR, Goodenough DA. 1984. Zonulae occludentes in junctional complex-enriched fractions from mouse liver: preliminary morphological and biochemical characterization. *J. Cell Biol.* 98:1209–21

Stevenson BR, Heintzelman MB, Anderson JM, Citi S, Mooseker MS. 1989. ZO-1 and cingulin: tight junction proteins with distinct identities and localizations. *Am. J. Physiol.* 257:C621–28

Stevenson BR, Siliciano JD, Mooseker MS, Goodenough DA. 1986. Identification of ZO-1: a high molecular weight polypeptide associated with the tight junction (zonula occludens) in a variety of epithelia. *J. Cell Biol.* 103:755–66

Stuart RO, Nigam SK. 1995. Regulated assembly of tight junctions by protein kinase C. *Proc. Natl. Acad. Sci. USA* 92:6072–76

Takahisa M, Togashi S, Suzuki T, Kobayashi M,

Murayama A, et al. 1996. The *Drosophila ta-mou* gene, a component of the activating pathway of extramacrochaetae expression, encodes a protein homologous to mammalian cell-cell junction-associated protein ZO-1. *Genes Dev.* 10:1783–95

Takeda H, Tsukita S. 1995. Effects of tyrosine phosphorylation on tight junctions in temperature-sensitive v-src-transfected MDCK cells. *Cell Struct. Funct.* 20:387–93

Takeuchi M, Hata Y, Hirao K, Toyoda A, Irie M, Takai Y. 1997. SAPAPS—a family of PSD-95/SAP90-associated proteins localized at postsynaptic density. *J. Biol. Chem.* 272:11943–51

Tsukita S, Furuse M, Itoh M. 1996. Molecular dissection of tight junctions. *Cell Struct. Funct.* 21:381–85

Tsukita S, Itoh M, Nagafuchi A, Yonemura S, Tsukita S. 1993. Submembranous junctional plaque proteins include potential tumor suppressor molecules. *J. Cell Biol.* 123:1049–53

Tsukita S, Tsukita S. 1989. Isolation of cell-to-cell adherens junctions from rat liver. *J. Cell Biol.* 108:31–41

Ueki K, Ramaswamy S, Billings SJ, Mohrenweiser HW, Louis DN. 1997. Chromosomal localization to 19q13.3, partial genomic structure and 5′ cDNA sequence of the human symplekin gene. *Som. Cell Mol. Gen.* 23:229–31

Van Itallie CM, Anderson JM. 1997. Occludin confers adhesiveness when expressed in fibroblasts. *J. Cell Sci.* 110:1113–21

Van Itallie CM, Balda MS, Anderson JM. 1995. Epidermal growth factor induces tyrosine phosphorylation and reorganization of the tight junction protein ZO-1 in A431 cells. *J. Cell Sci.* 108:1735–42

van Meer G, Gumbiner B, Simons K. 1986. The tight junction does not allow lipid molecules to diffuse from one epithelial cell to the next. *Nature* 322:639–41

Weber E, Berta G, Tousson A, St. John P, Green MW, et al. 1994. Expression and polarized targeting of a Rab3 isoform in epithelial cells. *J. Cell Biol.* 125:583–94

Willott E, Balda MS, Fanning AS, Jameson B, Van Itallie C, et al. 1993. The tight junction protein ZO-1 is homologous to the *Drosophila* discs-large tumor suppressor protein of septate junctions. *Proc. Natl. Acad. Sci. USA* 90:7834–38

Willott E, Balda SM, Heintzelman M, Jameson B, Anderson JM. 1992. Localization and differential expression of two isoforms of the tight junction protein ZO-1. *Am. J. Physiol.* 262:C1119–24

Wong V. 1997. Phosphorylation of occludin correlates with occludin localization and function at the tight junction. *Am. J. Physiol.* 273: C1859–67

Wong V, Gumbiner BM. 1997. A synthetic peptide corresponding to the extracellular domain of occludin perturbs the tight junction permeability barrier. *J. Cell Biol.* 136:399–409

Woods DF, Bryant PJ. 1991. The discs-large tumor suppressor gene of Drosophila encodes a guanylate kinase homolog localized at septate junctions. *Cell* 66:451–64

Woods DF, Hough C, Peel D, Callaini G, Bryant PJ. 1996. Dlg protein is required for junction structure, cell polarity, and proliferation control in *Drosophila* epithelia. *J. Cell Biol.* 134:1469–82

Woods DF, Wu JW, Bryant PJ. 1997. Localization of proteins to the apico-lateral junctions of *Drosophila* epithelia. *Dev. Genet.* 20:111–18

Yamamoto T, Harada N, Kano K, Taya S, Canaani E, et al. 1997. The Ras target AF-6 interacts with ZO-1 and serves as a peripheral component of tight junctions in epithelial cells. *J. Cell Biol.* 139:785–95

Yap AS, Mullin JM, Stevenson BR. 1998. Molecular analyses of tight junction physiology: insights and paradoxes. *J. Membr. Biol.* 163:159–67

Zahraoui A, Joberty G, Arpin M, Fontaine JJ, Hellio R, et al. 1994. A small rab GTPase is distributed in cytoplasmic vesicles in non-polarized cells but colocalizes with the tight junction marker ZO-1 in polarized epithelial cells. *J. Cell Biol.* 124:101–15

Zhong Y, Enomoto K, Isomura H, Sawada N, Minase T, et al. 1994. Localization of the 7h6 antigen at tight junctions correlates with the paracellular barrier function of MDCK cells. *Exp. Cell Res.* 214:614–20

Zhong YT, Saitoh T, Minase T, Sawada N, Enomoto K, Mori M. 1993. Monoclonal antibody 7H6 reacts with a novel tight junction-associated protein distinct from ZO-1, cingulin and ZO-2. *J. Cell Biol.* 120:477–83

Annu. Rev. Cell Dev. Biol. 1998. 14:111–36

FUNCTIONS OF LIPID RAFTS IN BIOLOGICAL MEMBRANES

D. A. Brown and E. London

Department of Biochemistry and Cell Biology, State University of New York at Stony Brook, Stony Brook, New York 11794-5215; e-mail: dbrown@mcbsgi.bio.sunysb.edu

KEY WORDS: membrane domain, glycosphingolipid, GPI-anchored protein, signal transduction, membrane trafficking

ABSTRACT

Recent studies showing that detergent-resistant membrane fragments can be isolated from cells suggest that biological membranes are not always in a liquid-crystalline phase. Instead, sphingolipid and cholesterol-rich membranes such as plasma membranes appear to exist, at least partially, in the liquid-ordered phase or a phase with similar properties. Sphingolipid and cholesterol-rich domains may exist as phase-separated "rafts" in the membrane. We discuss the relationship between detergent-resistant membranes, rafts, caveolae, and low-density plasma membrane fragments. We also discuss possible functions of lipid rafts in membranes. Signal transduction through the high-affinity receptor for IgE on basophils, and possibly through related receptors on other hematopoietic cells, appears to be enhanced by association with rafts. Raft association may also aid in signaling through proteins anchored by glycosylphosphatidylinositol, particularly in hematopoietic cells and neurons. Rafts may also function in sorting and trafficking through the secretory and endocytic pathways.

CONTENTS

1081-0706/98/1115-0111$08.00

INTRODUCTION

Because most biological phospholipids have low acyl chain melting temperatures (T_m), cellular membranes are generally thought to exist in a fluid, liquid-crystalline (l_c) phase. However, the plasma membrane and some organelles of the secretory and endocytic pathways in eukaryotic cells are rich in sphingolipids, which have elevated T_m, and sterols, which can have profound effects on membrane phase (Silvius et al 1996). This mixture of lipids raises the possibility of complex phase behavior in these membranes.

In fact, a number of recent studies suggest that eukaryotic cell plasma membranes are not entirely in the conventional l_c phase (Brown & London 1998). Instead, they may be, at least partially, in the cholesterol-rich liquid-ordered (l_o) phase. The l_o phase is characterized by a high degree of acyl chain order and is favored by high-T_m lipids with saturated acyl chains such as sphingolipids, when they are mixed with cholesterol. The strongest experimental support for this idea has come from a seemingly unrelated finding; i.e. in the cold, plasma membranes are partially resistant to solubilization by non-ionic detergents such as Triton X-100 (Brown & London 1998). After Triton extraction, insoluble lipids remain in the form of detergent-resistant membranes (DRMs; also called detergent-insoluble glycolipid-enriched membranes or DIGs) (Simons & Ikonen 1997).

We recently reviewed the evidence equating DRMs and lipid bilayers in the l_o phase and the possible domain structure that could result from formation of a separate l_o phase in biological membranes (Brown & London 1998). Readers are referred to this and three other recent reviews of sphingolipid and cholesterol-rich membranes (Simons & Ikonen 1997, Brown 1998, Rietveld & Simons 1998). Due to space limitations, these topics are summarized only briefly in this review. Here, we first discuss the relationship between DRMs, lipid rafts, caveolae, and low-density plasma membrane fragments. We then focus on how phase separation may function in biological membranes.

DRMS, RAFTS, CAVEOLAE, AND LOW-DENSITY MEMBRANES

DRMs

Most of the sphingolipids and some of the cholesterol in mammalian cell membranes are detergent-resistant in the cold, and can be isolated as DRMs (Brown & Rose 1992). In contrast, most of the cellular phospholipid is detergent soluble. Detergent-insolubility was found to correlate with lipid T_m, providing a clue that insolubility of cellular lipids might reflect their phase behavior (Schroeder et al 1994). Further support for this link came from findings that genuine l_o phase model membranes are detergent resistant and that DRMs isolated from cells have physical properties similar to those of l_o phase membranes (Schroeder et al 1994, Ahmed et al 1997, Schroeder et al 1998).

DRMs can be isolated from almost all mammalian cell types. Immature oligo-dendrocytes (Krämer et al 1997) and immature hippocampal neurons (C Dotti, unpublished data) are exceptions in that they are very poor sources of DRMs. However, as hippocampal neurons mature, their sphingomyelin content and their ability to produce DRMs both increase (C Dotti, unpublished data), suggesting that a high sphingolipid content is required for DRM formation. DRMs have not been well studied in other eukaryotes, although they have been isolated from *Saccharomyces cerevisiae* (Kübler et al 1996) and possibly from *Tetrahymena* (Zhang & Thompson 1997).

DRMs isolated from mammalian cell lysates have the appearance of vesicles, sometimes mixed with membrane sheets. Most probably originate from the plasma membrane, although some are also derived from intracellular membranes. However, DRMs examined in situ look very different, as first shown by Mayor & Maxfield (1995a). Detergent-resistant plasma membrane is a continuous sheet, interrupted by holes similar to those in Swiss cheese (Figure 1). Thus plasma membrane–derived DRMs do not exist as vesicles in cells. In fact, they may not be a collection of discrete structures, as the term DRMs suggests. This will be important later, when we consider the possible domain organization of the plasma membrane, and the relationship between DRMs and other structures such as caveolae.

HOW PROTEINS AND LIPIDS ASSOCIATE WITH DRMS   A specific group of membrane proteins is present in DRMs when they are isolated from mammalian cell lysates. Because DRMs are in an l_o-like state when they are isolated, they should be the molecules with the greatest tendency to partition into an ordered environment that is enriched in lipids with saturated acyl chains. In agreement with this idea, sphingolipids are enriched in DRMs, whereas phospholipids are

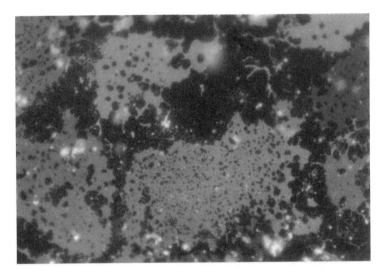

Figure 1   Detergent-resistant plasma membrane (DRM). COS cells were removed from glass coverslips by sonication, leaving a plasma membrane sheet behind as described by Huang et al (1997). After fixation, the membrane was incubated with 1% Triton X-100 for 30 min at 4°C and washed. DiI, a fluorescent lipophilic probe that should partition into any membrane under these conditions, was then added to visualize DRMs.

relatively depleted (Brown & Rose 1992). As expected from their high T_m, glycosphingolipids are enriched in DRMs. However, as sphingomyelin and cholesterol-rich DRMs can be isolated from mammalian cells that do not contain glycosphingolipids (K Ivarson, K Grove & DA Brown, unpublished data), these lipids are not absolutely required for DRM formation.

Surprisingly, phosphatidylinositol 4,5-bisphosphate (PtdIns 4,5-P_2) is enriched in DRMs, although its acyl chains are highly unsaturated (Pike & Casey 1996). The DRM-associated pool of PtdIns 4,5-P_2 is preferentially turned over in response to bradykinin and EGF, suggesting that this localization is important in signaling. It will be interesting to determine how PtdIns 4,5-P_2 is localized to these membranes.

Many DRM proteins are linked to saturated acyl chains, which is likely to make them prefer an ordered environment. Proteins can be linked to saturated acyl chains in two ways; either in the form of a glycosylphosphatidylinositol (GPI) anchor (McConville & Ferguson 1993) or through acylation with myristate or palmitate. Except in the DRM-poor cells noted above, GPI-anchored proteins in mammalian cells generally associate with DRMs, in a manner that requires the GPI anchor (Rodgers et al 1994, Arreaza & Brown 1995). The importance of acylation in DRM targeting has been shown most clearly for Src family nonreceptor protein tyrosine kinases (Resh 1994, Milligan et al 1995, Robbins et al 1995). With a few exceptions (Lisanti et al 1994, Dorahy et al 1996), most groups have found that association of these kinases with DRMs requires dual modification by both myristate and palmitate (Shenoy-Scaria et al 1994, Robbins et al 1995). Several other palmitoylated DRM proteins have also been identified (Brown & London 1997), and acylation may be a widely used DRM targeting signal. In fact, most of the proteins in DRMs isolated from the MDCK cultured epithelial cell line are either GPI anchored or acylated (KA Melkonian & DA Brown, unpublished data.) Mutation of either palmitoylation site in the dually palmitoylated neuronal protein GAP-43 (Maekawa et al 1997) blocks association with DRM (S Arni, SA Keilbaugh & DA Brown, unpublished data). Similarly, mutation of any of the three palmitoylation sites of the transmembrane influenza hemagglutinin protein blocks DRM association (MG Roth, unpublished data). Caveolin, a marker of caveolae (see below), may be unusual, as elimination of its three palmitoylation sites does not affect association with DRMs (Dietzen et al 1995). GPI-anchorage and acylation are the only known signals for DRM targeting. Other signals must exist, however, as some DRM proteins contain neither modification.

Rafts

Several early studies suggested that glycosphingolipids might cluster in membranes (Thompson & Tillack 1985). Simons & van Meer (1988) proposed that these glycolipid rafts might be involved in sorting (see below). Lipids in the rafts were suggested to be clustered by a network of hydrogen bonds. Glycosphingolipid-rich DRMs, discovered later, were presumed to be isolated rafts (Brown & Rose 1992). Further work showed that lipids associate with DRMs based largely on their degree of acyl chain order (Schroeder et al 1994). This appears to be a more important determinant of DRM association than hydrogen bonding capability (Brown & London 1998). Thus the focus of raft research has shifted to cholesterol and sphingolipid-rich ordered domains that may have characteristics of the l_o phase. The term rafts has recently been adapted to refer to such domains (Rietveld & Simons 1998), and we use the word in this sense here.

DO RAFTS EXIST IN CELL MEMBRANES? Although detergent-insolubility studies strongly suggest that plasma membranes are not in the l_c state, a key unanswered question is whether membranes contain discrete domains in different phases. It is possible that DRMs exist in intact cell membranes as rafts floating in a detergent-soluble l_c phase sea. [Similarly, in very sphingolipid-rich membranes, discrete l_c phase domains could exist in a continuous l_o-like sea (Rietveld & Simons 1998).] Model membrane studies show that these are viable models, because liposomes with sphingolipid and cholesterol levels similar to those in the plasma membrane are partially detergent insoluble (mimicking the behavior of cell membranes); they also show phase separation (Ahmed et al 1997, Schroeder et al 1998). However, it is important to note that partial detergent insolubility by itself does not prove that membranes contain rafts. As we have discussed, membranes present in a single uniform phase with properties intermediate between the l_o and l_c phases could also exhibit partial insolubility (Brown & London 1998). In this case, although rafts would not exist constitutively, they might form in a regulated manner.

Morphological studies have provided further insight into the question of whether rafts exist. Proteins (such as GPI-anchored proteins) and lipids (such as glycosphingolipids) that have an affinity for an ordered environment should partition into rafts if they are present and should act as useful morphological markers. The conclusion of several studies using this approach is that if rafts exist, they are very difficult to see. GPI-anchored proteins generally appear uniformly distributed in the plasma membrane (Maxfield & Mayor 1997), and it has been difficult to obtain evidence of glycosphingolipid clusters larger than a few molecules (Rock et al 1990).

However, there is much better evidence that rafts exist after certain proteins and lipids are clustered in the membrane. One of the best examples is the IgE receptor in basophils (see below). Additional evidence comes from the fact that proteins that associate with DRMs and thus are expected to prefer an ordered environment can cocluster when both are clustered independently. This has been shown for two different GPI-anchored proteins (Mayor et al 1994) and recently also for a GPI-anchored protein and a transmembrane DRM protein (T Harder, P Scheiffele, P Verkade & K Simons, unpublished data). The affinity of these independently clustered proteins for each other suggests that both are present in rafts.

We have incorporated these observations into three possible models for raft structure (Brown & London 1998). Briefly, stable rafts might exist, but individual proteins and lipids might have a relatively low affinity for them. The affinity might be increased by clustering. Alternatively, rafts might be very small, and might coalesce when the components are clustered. Finally, it is even possible that clustering of components might induce phase separation and cause raft formation. In any case, these studies highlight the importance of clustering of proteins and lipids that have an affinity for an ordered environment in triggering the stable association of these molecules with large rafts. This property must be kept in mind when considering how rafts may function.

A major outstanding question is how (or whether) rafts form in the cytoplasmic leaflet of the bilayer (discussed further by Rietveld & Simons 1998). The fact that Src-family kinases are present in DRMs, although their acyl chains have access only to the inner leaflet, suggests that rafts exist there, as does the fact that DRMs have a bilayer appearance (Brown & Rose 1992). However, sphingolipids are largely concentrated in the extracellular leaflet. Some glycerophospholipids may also participate in raft formation, a property that could be critical in the inner leaflet (Brown & London 1997). How rafts in opposite leaflets might communicate remains a mystery. Monolayer coupling in sphingomyelin-containing bilayers has been observed in model systems (Schmidt et al 1978), and it is conceivable that the long sphingolipid acyl chains affect phospholipid organization in the opposite leaflet.

Caveolae

Caveolae (recently reviewed by Parton 1996, Anderson 1998, Okamoto et al 1998) are 50–70-nm plasma membrane pits implicated in endocytosis, lipid traffic, and signal transduction. A 22-kDa protein, caveolin (VIP21), is closely associated with caveolae and may play an important structural role in their formation (Rothberg et al 1992, Fra et al 1995). Caveolin is also present in the Golgi/*trans*-Golgi network (TGN) and in post-Golgi transport vesicles (Dupree et al 1993), although caveolae have not been detected in intracellular membranes. The function of Golgi caveolin and the relationship between the Golgi and cell-surface pools of the protein are not known, although the presence of caveolin in transport vesicles suggests a role in vesicle formation (Simons & Ikonen 1997, Anderson 1998). In addition, several observations suggest that caveolae and/or caveolin are important in cholesterol traffic (Anderson 1998, Rietveld & Simons 1998).

It was recently proposed that the term caveolae be broadened beyond its original definition (Anderson 1998). The rationale for this suggestion is twofold. First, caveolae are dynamic structures, and their degree of invagination can be regulated. Under some experimental conditions, caveolae flatten and are not detectable as invaginations. Thus the original definition may seem too limited. Second, as described below, fragmented plasma membrane can be fractionated, and a low-density subfraction that is enriched in caveolae can be isolated. Low-density membranes with similar properties can be isolated from cells that do not contain caveolae. Thus it was proposed that the word caveolae be broadened to include these membranes.

However, the degree of similarity between these membranes and caveolae is not clear, and the membrane of invaginated caveolae may have unusual properties that are not shared by other membranes. For these reasons, we use the word caveolae here to refer only to caveolin-associated plasma membrane invaginations. It should be kept in mind that their morphology may be altered under some conditions.

Several observations initially suggested that DRMs exist in cells as rafts within caveolae. First, DRM markers such as GPI-anchored proteins and glycosphingolipids can concentrate in caveolae (although see below). Caveolin, the best marker of caveolae, is also concentrated in DRMs. In addition, isolated DRMs sometimes have the size and shape of caveolae (Chang et al 1994).

However, further results show that DRMs are not the same as caveolae. First, it now appears that most GPI-anchored proteins are not constitutively concentrated in caveolae but rather show a uniform distribution in the plasma membrane (Maxfield & Mayor 1997, Brown & London 1998). GPI-anchored proteins move into, or close to (Schnitzer et al 1995), caveolae only after being clustered in the membrane by antibody-mediated cross-linking. As a further indication that DRMs and caveolae are not the same, DRMs can be isolated from cells that do not have caveolae. Finally, in situ visualization (Figure 1) clearly shows that DRMs are not restricted to caveolae.

LIPID COMPOSITION   Caveolae are widely believed to be enriched in cholesterol and sphingolipids. However, this belief leans heavily on the assumptions that all DRMs are caveolae and that DRMs exist in membranes as distinct sphingolipid/cholesterol-rich rafts. As discussed above, the origin of DRMs is not as clear as it initially appeared. For this reason, data on the lipid composition of caveolae must be carefully re-examined.

The strongest evidence that sphingolipids are enriched in caveolae is that the ganglioside GM1 is concentrated in caveolae when detected with cholera toxin (Tran et al 1987, Parton 1994). However, cholera toxin is pentavalent. Thus GM1, like GPI-anchored proteins, may be concentrated in caveolae only after it is aggregated. Consistent with this possibility, cholera toxin-bound GM1 is more detergent insoluble than is free GM1 (Hagmann & Fishman 1982). This suggests that toxin binding increases the affinity of the lipid for an ordered environment. The distribution of GM1 has not been examined with a monovalent probe and remains uncertain.

The plasma membrane distribution of sphingomyelin and several neutral glycosphingolipids has also been examined (Fujimoto 1996). They were found to be randomly distributed in the membrane but concentrated in caveolae after being clustered. Another study has been cited as evidence that sphingomyelin is concentrated in caveolae (Liu & Anderson 1995). Fifty to seventy percent of the total plasma membrane sphingomyelin was found in low-density caveolin-rich membranes thought to be purified caveolae. However, as the fraction of total plasma membrane lipid in these fractions was not determined, it is not known if sphingomyelin was enriched there over its concentration in bulk membrane. In addition, it is now clear that these low-density membranes are not homogeneous caveolae (see below).

It is also not clear if cholesterol is enriched in caveolae. In an early study, the cholesterol-binding compound filipin preferentially labeled rings around the necks of caveolae when added to cells for a short time (Simionescu et al 1983). After longer exposure to the drug, heavy labeling of the entire plasma membrane was generally observed. As the authors pointed out, rings of filipin around caveolae could reflect either a concentration of cholesterol or a difference in the accessibility of cholesterol to the probe. Two later studies suggested that cholesterol is enriched in caveolae. First, nystatin, which complexes with cholesterol, caused caveolae to flatten and prevented GPI-anchored proteins from concentrating in them (Rothberg et al 1992). In a second study, caveolin was expressed in lymphocytes, which do not normally contain caveolae. Expression of caveolin in these cells (a procedure that induces formation of caveolae) (Fra et al 1995) selectively increased the cholesterol:protein ratio in a low-density caveolae-containing plasma membrane fraction, suggesting that the presence of caveolin caused an enrichment of cholesterol (Smart et al 1996). In another study, however, the distribution of cholesterol in the plasma membrane was examined morphologically using a modified biotinylated perfringolysin O toxin (Fujimoto et al 1997). Cholesterol detected with this reagent appeared evenly distributed in the membrane unless it was first clustered by cross-linking with streptavidin. Only then was it concentrated in caveolae-rich regions of the plasma membrane.

Thus the question of whether sphingolipids and cholesterol are concentrated in caveolae has not been resolved. Nevertheless, it is clear that GPI-anchored proteins and glycosphingolipids, which should prefer an ordered environment, concentrate in or near caveolae when they are clustered. This is the best indication that the lipid environment in caveolae may be more ordered than the surrounding membrane. It is not clear how this is accomplished, although caveolar proteins (possibly caveolin itself) are likely to play an important role.

PURIFICATION   Several recently described methods for purifying caveolae have provided a critical advance in the biochemical characterization of these structures (Anderson 1998). However, the purity of the isolated caveolae remains somewhat controversial. For instance, caveolae isolated from endothelial cells by two groups using similar techniques contain different proteins (Schnitzer et al 1995, Stan et al 1997). In one of the most widely used methods, low-density caveolae are separated from high-density bulk plasma membrane on Optiprep gradients (Smart et al 1995). However, a recent study of heterotrimeric G proteins showed that caveolae are not the only membranes in this fraction (Huang et al 1997). This was demonstrated by examining the distribution of $G_{i\alpha}$ between light and heavy membranes and also its plasma membrane localization, as determined by electron microscopy. Although almost all the $G_{i\alpha}$ was present in the gradient fractions proposed to contain purified caveolae (Smart et al 1995), only a small fraction of the protein was present in caveolae as detected morphologically (Huang et al 1997). It is thus difficult to determine what fraction of these low-density membranes are actually caveolae.

Low-Density Plasma Membrane Fragments

Fragmented plasma membrane from a variety of cells including lymphocytes (Hoessli & Rungger-Brändle 1983, Arni et al 1996, Smart et al 1996), fibroblasts (Smart et al 1995), epithelial cells (Huang et al 1997), and neurons (Wu et al 1997) can be separated into high- and low-density fractions on density gradients. The low-density membranes are enriched in GPI-anchored proteins and caveolin, suggesting that they are rafts. However, where the lipid composition has been examined, these membranes, compared with high-density membranes, do not appear to be enriched in cholesterol or sphingolipid (Hoessli & Rungger-Brändle 1983, Arni et al 1996). In another study, light membranes from neurons were reported to be enriched in cholesterol, sphingomyelin, phosphatidylcholine, and phosphatidylethanolamine compared with heavy membranes (Wu et al 1997). However, lipids isolated from light and heavy membranes containing equal amounts of protein were compared. Because light membranes have a higher lipid:protein ratio, even if the lipid composition of the two fractions were identical, every lipid would appear to be enriched in a light membrane sampled for equal amounts of protein. There was no indication of a difference in lipid composition between the two membranes in this study.

In summary, lipid analysis has not proven that low-density plasma membrane fragments correspond to rafts. Nonetheless, the fact that a number of key signaling molecules are enriched in the low-density membranes underscores their significance (Anderson 1998). Further characterization of these membranes will be very important.

RAFTS AND SIGNAL TRANSDUCTION

Rafts may be important in transmembrane signal transduction at the cell surface. Most of the evidence for this role comes from studies of signaling through GPI-anchored proteins, as is discussed in the following section. First, however, we describe how transmembraneous receptor proteins may also associate with rafts during signaling in some hematopoietic cells.

Transmembrane Signaling Proteins in Hematopoietic Cells

FCεRI   The best evidence for the involvement of rafts in signaling comes from studies of FcεRI, the receptor for IgE on basophils and mast cells. IgE binds constitutively to cell-surface FcεRI. Aggregation of FcεRI by binding of antigen to FcεRI-bound IgE activates the associated Src-family kinase, Lyn, initiating

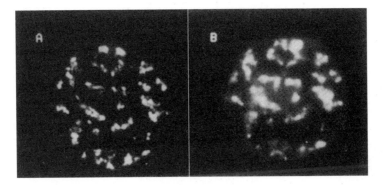

Figure 2   DiI colocalizes with clustered IgE receptor. DiI was incorporated into the plasma membrane of RBL cultured basophilic leukemia cells, where it appeared uniformly distributed (Thomas et al 1994). Cell-surface FcεRI was then clustered with biotinylated IgE and streptavidin before visualization of FcεRI; visualized with (*A*) FITC-IgE and (*B*) diI, in the same cell. Reproduced with permission from Thomas et al (1994).

a signaling cascade that culminates in degranulation (Field et al 1997). In an elegant series of studies, FcεRI-bound biotinylated IgE was clustered with streptavidin, generating large, easily detectable cell-surface clusters. Strikingly, as shown in Figure 2, a saturated-chain lipid probe, diI, colocalized with clustered receptors (Thomas et al 1994). DiI is known to partition preferentially into more-ordered gel phase domains in two-phase model membranes (Spink et al 1990). Of several other fluorescent probes examined, regardless of charge, only those predicted to prefer an ordered environment coclustered with the receptor (Thomas et al 1994). Similar results were obtained from another group when FcεRI was clustered by addition of antigen. In this study, receptor clusters colocalized with clustered GM1 (Stauffer & Meyer 1997).

Field et al showed that a fraction of FcεRI becomes detergent insoluble by associating with DRMs when it is clustered (Field et al 1997). Two additional observations showed that association of the receptor with DRMs correlates with signaling. First, the receptor is recruited into DRMs and phosphorylated by Lyn with the same kinetics. More strikingly, only the receptor that is in DRMs serves as a substrate for Lyn (Field et al 1997). These studies provide the clearest indication to date that rafts can form under physiological conditions in cell membranes. They show that clustering of FcεRI leads to formation, stabilization, or reorganization of rafts in the membrane and that the rafts can be visualized with diI. These studies also suggest a role for rafts in signaling.

OTHER RECEPTORS   Signaling in a variety of hematopoietic cells (including basophils) involves tyrosine phosphorylation of conserved sequences in the cytoplasmic domains of cell-surface receptors by Src-family kinases (Isakov

1997). This mechanistic similarity suggests that rafts are important in signaling in other cells as well as in basophils. For example, antibody-mediated cross-linking of the cell-surface transmembrane protein CD20 triggers signaling in B cells and tumor cells and recruits the protein into DRMs (Deans et al 1998).

Cell-surface receptors do not always associate with DRMs, possibly implying that they do not associate with rafts. However, in vitro studies have shown that detergent insolubility is not always a perfect measure of the l_o phase (Brown & London 1998). Receptors could have a moderate affinity for rafts in vivo and still not associate stably with DRMs. In fact, although the studies described above show that FcεRI associates with rafts, detergent insolubility of the receptor is somewhat difficult to detect (Field et al 1997).

Additional indirect evidence suggests that transmembrane receptors associate with rafts during signaling. For instance, activation of T cells through the T cell receptor (TCR) is impaired in cells that are defective for GPI anchor synthesis (Romagnoli & Bron 1997). Cross-linking of GPI-anchored proteins in these cells can stimulate signaling, in a manner that may involve rafts (see below). Thus recruitment of the TCR to rafts via association with GPI-anchored proteins may enhance its signaling. It is also interesting to note that depletion of cellular cholesterol can inhibit signaling in mast cells (Shakarjian et al 1993) and T cells (Stulnig et al 1997), possibly by affecting the structure of rafts.

How might association of receptors with rafts be important in signaling? One possibility is suggested by the puzzling nature of signaling in T cells (Germain 1997). The TCR complex and peptide-bound MHC molecules are both monomeric and interact with only low affinity. However, productive signaling appears to require the formation of oligomeric complexes of these molecules. It is not clear how these oligomeric complexes form. It has been proposed that low-affinity homophilic interactions between molecules of TCR, MHC, and the co-receptor CD4 may cooperate to form a stable complex (Germain 1997). Recruitment of these proteins into rafts could concentrate them enough to facilitate protein-protein interactions.

In addition, the activity of Src-family kinases may be inhibited (Rodgers & Rose 1996) or stimulated (Arni et al 1996, Kabouridis et al 1997) by association with rafts. For instance, in T cells, DRM-associated Lck is less active than detergent-soluble Lck, probably because CD45, the tyrosine phosphatase required for activation of Lck, is excluded from rafts (Rodgers & Rose 1996).

Signaling Through GPI-Anchored Proteins

Clustering or ligation of cell-surface GPI-anchored proteins can trigger transmembrane signal transduction. In some cases this occurs through activation of Src-family kinases (Brown 1993, Zisch et al 1995). Because neither protein penetrates the bilayer, how they communicate—and how GPI-anchored proteins send any information across the membrane—present a puzzle. A reasonable scenario is that GPI-anchored proteins bind in *cis* (in the plane of the membrane) to transmembrane proteins. These proteins could transmit signals across the membrane, for instance, by binding directly or indirectly to Src-family kinases. In the following, we consider GPI-anchored proteins known to be involved in signaling and the progress made in identifying some of their transmembrane signaling partners. We also discuss how rafts may be involved in these signaling pathways.

HEMATOPOIETIC CELLS   Antibody-mediated cross-linking of GPI-anchored proteins on the surface of most hematopoietic cells can stimulate Src-family kinases, leading to signaling events that include calcium flux as well as some downstream events (Robinson 1991, Brown 1993, Dráberová & Dráber 1993, Morgan et al 1993, van den Berg et al 1995).

A GPI-anchored protein for which *cis* signaling partners have been identified is FcγRIIIb (CD16), a member of the FcγR family of IgG receptors. Binding of circulating immune complexes to Fcγ receptors clusters the receptors and stimulates signaling (Unkeless et al 1995, Green et al 1997). FcγRIIIb, the only GPI-anchored FcγR, is restricted to primate neutrophils, where it coexists with the more widely distributed transmembrane form of the protein, FcγRIIa. Although the role of FcγRIIIb in signaling was controversial, it is now clear that clustering of this protein by itself can mediate calcium flux. Further signaling events require FcγRIIa, including its cytoplasmic domain. However, signaling through FcγRIIa is enhanced by coclustering with FcγRIIIb, suggesting a unique role for the GPI-anchored form of the protein. In fact, in neutrophils and transfected T cells, coclustering of FcγRIIa with either FcγRIIIb or unrelated GPI-anchored proteins enhances calcium flux, in a manner that depends on the GPI anchor (Green et al 1997). This finding highlights the role of the GPI anchor in this process.

GPI-anchored proteins can affect integrin signaling in hematopoietic cells. FcγRIIIb, as well as two other GPI-anchored proteins, the urokinase-type plasminogen activator receptor (uPAR, CD87) and CD14, the receptor for lipopolysaccharide, can bind in *cis* to β_2 integrins, which are found only on hematopoietic cells (Stockinger 1997, Todd & Petty 1997). These interactions, which are sometimes reversible and physiologically regulated, appear to have important and complex effects on integrin signaling and function (Todd & Petty 1997).

NEURONS   Binding of ligands to several GPI-anchored proteins in neurons can transmit signals across the membrane. One of the best characterized is the GPI-anchored protein contactin (F3, F11), which appears to mediate interactions of neurons with the local environment during development (Peles et al 1997).

Proteins that bind contactin both in *cis* and in *trans* (i.e. on adjacent cells) have been identified. Binding of the receptor-type protein tyrosine phosphatase β (RPTPβ) to contactin in *trans* can stimulate signaling by contactin. A transmembrane protein, Caspr (contactin-associated protein), binds contactin in *cis* (Peles et al 1997). Contactin was shown to provide a link between RPTPβ and Caspr in adjacent cells. Caspr is a good candidate for a *cis* signaling partner for contactin because it contains a mosaic of domains implicated in protein-protein interactions (Peles et al 1997). In particular, a Pro-rich region in the cytoplasmic domain of Caspr was shown to bind in vitro to SH3 domains of a subset of proteins, including those of Src and Fyn. (However, interaction between Caspr and Src in vivo could not be demonstrated.) Caspr associates with a Triton-insoluble fraction that might be either DRMs or cytoskeleton (Einheber et al 1997).

Contactin also binds the transmembrane neuronal immunoglobulin-superfamily members Ng-CAM (Brümmendorf et al 1993) and Nr-CAM (Morales et al 1993), although the role of this interaction in signaling through contactin is not clear. Interactions between contactin, L1 (the mouse homologue of Ng-CAM), and Fyn were demonstrated by coimmunoprecipitation from mouse brain (Olive et al 1995).

Several other neuronal GPI-anchored receptors can mediate signaling upon ligand binding; one example is Thy-1 (Doherty et al 1993). In other cases, such as the receptors for ciliary neurotrophic factor (CNTF) (Economides et al 1995), glial cell neurotrophic factor (GDNF) (Massagué 1996), and the closely related neurturin (Buj-Bello et al 1997), multi-subunit receptor complexes contain a GPI-anchored protein component. GPI-anchored proteins can also act as ligands for EPH-family receptor tyrosine kinases in adjacent cells (Davis et al 1994).

OTHER CELLS   Signaling through GPI-anchored proteins appears to be uncommon in cells other than hematopoietic cells or neurons. However, uPAR can mediate signaling in a variety of mammalian cells. uPAR is the receptor for the urokinase-type plasminogen activator (uPA), which cleaves plasminogen to plasmin. Signaling through the uPA/uPAR complex has been implicated in cell adhesion, migration, and differentiation independently of the enzymatic activity of uPA (Yebra et al 1996, Planus et al 1997). Its *cis* interactions with integrins appear to be important in this signaling, as was mentioned above for interactions between β_2 integrins and uPAR in neutrophils. For example, uPAR cooperates with the integrin $\alpha v \beta 5$ in mediating migration of carcinoma cells on vitronectin (Yebra et al 1996). In another study, embryonic kidney cells were shown to bind fibronectin via a $\beta 1$ integrin (Wei et al 1996). Expression of uPAR (which binds vitronectin in vitro) in these cells prevented them from binding to fibronectin. However, the transfected cells now bound vitronectin, in a manner that required both uPAR and the integrin cytoplasmic domain. This study showed that uPAR and the integrin could cooperate to mediate binding of cells to vitronectin.

ROLE OF RAFTS IN SIGNALING EVENTS   It is not known whether association of GPI-anchored proteins with rafts is important in any of these signaling pathways. The role of rafts may differ between proteins and between cell types. At one extreme, the fact that soluble forms of the GPI-anchored subunits of CNTFR and GDNFR can substitute for the GPI-anchored forms (Economides et al 1995, Massagué 1996) suggests that these proteins do not need to associate with rafts in order to signal.

In other cases, the presence of GPI-anchored and associated signaling proteins in DRMs and/or caveolae suggests that localization of the proteins in rafts may be important. For instance, DRMs containing both GPI-anchored proteins and Src-family kinases can be isolated from hematopoietic cells (Brown 1993) and neurons (Olive et al 1995, Zisch et al 1995). In addition, uPAR, β_2 integrins, and Src-family kinases have been isolated from monocytes in the same DRMs (Bohuslav et al 1995), and uPAR, integrins, and caveolin formed complexes in transfected fibroblasts, suggesting that the protein complex might localize to caveolae in these cells (Wei et al 1996). Another study has also shown that certain integrins can be coimmunoprecipitated with caveolin in fibroblasts (Wary et al 1996). It should be cautioned, however, that the presence of two proteins in the same DRM does not demonstrate that they interact (Mayor & Maxfield 1995a). For example, even if they did not interact directly, two proteins in DRMs might be coimmunoprecipitated if the entire DRM were isolated in the process. In fact, proteins could be linked via association with DRMs even if, by some criteria, they appear to be fully solubilized. As an example, although a GPI-anchored protein could no longer be pelleted by centrifugation after detergent extraction at 37°C, it still had a low density, thus indicating that it associated with DRM lipid (Naslavsky et al 1997).

There may be two distinct paradigms for signaling through GPI-anchored proteins. The first and best characterized model is specific binding of GPI-anchored proteins with signaling capability to one or more transmembrane proteins in *cis*. As discussed above, in some cases, such as CNTFR and GDNFR, association of these complexes with rafts does not appear to be crucial for signaling. In other cases, such as the binding of FcγRIIIb or uPAR to β_2 integrins (described above), association of the complexes with rafts may facilitate signaling.

A second paradigm may be found in some hematopoietic cells (for example, T cells) that can be stimulated by clustering of virtually any GPI-anchored protein (Robinson 1991). This lack of specificity could result from binding of an unidentified linker protein to the GPI anchor itself. However, it is interesting that no GPI-anchored proteins in T cells have been shown to bind β_2

integrins (Stockinger 1997) nor have any transmembrane signaling partners for GPI-anchored proteins in T cells been identified. This may mean that signaling uses a different mechanism; GPI-anchored proteins may not bind directly to transmembrane signaling partners. Instead, rafts that are formed or stabilized when GPI-anchored proteins are clustered may play an important role in signaling through GPI-anchored proteins in T cells. For instance, transmembrane proteins that are downstream of GPI-anchored proteins in signaling might be concentrated and activated simply by partitioning into these rafts, without binding the GPI-anchored protein directly. It is even conceivable that in some cases no transmembrane linker protein is involved and that rafts in the outer bilayer leaflet are somehow coupled to rafts in the inner leaflet, possibly through monolayer coupling, as mentioned above (Schmidt et al 1978).

In either of these models, how would clustering of GPI-anchored proteins enhance signaling? This would depend on the structure of rafts in the membranes (Brown & London 1998). If rafts normally contain only a few molecules, then clustering of GPI-anchored proteins would cause small rafts to coalesce, bringing raft-associated transmembrane proteins close together. Alternatively, clustering of GPI-anchored proteins might induce formation of rafts in a previously uniform membrane, allowing recruitment of transmembrane proteins with an affinity for rafts.

Signaling in Caveolae

Several groups have found that a variety of cell-surface signaling pathways are concentrated in caveolae or in low-density plasma membrane domains (Anderson 1998). [However, in contrast, one group failed to detect an enrichment of signaling molecules in purified caveolae (Stan et al 1997).] Several signaling proteins, including heterotrimeric G proteins, Ras, Src, endothelial nitric oxide synthase (eNOS), and protein kinase C have been reported to bind caveolin directly and to be inactivated when bound (Oka et al 1997, Okamoto et al 1998). It should be noted that another group failed to detect binding of G proteins to caveolin or an effect of caveolin on the activity of $G_{o\alpha}$ (Huang et al 1997).) Exciting recent studies have shown that eNOS can be up- or down-regulated by alternative binding to either caveolin or calmodulin (Feron et al 1998). Thus with the divergent reports as caveats, most studies point to an important role for caveolae as signaling centers, as reviewed in detail elsewhere (Anderson 1998, Okamoto et al 1998). The role of the caveolar lipid environment in signaling remains to be explored.

CELL-SURFACE PROTEOLYSIS

Two cell-surface proteases may be regulated by association with rafts or caveolae. The first is uPA. uPAR (the receptor for uPA) appears to be constitutively localized to caveolae in melanoma cells, as detected morphologically (Stahl & Mueller 1995). As most GPI-anchored proteins localize to caveolae only after cross-linking (Maxfield & Mayor 1997), uPAR may be concentrated there either by binding to other caveolar proteins, or through an unusually high affinity for an ordered lipid environment. Treatment of cells with nystatin or filipin to disrupt caveolae inhibits cell-surface plasmin generation by uPA, suggesting that caveolar localization may regulate uPA enzymatic activity (Stahl & Mueller 1995).

A second example is the coagulation cascade on endothelial cells. This involves tissue factor (TF), a transmembraneous protease receptor. Briefly, a proteolytically active complex formed by TF and the serine protease factor VIIa can be inhibited by binding of other components (Sevinsky et al 1996). During this down-regulation process, the complex was shown to move into caveolae and gain an affinity for DRMs by associating with an unidentified GPI-anchored protein (Sevinsky et al 1996). The complex in DRMs was inhibited more than would be expected from binding of inhibitory proteins, suggesting that the membrane environment itself has an additional inhibitory effect. Thus regulating the activity of cell-surface proteases such as uPA and the TF complex may be an important function of rafts and/or caveolae.

SECRETORY AND ENDOCYTIC PATHWAYS

Membranes of the Golgi, TGN, and endocytic pathway can contain significant amounts of cholesterol and sphingolipid (Steer et al 1984, Coxey et al 1993, Cluett & Machamer 1996) and may have some l_o-like character. In agreement with this idea, a GPI-anchored protein first becomes Triton-insoluble in the medial Golgi during biosynthetic transport (Brown & Rose 1992). However, there is no direct evidence that rafts form in intracellular membranes. Because these membranes are difficult to access with externally added probes, the morphological approaches that have provided evidence for raft formation in the plasma membrane have not been applicable.

Regardless, it has been suggested that rafts function in sorting of lipids and proteins in the secretory and endocytic pathways. This could explain how the distinct lipid compositions of the plasma membrane and organelles of the secretory pathway are maintained in the face of membrane traffic in both directions through the pathway. Lipids could be sorted by preferential inclusion of rafts in nascent transport vesicles. Alternatively, rafts might be selectively excluded from the vesicles. Furthermore, sorting of cargo proteins could be coupled to lipid sorting if the proteins partitioned preferentially into rafts (Bretscher & Munro 1993, Simons & Ikonen 1997). As described in the next sections, such sorting mechanisms have been proposed to operate at several steps in the secretory and endocytic pathways.

Sorting in Epithelial Cells and Neurons

Coupled sorting of lipid microdomains and proteins was first proposed by Simons and van Meer in a model for sorting of apical and basolateral proteins and lipids in polarized epithelial cells (Simons & van Meer 1988). Glycosphingolipids are more abundant in apical than basolateral membranes. To explain this distribution, glycosphingolipid-rich rafts containing apically directed proteins were proposed to form in the TGN and to be packaged into apical transport vesicles. A similar mechanism has been proposed to mediate sorting of axonal and dendritic membrane proteins in neurons; axonal proteins may associate with rafts (Dotti et al 1991).

The behavior of GPI-anchored proteins initially appeared to provide experimental support for the raft model (Brown & Rose 1992). These proteins, which partition into DRMs during biosynthetic transport, are targeted apically in epithelial cells. This correlation suggested that DRM association might lead to apical targeting. This suggestion was strengthened by other evidence (independent of DRM association) that GPI anchors were apical sorting signals (see below). Thus the idea that the anchors mediated sorting by partitioning into rafts was very appealing. However, as discussed next, further findings forced a re-evaluation, and showed that—apart from DRM association—there is no evidence that GPI anchors play a role in apical sorting. Furthermore, although several apical proteins in intestinal cells associate with DRMs (Danielsen 1995), DRM association does not correlate well with apical targeting of transmembrane proteins in MDCK cells (Sargiacomo et al 1993, Melkonian et al 1995, Arreaza & Brown 1995).

The evidence implicating GPI anchors in sorting came from studies of hybrid proteins expressed in MDCK cells (Brown et al 1989, Lisanti et al 1989). For example, PLAP-G, a fusion protein containing the extracellular domain of the GPI-anchored placental alkaline phosphatase (PLAP) linked to the transmembrane and cytoplasmic domains of the vesicular stomatitis virus glycoprotein (VSV G), is targeted to the basolateral membrane (Figure 3). One interpretation of this result is that GPI anchors are apical sorting signals. However, the data are equally consistent with the opposite conclusion: that signals in the cytoplasmic domains of the basolateral proteins contain positive signals. In fact, cytoplasmic domains of basolateral proteins are now generally believed to contain such positive signals. Furthermore, the apical localization of two additional hybrid proteins, PLAP654t (Casanova et al 1991) and PLAP-HA (Arreaza & Brown 1995), showed that the GPI anchor is not required for apical targeting of PLAP (see Figure 3 for details). In addition, PLAP-HA is detergent soluble, indicating that DRM association is not required for apical targeting.

Apical/basolateral sorting now appears to be very complex and may involve a hierarchy of sorting signals (Mays et al 1995, Yeaman et al 1997, Simons &

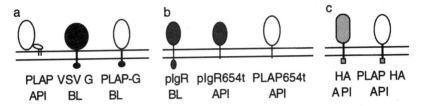

Figure 3   The GPI anchor is not required for apical sorting of PLAP. (*a*) Placental alkaline phosphatase (PLAP), a GPI-anchored protein, is apical, wheras PLAP-G, a hybrid protein containing the extracellular domain of PLAP and the transmembrane and cytoplasmic domains of the basolateral vesicular stomatitis glycoprotein (VSV G), is basolateral (Brown et al 1989). One explanation of this result is that the GPI anchor of PLAP is an apical signal. Alternatively, a dominant signal contributed by VSV G might specify basolateral targeting of PLAP-G. (*b*) The polymeric immunoglobulin receptor (pIgR) is targeted basolaterally by a signal in the cytoplasmic domain (Casanova et al 1991). pIgR654t (a truncated pIgR with a two–amino acid cytoplasmic domain) is apical (Casanova et al 1991). PLAP654t (PLAP fused to the transmembrane and cytoplasmic domains of pIgR654t) is also apical, indicating that GPI anchorage is not required for apical targeting of PLAP. (*c*) Influenza hemagglutinin and the PLAP HA hybrid are both apical (Arreaza & Brown 1995). As the short cytoplasmic domains of PLAP HA and especially PLAP654t are unlikely to contain apical signals, apical sorting of PLAP, PLAP654t, and PLAP HA may require a signal in the PLAP extracellular domain. Such a signal would be recessive to a basolateral signal in the cytoplasmic domain of VSV G, explaining basolateral targeting of PLAP-G.

Ikonen 1997, Weimbs et al 1997). It is generally believed that basolateral sorting signals are located in the cytoplasmic domains of proteins to be sorted, whereas apical signals are in extracellular domains. If two conflicting signals are present in the same protein, one may be dominant and specify targeting. Thus apical transport of PLAP could be mediated by a signal anywhere in the protein, if this signal is recessive to a basolateral signal in the cytoplasmic domain of PLAP-G.

On the other hand, studies showing that reducing cellular cholesterol or sphingolipid levels can lead to selective mis-sorting of apical and axonal proteins support the raft model. For instance, inhibition of sphingolipid synthesis caused mis-sorting of a GPI-anchored protein in MDCK cells (Mays et al 1995). In addition, inhibition of sphingolipid synthesis with fumonisin caused mis-sorting of a GPI-anchored protein that is normally targeted to axons in primary hippocampal neurons, and increased its Triton solubility (Ledesma et al 1998). Depletion of cellular cholesterol by 60 to 70% in MDCK cells caused mis-sorting of the apical influenza hemagglutinin (HA) protein, which associates with DRMs (Keller & Simons 1998). However, in another study, a more modest reduction in cellular cholesterol in these cells did not affect sorting of a GPI-anchored protein, although its detergent solubility was increased (Hannan & Edidin 1996).

Although the raft model for sorting is appealing, several questions about it have been raised (Weimbs et al 1997). For example, it is surprising that DRMs are rich in sphingomyelin (Brown & Rose 1992), which is not apically targeted (Simons & van Meer 1988), and that several basolateral proteins associate with DRMs (Sargiacomo et al 1993, Melkonian et al 1995). Further study will be required to conclusively demonstrate the involvement of rafts in apical sorting.

Cholesterol and Protein Sorting in the Golgi

There is a gradient of cholesterol across the Golgi cisternae, with higher levels on the *trans* side (Coxey et al 1993). To explain this gradient, it was proposed that cholesterol-rich membrane domains are selectively transported forward through the Golgi toward the plasma membrane (Bretscher & Munro 1993). Cholesterol-poor domains may be left behind or actively transported in the opposite direction by retrograde transport. As plasma membrane proteins often have longer transmembrane spans than do Golgi proteins, they might partition preferentially into the thicker cholesterol-rich domains, leaving Golgi proteins in cholesterol-poor domains in the Golgi. In support of this model, mutagenesis studies showed that the same protein can be directed to either the Golgi or plasma membrane by altering the length of the transmembrane span (Munro 1995). In addition, model membrane studies have shown that insertion of a hydrophobic peptide into a bilayer requires the proper relationship between membrane width (which is affected by cholesterol content) and peptide length (Ren et al 1997, Webb et al 1998).

ER to Golgi Transport of GPI-Anchored Proteins in Yeast

ER to Golgi transport of GPI-anchored proteins in yeast is selectively retarded when sphingolipid synthesis is inhibited (Skrzypek et al 1997, Sütterlin et al 1997). This suggests that rafts form in the ER and that GPI-anchored proteins must partition into them for efficient transport (Sütterlin et al 1997). However, the concentration of sphingolipids in the yeast ER is very low (Patton & Lester 1991), arguing against spontaneous formation of rafts. Additional information came from an in vitro budding assay, measuring packaging of the GPI-anchored protein Gas1p into transport vesicles that bud from ER membranes. The assay was performed using ER membranes from either wild-type yeast or from a mutant strain that is defective for sphingolipid synthesis and for ER to Golgi transport of Gas1p in vivo (Sütterlin et al 1997). Gas1p packaging was equally efficient in both cases. Thus slow transport of GPI-anchored proteins in the mutant does not result from an inability to associate with any sphinoglipid-rich rafts in the ER, but from defects in a step after vesicle budding.

Rafts in Endosomes

A provocative observation suggests that rafts exist in endocytic compartments in fibroblasts. A GPI-anchored protein delivered to early endosomes after internalization was found to recycle to the cell surface more slowly than bulk membrane

(Mayor & Maxfield 1995b). However, after depletion of cholesterol (Mayor & Maxfield 1995b, Maxfield & Mayor 1997) or sphingolipids (Chatterjee et al 1997), GPI-anchored proteins recycle as fast as bulk membrane. Association of GPI-anchored proteins with rafts in the endocytic pathway may slow their recycling.

RAFTS AND DISEASE

Some pathogens may take advantage of the ordered state of mammalian cell membranes for infection. For example, fusion of simian forest virus with endosomal membranes during infection requires both sphingolipid (Nieva et al 1994) and cholesterol (Phalen & Kielian 1991). Another virus, SV40, can be internalized into mammalian cells via caveolae and then delivered to the lumen of the ER (Stang et al 1997). Internalization of pathogenic *Escherichia coli* via caveolae may promote pathogen survival by preventing fusion of phagosomes with lysosomes (Baorto et al 1997). Some evidence suggests that aerolysin toxin (Abrami et al 1998), cholera toxin (Tran et al 1987), and Shiga toxin (Sandvig et al 1996) enter mammalian cells via rafts. As detailed elsewhere, rafts may also be involved in prion diseases, Alzheimer's disease, and cancer (Anderson 1998). Further work will show whether the properties of rafts can be used in treatment or prevention of any of these diseases.

ACKNOWLEDGMENTS

We thank C Dotti, MG Roth, and K Simons for sharing unpublished data. Work on this article was supported by National Institutes of Health Grants GM 47897 (to DAB) and GM 48596 (to EL).

Visit the *Annual Reviews home page* at
http://www.AnnualReviews.org

Literature Cited

Abrami L, Fivaz M, Glauser P-E, Parton RG, van der Goot FG. 1998. A pore-forming toxin interacts with a GPI-anchored protein and causes vacuolation of the endoplasmic reticulum. *J. Cell Biol.* 140:525–40

Ahmed SN, Brown DA, London E. 1997. On the origin of sphingolipid-cholesterol rich detergent-insoluble domains in cell membranes: Physiological concentrations of cholesterol and sphingolipid induce formation of a detergent-insoluble, liquid-ordered lipid phase in model membranes. *Biochemistry* 36:10944–53

Anderson RGW. 1998. The caveolae membrane system. *Annu. Rev. Biochem.* In press

Arni S, Ilangumaran S, van Echten-Deckert G, Sandhoff K, Poincelet M, et al. 1996. Differential regulation of Src-family protein tyrosine kinases in GPI domains of T lymphocyte plasma membranes. *Biochem. Biophys. Res. Commun.* 225:801–7

Arreaza G, Brown DA. 1995. Sorting and intracellular trafficking of a glycosylphosphatidylinositol-anchored protein and two hybrid proteins with the same ectodomain in MDCK kidney epithelial cells. *J. Biol. Chem.* 270:23641–47

Baorto DM, Gao Z, Malaviya R, Dustin ML, van

der Merwe A, et al. 1997. Survival of FimH-expressing enterobacteria in macrophages relies on glycolipid traffic. *Nature* 389:636–39

Bohuslav J, Horejsí V, Hansmann C, Stöckl J, Weidle UH, et al. 1995. Urokinase plasminogen activator receptor, β2-integrins, and Src-kinases within a single receptor complex of human monocytes. *J. Exp. Med.* 181:1381–89

Bretscher MS, Munro S. 1993. Cholesterol and the Golgi apparatus. *Science* 261:1280–81

Brown D. 1993. The tyrosine kinase connection: how GPI-anchored proteins activate T cells. *Curr. Opin. Immunol.* 5:349–54

Brown DA, Crise B, Rose JK. 1989. Mechanism of membrane anchoring affects polarized expression of two proteins in MDCK cells. *Science* 245:1499–501

Brown DA, London E. 1997. Structure of detergent-resistant membrane domains: Does phase separation occur in biological membranes? *Biochem. Biophys. Res. Commun.* 240:1–7

Brown DA, London E. 1998. Structure and function of ordered lipid domains in biological membranes. *J. Membr. Biol.* In press

Brown DA, Rose JK. 1992. Sorting of GPI-anchored proteins to glycolipid-enriched membrane subdomains during transport to the apical cell surface. *Cell* 68:533–44

Brown RE. 1998. Sphingolipid organization in biomembranes: what physical studies of model membranes reveal. *J. Cell Sci.* 111:1–9

Brümmendorf T, Hubert M, Treubert U, Leuschner R, Tárnok A, et al. 1993. The axonal recognition molecule F11 is a multifunctional protein: specific domains mediate interactions with Ng-CAM and restrictin. *Neuron* 10:711–27

Buj-Bello A, Adu J, Pinon LG, Horton A, Thompson J, et al. 1997. Neurturin responsiveness requires a GPI-linked receptor and the Ret receptor tyrosine kinase. *Nature* 387:721–24

Casanova JE, Apodaca G, Mostov KE. 1991. An autonomous signal for basolateral sorting in the cytoplasmic domain of the polymeric immunoglobulin receptor. *Cell* 66:65–75

Chang W-J, Ying Y-s, Rothberg KG, Hooper NM, Turner AJ, et al. 1994. Purification and characterization of smooth muscle cell caveolae. *J. Cell Biol.* 126:127–38

Chatterjee S, Stevens VL, Mayor S. 1997. Lipid dependent retention of GPI-anchored proteins in the endocytic pathway of mammalian cells. *Mol. Biol. Cell.* 8:302a (Abstr.)

Cluett EB, Machamer CE. 1996. The envelope of vaccinia virus reveals an unusual phospholipid in Golgi complex membranes. *J. Cell Sci.* 109:2121–31

Coxey RA, Pentchev PG, Campbell G,

Blanchette-Mackie EJ. 1993. Differential accumulation of cholesterol in Golgi compartments of normal and Niemann-Pick Type C fibroblasts incubated with LDL: a cytochemical freeze-fracture study. *J. Lipid Res.* 34:1165–76

Danielsen EM. 1995. Involvement of detergent-insoluble complexes in the intracellular transport of intestinal brush border enzymes. *Biochemistry* 34:1596–605

Davis S, Gale NW, Aldrich TH, Maisonpierre PC, Lhotak V, et al. 1994. Ligands for EPH-related receptor tyrosine kinases that require membrane attachment or clustering for activity. *Science* 266:816–19

Deans JP, Robbins SM, Polyak MJ, Savage JA. 1998. Rapid redistribution of CD20 to a low density detergent-insoluble membrane compartment. *J. Biol. Chem.* 273:344–48

Dietzen DJ, Hastings WR, Lublin DM. 1995. Caveolin is palmitoylated on multiple cysteine residues: Palmitoylation is not necessary for localization of caveolin to caveolae. *J. Biol. Chem.* 270:6838–42

Doherty P, Singh A, Rimon G, Bolsover SR, Walsh FS. 1993. Thy-1 antibody-triggered neurite outgrowth requires an influx of calcium into neurons via N- and L-type calcium channels. *J. Cell Biol.* 122:181–89

Dorahy DJ, Lincz LF, Meldrum CJ, Burns GF. 1996. Biochemical isolation of a membrane microdomain from resting platelets highly enriched in the plasma membrane glycoprotein CD36. *Biochem. J.* 319:67–72

Dotti CG, Parton RG, Simons K. 1991. Polarized sorting of glypiated proteins in hippocampal neurons. *Nature* 349:158–61

Dráberová L, Dráber P 1993. Thy-1 glycoprotein and Src-like protein-tyrosine kinase p53/p56^{lyn} are associated in large detergent-resistant complexes in rat basophilic leukemia cells. *Proc. Natl. Acad. Sci. USA* 90:3611–15

Dupree P, Parton RG, Raposo G, Kurzchalia TV, Simons K. 1993. Caveolae and sorting in the *trans*-Golgi network of epithelial cells. *EMBO J.* 12:1597–605

Economides AN, Ravetch JV, Yancopoulos GD, Stahl N. 1995. Designer cytokines: targeting actions to cells of choice. *Science* 270:1351–53

Einheber S, Zanazzi G, Ching W, Scherer W, Milner TA, et al. 1997. The axonal membrane protein Caspr, a homologue of neurexin IV, is a component of the septate-like paranodal junctions that assemble during myelination. *J. Cell Biol.* 139:1495–506

Feron O, Saldana F, Michel JB, Michel T. 1998. The endothelial nitric-oxide synthase-caveolin regulatory cycle. *J. Biol. Chem.* 273:3125–28

Field KA, Holowka D, Baird B. 1997. Compart-mentalized activation of the high affinity immunoglobulin E receptor within membrane domains. *J. Biol. Chem.* 272:4276–80

Fra AM, Williamson E, Simons K, Parton RG. 1995. De novo formation of caveolae in lymphocytes by expression of VIP21-caveolin. *Proc. Natl. Acad. Sci. USA* 92:8655–59

Fujimoto T. 1996. GPI-anchored proteins, glycosphingolipids, and sphingomyelin are sequestered to caveolae only after crosslinking. *J. Histochem. Cytochem.* 44:929–41

Fujimoto T, Hayashi M, Iwamoto M, Ohno-Iwashita Y. 1997. Crosslinked plasmalemmal cholesterol is sequestered to caveolae: analysis with a new cytochemical probe. *J. Histochem. Cytochem.* 45:1197–205

Germain RN. 1997. T-cell signaling: the importance of receptor clustering. *Curr. Biol.* 7:R640–44

Green JM, Schreiber AD, Brown EJ. 1997. Role for a glycan phosphoinositol anchor in Fcγ receptor synergy. *J. Cell Biol.* 139:1209–18

Hagmann J, Fishman PH. 1982. Detergent extraction of cholera toxin and gangliosides from cultured cells and isolated membranes. *Biochim. Biophys. Acta* 720:181–87

Hannan LA, Edidin M. 1996. Traffic, polarity, and detergent solubility of a glycosyl-phosphatidylinositol-anchored protein after LDL-deprivation of MDCK cells. *J. Cell Biol.* 133:1265–76

Hoessli DC, Rungger-Brändle E. 1983. Isolation of plasma membrane domains from murine T lymphocytes. *Proc. Natl. Acad. Sci. USA* 80:439–43

Huang C, Hepler JR, Chen LT, Gilman AG, Anderson RGW, et al. 1997. Organization of G proteins and adenylyl cyclase at the plasma membrane. *Mol. Biol. Cell.* 8:2365–78

Isakov N. 1997. Immunoreceptor tyrosine-based activation motif (ITAM), a unique module linking antigen and Fc receptors to their signaling cascades. *J. Leuk. Biol.* 61:6–16

Kabouridis P, Magee AI, Ley SC. 1997. S-acylation of LCK protein tyrosine kinase is essential for its signalling function in T lymphocytes. *EMBO J.* 16:4983–98

Keller P, Simons K. 1998. Cholesterol is required for surface transport of influenza virus hemagglutinin. *J. Cell Biol.* 141:1357–67

Krämer E-M, Koch T, Niehaus A, Trotter J. 1997. Oligodendrocytes direct glycosyl phosphatidylinositol-anchored proteins to the myelin sheath in glycosphingolipid-rich complexes. *J. Biol. Chem.* 272:8937–45

Kübler E, Dohlman HG, Lisanti MP. 1996. Identification of Triton X-100 insoluble membrane domains in the yeast *Saccharomyces cerevisiae*. *J. Biol. Chem.* 271:32975–80

Ledesma MD, Simons K, Dotti CG. 1998.

Neuronal polarity: essential role of protein-lipid complexes in axonal sorting. *Proc. Natl. Acad. Sci. USA* 95:3966–71

Lisanti MP, Caras IW, Davitz MA, Rodriguez-Boulan E. 1989. A glycosphingolipid membrane anchor acts as an apical targeting signal in polarized epithelial cells. *J. Cell Biol.* 109:2145–56

Lisanti MP, Scherer PE, Vidugiriene J, Tang Z, Hermanowski-Vosatka A, et al. 1994. Characterization of caveolin-rich membrane domains isolated from an endothelial-rich source. *J. Cell Biol.* 126:111–26

Liu P, Anderson RGW. 1995. Compartmentalized production of ceramide at the cell surface. *J. Biol. Chem.* 270:27179–85

Maekawa S, Kumanogoh H, Funatsu N, Takei N, Inoue K, et al. 1997. Identification of NAP-22 and GAP-43 (neuromodulin) as major protein components in a Triton insoluble low density fraction of rat brain. *Biochim. Biophys. Acta* 1323:1–5

Massagué J. 1996. Crossing receptor boundaries. *Nature* 382:29–30

Maxfield FR, Mayor S. 1997. Cell surface dynamics of GPI-anchored proteins. *Adv. Exp. Med. Biol.* 419:355–64

Mayor S, Maxfield FR. 1995a. Insolubility and redistribution of GPI-anchored proteins at the cell surface after detergent treatment. *Mol. Biol. Cell.* 6:929–44

Mayor S, Maxfield FR. 1995b. Cholesterol-dependent sorting of GPI-anchored proteins in endosomes. *Mol. Biol. Cell.* 6:231a (Abstr.)

Mayor S, Rothberg KG, Maxfield FR. 1994. Sequestration of GPI-anchored proteins in caveolae triggered by cross-linking. *Science* 264:1948–51

Mays RW, Siemers KA, Fritz BA, Lowe AW, van Meer G, et al. 1995. Hierarchy of mechanisms involved in generating Na/K-ATPase polarity in MDCK epithelial cells. *J. Cell Biol.* 130:1105–15

McConville MJ, Ferguson MAJ. 1993. The structure, biosynthesis and function of glycosylated phosphatidylinositols in the parasitic protozoa and higher eukaryotes. *Biochem. J.* 294:305–24

Melkonian KA, Chu T, Tortorella LB, Brown DA. 1995. Characterization of proteins in detergent-resistant membrane complexes from Madin-Darby canine kidney epithelial cells. *Biochemistry* 34:16161–70

Milligan G, Parenti M, Magee AI. 1995. The dynamic role of palmitoylation in signal transduction. *Trends Biochem. Sci.* 20:181–87

Morales G, Hubert M, Brümmendorf T, Treubert U, Tárnok A, et al. 1993. Induction of axonal growth by heterophilic interactions between the cell surface recognition proteins

F11 and Nr-CAM/Bravo. *Neuron* 11:1113–22

Morgan BP, van den Berg CW, Davies EV, Hallett MB, Horejsi V. 1993. Cross-linking of CD59 and of other glycosyl phosphatidylinositol-anchored molecules on neutrophils triggers cell activation via tyrosine kinase. *Eur. J. Immunol.* 23:2841–50

Munro S. 1995. An investigation of the role of transmembrane domains in Golgi protein retention. *EMBO J.* 14:4695–704

Naslavsky N, Stein R, Yanai A, Friedlander G, Taraboulos A. 1997. Characterization of detergent-insoluble complexes containing the cellular prion protein and its scrapie isoform. *J. Biol. Chem.* 272:6324–31

Nieva JL, Bron R, Corver J, Wilschut J. 1994. Membrane fusion of Semliki forest virus requires sphingolipids in the target membrane. *EMBO J.* 13:2797–2804

Oka N, Yamamoto M, Schwencke C, Kawabe J-i, Ebina T, et al. 1997. Caveolin interaction with protein kinase C. *J. Biol. Chem.* 272:33416–21

Okamoto T, Schlegel A, Scherer PE, Lisanti MP. 1998. Caveolins: a family of scaffolding proteins for organizing pre-assembled signaling complexes at the plasma membrane. *J. Biol. Chem.* 273:5419–22

Olive S, Dubois C, Schachner M, Rougon G. 1995. The F3 neuronal glycosylphosphatidylinositol-linked molecule is localized to glycolipid-enriched membrane subdomains and interacts with L1 and Fyn kinase in cerebellum. *J. Neurochem.* 65:2307–17

Parton RG. 1994. Ultrastructural localization of gangliosides; GM1 is concentrated in caveolae. *J. Histochem. Cytochem.* 42:155–66

Parton RG. 1996. Caveolae and caveolins. *Curr. Opin. Cell Biol.* 8:542–48

Patton JL, Lester RL. 1991. The phosphoinositol sphingolipids of *Saccharomyces cerevisiae* are highly localized in the plasma membrane. *J. Bacteriol.* 173:3101–8

Peles E, Nativ M, Lustig M, Grumet M, Schilling J, et al. 1997. Identification of a novel contactin-associated transmembrane receptor with multiple domains implicated in protein-protein interactions. *EMBO J.* 16:978–88

Phalen T, Kielian M. 1991. Cholesterol is required for infection by Semliki forest virus. *J. Cell Biol.* 112:615–23

Pike LJ, Casey L. 1996. Localization and turnover of phosphatidylinositol 4,5-bisphosphate in caveolin-enriched membrane domains. *J. Biol. Chem.* 271:26453–56

Planus E, Barlovatz-Meimon G, Rogers RA, Bonavaud S, Ingber DE, et al. 1997. Binding of urokinase to plasminogen activator type-1 mediates cell adhesion and spreading. *J. Cell Sci.* 110:1091–98

Ren J, Lew S, Wang Z, London E. 1997. Transmembrane orientation of hydrophobic α-helices is regulated both by the relationship of helix length to bilayer thickness and by the cholesterol concentration. *Biochemistry* 36:10213–20

Resh MD. 1994. Myristylation and palmitylation of Src family members: the fats of the matter. *Cell* 76:411–13

Rietveld A, Simons K. 1998. The differential miscibility of lipids as the basis for the formation of functional membrane rafts. *Biochim. Biophys. Acta.* In press

Robbins SM, Quintrell NA, Bishop JM. 1995. Myristoylation and differential palmitoylation of the HCK protein-tyrosine kinases govern their attachment to membranes and association with caveolae. *Mol. Cell. Biol.* 15:3507–15

Robinson PJ. 1991. Phosphatidylinositol membrane anchors and T-cell activation. *Immunol. Today* 12:35–41

Rock P, Allietta M, Young WW Jr, Thompson TE, Tillack TW. 1990. Organization of glycosphingolipids in phosphatidylcholine bilayers: use of antibody molecules and Fab fragments as morphologic markers. *Biochemistry* 29:8484–90

Rodgers W, Crise B, Rose JK. 1994. Signals determining protein tyrosine kinase and glycosyl-phosphatidylinositol-anchored protein targeting to a glycolipid-enriched membrane fraction. *Mol. Cell. Biol.* 14:5384–91

Rodgers W, Rose JK. 1996. Exclusion of CD45 inhibits activity of p56^{lck} associated with glycolipid-enriched membrane domains. *J. Cell Biol.* 135:1515–24

Romagnoli P, Bron C. 1997. Phosphatidylinositol-based glycolipid-anchored proteins enhance proximal TCR signaling events. *J. Immunol.* 158:5757–64

Rothberg KG, Heuser JE, Donzell WC, Ying Y-S, Glenney JR, Anderson RGW. 1992. Caveolin, a protein component of caveolae membrane coats. *Cell* 68:673–82

Sandvig K, Garred O, van Helvoort A, van Meer G, van Deurs B. 1996. Importance of glycolipid synthesis for butyric acid-induced sensitization to Shiga toxin and intracellular sorting of toxin in A431 cells. *Mol. Biol. Cell.* 7:1391–404

Sargiacomo M, Sudol M, Tang Z, Lisanti MP. 1993. Signal transducing molecules and glycosyl-phosphatidylinositol-linked proteins form a caveolin-rich insoluble complex in MDCK cells. *J. Cell Biol.* 122:789–807

Schmidt CF, Barenholz Y, Huang C, Thompson TE. 1978. Monolayer coupling in sphingomyelin bilayer systems. *Nature* 271:775–77

Schnitzer JE, McIntosh DP, Dvorak AM, Liu J, Oh P. 1995. Separation of caveolae from associated microdomains of GPI-anchored proteins. *Science* 269:1435–39

Schroeder RJ, Ahmed SN, Zhu Y, London E, Brown DA. 1998. Cholesterol and sphingolipid enhance the Triton X-100-insolubility of GPI-anchored proteins by promoting the formation of detergent-insoluble ordered membrane domains. *J. Biol. Chem.* 273:1150–57

Schroeder R, London E, Brown DA. 1994. Interactions between saturated acyl chains confer detergent resistance on lipids and GPI-anchored proteins: GPI-anchored proteins in liposomes and cells show similar behavior. *Proc. Natl. Acad. Sci. USA* 91:12130–34

Sevinsky JR, Rao LVM, Ruf W. 1996. Ligand-induced protease receptor translocation into caveolae: a mechanism for regulating cell surface proteolysis of the tissue factor-dependent coagulation pathway. *J. Cell. Biol.* 133:293–304

Shakarjian MP, Eiseman E, Penhallow RC, Bolen JB. 1993. 3-hydroxy-3-methylglutaryl-coenzyme A reductase inhibition in a rat mast cell line. Impairment of tyrosine kinase-dependent signal transduction and the subsequent degranulation response. *J. Biol. Chem.* 268:15252–59

Shenoy-Scaria AM, Dietzen DJ, Kwong J, Link DC, Lublin DM. 1994. Cysteine3 of Src family protein tyrosine kinases determines palmitoylation and localization in caveolae. *J. Cell Biol.* 126:353–64

Silvius JR, del Guidice D, Lafleur M. 1996. Cholesterol at different bilayer concentrations can promote or antagonize lateral segregation of phospholipids of differing acyl chain length. *Biochemistry* 35:15198–208

Simionescu N, Lupu F, Simionescu M. 1983. Rings of membrane sterols surround the openings of vesicles and fenestrae, in capillary endothelium. *J. Cell Biol.* 97:1592–600

Simons K, Ikonen E. 1997. Functional rafts in cell membranes. *Nature* 387:569–72

Simons K, van Meer G. 1988. Lipid sorting in epithelial cells. *Biochemistry* 27:6197–202

Skrzypek M, Lester RL, Dickson RC. 1997. Suppressor gene analysis reveals an essential role for sphingolipids in transport of glycosylphosphatidylinositol-anchored proteins in *Saccharomyces cerevisiae*. *J. Bacteriol.* 179:1513–20

Smart EJ, Ying Y-s, Donzell WC, Anderson RGW. 1996. A role for caveolin in transport of cholesterol from endoplasmic reticulum to plasma membrane. *J. Biol. Chem.* 271:29427–35

Smart EJ, Ying Y-s, Mineo C, Anderson RGW. 1995. A detergent-free method for purifying caveolae membrane from tissue culture cells. *Proc. Natl. Acad. Sci. USA* 92:10104–8

Spink CH, Yeager MD, Feigenson GW. 1990. Partitioning behavior of indocarbocyanine probes between coexisting gel and fluid phases in model membranes. *Biochim. Biophys. Acta* 1023:25–33

Stahl A, Mueller BM. 1995. The urokinase-type plasminogen activator receptor, a GPI-linked protein, is localized in caveolae. *J. Cell Biol.* 129:335–44

Stan R-V, Roberts WG, Predescu D, Ihida K, Saucan L, et al. 1997. Immunoisolation and partial characterization of endothelial plasmalemmal vesicles (caveolae). *Mol. Biol. Cell.* 8:595–605

Stang E, Kartenbeck J, Parton RG. 1997. Major histocompatibility complex Class I molecules mediate association of SV40 with caveolae. *Mol. Biol. Cell.* 8:47–57

Stauffer TP, Meyer T. 1997. Compartmentalized IgE receptor-mediated signal transduction in living cells. *J. Cell Biol.* 139:1447–54

Steer CJ, Bisher M, Blumenthal R, Steven AC. 1984. Detection of membrane cholesterol by filipin in isolated rat liver coated vesicles is dependent upon removal of the clathrin coat. *J. Cell Biol.* 99:315–19

Stockinger H. 1997. Interaction of GPI-anchored cell surface proteins and complement receptor type 3. *Exp. Clin. Immunogenet.* 14:5–10

Stulnig TM, Berger M, Sigmund T, Stockinger H, Horejsí V, et al. 1997. Signal transduction via glycosyl phosphatidylinositol-anchored proteins in T cells is inhibited by lowering cellular cholesterol. *J. Biol. Chem.* 272:19242–47

Sütterlin C, Doering TL, Schimmöller F, Schröeder S, Riezman H. 1997. Specific requirements for the ER to Golgi transport of GPI-anchored proteins in yeast. *J. Cell Sci.* 110:2703–14

Thomas JL, Holowka D, Baird B, Webb WW. 1994. Large scale co-aggregation of fluorescent lipid probes with cell surface proteins. *J. Cell Biol.* 125:795–802

Thompson TE, Tillack TW. 1985. Organization of glycosphingolipids in bilayers and plasma membranes of mammalian cells. *Annu. Rev. Biophys. Chem.* 14:361–86

Todd RF III, Petty HR. 1997. Beta 2 (CD11/CD18) integrins can serve as signaling partners for other leukocyte receptors. *J. Lab. Clin. Med.* 129:492–98

Tran D, Carpentier J-L, Sawano F, Gorden P, Orci L. 1987. Ligands internalized through coated or noncoated invaginations follow a common intracellular pathway. *Proc. Natl. Acad. Sci. USA* 84:7957–61

Unkeless JC, Shen Z, Lin C-W, DeBeus E. 1995.

Function of human FcγRIIA and FcγRIIIB. *Semin. Immunol.* 7:37–44

van den Berg CW, Cinek T, Hallett MB, Horejsí V, Morgan BP. 1995. Exogenous glycosyl phosphatidylinositol-anchored CD59 associates with kinases in membrane clusters on U937 cells and becomes Ca^{2+}-signaling competent. *J. Cell Biol.* 131:669–77

Wary KK, Mainiero F, Isakoff SJ, Marcantonio EE, Giancotti FG. 1996. The adaptor protein Shc couples a class of integrins to the control of cell cycle progression. *Cell* 87:733–43

Webb RJ, East JM, Sharma RP, Lee AG. 1998. Hydrophobic mismatch and the incorporation of peptides into lipid bilayers: a possible mechanism for retention in the Golgi. *Biochemistry* 37:673–79

Wei Y, Lukashev M, Simon DI, Bodary SC, Rosenberg S, et al. 1996. Regulation of integrin function by the urokinase receptor. *Science* 273:1551–55

Weimbs T, Low SH, Chapin SJ, Mostov KE. 1997. Apical targeting in polarized epithelial cells: there's more afloat than rafts. *Trends Cell Biol.* 7:393–99

Wu C, Butz S, Ying Y-s, Anderson RGW. 1997. Tyrosine kinase receptors concentrated in caveolae-like domains from neuronal plasma membrane. *J. Biol. Chem.* 272:3554–59

Yeaman C, le Gall AH, Baldwin AN, Monlauzeur L, le Bivic A, et al. 1997. The O-glycosylated stalk domain is required for apical sorting of neurotrophin receptors in polarized MDCK cells. *J. Cell Biol.* 139:929–40

Yebra M, Parry GCN, Strömblad S, Mackman N, Rosenberg S, et al. 1996. Requirement of receptor-bound urokinase-type plasminogen activator for integrin $\alpha v \beta 5$-directed cell migration. *J. Biol. Chem.* 271:29393–99

Zhang X, Thompson GA Jr. 1997. An apparent association between glycosylphosphatidylinositol-anchored proteins and a sphingolipid in *Tetrahymena mimbres. Biochem. J.* 323:197–206

Zisch AH, D'Alessandri L, Amrein K, Ranscht B, Winterhalter KH, et al. 1995. The glypiated neuronal cell adhesion molecule contactin/F11 complexes with Src-family protein tyrosine kinase Fyn. *Mol. Cell. Neurosci.* 6:263–79

Annu. Rev. Cell Dev. Biol. 1998. 14:137–66

INTRACELLULAR PATHOGENS AND THE ACTIN CYTOSKELETON

S. Dramsi and P. Cossart

Unité des Interactions Bactéries-Cellules, Institut Pasteur, 28 rue du Dr. Roux, 75724 Paris, Cedex 15, France; e-mail: pcossart@pasteur.fr

KEY WORDS: invasion, phagocytosis, signal transduction, phospholipids, actin-based motility

ABSTRACT

Many pathogens actively exploit the actin cytoskeleton during infection. This exploitation may take place during entry into mammalian cells after engagement of a receptor and/or as series of signaling events culminating in the engulfment of the microorganism. Although actin rearrangements are a common feature of most internalization events (e.g. entry of *Listeria, Salmonella, Shigella, Yersinia, Neisseria,* and *Bartonella*), bacterial and other cellular factors involved in entry are specific to each bacterium. Another step during which pathogens harness the actin cytoskeleton takes place in the cytosol, within which some bacteria (*Listeria, Shigella, Rickettsia*) or viruses (vaccinia virus) are able to move. Movement is coupled to a polarized actin polymerization process, with the formation of characteristic actin tails. Increasing attention has focused on this phenomenon due to its striking similarity to cellular events occurring at the leading edge of locomoting cells. Thus pathogens are convenient systems in which to study actin cytoskeleton rearrangements in response to stimuli at the plasma membrane or inside cells.

CONTENTS

137

1081-0706/98/1115-0137$08.00

INTRODUCTION

The cytoskeleton is a dynamic network of intracellular proteinaceous structural elements responsible for cell shape, motility, migration, polarity, and maintenance of intercellular contacts involved in tissue architecture. The many roles played by the cytoskeleton are mainly due to its capacity to continuously assemble or disassemble. The basic building blocks of the cytoskeleton include actin filaments (about 7 nm in diameter), microtubules (about 25 nm in diameter), and a variety of intermediate filaments (about 10 nm in diameter). Each filament type is composed of linear polymers of globular protein subunits that are assembled and disassembled in a precisely regulated fashion, sometimes at astonishing rates.

The high plasticity of the cytoskeleton is often exploited by pathogens during entry into cells, which are normally non-phagocytic, and in some cases during dissemination of these pathogens in cells and tissues. The role of microtubules has been recognized in only a few cases (Donnenberg et al 1990, Oelschlaeger et al 1993, Kuhn 1998). It is mainly the actin cytoskeleton that appears to play a critical role in infection and is the topic of this review.

Monomeric actin (G-actin) is a 43-kDa globular protein. In vitro studies have shown that actin filament (F-actin) assembly starts with the formation of a thermodynamically unstable trimer that rapidly grows into a filament by addition of new monomers. In the assembly process, trimer formation, also called the nucleation step, is the rate-limiting event. The two ends of the actin filament are structurally and functionally different. Growth of actin filaments is five to ten times faster at the $(+)$ ends, the barbed ends, than at the $(-)$ ends, or pointed ends. Within the cell, actin polymerization is highly controlled by actin-sequestering proteins, as well as by capping proteins. Other actin-binding proteins are able to cross-link or bundle or sever actin filaments. Often, these actin-binding proteins have several functions, depending on the ligand bound (Ca^{2+} or PIP2). No nucleator of actin has been isolated thus far.

The first part of this review describes the different strategies devised by invasive bacteria to exploit the dynamic properties of the actin cytoskeleton in order to promote their internalization. The second part discusses what is currently known about the actin-based motility of some intracellular pathogens. Both types of actin cytoskeleton subversion, i.e. actin reorganization during entry and bacterially induced actin assembly during intra- and intercellular movement, may likely contribute to a better understanding of actin rearrangements in response to ligand receptor signaling or to other stimuli.

BACTERIAL ENTRY INTO MAMMALIAN CELLS

Many pathogenic microorganisms have the capacity to induce their own uptake into non-phagocytic mammalian cells. The entry process is similar to phagocytosis and requires reorganization of the actin cytoskeleton underlying the plasma membrane that contacts the pathogen. Exploitation of the cytoskeleton by pathogenic bacteria during entry can be divided into two general mechanisms according to the type of morphological changes that occur in the host cell. These mechanisms—the zipper and trigger—were first proposed for particle phagocytosis (Swanson & Baer 1995). Entry of *Yersinia, Listeria,* and *Neisseria* into epithelial cells, which does not result in major remodeling of the cell surface, is reminiscent of the classical model of zipper phagocytosis of erythocytes by macrophages, via the Fc receptor (Figure 1). The zipper model implies interaction of a bacterial ligand with a host cell receptor. In contrast, entry of *Salmonella* or *Shigella* into epithelial cells and macrophages indicates

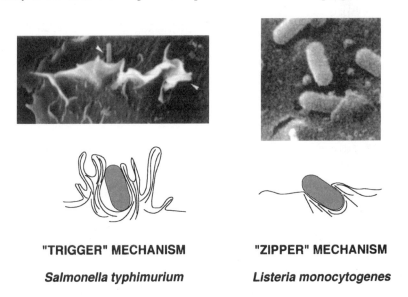

"TRIGGER" MECHANISM   **"ZIPPER" MECHANISM**

Salmonella typhimurium   *Listeria monocytogenes*

Figure 1   The two mechanisms of phagocytosis induced by bacterial pathogens. (*Top left*) *Salmonella*-induced ruffles during entry into epithelial cell. (*Top right*) Entry of *L. monocytogenes* into epithelial cells by a zipper mechanism (adapted with permission from Mengaud et al 1996). (*Bottom drawings*) Schematic diagram of phagocytosis by zipper and trigger mechanisms.

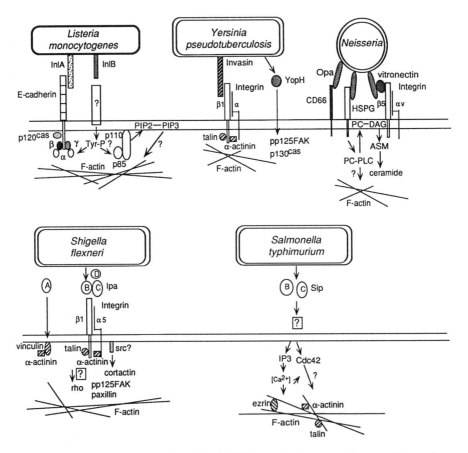

Figure 2 Schematic representation of the initial interactions between pathogen and host cell leading to bacterial uptake (for details, see text).

an indiscriminately triggered response that mimics the membrane ruffling induced by growth factors (Figures 1 and 2). In the trigger model, the nature of the interaction between the host cell and the pathogen may be more complex. For example, the pathogen may direct the delivery of a protein into the mammalian cytosol where it can exert a direct effect on the host cytoskeleton, resulting in rapid actin rearrangements leading to uptake. Recent work has shown that several host signaling pathways (tyrosine phosphorylation, lipid metabolism, activation of small G proteins) may lead to these actin rearrangements and that pathogens have evolved various strategies to induce their uptake by mammalian cells (Finlay & Cossart 1997, Ireton & Cossart 1998).

Entry Via a Zipper Mechanism

LISTERIA   *Listeria monocytogenes* is the etiologic agent of listeriosis, a disease whose features are meningitis, meningo-encephalitis, and abortions. This bacterium is characterized in vivo as well as in vitro by its capacity to enter a wide variety of cell types (Ireton & Cossart 1997). Two bacterial surface proteins involved in entry of *L. monocytogenes* into cultured cells are known, InlA (internalin) and InlB. InlA is a 80-kDa protein that contains a region of leucine-rich repeats (LLRs). It is needed for entry into the human intestinal epithelial cell line Caco-2. Expression of InlA in the non-invasive bacterium *Listeria innocua* renders this organism capable of invading Caco-2 cells, suggesting that InlA may be sufficient for entry (Gaillard et al 1991, Dramsi et al 1993, 1995). Recently, uptake of InlA-coated beads into cells expressing the InlA receptor showed that InlA is indeed sufficient (Lecuit et al 1997).

The InlA receptor is E-cadherin, a 110-kDa glycoprotein responsible for Ca^{2+}-dependent cell-cell adhesion through homophilic interactions (Mengaud et al 1996). E-cadherin is expressed primarily in epithelial tissues and plays a critical role in cell sorting during development and in maintenance of adult tissue architecture (Näthke et al 1995). The only other known heterophilic ligand for E-cadherin is the $\alpha_E\beta_7$ integrin, which mediates adhesion between intraepithelial lymphocytes and enterocytes (Cepek et al 1994, Karecla et al 1995). In polarized epithelial cells, E-cadherin is localized mainly at the basolateral membrane and is concentrated at the adherens junctions (Boller et al 1985, Cepek et al 1994). In agreement with this distribution, InlA-mediated entry occurs primarily at the basolateral face in Caco-2 cells (Temm-Grove et al 1994, Gaillard & Finlay 1996).

The extracellular region of E-cadherin consists of five modules (Overduin et al 1995, Shapiro et al 1995). The sequence HAV located in the first module is thought to be needed for homophilic interactions (Takeichi 1996). The cytoplasmic domain of E-cadherin associates with the catenins, which interact with the actin cytoskeleton. The presence of the cytoplasmic domain is essential for strong homophilic cell-cell interactions. Interestingly, this region is not required for interaction between $\alpha_E\beta_7$ and E-cadherin (Karecla et al 1996). Recent results indicate that the cytoplasmic domain of E-cadherin is not required for InlA-mediated adhesion but is required for efficient internalization, suggesting that InlA-mediated entry requires the catenins (M Lecuit, S Dramsi & P Cossart, unpublished results). The extracellular region of E-cadherin interacting with InlA is not known.

InlB, a 67-kDa protein homologous to InlA, also contains a LLR region. InlB mediates entry into a wide variety of cells, including cultured hepatocytes, and in epithelial or fibroblastic cell lines such as HEp-2, HeLa, Vero, CHO, and L2 (Dramsi et al 1995, 1997; Ireton et al 1996). Coating of normally non-invasive bacteria or inert latex beads with InlB leads to internalization into mammalian cells (Braun et al 1998). InlB, similar to InlA, is thus sufficient to promote internalization. The InlB receptor has not been identified.

Tyrosine phosphorylation and cytoskeletal rearrangements are required for both InlA- and InlB-mediated entry because inhibitors of tyrosine kinases (genistein) and actin polymerization (cytochalasin D) impair bacterial internalization (Gaillard et al 1987, Tang et al 1994, Velge et al 1994). However, the kinases involved have not been identified. Note that neither tyrosine kinase inhibitors nor cytochalasin D inhibit bacterial adhesion, highlighting the role of the actin cytoskeleton in uptake. Another signaling protein needed for entry, but not adhesion, is the phosphoinositide PI 3-kinase p85α-p110, as shown by a decrease in entry after transfection with a dominant-negative form of p85, and upon cell pretreatment with PI 3-kinase inhibitors such as wortmannin or LY2924002 (Ireton et al 1996). Inhibition of entry is cell-type dependent with a maximal effect in Vero cells. In these cells, PI 3-kinase is activated upon entry, leading to rapid increases in the lipid products of PI 3-kinase. This activation requires InlB, tyrosine phosphorylation in the host cell, and association of p85α with one or more tyrosine phosphorylated proteins. Pretreatment of Vero cells with cytochalasin D does not impair activation of PI 3-kinase, suggesting that stimulation of this kinase is obtained by extracellular adhesive bacteria and precedes cytoskeletal rearrangements (Ireton et al 1996). How activation of PI 3-kinase stimulates entry of *L. monocytogenes* is unknown. One attractive possibility, recently shown in platelets, is that the lipid products of PI 3-kinase may directly affect actin assembly by uncapping barbed ends of actin filaments (Hartwig et al 1995, 1996). Increasing evidence also suggests that one important role of PI 3-kinase products is to recruit proteins at the plasma membrane. PH or SH2-domain–containing proteins are known to bind to PI(3,4,5)P$_3$ (Toker & Cantley 1997). During entry of *L. monocytogenes*, this type of protein could be responsible for the rearrangements of the actin cytoskeleton. It is also known that PI 3-kinase can interact with the small GTPase Rac (Tolias et al 1995). This interaction may also be involved in the cytoskeletal changes needed for entry.

YERSINIA   The first and best-studied invasion system is that of the enteropathogenic bacterium *Yersinia pseudotuberculosis*, which uses a 986–amino acid outer membrane protein, called invasin, to enter into mammalian cells (Isberg et al 1987). Internalization of *Escherichia coli*–expressing invasin or of invasin-coated beads by cultured epithelial cells was the first demonstration that a bacterial factor by itself is sufficient to mediate uptake (for a review, see Isberg &

Tran Van Nhieu 1995). The cellular receptor for invasin was identified as a $\beta 1$ subunit–containing integrin (Isberg & Leong 1990). Integrins are heterodimers made of a combination of α and β chains. They mediate cell-cell interactions and adhesion to the extracellular matrix. Invasin binds to its receptor with an $\approx$100-fold higher affinity than do the natural ligands such as fibronectin. This high-affinity binding of invasin to $\beta 1$ integrins guides extension of the membrane around the bacterium to form a tight-fitting phagosome that internalizes the bacterium in a zipper-like process. The efficiency of internalization correlates with both the affinity of invasin for integrin and the densities of ligand and receptor present on the bacterium and the cell surface, respectively (Tran Van Nhieu & Isberg 1993).

Invasin-mediated entry is inhibited by cytochalasin D (Finlay & Falkow 1988). It was thus speculated that direct association of integrins with the cytoskeleton would be critical for internalization. Experiments using chimeric receptors demonstrated that the 47 amino acids of the $\beta 1$ cytoplasmic domain contain sufficient information to target integrins to adhesion plaques. Talin and α-actinin, two cytoplasmic proteins localized in focal adhesions, appear to interact directly with this $\beta 1$ domain (Horwitz et al 1986, Otey et al 1993). Interestingly, mutations in the $\beta 1$ cytoplasmic domain that reduce interaction with the cytoskeleton increase bacterial uptake, whereas mutations that impair bacterial uptake are in the NPIY sequence, a signature of clathrin-mediated endocytosis. Replacement of this NPIY motif by another endocytosis internalization sequence, PPGY, resulted in efficient integrin-mediated bacterial internalization. In agreement with these data, endocytic factors including clathrin and the adaptor protein AP-2, as shown by electron microscopy, are found beneath bacteria in the early stages of internalization. Moreover, inhibition experiments with anti-AP-2-antibodies also indicate a role for clathrin-mediated endocytosis in integrin-mediated bacterial internalization (Tran Van Nhieu et al 1996). Although actin is involved in bacterial entry, the role of this endocytotic pathway remains to be defined. In fact, internalization of $\alpha_5\beta_1$ integrins through clathrin-mediated endocytosis is also unclear. The two NPXY motifs present in the $\beta 1$ cytoplasmic domain are not responsible for the $\alpha_5\beta_1$ integrin endocytosis in CHO cells (Vignoud et al 1994), and a recent report indicates that these motifs are required for the recruitment of integrins in focal adhesions but are not the talin-binding sites (Vignoud et al 1997).

Signal transduction via tyrosine phosphorylation is needed because inhibitors of tyrosine kinase prevent entry (Rosenshine et al 1992). Two of the tyrosine-phosphorylated proteins that act downstream of integrin engagement during invasion by *Yersinia* are p130^{cas} and focal adhesion kinase (FAK). These proteins are normally present in focal adhesions. They colocalize with integrins, participate in integrin-mediated signaling, and were recently identified as targets of an anti-phagocytic mechanism used by *Yersinia* to prevent internalization (Black & Bliska 1997, Persson et al 1997). Direct evidence for the role of these proteins in invasin-mediated entry will need further study.

NEISSERIA   Entry of *Neisseria gonorrhoeae* into human epithelial cells is multifactorial (for a recent review, see Jerse & Rest 1997). Initial attachment is mediated by pili, followed by tight adherence via the phase-variable colony opacity (Opa) proteins. Opa proteins are a family of 11 outer membrane proteins variably expressed at the surface of the bacterium (Bhat et al 1991, Chen et al 1992). However, only one Opa protein, called OpaA or Opa30 or Opa50, confers invasion into epithelial cells (Makino et al 1991, Simon & Rest 1992, Kupsch et al 1993). This entry is mediated by heparan sulfate proteoglycan (HSPG) receptors of the syndecan family expressed on the target cell surface (Chen et al 1995, Van Putten & Paul 1995). However, in CHO cells, interaction between OpaA and HSPG promotes only adhesion without internalization. Interestingly, it has been shown that the presence of serum-derived vitronectin allows entry of *N. gonorrhoeae* into CHO cells. In fact, OpaA can bind purified vitronectin and may drive bacterial internalization through the vitronectin receptor (Duensing & Van Putten 1997, Gomez-Duarte et al 1997).

Other Opa proteins such as Opa52 permit interaction with phagocytic cells. Several reports identified the receptors of these Opa proteins as members of the CD66 family (Chen & Gotschlich 1996, Virji et al 1996, Chen et al 1997, Bos et al 1997, Gray-Owen et al 1997). These receptor molecules, members of the immunoglobulin superfamily, are also present in epithelial cells. Thus multiple interactions may occur in epithelial cells, and these interactions may vary with the cell lines used or with the Opas expressed.

In Chang conjunctiva epithelial cells, Opa-dependent internalization is blocked by cytochalasin D. However, the local bacterium-associated accumulation of F-actin that accompanies Opa-mediated uptake is not affected by cytochalasin D treatment (Grassmé et al 1996). Whether the highly efficient recruitment of F-actin by gonococci involves a clustering of cytochalasin D–insensitive cortical (perhaps receptor-linked) actin filaments or whether cytochalasin D treatment is not absolutely efficient remains to be determined (Grassmé et al 1996). A recent report demonstrates a role for lipid metabolism in entry of *N. gonorrhoeae* into epithelial cells. Infection results in activation of phosphatidylcholine-specific phospholipase C (PC-PLC) and production of diacylglycerol (DAG), which in turn leads to stimulation of acidic sphingomyelinase (ASM). Pharmacological and genetic studies suggest that production of ceramide by ASM is required for invasion by *N. gonorrhoeae* (Grassmé et al 1997). It is presently unclear how this lipid affects neisserial invasion. How the Opa-HSPG interaction is coupled to these enzymes and whether the lipids produced play a role in actin cytoskeleton rearrangements are also not understood. In mammalian cells, rearrangements of actin cytoskeleton mediated by ligand-receptor interaction leading to membrane ruffling, actin stress fiber formation, or filopodia formation are controlled by small GTP-binding proteins of the Rho family (Rac, Rho, and Cdc42) (Hall 1998). Recently, these proteins have also been shown to play a role in phagocytosis (Cox et al 1997, Hackam et al 1997). It was anticipated that invasive bacteria might regulate rho GTPases to induce cytoskeletal changes needed for uptake. In neutrophils, the GTPase Rac is activated upon infection with *Neisseria*, and Rac activity is needed for efficient CD66-mediated uptake. Rac activation appears to be controlled by Src-family kinases (Hauck et al 1998). It has not been reported whether invasion of epithelial cells by *N. gonorrhoeae* also involves Rac and Src kinases.

Entry Via a Trigger-Type Mechanism

SALMONELLA   In contrast to *Listeria* and *Yersinia*, the mechanisms of *Salmonella* entry appear more complex. On the bacterial side, more than 20 gene products are necessary to trigger uptake (Galan 1996). On the cellular side, on initial contact *Salmonella typhimurium* enacts a dramatic response on the epithelial cell surface, characterized by large membrane projections similar to membrane ruffles induced by some growth factors or oncogenes (Francis et al 1992, 1993; Alpuche-Aranda et al 1994). Cytoskeletal rearrangements culminate in the formation of plasma membrane projections that lead to bacterial engulfment and passive entry of other bacteria or particles located in the vicinity of these highly dynamic membranes in a process similar to macropinocytosis (Francis et al 1992, 1993, Alpuche-Aranda et al 1994).

S. typhimurium has multiple genetic loci involved in invasion that are clustered in one region on its chromosome called a pathogenicity island SPI1 (Galan 1996). Many of the bacterial proteins required for uptake of *Salmonella* comprise a type III secretion system. This apparatus, constituted by the *inv/spa/prg* loci, is found in many gram-negative pathogens and allows the localized translocation of effector proteins onto or inside a mammalian cell (for a review, see Galan & Bliska 1996). Proteins secreted by such systems lack typical signal sequences, are not processed during translocation, and do not have a periplasmic intermediate. It is clear that most of the *inv/spa/prg* loci of *S. typhimurium* encode products that share significant homology with products of other pathogenic species. Indeed, several *Shigella* virulence genes can complement non-invasive mutations of *S. typhimurium* (Hermant et al 1995, Hueck et al 1995). To date, by analogy with the situation in *Shigella,* two proteins secreted via the specialized type III secretion system are candidates for effectors of *S. typhimurium* entry into a host cell: SipB and SipC (Kaniga et al 1995). Direct evidence for the involvement of these proteins in invasion and cytoskeleton rearrangements awaits further study.

The receptor(s) to which *Salmonella*-secreted proteins bind is unknown. Invasion of Henle-407 cells by *S. typhimurium* has been associated with tyrosine phosphorylation of the epidermal growth factor (EGF) receptor (Galan et al 1992). Further studies indicated that the EGF receptor is not required for *Salmonella* internalization and that activation of this receptor is probably an indirect phenomenon (Francis et al 1993, Jones et al 1993). *S. typhimurium* initiates a cascade of host cell signaling events that lead to uptake. Increases in inositol phosphates, calcium fluxes, and changes in lipid metabolism have been implicated in *Salmonella* entry (Black et al 1993, Pace et al 1993). It seems likely that the bacterium stimulates host phospholipase C, thus inducing IP_3 production, which in turn mobilizes Ca^{2+} from intracellular stores. Calcium fluxes could affect uptake by controlling activities of various actin-binding proteins such as α-actinin, talin, and ezrin, which are recruited to the site of entry (Finlay & Ruschkowski 1991). A recent study indicates that Cdc42 is required in *Salmonella*-induced internalization (Chen et al 1996). A minor role has been attributed to Rac, whereas Rho is not required. The mechanism of activation of Cdc42 is not known, but it probably does not involve tyrosine phosphorylation because tyrosine kinase inhibitors do not significantly block entry (Rosenshine et al 1992). It is presently not clear how all these signaling events are related and what the precise sequence of events is that leads to bacterial internalization. Note that *Salmonella* seems to be insensitive to inhibitors that affect entry of most other bacteria, including tyrosine kinase inhibitors. It is also insensitive to wortmannin, which apparently increases the level of entry (Ireton et al 1996).

SHIGELLA   *Shigella* invasion into epithelial cells closely resembles *Salmonella* invasion, although the two bacteria in vivo target different cells. Internalization results from the coalescence of many membrane projections that, as in the case of *Salmonella*, first surround the bacterial body. These cellular projections are sustained by bundles of parallel actin filaments, whose positive ends are pointing to the tip of the projections (Adam et al 1995). Massive actin polymerization at the sites of bacterial entry characterizes *Shigella* internalization. Myosin S1 decoration of actin filaments has revealed discrete actin nucleation sites in close proximity to the contact site underneath the pathogen. These nucleation sites are where long actin filaments are assembled and bundled (Adam et al 1995). Fimbrin appears to play a key role in this process (see below). Several other cytoskeleton-associated proteins are recruited to the foci of *Shigella* entry. Some are well-known components of focal adhesion plaques including vinculin, paxillin, talin, α-actinin and pp125[FAK], whereas others are associated with the cortical actin network, such as cortactin, or with the brush border, such as plastin/fimbrin and ezrin. Plastin, which has a well-characterized actin-bundling activity, was shown to be involved in *Shigella*-induced membrane extensions, through the use of cells transfected with a dominant-negative form of plastin (Adam et al 1995). A recent report indicates that vinculin, a protein involved in indirectly linking actin filaments to the plasma membrane, is involved in efficient uptake of *Shigella* (Tran Van Nhieu et al 1997). IpaA, a bacterial protein secreted upon cell contact (see below), rapidly associates with vinculin during bacterial invasion. Although an *ipaA* mutant recruits vinculin at the site of entry, it is impaired in recruitment of α-actinin, a vinculin actin-binding protein. It is probable that in the wild-type strain, the IpaA-vinculin interaction activates vinculin and initiates the formation of focal adhesion-like structures required for efficient invasion. The small G-protein Rho, known to be involved in focal adhesion plaques and stress fiber formation, is needed for *Shigella*-induced cytoskeletal rearrangements and bacterial internalization (Adam et al 1996, Watarai et al 1997). Cortactin, pp125^{FAK} and paxillin become tyrosine-phosphorylated proteins upon entry. Since tyrosine kinase inhibitors affect *Shigella* uptake (Dehio et al 1995, Watarai et al 1996), the proteins may play an important role during bacterial invasion. Interestingly, the proto-oncoprotein pp60^{c-src}, a protein tyrosine kinase involved in the regulation of the actin cytoskeleton, is also recruited to *Shigella*-induced membrane extensions, where it specifically phosphorylates one of its substrates, cortactin. In addition, transient overexpression of c-*src* in transfected cells induces membrane ruffling and stimulates entry of normally non-invasive *Shigella* mutants. However, a definitive role for pp60^{c-src} in *Shigella* entry has not been established.

On the bacterial side, IpaB, IpaC, and IpaD are the proteins originally identified as being required for entry (Ménard et al 1996a). These proteins are secreted by the Mxi/Spa translocon, which is a member of the type III secretion system. Ipa proteins are secreted upon contact with the host cell or in the presence of serum. This contact-mediated secretion seems to be a specific property of type III secretion systems. IpaB and IpaC associate into a soluble complex that can be immunopurified on latex beads. These beads are sufficient to cause membrane ruffling and can be internalized in HeLa cells (Ménard et al 1996b). The recent results with IpaA (Tran Van Nhieu et al 1997) suggest that IpaA acts in concert with and controls the effects of the IpaB-IpaC complex. Immunolocalization of IpaC during bead uptake showed that a proportion of this protein is detached from the beads and is found in endocytic vesicles at a distance from the internalized beads, suggesting that Ipa complexes can act as soluble effectors. One of the receptors that mediates *Shigella* entry is the $\alpha_5\beta_1$ integrin (Watarai et al 1996). A secreted complex of IpaB, IpaC, and IpaD proteins can interact with purified $\alpha_5\beta_1$ integrin, and transfection experiments in CHO cells demonstrate that increasing expression of this integrin increases the level of uptake of *Shigella*. In addition, clustering of $\alpha_5\beta_1$ integrins is observed near invading bacteria. The fact that this integrin is also the receptor for the invasin protein of *Yersinia* raises the possibility that the same receptor can be exploited in different ways to cause remarkably different mechanisms (zipper or trigger).

The Particular Case of Bartonella

Bartonella henselae is a newly recognized human pathogen shown to enter cultured epithelial cells by a process inhibited by cytochalasin D. Initial adherence is mediated by the expression of type IV-like pili, which in turn permits subsequent invasion (Batterman et al 1995). In general, bacterial pathogens are internalized as individuals, or occasionally as small groups of two or three cells. In contrast, entry of *B. henselae* was noted to occur by single cells or by large clumps (Batterman et al 1995, Dehio et al 1997). Dehio and colleagues have described this aggregate as an "invasome" in the entry of *B. henselae* in endothelial cells. This structure forms on the host cell and is slowly engulfed over a period of about 24 h by a mechanism that requires reorganization of the host cytoskeleton. A spontaneous mutant strain was found to be impaired in invasome formation, suggesting that the formation of invasomes is dependent on the expression of specific bacterial determinants. However, this mutant can still enter into endothelial cells by an alternative pathway, giving rise to intracellular bacteria residing in perinuclear localizing phagosomes. Entry by this alternative pathway, which is more rapid, is also observed with the wild-type strain. Interestingly, invasome-mediated internalization appears to down-regulate this alternative process of cell invasion. It will be interesting to see which type of internalization occurs in vivo (Dehio et al 1997).

ACTIN-BASED MOTILITY

Although rearrangements of the cytoskeleton appear as an absolute requirement for entry of most bacterial pathogens, the exploitation of the cytoskeleton at a later stage of the infection, i.e. during intracellular life, seems restricted to several intracellular bacteria, including *Listeria*, *Shigella*, and *Rickettsias*, that have the capacity to escape from the phagocytic vacuole. Once inside the host cytoplasm, bacteria both divide and induce the polymerization of host actin around them. This actin coat then rearranges into a tail located at one end of the bacterium. Actin assembly propels the bacteria inside the cytosol. When moving bacteria reach the plasma membrane, they push out long protrusions that are taken up by neighboring cells, allowing the infection to spread from cell to cell within tissues. As recently discovered, vaccinia virus can also move using this actin-based motility. These few pathogens appear as simplified models to study the molecular basis of cell motility. We discuss below the current hypothesis concerning the mechanisms by which these organisms succeed to polymerize actin and move. Since this field has been extensively reviewed recently (Theriot 1995, Cossart 1995, 1997, Lasa & Cossart 1996, Ireton & Cossart 1997, Smith & Portnoy 1997, Lasa et al 1998), we overview the phenomenon and pinpoint the most relevant questions.

Thermodynamics and Morphological Aspects of Actin-Based Movement

Video-microscopy has played a key role in demonstrating the direct coupling between actin polymerization and bacterial movement. In pioneering work Ogawa and colleagues (1968) first showed by phase-contrast time-lapse cine-matography that *Shigella flexneri* bacilli moved independently from the cellular organelles and could be seen at the tip of microfibrillar structures protruding from the host cell surface (Ogawa et al 1968). Genetic approaches then helped to identify a genetic locus required for this movement and demonstrated that this movement correlated with actin tails detected at one end of the *Shigella*. Formation of actin tails was totally inhibited by cytochalasin D (Makino et al 1986, Bernardini et al 1989). A similar phenomenon was discovered for *Listeria* (Tilney & Portnoy 1989, Mounier et al 1990). Listerial movement can take place in cytoplasmic extracts of *Xenopus laevis* eggs (Theriot et al 1994). The speed of bacterial movement and density profiles of actin tails in these extracts indicate that they provide a reasonable substitute for the cytoplasm of mammalian cells. Interestingly, *Rickettsia conorii* moves in these cytoplasmic extracts albeit slower than *Listeria* (V Villiers, E Gouin, I Lasa & P Cossart, unpublished data) whereas *S. flexneri* does not (Kocks et al 1995).

With a combination of video-microscopy and microinjection of rhodamine-labeled or photo-activated actin monomers (Dabiri et al 1990, Sanger et al 1992, Theriot et al 1992), it was established (*a*) that polymerization takes place at the rear of the bacterium and the newly formed actin tails remain stationary in the cytoplasm and (*b*) that the rate of incorporation of actin monomers approximates the rate of bacterial movement, suggesting that actin polymerization itself provides the energy for translocation. *Listeria* move at speeds ranging from 0.05 to 0.25 μm per s, and the tail length is linearly related to speed of movement. Measurements of fluorescence decay (rate of depolymerization) indicate that the half life of F-actin is identical among different tails and in various regions of a single tail.

The structure of the actin tail is a matter of debate. Tilney & Portnoy first observed that when the filaments are decorated with the S1 fragment of myosin, the arrowheads formed by the S1 fragment often point away from the bacteria, indicating that rapidly growing barbed ends are associated with or close to the bacterial surface. Moreover, in the actin tails, actin filaments generally appeared short, with an average length of 0.2 μm (about 73 actin monomers) (Tilney & Portnoy 1989, Tilney et al 1992a,b). Recently, Small and colleagues re-examined the structure of the tails (Sechi et al 1997). They observed that in the protrusions formed during cell-cell spread of the bacteria, the comet tail has a core of long axial filaments obscured in the proximal region close to the bacterium by a high density of randomly oriented, short filaments. Our unpublished observations indicate that in the cytosol, *Listeria* have heterogenous tails composed of a part close to the bacteria made of numerous short actin filaments and a second part made of longer actin filaments; these longer filaments, however, are shorter than those detected in the protrusions (H Gantelet, H Ohayon, E Gouin, I Lasa, P Gounon & P Cossart, unpublished data) (Figure 3). *Rickettsia* (Teysseire et al 1992, Heinzen et al 1993) and *Shigella* tails (Prévost et al 1992) appear different from those of *Listeria*, suggesting that these two bacteria behave differently from *Listeria. Rickettsia* comet tails are made of a restricted number of long actin filaments (V Villiers, H Gantelet, H Ohayon, E Gouin, I Lasa, P Gounon & P Cossart, unpublished results). Complete knowledge of the structure of the different actin tails will be of the utmost importance to understand the dynamics of the actin polymerization process.

The Bacterial Factors Involved in Actin-Based Motility

Isolation of mutants unable to induce actin polymerization allowed the identification of bacterial genes involved in this process: *actA* from *L. monocytogenes* (Domann et al 1992, Kocks et al 1992) and *icsA* (or *virG*) from *S. flexneri* (Bernardini et al 1989). The *iactA* gene from *L. ivanovii* was then isolated based on its homology with *actA* (Gouin et al 1995, Kreft et al 1995). The gene responsible for the actin polymerization process in *Rickettsia* is unknown.

The actA Gene of L. monocytogenes

The *actA* gene encodes a mature protein of 610 amino acids with a C-terminal hydrophobic region involved in anchoring to the bacterial membrane. ActA can be artificially divided into three domains: an N-terminal domain (1–234; amino acids numbering, as in Kocks et al 1992) that is highly charged, a central domain (235–395) with a striking succession of proline/glutamic acid-rich repeats, and a C-terminal region (396–555). Recent amino acid comparisons suggest that ActA might be a composite protein with similarities to domains in some eukaryotic proteins associated with actin cytoskeleton. The N-terminal domain of ActA has sequence similarity with the C-terminal actin-binding domain of human vinculin (Lasa et al 1998). The central proline-rich region shares some similarity with the proline-rich domain of vinculin and zyxin, and the C-terminal domain of ActA has sequence similarity with zyxin (Golsteyn et al 1997).

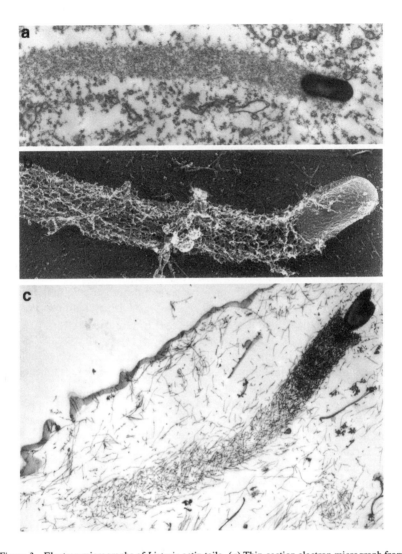

Figure 3   Electron micrographs of *Listeria* actin tails. (*a*) Thin-section electron micrograph from an infected tissue culture cell showing moving bacterium associated with an F-actin comet tail (reprinted with permission from Kocks et al 1992). (*b*) Three-dimensional visualization of actin comet tail by quick-freeze/deep-etch technique (Heuser 1980; micrograph courtesy of Heuser). (*c*) Thin section through a *Listeria* with a tail whose actin filaments have been decorated with subfragment 1 (S1) of myosin (Tilney & Tilney 1994).

ActA is a surface protein with a polar distribution on the bacterial body. It is present in maximal amounts at one pole and decreases in concentration toward the other (Kocks et al 1993). In infected cells, the ActA-expressing pole colocalizes with the site of actin assembly, suggesting that the ActA distribution predetermines actin assembly and movement in the direction of the non–ActA-expressing pole. ActA cannot be detected in the actin tail (Kocks et al 1992, Niebuhr et al 1993).

Tranfection of the *actA* gene in eukaryotic cells (Pistor et al 1994, Friederich et al 1995) and heterologous expression of *actA* in the non-pathogenic *L. innocua* (Kocks et al 1995) have unambiguously demonstrated that ActA is sufficient to induce actin assembly. In another approach, coating of *Streptococcus pneumoniae* with a recombinant ActA-LytA hybrid protein resulted in bacteria able to induce actin assembly in *Xenopus* eggs extracts but unable to move unless bacterial division had occurred that generated some polarization of ActA on the bacterial surface (Smith & Portnoy 1995). This experiment reinforced the view that the polar distribution of ActA on the bacterial surface is critical for movement.

Functional regions of ActA were identified either by transfection of various parts of *actA* in eukaryotic cells or by generating internal deletions in *actA* (Friederich et al 1995, Lasa et al 1995, Pistor et al 1995, Smith & Portnoy 1996). Results indicate that the C-terminal part is not involved in ActA function. The central proline-rich region is not absolutely essential either but acts as a stimulator. Indeed, its absence results in shortened tails and slower motility. In contrast, the N-terminal domain of ActA (ActA-N) is essential for motility and expression of ActA-N fused to the ω fragment of β-galactosidase in *L. monocytogenes* $\Delta actA$ is sufficient to induce actin assembly and movement in *Xenopus* eggs extracts, demonstrating that this domain contains all the elements necessary for the tail formation (Lasa et al 1997). A detailed analysis of ActA variants in which small regions of the N-terminal domain were deleted allowed the identification of two essential regions. The first region (T), amino acids 117–121, is critical for actin tail formation but does not impair actin assembly. The second region (C), amino acids 21–97, is apparently involved in maintenance of the continuity of the actin tail formation because deletion of this region leads to discontinuous comet tails in *Xenopus* eggs extracts (Lasa et al 1997).

Experiments with the yeast two-hybrid system indicate that the N-terminal domain of ActA forms homodimers. This result was confirmed by direct chemical cross-linking on bacteria grown in broth (Mourrain et al 1997). The role of dimerization in actin-based motility has not been established. To date, the only modification reported for ActA is phosphorylation. However, whether phosphorylation is required for ActA function is still an open question (Brundage et al 1993).

The icsA Gene of S. flexneri

The *icsA/virG* gene located on the virulence plasmid of *S. flexneri* encodes an outer membrane protein of 1102 amino acids, named IcsA/VirG (Makino et al 1986, Lett et al 1989). The only remarkable feature of the sequence is the presence of six glycine-rich repeats of 32–34 amino acids (residues 105–307). The protein is anchored in the outer membrane by the C-terminal domain (IcsAβ; residues 759–1102) forming a β-barrel structure through which the N-terminal domain (IcsAα, residues 53–758) is translocated across the outer membrane (Suzuki & Sasakawa 1995). After the anchoring step, a specific serine protease (SopA or IcsP), closely related to the proteases OmpT and OmpP of *E. coli*, cleaves a small proportion of the IcsA protein (25–50%) between residues 758 and 759 (Egile et al 1997, Shere et al 1997). IcsA, like ActA, is asymmetrically distributed on the bacterial surface and is located in infected cells at the pole of the bacterium where actin polymerization occurs (Goldberg et al 1993). It has been proposed that the cleavage by SopA could increase the asymmetric distribution of IcsA on the bacterial surface. Accordingly, a *S. flexneri* ΔsopA strain retains its ability to accumulate actin but correct actin tail formation is affected (Egile et al 1997). In contrast, Shere and colleagues report that the *icsP* mutant displays significantly increased rates of actin-based motility in PtK2 cells (Shere et al 1997).

Expression of IcsA in an *E. coli* ΔompT strain allows *E. coli* to move in *Xenopus* cytoplasmic extracts, demonstrating that IcsA is sufficient to induce actin polymerization (Goldberg & Theriot 1995, Kocks et al 1995). Two critical regions for IcsA function were identified (in residues 103–319 and 320–508) by expressing IcsA variants in a *S. flexneri* ΔicsA mutant strain. These two regions span the domain known to interact with vinculin (Suzuki et al 1996).

The Cellular Factors Involved in Actin-Based Motility

Characterization of the host proteins that might be involved in the formation of actin tails induced by intracellular pathogens has been largely based on colocalization of proteins by immunohistochemical studies (Table 1). However, detection of some of these proteins may be solely a consequence of the high F-actin density in the tails. Thus a functional analysis is necessary to demonstrate the role, if any, of these proteins in actin-based motility. Note that detection of a protein at the front of the actin tail, close to the bacterium, is a good indication that the host protein might be involved in the first step of the process. Since all attempts to demonstrate a direct binding between actin and

Table 1 Proteins present in the actin tails

Bacteria	Protein	Localization	Interaction with IcsA/ActA	Reference
Listeria	α-actinin	Tail	—	a, b, c
	Tropomyosin	Tail	—	a
	Fimbrin/plastin	Tail	—	d
	Profilin	Bacterial pole	—	e, f
	Vinculin	Tail	—	c
	Talin	Tail	—	c
	Villin	Tail	—	g
	Ezrin (radixin)	Tail	—	g
	VASP	Bacterial pole	+	h
	MENA	Bacterial pole	+	i
	Arp2/Arp3 Complex	Tail/bacterial pole	—	j
	Cofilin	Tail	?	k, l
	CapZ	Tail	—	l
	Coronin	Tail	—	l
	Rac	Tail	—	l
Shigella	Fimbrin/Plastin	Bacterial pole	?	m
	VASP	Tail	?	h
	Vinculin	Tail/bacterial pole	+	n

[a]Dabiri et al 1990, [b]Sanger et al 1992, [c]Dold et al 1994, [d]Kocks & Cossart 1994, [e]Theriot et al 1994, [f]Smith et al 1996, [g]Temm-Grove et al 1994, [h]Chakraborty et al 1995, [i]Gertler et al 1996, [j]Welch et al 1997, [k]Rosenblatt et al 1997, [l]David et al 1998, [m]Prévost et al 1992, [n]Kadurugamuwa et al 1991.

ActA have failed, identification of the proteins that interact with ActA remains the challenge.

To date, the only protein able to bind directly to ActA is the vasodilator-stimulated phosphoprotein (VASP) and a murine protein relative of VASP, MENA (Chakraborty et al 1995, Gertler et al 1996, Niebuhr et al 1997). In *Listeria*-infected cells, VASP colocalizes with the front portion of the actin tail. It is a tetramer of four 46–50 kDa subunits that is normally localized at focal contacts and in the cell cortex (Reinhard et al 1992). VASP contains proline-rich sequences and is the first ligand identified for profilin, a protein known to bind polyproline stretches and able to promote actin polymerization when barbed ends are free (Pantaloni & Carlier 1993, Reinhard et al 1995a). Besides ActA and profilin, VASP is able to bind zyxin and vinculin, which both contain proline-rich repeats similar to those of ActA (Reinhard et al 1995b, 1996). In agreement with these observations, experiments with ActA variants and peptides indicate that VASP binds to the proline-rich region of ActA (Chakraborty et al 1995, Gertler et al 1996, Lasa et al 1997, Niebuhr et al 1997) (Table 1). Like the localization by VASP, profilin has been localized to the bacterial pole close to the tail (Theriot et al 1994). Profilin recruitment at the bacterial pole is impaired by deletion of the central proline-rich region of ActA, indicating that the role of this region is to recruit both VASP and profilin (142). Because the proline-rich region of ActA is not absolutely essential, VASP and profilin should be considered accessory factors stimulating the events taking place in the N-terminal part of ActA.

Recently, a seven polypeptide complex isolated from human platelets and containing two actin-related proteins, Arp2 and Arp3, was shown to elicit actin filament accumulation on the surface of *Listeria* (Welch et al 1997). The Arp2/Arp3 complex was first described in *Acanthamoeba castellanii* using affinity chromatography of amoeba cytosol on a profilin-agarose column (Machewski et al 1994). It is not known whether this complex is responsible for actin nucleation in intact host cells or if it binds to the N-terminal part of ActA.

Cofilin/ADF, which belongs to a group of small (15–22 kDa) actin-binding proteins, was also identified in the *Listeria* actin-based motility. Cofilin/ADF is a protein with affinity for ADP-actin; it can increase the off rate at the pointed ends of actin filaments and enhance filament turnover. Both depletion and addition experiments in cytoplasmic extracts indicate that cofilin is critical for the dynamics of the process (Carlier et al 1997, Rosenblatt et al 1997). α-Actinin is a dimeric protein that cross-links F-actin. Microinjection of a dominant-negative form of α-actinin leads to the disappearance of protrusions and actin tails, indicating that cross-linking of actin filaments is also critical for tail formation (Dold et al 1994).

In the case of *Shigella*, the situation appears different. VASP is detected in the whole actin tail (Chakraborty et al 1995). IcsA has not been reported to bind VASP directly, but microinjection of peptides corresponding to the VASP proline-rich peptide (GPPPPP)$_3$ or to the ActA proline-rich repeat (FEFPPPPTDE) blocks *Shigella* movement (Zeile et al 1996). The 85-kDa domain of IcsA (IcsAα) is able to interact with the head domain of vinculin, a protein normally responsible for the link between actin filaments and integrins via talin and α-actinin in the focal contacts (Suzuki et al 1996). As recently shown, the head region of vinculin can be generated by vinculin proteolysis in *Shigella*-infected cells and is localized to the back of motile bacteria (Laine et al 1997). In addition, microinjection of the head domain of vinculin increases *Shigella* motility (Laine et al 1997). The role of vinculin is controversial. A recent report indicates that *Shigella* movement is not impaired in vinculin-deficient cells (Goldberg 1997). In contrast, another study indicates that these vinculin-deficient cells are still expressing vinculin (Southwick et al 1997). Because vinculin has an ActA-like proline-rich motif that interacts with VASP, one hypothesis is that vinculin bound to IcsA could recruit VASP, which would then play the same role as in ActA, i.e. recruitment of profilin. The role of profilin in *Shigella*-infected cells has not been documented.

Current Models of ActA/IcsA-Induced Actin-Based Motility

The mechanism of actin polymerization induced by ActA is still not understood. Initial models were largely based on the idea that ActA could be a nucleator or could recruit a nucleator in the host cell. Several lines of evidence suggest that ActA is not directly responsible for the actin polymerization. Whether the Arp2/Arp3 complex is the cellular nucleator recruited by ActA remains to be demonstrated. ActA could also control movement by generating or regulating the availability of free barbed ends of actin filaments. In the context of our recent findings (*a*) that ActA is a dimer and (*b*) that small deletions in the N-terminal domain of ActA lead to various phenotypes (absence of tails or stripped tails), we propose the following model (Figure 4).

In a first step, free barbed ends are generated in the vicinity of the bacteria either by nucleation of actin monomers or by uncapping or severing of pre-existing filaments. The roles of the N-terminal domain of ActA and/or of the Arp2/Arp3 complex in this process are unknown. The second step is monomer addition, i.e. elongation at the free barbed ends generated in the first step, leading to bacterial propulsion. The VASP profilin complex bound to the central proline-rich region of ActA could provide competent actin monomers to the N-terminal domain and increase the efficiency of the process. In the last step, filaments are capped, released, and cross-linked while new free barbed ends are generated in the vicinity of the bacteria. The balance between the capping/release events and the generation of free barbed ends allows continuity of the process. This balance is absolutely critical and any cues affecting this balance will induce either absence of tail or discontinuous tails. Recent data reveal that the stripped tail phenotype can be obtained by deleting regions other than the region covering residues 21–97 (E Gouin, V Villiers, H Gantelet & P Cossart, unpublished results). A similar phenotype was infrequently observed in cell-free extracts (Fung & Theriot 1997, and our unpublished observations). These data reinforce the idea that actin-based movement occurs when a certain threshold of free barbed ends is reached. This threshold may be affected by the capping proteins, a class that deserves more investigation. We have recently shown that the capping protein CapZ is recruited by *Listeria* (V David, E Gouin & P Cossart, unpublished data). The way in which *Shigella* recruits actin may be similar to that of *Listeria*, with vinculin acting as a VASP-recruiting protein (Figure 4).

The Vaccinia Virus

Vaccinia virus had been shown to induce the formation of protrusions similar to those of *Listeria*, *Shigella*, and *Rickettsia* (Hiller et al 1981). It is now established that this virus can move within the cytoplasm of the host cells by

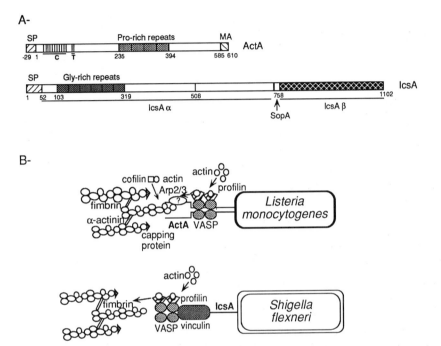

Figure 4   Models of actin assembly induced by *L. monocytogenes* and *S. flexneri*. (A) Schematic representation of ActA and IcsA. Amino acids are numbered as in Kocks et al (1992) for ActA and as in Goldberg et al (1994) for IcsA. The signal peptide (SP), membrane anchor (MA and IcsAβ), and the regions important for protein function are indicated. The N-terminal domain of ActA contains all the elements necessary for actin-based motility. The α-domain of IcsA is exposed on the surface of the bacteria and contains a region of glycine-rich repeats (residues 105–307), whereas the β-domain is embedded in the outer membrane. (B) Hypothetical models of actin assembly induced by ActA and IcsA. (*Top*) ActA is represented as a dimer. The proline-rich region of ActA interacts with VASP, which in turn binds the profilin-actin complex. This complex is believed to fuel the actin polymerization process by providing competent actin monomers in the vicinity of the bacterium. Actin polymerization starts with the generation of free barbed ends either by nucleation (via the Arp2/Arp3 complex?) or by severing or uncapping of pre-existing F-actin filaments. Thus elongation proceeds until release, capping, and cross-linking of the actin filaments present in the comet tail (for details, see text). (*Bottom*) IcsA is represented as a monomer. The N-terminal region of IcsA interacts with vinculin, which can in turn recruit the VASP-profilin-actin complex (see above).

forming actin tails very similar to those of bacteria (Cudmore et al 1995, 1996). However, only one particular form of the virus, called IEV (for intracellular enveloped virus), corresponding to the final step of the virus maturation, is able to induce actin assembly. The IEV form of the virus is enveloped by two membranes derived from the *trans*-Golgi network. Attempts, using a variety of mutants, to identify a viral protein involved in actin-based motility have failed. It appears that a tyrosine-phosphorylated protein is specifically recruited at the base of the actin tail (M Way, personal communication). Its identification is in progress. Whether this motility is similar to that of endosomes moving in lanthanum- or zinc-treated cells (Heuser & Morisaki 1992) or in cell extracts (Marchand et al 1995) is highly possible. Like the enteropathogenic *Escherichia coli* (EPEC) (see below), vaccinia virus represents a good model system for addressing the origin of cytoskeletal rearrangements at a membrane.

Actin-Based Motility of Extracellular Bacteria

EPECs are gram-negative bacteria responsible for diarrhea. They colonize the intestine, form small colonies, and induce the degeneration of microvilli, a phenomenon called attaching and effacing phenotype. Bacteria adhere tightly to the host cell surface and induce the localized formation of bundles of actin filaments just underneath the attachment sites. Beneath some of the bacteria, the actin filaments become organized into membrane encased protruberances that extend up to 6 μm above the cell surface, creating pedestals on which the EPEC bacilli rest horizontally. The concentration of non-muscle isoforms of myosin II and tropomyosin near the base of the pedestals suggests a similarity of these structures to the brush border microvilli. Video-microscopy indicates that these EPEC pedestals can bend and undulate, alternately growing longer and shorter while remaining tethered in place (Sanger et al 1996). Some of the attached EPECs also translocate along the cell surface, reaching speeds of 0.007 μm/s. Both types of movement are inhibited by cytochalasin D, indicating that actin polymerization in the pedestals is required for the motility of EPEC on the host cell surface. While this model shares similarities with the *Listeria* or *Shigella* systems, the main difference is the presence of a membrane between the pathogen and the cell cytoskeleton, as in the case of vaccinia virus. Recently, a two-protein complex required for the intimate attachment of the bacteria has been identified (Rosenshine et al 1996, Kenny & Finlay 1997). Intriguingly, the bacteria first inserts a protein named Tir in the plasma membrane. Tir becomes phosphorylated and in turn acts as a receptor for intimin, a protein similar to invasin. However, the phosphorylation of Tir does not seem to be required for adhesion. How these events induce rearrangements of the cytoskeleton is unknown. This phenomenon is very similar to that described by Forscher and colleagues, who showed that polycationic beads, which bind to the surface of nerve cell growth cones, can induce actin filament assembly inside cells. These beads can then move along the cell suface at the rate of 10 μm/min, and actin tails can be detected underneath moving bacteria (Forscher et al 1992, Sanger & Sanger 1992). Similar to vaccinia virus, EPEC may represent a good system to understand actin-cytoskeleton rearrangements after signaling at a plasma membrane.

CONCLUSION

We have focused on two events important for bacterial pathogenesis that require rearrangements of the host actin cytoskeleton: entry into non-phagocytic cells and actin-based motility. Our knowledge of the morphological events taking place during these processes has greatly improved. Some of the key cellular proteins involved have been identified, but a complete reconstitution of the scenario taking place during both types of events is far from being reached. There may be two reasons for this: First, the signaling pathways used by bacteria are just being discovered or have not yet been discovered. For example, the targets of activated small GTPases are only starting to be identified. The same holds true for the downstream targets of the phospholipids generated by PI 3-kinases. Second, some putative key regulators, including Ca^{2+} and the phospholipids, have not been considered in detail. Another important issue is the role of the plasma membrane composition. Are there plasma membrane subdomains—raft membrane microdomains—that the bacteria prefer for entry?

The field of microbial pathogenesis has now met the field of cell biology, and the list of tools that bacteria provide to address specific questions in cell biology is constantly increasing. If it is well recognized that some clostridial toxins are useful tools for investigating signaling pathways regulating the cytoskeleton (ActA or IcsA also provide valuable objects to address actin-based motility), it is less well known that purified proteins such as internalin or InlB, Ipas, or Sips could also be used to analyze cell adhesion or signaling pathways. As illustrated in this review, a new discipline has emerged, i.e. cellular microbiology (Cossart et al 1996), that should be a benefit to both microbiologists and cell biologists.

ACKNOWLEDGMENTS

We thank John Heuser (Washington University) for kindly providing the electron micrograph presented in Figure 2*b*. We apologize to those whose work could not be cited due to space limitations. Work in our laboratory receives financial support from ARC (CT 9223), DRET(DGA97/69), EC(BMH4-CT96-0659), and the Pasteur Institute.

Literature Cited

Adam T, Arpin M, Prévost MC, Gounon P, Sansonetti PJ. 1995. Cytoskeletal rearrangements during entry of *Shigella flexneri* into HeLa cells. *J. Cell. Biol.* 129:367–81

Adam T, Giry M, Boquet P, Sansonetti P. 1996. Rho-dependent membrane folding causes *Shigella* entry into epithelial cells. *EMBO J.* 15:3315–21

Alpuche-Aranda CM, Racoosin EL, Swanson JA, Miller SI. 1994. *Salmonella* stimulate macrophage pinocytosis and persist within spacious phagosomes. *J. Exp. Med.* 179:601–8

Batterman HJ, Peek JA, Loutit JS, Falkow S, Tompkins LS. 1995. *Bartonella henselae* and *Bartonella quintana* adherence to and entry into cultured human epithelial cells. *Infect. Immun.* 63:4553–56

Bernardini ML, Mounier J, D'Hauteville H, Coquis-Rondon M, Sansonetti PJ. 1989. Identification of *icsA*, a plasmid locus of *Shigella flexneri* that governs bacterial intra- and intercellular spread through interaction with F-actin. *Proc. Natl. Acad. Sci. USA* 86:3867–71

Bhat KS, Gibbs CP, Barrera O, Morrison SG, Jähnig F, et al. 1991. The opacity proteins of *Neisseria gonorrhoeae* strain MS11 are encoded by a family of 11 complete genes. *Mol. Microbiol.* 5:1889–901

Black DS, Bliska JB. 1997. Identification of p130^{Cas} as a substrate of *Yersinia* YopH(Yop51), a bacterial protein tyrosine phosphatase that translocates into mammalian cells and targets focal adhesions. *EMBO J.* 16:2730–44

Bliska JB, Galan JE, Falkow S. 1993. Signal transduction in the mammalian cell during bacterial attachment and entry. *Cell* 73:903–20

Boller K, Vestweber D, Kemler R. 1985. Cell-adhesion molecule uvomorulin is localized in the intermediate junctions of adult intestinal epithelial cells. *J. Cell Biol.* 100:327–32

Bos MP, Grunert F, Belland RJ. 1997. Differential recognition of members of the carcinoembryonic antigen family by Opa variants of *Neisseria gonorrhoeae*. *Infect. Immun.* 65:2353–61

Braun L, Ohayon H, Cossart P. 1998. The InlB protein of *Listeria monocytogenes* is sufficient to promote entry into mammalian cells. *Mol. Microbiol.* 27:1077–87

Brundage RA, Smith GA, Camilli A, Theriot J,

Portnoy DA. 1993. Expression and phosphorylation of the *Listeria monocytogenes* ActA protein in mammalian cells. *Proc. Natl. Acad. Sci. USA* 90:11890–94

Carlier MF, Laurent V, Santolini J, Melki R, Didry D, et al. 1997. Actin depolymerizing factor (ADF/cofilin) enhances the rate of filament turnover: implication in actin-based motility. *J. Cell Biol.* 136:1307–22

Cepek KL, Shaw SK, Parker CM, Russell GJ, Morrow JS, et al. 1994. Adhesion between epithelial cells and T lymphocytes mediated by E-cadherin and the $\alpha_E\beta_7$ integrin. *Nature* 372:190–93

Chakraborty T, Ebel F, Dommann E, Niebuhr K, Gerstel B, et al. 1995. A focal adhesion factor directly linking intracellularly motile *Listeria monocytogenes* and *Listeria ivanovii* to the actin-based cytoskeleton of mammalian cells. *EMBO J.* 14:1314–21

Chen L-M, Hobbie S, Galan JE. 1996. Requirement of cdc42 for *Salmonella*-induced cytoskeletal and nuclear responses. *Science* 274:2115–18

Chen T, Belland RJ, Wilson J, Swanson J. 1995. Adherence of Pilus- Opa+ gonococci to epithelial cells in vitro involves heparan sulfate. *J. Exp. Med.* 182:511–17

Chen T, Gotschlich EC. 1996. CGM1a antigen of neutrophils, a receptor of gonococcal opacity protein. *Proc. Natl. Acad. Sci. USA* 93:14851–56

Chen T, Grunert F, Medina-Marino A, Gotschlich E. 1997. Several carcinoembryonic antigens (CD66) serve as receptors for gonococcal opacity proteins. *J. Exp. Med.* 185:1557–64

Chen T, Swanson J, Fischer SH. 1992. Human neutrophil response to recombinant Neisserial opacity proteins. *Mol. Microbiol.* 6:1729–37

Cossart P. 1995. Bacterial actin based motility. *Curr. Opin. Cell. Biol.* 7:94–101

Cossart P. 1997. Subversion of the mammalian cell cytoskeleton by invasive bacteria. *J. Clin. Invest.* 99:2307–11

Cossart P, Boquet P, Normark S, Rappuoli R. 1996. Cellular microbiology emerging. *Science* 271:315–16

Cox D, Chang P, Zhang Q, Gopal Reddy P, et al. 1997. Requirements for both Rac1 and Cdc42 in membrane ruffling and phagocytosis in leucocytes. *J. Exp. Med.* 186:1487–94

Cudmore S, Cossart P, Griffiths G, Way M.

1995. Actin-based motility of vaccinia virus. *Nature* 378:636–38

Cudmore S, Reckmann I, Griffiths G, Way M. 1996. Vaccinia virus: a model system for actin-membrane interactions. *J. Cell Sci.* 109:1739–47

Dabiri GA, Sanger JM, Portnoy DA, Southwick FS. 1990. *Listeria monocytogenes* moves rapidly through the host-cell cytoplasm by inducing directional actin assembly. *Proc. Natl. Acad. Sci. USA* 87:6068–72

Dehio C, Meyer M, Berger J, Schwarz H, Lanz C. 1997. Interaction of *Bartonella henselae* with endothelial cells results in bacterial aggregation on the cell surface and the subsequent engulfment and internalisation of the bacterial aggregate by a unique structure, the invasome. *J. Cell Sci.* 110:2141–54

Dehio C, Prévost MC, Sansonsetti PJ. 1995. Invasion of epithelial cells by *Shigella flexneri* induces tyrosine phosphorylation of cortactin by a pp60^{c-Src} mediated signaling pathway. *EMBO J.* 14:2471–82

Dold FG, Sanger JM, Sanger JW. 1994. Intact alpha-actinin molecules are needed for both the assembly of actin into tails and the locomotion of *Listeria monocytogenes* inside infected cells. *Cell Motil. Cytoskelet.* 28:97–107

Domann E, Wehland J, Rohde M, Pistor S, Hartl M, et al. 1992. A novel bacterial gene in *Listeria monocytogenes* required for host cell microfilament interaction with homology to the proline-rich region of vinculin. *EMBO J.* 11:1981–90

Donnenberg MS, Donohue-Rolfe A, Keusch GT. 1990. A comparison of HEp-2 cell invasion by enteropathogenic and enteroinvasive *Escherichia coli*. *FEMS Microbiol. Lett.* 69:83–86

Dramsi S, Biswas I, Maguin E, Braun L, Mastroeni P, Cossart P. 1995. Entry of *L. monocytogenes* into hepatocytes requires expression of InlB, a surface protein of the internalin multigene family. *Mol. Microbiol.* 16:251–61

Dramsi S, Dehoux P, Cossart P. 1993. Common features of gram-positive bacterial proteins involved in cell recognition. *Mol. Microbiol.* 9:1119–22

Dramsi S, Dehoux P, Lebrun M, Goossens P, Cossart P. 1997. Identification of four new members of the internalin multigene family in *Listeria monocytogenes* strain EGD. *Infect. Immun.* 65:1615–25

Duensing TD, Van Putten JPM. 1997. Vitronectin mediates internalization of *Neisseria gonorrhoeae* by Chinese hamster ovary cells. *Infect. Immun.* 65:964–70

Egile C, d'Hauteville H, Parsot C, Sansonetti PJ. 1997. SopA, the outer membrane protease responsible for polar localisation of IcsA in *Shigella flexneri*. *Mol. Microbiol.* 23:1063–74

Finlay BB, Cossart P. 1997. Exploitation of mammalian host cell functions by bacterial pathogens. *Science* 276:718–25

Finlay BB, Falkow S. 1988. Comparison of the invasion strategies used by *Salmonella choleraesuis*, *Shigella flexneri* and *Yersinia enterocolitica* to enter cultured animal cells: endosome acidification is not required for bacterial invasion or intracellular replication. *Biochimie* 70:1089–99

Finlay BB, Ruschkowski S. 1991. Cytoskeletal rearrangements accompanying *Salmonella* entry into epithelial cells. *J. Cell Sci.* 99:283–96

Forscher P, Lin CH, Thompson C. 1992. Novel form of growth cone motility involving site-directed actin filament assembly. *Nature* 357:515–18

Francis CL, Ryan TA, Jones BD, Smith SJ, Falkow S. 1993. Ruffles induced by *Salmonella* and other stimuli direct macropinocytosis of bacteria. *Nature* 364:639–42

Francis CL, Starnbach MN, Falkow S. 1992. Morphological and cytoskeletal changes in epithelial cells occur immediately upon interaction with *Salmonella typhimurium* grown under low-oxygen conditions. *Mol. Microbiol.* 6:3077–87

Friederich E, Gouin E, Hellio R, Kocks C, Cossart P, Louvard D. 1995. Targeting of *Listeria monocytogenes* ActA protein to the plasma membrane as a tool to dissect both actin-based cell morphogenesis and ActA function. *EMBO J.* 14:2731–44

Fung DC, Theriot JA. 1997. Unusual hopping movement of *Listeria monocytogenes* and the relationship between actin polymerization and movement. *Mol. Biol. Cell* S8:167a

Gaillard J-L, Berche P, Frehel C, Gouin E, Cossart P. 1991. Entry of L. monocytogenes into cells is mediated by internalin, a repeat protein reminiscent of surface antigens from gram-positive cocci. *Cell* 65:1127–41

Gaillard JL, Berche P, Mounier J, Richard S, Sansonetti PJ. 1987. In vitro model of penetration and intracellular growth of *L. monocytogenes* in the human enterocyte-like cell line Caco-2. *Infect. Immun.* 55:2822–29

Gaillard JL, Finlay BB. 1996. Effect of cell polarization and differentiation on entry of *Listeria monocytogenes* into enterocyte-like Caco-2 cell line. *Infect. Immun.* 64:1299–308

Galan JE. 1996. Molecular genetic bases of *Salmonella* entry into host cells. *Mol. Microbiol.* 20:263–71

Galan JE, Bliska JB. 1996. Cross-talk between bacterial pathogens and their host cells. *Annu. Rev. Cell Dev. Biol.* 12:221–55

Galan JE, Pace J, Hayman MJ. 1992. Involvement of the epidermal growth factor in the invasion of epithelial cells by *Salmonella typhimurium*. *Nature* 357:588–89

Gertler FB, Niebuhr K, Reinhard M, Wehland J, Soriano P. 1996. Mena, a relative of VASP and Drosophila Enabled, is implicated in the control of microfilament dynamics. *Cell* 87:227–39

Goldberg M. 1997. *Shigella* actin-based motility in the absence of vinculin. *Cell Motil. Cytoskelet.* 37:44–53

Goldberg M, Bařzu O, Parsot C, Sansonetti PJ. 1993. Unipolar localization and ATPase activity of IcsA, a *Shigella flexneri* protein involved in intracellular movement. *J. Bacteriol.* 175:2189–96

Goldberg M, Theriot J, Sansonetti PJ. 1994. Regulation of surface presentation of IcsA, a *Shigella* protein essential to intracellular movement and spread, is growth phase dependent. *Infect. Immun.* 62:5664–68

Goldberg MA, Theriot JA. 1995. *Shigella flexneri* surface protein IcsA is sufficient to direct actin-based motility. *Proc. Natl. Acad. Sci. USA* 92:6572–76

Golsteyn RM, Beckerle M, Koay T, Friederich E. 1997. Structural and functional similarities between the human cytoskeletal protein zyxin and the ActA protein of *Listeria monocytogenes*. *J. Cell Sci.* 110:1893–906

Gomez-Duarte OG, Dehio M, Guzman CA, Chhatwal GS, Dehio C, Meyer T. 1997. Binding of vitronectin to Opa-expressing *Neisseria gonorrhoeae* mediates invasion of HeLa cells. *Infect. Immun.* 65:3857–66

Gouin E, Dehoux P, Mengaud J, Kocks C, Cossart P. 1995. *iactA* of *Listeria ivanovii* although distantly related to *Listeria monocytogenes actA* restores actin tail formation in a *L. monocytogenes actA* mutant. *Infect. Immun.* 63:2729–37

Grassmé H, Gulbins E, Brenner B, Ferlinz K, Sandhoff K, et al. 1997. Acidic shingomyelinase mediates entry of Neisseria gonorrhoeae into non-phagocytic cells. *Cell* 91:605–15

Grassmé HUC, Ireland RM, Van Putten JPM. 1996. Gonococcal opacity protein promotes bacterial entry-associated rearrangements of the epithelial cell actin cytoskeleton. *Infect. Immun.* 64:1621–30

Gray-Owen SD, Dehio C, Haude A, Grunert F, Meyer TF. 1997. CD66 carcinoembryonic antigens mediate interactions between Opa-expressing *Neisseria gonorrhoeae* and human polymorphonuclear phagocytes. *EMBO J.* 16:3435–45

Hackam DJ, Rotstein OD, Schreiber A, Zhang W, Grinstein S. 1997. Rho is required for the initiation of calcium signaling and phagocytosis by Fcγ receptors in macrophages. *J. Exp. Med.* 186:955–66

Hall A. 1998. Rho GTPases and the actin cytoskeleton. *Science* 279:509–15

Hartwig JH, Bokoch G, Carpenter CL, Janmey PA, Taylor LA, et al. 1995. Thrombin receptor ligation and activated rac uncap actin filament barbed ends through phosphoinositide synthesis in permeabilized human platelets. *Cell* 82:643–53

Hartwig JH, Kung S, Kovacsovics T, Janmey PA, Cantley LC, et al. 1996. D3 phosphoinositides and outside-in integrin signaling by glycoprotein IIb-IIIa mediate platelet actin assembly and filopodial extension induced by phorbol 12-myristate 13-acetate. *J. Biol. Chem.* 271:32986–93

Hauck CR, Meyer TF, Lang F, Gulbins E. 1998. CD66-mediated phagocytosis of Opa$_{52}$ *Neisseria gonorrhoeae* requires a Src-like tyrosine kinase-and Rac1-dependent signalling pathway. *EMBO J.* 17:443–54

Heinzen RA, Hayes SF, Peacock MG, Hackstadt T. 1993. Directional actin polymerization associated with spotted fever group *Rickettsia* infection of vero cells. *Infect. Immun.* 61:1926–35

Hermant D, Ménard R, Arricau N, Parsot C, Popoff MY. 1995. Functional conservation of *Salmonella* and *Shigella* effectors for entry into epithelial cells. *Mol. Microbiol.* 17:781–89

Heuser JE. 1980. The quick-freeze, deep-etch method of preparing samples for high resolution, 3-D electron microscopy. *Trends Biochem. Sci.* 6:64–68

Heuser JE, Morisaki JH. 1992. Time-lapse video microscopy of endosomal rocketing of La/Zn treated cells. *Mol. Biol. Cell* 3S:A172

Hiller G, Jungwirth C, Weber K. 1981. Fluorescence microscopical analysis of the life cycle of vaccinia virus in the chick embryo fibroblasts. *Exp. Cell Res.* 132:81–87

Horwitz A, Duggan K, Burk C, Beckerle MC, Burridge K. 1986. Interaction of plasma membrane fibronectin receptor with talin-a transmembrane linkage. *Nature* 320:531–33

Hueck CJ, Hantman MJ, Bajaj V, Johnston C, Lee CA, Miller SI. 1995. *Salmonella typhimurium* secreted invasion determinants are homologous to *Shigella* Ipa proteins. *Mol. Microbiol.* 18:479–90

Ireton K, Cossart P. 1997. Host pathogen interactions during entry and actin-based movement of *Listeria monocytogenes*. *Annu. Rev. Genet.* 31:113–38

Ireton K, Cossart P. 1998. Interaction of invasive bacteria with host signaling pathways. *Curr. Opin. Cell Biol.*

Ireton K, Payrastre B, Chap H, Ogawa W, Sakaue H, et al. 1996. A role for phosphoinositide 3-kinase in bacterial invasion. *Science* 274:780–82

Isberg RR, Leong JM. 1990. Multiple β_1 chain integrins are receptors for invasin, a protein that promotes bacterial penetration into mammalian cells. *Cell* 60:861–71

Isberg RR, Tran Van Nhieu G. 1995. The mechanism of phagocytic uptake promoted by invasin-integrin interaction. *Trends Cell Biol.* 5:120–24

Isberg RR, Voorhis DL, Falkow S. 1987. Identification of invasin: a protein that allows enteric bacteria to penetrate cultured mammalian cells. *Cell* 50:769–78

Jerse AE, Rest RF. 1997. Adhesion and invasion by the pathogenic *Neisseria. Trends Microbiol.* 5:217–21

Jones BD, Paterson HF, Hall F, Falkow S. 1993. *Salmonella typhimurium* induces membrane ruffling by a growth factor independent mechanism. *Proc. Natl. Acad. Sci. USA* 90:10390–94

Kadurugamuwa JL, Rohde M, Wehland J, Timmis KN. 1991. Intercellular spread of *Shigella flexneri* through a monolayer mediated by membranous protrusions and associated with reorganization of the cytoskeletal protein vinculin. *Infect. Immun.* 59:3463–71

Kaniga K, Tucker S, Trollinger D, Galan JE. 1995. Homologs of the *Shigella* IpaB and IpaC invasins are required for *Salmonella typhimurium* entry into cultured epithelial cells. *J. Bacteriol.* 177:3965–71

Karecla PI, Green SJ, Bowden SJ, Coadwell J, Kilshaw PJ. 1996. Identification of a binding site for integrin $\alpha_E\beta_7$ in the N-terminal domain of E-cadherin. *J. Biol. Chem.* 271:30909–15

Karecla PI, Bowden SJ, Green SJ, Kilshaw PJ. 1995. Recognition of E-cadherin on epithelial cells by the mucosal T cell integrin $\alpha_{M290}\beta_7$ ($\alpha_E\beta_7$). *Eur. J. Immunol.* 25:852–56

Kenny B, Finlay BB. 1997. Intimin-dependent binding of enteropathogenic *Escherichia coli* to host cells triggers novel signalling events, including tyrosine phosphorylation of phospholipase C-γ1. *Infec. Immun.* 65:2528–36

Kocks C, Cossart P. 1994. Directional actin assembly by *Listeria monocytogenes* at the site of polar surface expression of the *actA* gene product involving the actin-bundling protein plastin (fimbrin). *Infect. Agents Dis.* 2:207–9

Kocks C, Gouin E, Tabouret M, Berche P, Ohayon H, Cossart P. 1992. Listeria monocytogenes-induced actin assembly requires the actA gene product, a surface protein. *Cell* 68:521–31

Kocks C, Hellio R, Gounon P, Ohayon H, Cossart P. 1993. Polarized distribution of *Listeria monocytogenes* surface protein ActA at the site of directional actin assembly. *J. Cell Sci.* 105:699–710

Kocks C, Marchand JB, Gouin E, d'Hauteville H, Sansonetti PJ, et al. 1995. The unrelated surface proteins ActA of *Listeria monocytogenes* and IcsA of *Shigella flexneri* are sufficient to confer actin-based motility to *L. innocua* and *E. coli* respectively. *Mol. Microbiol.* 18:413–23

Kreft J, Dumbsky M, Theiss S. 1995. The actin polymerization protein from *Listeria ivanovii* is a large repeat protein which shows only limited amino-acid sequence homology to ActA from *Listeria monocytogenes. FEMS Microbiol. Lett.* 126:113–22

Kuhn M. 1998. The microtubule depolymerizing drugs nocodazole and colchicine inhibit the uptake of *Listeria monocytogenes* by P388D1 macrophages. *FEMS Microbiol. Lett.* 160:87–90

Kupsch E-M, Knepper B, Kuroki T, Heuer I, Meyer TF. 1993. Variable opacity (Opa) outer membrane proteins account for the cell tropisms displayed by *Neisseria gonorrhoeae* for human leukocytes and epithelial cells. *EMBO J.* 12:641–50

Laine RO, Zeile W, Kang F, Purich DL, Southwick FS. 1997. Vinculin proteolysis unmasks an ActA homolog for actin-based *Shigella* motility. *J. Cell Biol.* 138:1255–64

Lasa I, Cossart P. 1996. Actin-based motility: toward a definition of the minimal requirements. *Trends Cell Biol.* 6:109–14

Lasa I, David V, Gouin E, Marchand J, Cossart P. 1995. The amino-terminal part of ActA is critical for the actin based motility of *Listeria monocytogenes*; the central proline-rich region acts as a stimulator. *Mol. Microbiol.* 18:425–36

Lasa I, Dehoux P, Cossart P. 1998. Actin polymerization and bacterial movement. *Biochem. Biophys. Acta* 1402:217–28

Lasa I, Gouin E, Goethals M, Vancompernolle K, David V, et al. 1997. Identification of two regions in the amino-terminal domain of ActA involved in the actin comet tail formation by *Listeria monocytogenes. EMBO J.* 16:1531–40

Lecuit M, Ohayon H, Braun L, Mengaud CP. 1997. Internalin of *Listeria monocytogenes* with an intact leucine-rich repeat region is sufficient to promote internalization. *Infect. Immun.* 65:5309–19

Lett M-C, Sasakawa C, Okada N, Sakai T, Makino S, et al. 1989. *virG*, a plasmid-coded virulence gene of *Shigella flexneri*: identification of the *virG* protein and determination of the complete coding sequence. *J. Bacteriol.* 171:353–59

Machewski LM, Atkinson SJ, Ampe C, Vandekerckhove J, Pollard TJ. 1994. Purification of a cortical complex containing two unconventional actins from *Acanthamoeba* by affinity chromatography on profilin-agarose. *J. Cell Biol.* 1:107–15

Makino S, Sasakawa C, Kamata K, Kurata T, Yoshikawa M. 1986. A genetic determinant required for continuous reinfection of adjacent cells on large plasmid in S. flexneri 2a. *Cell* 46:551–55

Makino S, Van Putten JPM, Meyer TF. 1991. Phase variation of the opacity outer membrane protein controls invasion by *Neisseria gonorrhoeae* into human epithelial cells. *EMBO J.* 10:1307–15

Marchand JB, Moreau P, Paoletti A, Cossart P, Carlier MF, Pantaloni D. 1995. Actin-based movement of *Listeria monocytogenes* in *Xenopus* egg extracts is due to local uncapping of the barbed ends of actin filaments at the bacterial surface and resulting shift in steady state of actin assembly. *J. Cell Biol.* 130:331–43

Ménard R, Dehio C, Sansonetti PJ. 1996a. Bacterial entry into epithelial cells: the paradigm of *Shigella*. *Trends Microbiol.* 4:220–26

Ménard R, Prévost MC, Gounon P, Sansonetti P, Dehio C. 1996b. The secreted Ipa complex of *Shigella flexneri* promotes entry into mammalian cells. *Proc. Natl. Acad. Sci. USA* 93:1254–58

Mengaud J, Ohayon H, Gounon P, Mège RM, Cossart P. 1996. E-cadherin is the receptor for internalin, a surface protein required for entry of Listeria monocytogenes into epithelial cells. *Cell* 84:923–32

Mounier J, Ryter A, Coquis-Rondon M, Sansonetti PJ. 1990. Intracellular and cell-to-cell spread of *Listeria monocytogenes* involves interaction with F-actin in the enterocyte-like cell line Caco-2. *Infect. Immun.* 58:1048–58

Mourrain P, Lasa I, Gautreau A, Gouin E, Pugsley A, Cossart P. 1997. ActA is a dimer. *Proc. Natl. Acad. Sci. USA* 94:10034–39

Näthke IS, Hinck L, Nelson JW. 1995. The cadherin/catenin complex: connections to multiple cellular processes involved in cell adhesion, proliferation and morphogenesis. *Semin. Dev. Biol.* 6:89–95

Niebuhr K, Chakraborty T, Rohde M, Gazlig T, Jansen B, et al. 1993. Localization of the ActA polypeptide of *Listeria monocytogenes* in infected tissue culture cell lines: ActA is not associated with actin comets. *Infect. Immun.* 61:2793–802

Niebuhr K, Ebel F, Frank R, Reinhard M, Domann E, et al. 1997. A novel proline-rich motif present in ActA of *Listeria monocytogenes* and cytoskeletal proteins is the ligand for the EVH1 domain, a protein module present in the Ena/VASP family. *EMBO J.* 16:5433–44

Oelschlaeger TA, Guerry P, Kopecko DJ. 1993. Unusual microtubule-dependent endocytosis mechanisms triggered by *Campylobacter jejuni* and *Citrobacter freundii*. *Proc. Natl. Acad. Sci. USA* 90:6884–88

Ogawa H, Nakamura A, Nakaya R. 1968. *Jpn. J. Med. Sci. Biol.* 21:259–73

Otey CA, Vazquez GB, Burridge K, Erickson BW. 1993. Mapping of the α-actinin binding site within the β1 integrin cytoplasmic domain. *J. Biol. Chem.* 268:21193–97

Overduin M, Harvey TS, Bagdy S, Tong KI, Yau P, et al. 1995. Solution structure of the epithelial cadherin domain responsible for selective cell adhesion. *Science* 267:386–89

Pace J, Hayman MJ, Galan J. 1993. Signal transduction and invasion of epithelial cells by *S. typhimurium*. *Cell* 72:505–14

Pantaloni D, Carlier MF. 1993. How profilin promotes actin filament assembly in the presence of thymosin β4. *Cell* 75:1007–14

Persson C, Carballeira N, Wolf-Watz H, Fällmann. 1997. The PTPase YopH inhibits uptake of *Yersinia*, tyrosine phosphorylation of p130^{Cas} and FAK, and the associated accumulation of these proteins in peripheral focal adhesions. *EMBO J.* 16:2307–18

Pistor S, Chakraborty T, Niebuhr K, Domann E, Wehland J. 1994. The ActA protein of *L. monocytogenes* acts as a nucleator inducing reorganization of the actin cytoskeleton. *EMBO J.* 13:758–63

Pistor S, Chakraborty T, Walter U, Wehland J. 1995. The bacterial actin nucleator protein ActA of *Listeria monocytogenes* contains multiple binding sites for host microfilament proteins. *Curr. Biol.* 5:517–25

Prévost MC, Lesourd M, Arpin M, Vernel F, Mounier J, et al. 1992. Unipolar reorganization of F-actin layer at bacterial division and bundling of actin filaments by plastin correlates with movement of *Shigella flexneri* within HeLa cells. *Infect. Immun.* 60:4088–99

Reinhard M, Giehl K, Abel K, Haffner C, Jarchau T, et al. 1995a. The proline-rich focal adhesion and microfilament protein VASP is a ligand for profilins. *EMBO J.* 14:1583–89

Reinhard M, Halbrügge M, Scheer U, Wiegand C, Jockusch BM, Walter U. 1992. The 45/50 kDa phosphoprotein VASP purified from human platelets is a novel protein associated with actin filaments and focal contacts. *EMBO J.* 11:2063–70

Reinhard M, Jouvenal K, Tripier D, Walter U. 1995b. Identification, purification, and characterization of a zyxin-related protein that binds the focal adhesion and mirofilament protein VASP (vasodilator-stimulated phosphoprotein). *Proc. Natl. Acad. Sci. USA* 92:7956–60

Reinhard M, Rudiger M, Jockusch BM, Walter U. 1996. VASP interaction with vinculin: a recurring theme of interactions with proline-rich motifs. *FEBS Lett.* 399:103–7

Rosenblatt J, Agnew BJ, Abe H, Barnburg JR, Mitchison TJ. 1997. *Xenopus* actin-depolymerizing factor/cofilin (XAC) is responsible for the turnover of actin filaments in *Listeria monocytogenes* tails. *J. Cell Biol.* 136:1323–32

Rosenshine I, Duronio V, Finlay BB. 1992. Protein tyrosine kinase inhibitors block invasin-promoted bacterial uptake by epithelial cells. *Infect. Immun.* 60:2211–17

Rosenshine I, Ruschkowski S, Stein M, Reinscheid DJ, Mills SD, Finlay BB. 1996. A pathogenic bacterium triggers epithelial signals to form a functional bacterial receptor that mediates actin pseudopod formation. *EMBO J.* 15:2613–24

Sanger JM, Chang R, Ashton F, Kaper JB, Sanger JW. 1996. Novel form of actin-based motility transports bacteria on the surfaces of infected cells. *Cell Motil. Cytoskelet.* 34:279–87

Sanger JM, Sanger JW, Southwick FS. 1992. Host cell actin assembly is necessary and likely to provide the propulsive force for intracellular movement of *Listeria monocytogenes. Infect. Immun.* 60:3609–19

Sanger JW, Sanger JM. 1992. Cell motility. Beads, bacteria and actin. *Nature* 357:442

Sechi AS, Wehland J, Small JV. 1997. The isolated comet tail pseudopodium of *Listeria monocytogenes:* a tail of two actin filament populations, long and axial and short and random. *J. Cell Biol.* 137:155–67

Shapiro L, Fannon AM, Kwong PD, Thompson A, Lehmann MS, et al. 1995. Structural basis of cell-cell adhesion by cadherins. *Nature* 374:327–37

Shere KD, Sallustio S, Manessis A, D'Aversa TG, Goldberg M. 1997. Disruption of IcsP, the major *Shigella* protease that cleaves IcsA, accelerates actin-based motility. *Mol. Microbiol.* 25:451–62

Simon D, Rest F. 1992. *Escherichia coli* expressing a *Neisseria gonorrhoeae* opacity associated outer membrane protein invade human cervical and endometrial cell lines. *Proc. Natl. Acad. Sci. USA* 89:5512–16

Smith GA, Portnoy DA. 1997. How the *Listeria monocytogenes* ActA protein converts actin polymerization into a motile force. *Trends Microbiol.* 5:272–76

Smith GA, Portnoy DA, Theriot JA. 1995. Asymmetric distribution of the *Listeria monocytogenes* ActA protein is required and sufficient to direct actin-based motility. *Mol. Microbiol.* 17:945–51

Smith GA, Theriot J, Portnoy D. 1996. The tandem repeat domain in the *Listeria monocytogenes* ActA protein controls the rate of actin-based motility, the percentage of moving bacteria, and the localization of vasodilator-stimulated phosphoprotein and profilin. *J. Cell Biol.* 135:647–60

Southwick FS, Adamson ED, Purich DL. 1997. Role of vinculin in *Shigella* actin-based motility in 5.51 and γ229 vinculin-deficient host cell. *Mol. Biol. Cell* S8:169a

Suzuki T, Sasakawa C. 1995. Extracellular transport of VirG protein in *Shigella. J. Biol. Chem.* 270:30874–80

Suzuki T, Shinsuke S, Sasakawa C. 1996. Functional analysis of *Shigella* VirG domains essential for interaction with vinculin and actin-based motility. *J. Biol. Chem.* 271:21878–85

Swanson JA, Baer SC. 1995. Phagocytosis by zippers and triggers. *Trends Cell Biol.* 5:89–93

Takeichi M. 1996. Morphogenetic roles of classic cadherins. *Curr. Opin. Cell Biol.* 7:619–27

Tang P, Rosenshine I, Finlay BB. 1994. *Listeria monocytogenes,* an invasive bacterium, stimulates MAP kinase upon attachment to epithelials cells. *Mol. Biol. Cell.* 5:455–64

Temm-Grove CT, Jockusch B, Rohde M, Niebuhr K, Chakraborty T, Wehland J. 1994. Exploitation of microfilament proteins by *Listeria monocytogenes:* microvillus-like composition of the comet tails and vectorial spreading in polarized epithelial sheets. *J. Cell Sci.* 107:2951–60

Teysseire N, Chiche-Portiche C, Raoult D. 1992. Intracellular movements of *Rickettsia conorii* and *R. typhi* based on actin polymerization. *Res. Microbiol.* 143:821–29

Theriot J. 1995. The cell biology of infection by intracellular bacterial pathogens. *Annu. Rev. Cell Dev. Biol.* 11:213–39

Theriot JA, Mitchison TJ, Tilney LG, Portnoy DA. 1992. The rate of actin-based motility of intracellular *Listeria monocytogenes* equals the rate of actin polymerization. *Nature* 357:257–60

Theriot JA, Rosenblatt J, Portnoy DA, Goldschmidt-Clermont PJ, Mitchison TJ. 1994. Involvement of profilin in the actin-based motility of L. monocytogenes in cells and in cell-free extracts. *Cell* 76:505–17

Tilney LG, DeRosier DJ, Tilney MS. 1992a. How *Listeria* exploits host cell actin to form its own cytoskeleton. I. Formation of a tail and how that tail might be involved in movement. *J. Cell Biol.* 118:71–81

Tilney LG, DeRosier DJ, Weber A, Tilney MS. 1992b. How *Listeria* exploits host cell actin to form its own cytoskeleton. II. Nucleation, Actin filament polarity, filament assembly, and evidence for a pointed end capper. *J. Cell Biol.* 118:83–93

Tilney LG, Portnoy DA. 1989. Actin filaments and the growth, movement, and spread of the intracellular bacterial parasite, *Listeria monocytogenes*. *J. Cell Biol.* 109:1597–608

Tilney LG, Tilney MS. 1994. Methods to vizualize actin polymerisation associated with bacterial invasion. *Methods Enzymol.* 236:476–81

Toker A, Cantley LG. 1997. Signalling through the lipid products of phosphoinositide-3-OH kinase. *Nature* 387:673–76

Tolias KF, Cantley LC, Carpenter CL. 1995. Rho family GTPases bind to phosphoinositide kinases. *J. Biol. Chem.* 270:17656–59

Tran Van Nhieu G, Ben-Ze'ev A, Sansonetti PJ. 1997. Modulation of bacterial entry in epithelial cells by association between vinculin and the *Shigella* IpaA invasin. *EMBO J.* 16:2717–29

Tran Van Nhieu G, Isberg R. 1993. Bacterial internalization mediated by $\beta 1$ chain integrins is determined by ligand affinity and receptor density. *EMBO J.* 12:1887–95

Tran Van Nhieu G, Krukonis ES, Reszka AA, Horwitz AF, Isberg RR. 1996. Mutations in the cytoplasmic domain of the integrin $\beta 1$ chain indicate a role for endocytosis factors in bacterial internalization. *J. Biol. Chem.* 271:7665–72

Van Putten JPM, Paul SM. 1995. Binding of syndecan-like cell surface proteoglycan receptors is required for *Neisseria gonorrhoeae* entry into human mucosal cells. *EMBO J.* 14:2144–54

Velge P, Bottreau E, Kaeffer B, Yurdusev N, Pardon P, Van Langendonck N. 1994. Protein tyrosine kinase inhibitors block the entries of *Listeria monocytogenes* and *Listeria ivanovii* into epithelial cells. *Microbiol. Pathol.* 17:37–50

Vignoud L, Albigès-Rizo C, Frachet P, Block MR. 1997. NPXY motifs control the recruitment of the $\alpha_5\beta_1$ integrin in focal adhesions independently of the association of talin with the $\beta 1$ chain. *J. Cell. Sci.* 110:1421–30

Vignoud L, Usson Y, Balzac F, Tarone G, Block MR. 1994. Internalization of the $\alpha_5\beta_1$ integrin does not depend on "NPXY" signals. *Biochem. Biophys. Res. Commun.* 199:603–11

Virji M, Makepeace K, Ferguson DJP, Watt SM. 1996. Carcinoembryonic antigens (CD66) on epithelial cells and neutrophils are receptors for Opa proteins of pathogenic *Neisseriae*. *Mol. Microbiol.* 22:941–50

Watarai M, Funato S, Sasakawa C. 1996. Interation of Ipa proteins of *Shigella flexneri* with $\alpha_5\beta_1$ integrin promotes entry of the bacteria into mammalian cells. *J. Exp. Med.* 183:991–99

Watarai M, Kamata Y, Kozaki S, Sasakawa C. 1997. rho, a small GTP-binding protein, is essential for *Shigella* invasion of epithelial cells. *J. Exp. Med.* 185:281–92

Welch MD, Iwamatsu A, Mitchison TJ. 1997. Actin polymerization is induced by Arp2/3 protein complex at the surface of *Listeria monocytogenes*. *Nature* 385:265–69

Zeile WL, Purich DL, Southwick FS. 1996. Recognition of two classes of oligoproline sequences in profilin-mediated acceleration of actin-based *Shigella* motility. *J. Cell Biol.* 133:49–59

Annu. Rev. Cell Dev. Biol. 1998. 14:167–96

TRANSCRIPTIONAL CONTROL OF MUSCLE DEVELOPMENT BY MYOCYTE ENHANCER FACTOR-2 (MEF2) PROTEINS

Brian L. Black* and Eric N. Olson

Department of Molecular Biology and Oncology, The University of Texas
Southwestern Medical Center, 5323 Harry Hines Blvd., Dallas, Texas 75235-9148;
e-mail: bblack@mednet.swmed.edu; eolson@hamon.swmed.edu

KEY WORDS: myogenesis, MADS-box, transcription factor, gene expression, cardiac
               development

ABSTRACT

Metazoans contain multiple types of muscle cells that share several common properties, including contractility, excitability, and expression of overlapping sets of muscle structural genes that mediate these functions. Recent biochemical and genetic studies have demonstrated that members of the myocyte enhancer factor-2 (MEF2) family of MADS (MCM1, agamous, deficiens, serum response factor)-box transcription factors play multiple roles in muscle cells to control myogenesis and morphogenesis. Like other MADS-box proteins, MEF2 proteins act combinatorially through protein-protein interactions with other transcription factors to control specific sets of target genes. Genetic studies in *Drosophila* have also begun to reveal the upstream elements of myogenic regulatory hierarchies that control MEF2 expression during development of skeletal, cardiac, and visceral muscle lineages. Paradoxically, MEF2 factors also regulate cell proliferation by functioning as endpoints for a variety of growth factor-regulated intracellular signaling pathways that are antagonistic to muscle differentiation. We discuss the diverse functions of this family of transcription factors, the ways in which they are regulated, and their mechanisms of action.

*Present address: Cardiovascular Research Institute, University of California, 505 Parnassus Avenue, San Francisco, CA 94143-0130; e-mail: brian_black@quickmail.ucsf.edu

167

CONTENTS

INTRODUCTION

Metazoans contain multiple muscle cell types that differ in morphology, patterns of gene expression, pharmacologic responsiveness, and proliferative potential. These muscle types share the properties of being contractile and excitable and express overlapping sets of muscle-specific genes. How different types of muscle cells arise during development and whether their myogenic regulatory programs depend on similar or distinct sets of transcription factors are intriguing questions that are beginning to be answered.

Recently, a family of transcription factors, the myocyte enhancer factor-2 (MEF2) family, has been shown to play a pivotal role in morphogenesis and myogenesis of skeletal, cardiac, and smooth muscle cells (Olson et al 1995). MEF2 factors [also referred to as RSRF (Related to Serum Response Factor)] are expressed in all developing muscle cell types, they bind a conserved DNA sequence in the control regions of the majority of muscle-specific genes, and loss-of-function studies indicate that they are essential for activation of muscle gene expression during embryogenesis. Biochemical and genetic studies in vertebrate and invertebrate organisms have shown that MEF2 factors regulate myogenesis through combinatorial interactions with other transcription factors. MEF2 factors are evolutionarily conserved and appear to function at the core of an ancient regulatory network for muscle formation. Paradoxically, MEF2 factors also appear to activate gene expression in response to mitogenic signaling pathways, which oppose muscle gene activation.

The expression and functions of MEF2 proteins are subject to multiple forms of positive and negative control, which serve to fine-tune the diverse transcriptional circuits in which these factors participate. We describe the structure, functions, and regulation of MEF2 factors and consider mechanisms that may account for the apparently antithetical activities of these factors in the control of cell differentiation and growth.

STRUCTURE-FUNCTION OF MEF2 FACTORS

MEF2 was originally identified as a DNA-binding activity from skeletal muscle cells that recognized a conserved A/T-rich DNA sequence in the muscle creatine kinase (MCK) enhancer (Gossett et al 1989). The MEF2-binding site has subsequently been identified in the control regions of nearly all skeletal and cardiac muscle genes (Table 1). For many of these genes it has been demonstrated that mutation of the MEF2-binding sites either extinguishes or severely diminishes their expression or that ectopically expressed MEF2 can activate their expression. These MEF2-dependent genes encode a wide array of proteins, including numerous muscle-specific enzymes and structural proteins, as well as other transcription factors.

In vertebrates, there are four *mef2* genes, referred to as *mef2a, -b, -c,* and *-d,* that are located on different chromosomes (Pollock & Treisman 1991, Yu et al 1992, Breitbart et al 1993, Leifer et al 1993, Martin et al 1993, 1994, McDermott et al 1993, Hidaka et al 1995, Hobson et al 1995, Ticho et al 1996, Molkentin et al 1996b, Suzuki et al 1996, Morisaki et al 1997). There is a single *mef2* gene in each of the genomes of *Drosophila* (Lilly et al 1994, Nguyen et al 1994), *Caenorhabditis elegans* (M Krause, personal communication), and sea urchins (J Venuti, personal communication). The intron-exon organization of the *mef2* genes from vertebrates and *Drosophila* is identical within the conserved regions of the genes, consistent with the notion that they evolved from a common ancestral *mef2* gene.

MEF2 Factors Belong to the MADS-Box Family of Transcriptional Regulators

The MADS-box is named for the first four members of the family to be identified: MCM1, a yeast factor involved in mating-type selection; Agamous and Deficiens, which act as homeotic factors that control leaf identity in plants; and serum-response factor (SRF), which regulates growth factor-inducible and muscle genes (Shore & Sharrocks 1995). The MADS-box is a 57-amino acid

Table 1   Genes regulated by MEF2

aldolase A	Joh et al 1991, Hidaka et al 1993, Salminen et al 1995
α-myosin heavy chain	Adolph et al 1993, Molkentin & Markham 1993, 1994
α-PS2 integrin	Ranganayakulu et al 1995
AMP deaminase I	Morisaki & Holmes 1993
beta-enolase (ENO3)	Feo et al 1995
BZLF1	Liu et al 1997
c-jun	Han & Prywes 1995, Rozek & Pfeifer 1995, Han et al 1997
desmin	Li & Capetenaki 1994, Kuisk et al 1996
D-mef2	R Cripps & E Olson, unpublished data
dystrophin	Nishio et al 1994, Klamut et al 1997
Gax	Andres et al 1995b, Skopicki et al 1997
GLUT4	Liu et al 1994
MRF4	Black et al 1995, Naidu et al 1995
muscle creatine kinase (MCK)	Amacher et al 1993, Cserjesi et al 1994, Ferrari et al 1997
myogenin	Edmondson et al 1992, Cheng et al 1993, Yee & Rigby 1993, Malik et al 1995
MyoD	Dechesne et al 1994, Leibham et al 1994, Wong et al 1994, Pinney et al 1995
myoglobin	Bassel-Duby et al 1992
myosin light chain 1/3	McGrew et al 1996, Rao et al 1996
myosin light chain 2 (Xenopus)	Chambers et al 1994
myosin light chain 2v	Navankasattusas et al 1992, Lee et al 1994, Ross et al 1996
Nur77	Woronicz et al 1995
phosphoglycerate mutase	Nakatsuji et al 1992
skeletal α-actin	Muscat et al 1992
smooth muscle myosin heavy chain	Katoh et al 1994
SR Ca²⁺ ATPase	Moriscot et al 1997
tropomyosin I (Drosophila)	MH Lin et al 1996, 1997, Lin & Storti 1997
troponin C	Gahlmann & Kedes 1993, Parmacek et al 1994
troponin Is	Nakayama et al 1996
troponin T	Wang et al 1994

motif located at the extreme N terminus of the MEF2 factors (Figure 1). This motif serves as a minimal DNA-binding domain, which requires an adjacent 29-amino acid extension, referred to as the MEF2 domain, for high-affinity DNA binding and dimerization (Molkentin et al 1996a). Within the MADS-box, the MEF2 factors share homology at several invariant residues with other members of the MADS-box family of transcription factors. These conserved residues are important for DNA sequence recognition. The MEF2 domain is unique to MEF2 factors, but other MADS-box proteins contain domains with analogous functions. In addition to its role in DNA binding, the MADS-box

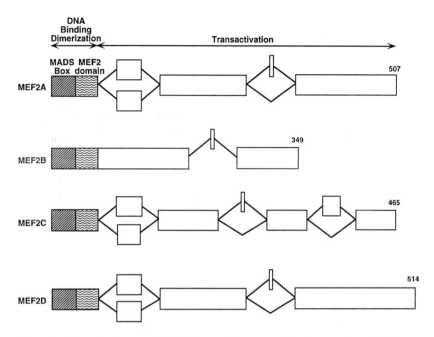

Figure 1 Schematic diagrams of MEF2 factors. Structures of the four vertebrate MEF2 gene products are shown. Alternative exons within the C-terminal activation domains are indicated, along with the number of amino acids in the longer form of each protein.

mediates dimerization of MADS-box proteins, and the MEF2 domain is important for interactions with accessory factors. MEF2 factors can homo- and heterodimerize, but they cannot interact with other MADS-box factors, suggesting that specific amino acid residues within the MADS-box that establish the dimerization interface are not conserved outside the MEF2 family. Given the multiplicity of MEF2 isoforms and the extensive alternative splicing that occurs within MEF2 transcripts, there is enormous potential for different heterodimeric associations among these factors. Thus far there have been only a few examples from in vitro assays or overexpression studies of functional differences among different MEF2 isoforms. Whether functional differences occur in vivo remains to be determined.

The vertebrate MEF2 gene products share about 50% amino acid identity overall and about 95% similarity throughout the highly conserved MADS-box and MEF2 domain, whereas they are divergent in their C-terminal regions. MEF2 factors from invertebrates are also highly homologous to the vertebrate factors in the MADS-box and MEF2 domain. The *Drosophila* MEF2 protein, referred to as D-MEF2, binds the same DNA sequence as its vertebrate counterparts and can activate transcription through the MEF2 site in mammalian cells (Lilly et al 1994, Nguyen et al 1994). Two factors with 67% homology to the MADS domains of vertebrate MEF2 proteins have also been identified in yeast (Dodou & Treisman 1997). These factors bind the same DNA sequence as the metazoan MEF2 factors.

The only MADS-box protein to be crystallized thus far is SRF (Pelligrini et al 1995). The structure of SRF bound to DNA reveals that the core DNA-binding domain adopts a novel structure composed of three distinct domains. The N-terminal portion of the MADS-box assumes a coiled-coil structure that contacts DNA, followed by a four-stranded β-sheet involved in both DNA binding and dimerization. C-terminal to the MADS-box of SRF is an extension that is oriented away from the DNA and is important for interactions with accessory factors. The extensive homology between the MADS-box of SRF and the MEF2 factors suggests that the DNA-binding domains of these proteins adopt similar conformations.

MADS-box proteins generally bind A/T-rich DNA sequences. SRF binds preferentially to the consensus sequence $CC(A/T)_6GG$, referred to as a CArG-box, whereas MEF2 binds $YTA(A/T)_4TAR$. MEF2A, -C, and -D have the same DNA binding specificity, whereas MEF2B binds the MEF2 consensus sequence with reduced affinity relative to the other family members (Pollock & Treisman 1991, Yu et al 1992, Molkentin et al 1996b). The ability of different MADS-box factors to discriminate between related A/T-rich binding sites is dependent on three basic amino acids at positions 1, 11, and 15 in the MADS-box that differ among the different factors (Nurrish & Treisman 1995). Sequences outside the MADS-box can also influence DNA binding specificity, as shown for SRF. Deletion of sequences N-terminal to the MADS-box of SRF relaxes its DNA binding specificity, allowing it to bind the MEF2 site, as well as to the CArG-box (Nurrish & Treisman 1995). Nucleotides flanking the MEF2 site have also been shown to profoundly influence DNA binding (Yu et al 1992, Andres et al 1995a, Fickett 1996b). MEF2, for example, can show vastly different binding to identical MEF2 sites that are flanked by different sequences. DNA-binding site selection using MEF2 from muscle and neural nuclear extracts has also demonstrated that the optimal target for MEF2 from neurons shows sequence constraints in the regions flanking the invariant A/T-core motif that are not observed with MEF2 factors from other cell types (Andres et al 1995a). Such sequence selectivity could, in principle, provide a mechanism for differential gene activation by MEF2 in different cell types.

The MADS-box and MEF2 domain are necessary and sufficient for DNA binding, but they lack transcriptional activity on their own. The C-terminal regions of MEF2 factors contain transcription activation domains and are subject to complex patterns of alternative splicing (Figure 1), with certain exons being present ubiquitously and others being muscle- or neural-specific. In MEF2A, an acidic exon with the sequence SEEEELEL is specific to muscle and neural cells in which MEF2 DNA-binding activity is detected and is absent in MEF2 transcripts from a variety of cell types in which MEF2A protein is not detected (Yu et al 1992). MEF2D contains a similar acidic exon (TEDHLDL), which is present only in transcripts from skeletal muscle, heart, and brain, and correlates with MEF2D-binding activity (Breitbart et al 1993, Martin et al 1994). The corresponding domain in MEF2C (SEDVDLLL) is present in transcripts from skeletal muscle only (McDermott et al 1993). Although the presence of these exons seems to correlate with high levels of MEF2 DNA-binding activity, their inclusion in MEF2 proteins is not absolutely essential for DNA-binding activity because overexpression of MEF2 isoforms lacking these exons in fibroblasts gives rise to MEF2 proteins that bind DNA efficiently. Moreover, as discussed below, MEF2 DNA-binding activity is detected in various cell types in which these acidic exons are not included in MEF2 transcripts.

There is relatively little amino acid homology between the C-terminal regions of different MEF2 gene products, except for the short acidic exons described above and four serine/threonine-rich regions (Figure 2). Certain of the latter regions are contained within transcription activation domains; the functions of the others remain to be determined. MEF2A has also been shown to contain a nuclear localization sequence at its extreme C-terminal region, which is conserved in MEF2C and MEF2D. When this sequence is deleted, MEF2A fails

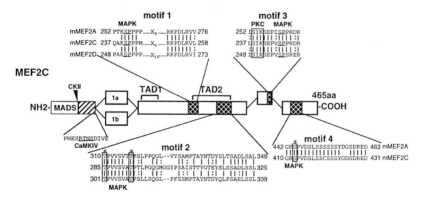

Figure 2 Conserved regions in the C terminus of MEF2 contain potential phosphorylation sites. Sites that are phosphorylated by p38 and ERK5 are marked with *asterisks*. Not all potential phosphorylation sites are shown. Some of these conserved stretches overlap with transactivation domains (TADs) that have been mapped by deletion analysis. PKC, protein kinase C site; MAPK, mitogen-activated protein kinase site; CKII casein kinase II site; CaMKIV, calcium-calmodulin kinase IV site.

to localize to the cell nucleus (Yu 1996). This nuclear localization signal is not present in MEF2B or D-MEF2, yet these factors still localize to the cell nucleus. Thus other sequences must mediate their nuclear localization. Of note, a mutant form of *Drosophila* MEF2 lacking only 25 residues from the extreme C-terminal region fails to localize efficiently to the nucleus in vivo (Ranganayakulu et al 1995). How the C-terminal sequences of that MEF2 factor participate in nuclear localization has not been addressed.

MEF2 factors, as well as other MADS-box proteins, have been shown to bend DNA upon high-affinity DNA binding. Meierhans et al (1997) showed that the MEF2 site is an inherently bendable sequence and it is this bendability that is one of the principal determinants recognized by MEF2C during in vitro DNA binding. This is consistent with the ability of two other MADS-box factors, SRF and MCM1, to bend DNA and affect transcriptional activation through selective DNA bending in vivo (West et al 1997, Acton et al 1997).

A hallmark of MADS-box proteins is their combinatorial associations with other MADS domain factors, as well as with other heterologous classes of transcriptional regulators (Shore & Sharrocks 1995, Riechmann & Meyerowitz 1997). This role for MADS-box proteins has been particularly well studied in plants where, through protein-protein interactions, these factors play a critical role in leaf specification and exert homeotic transformations in specialized leaf structures when any of the MADS-box genes are mutated (Theissen & Saedler 1995, Theissen et al 1996, Riechmann & Meyerowitz 1997). SRF and MCM1 also interact with a variety of positive and negative cofactors that determine the pattern of gene expression activated by these factors (reviewed in Shore & Sharrocks 1995). Recent evidence indicates that protein-protein interactions play a critical role in determining the target genes for MEF2 proteins (see below).

REGULATION OF MEF2 EXPRESSION AND ACTIVITY

Although the importance of MEF2 for muscle gene activation is undisputed, the cell type distribution of MEF2 proteins has been the subject of controversy. Numerous studies have described MEF2 DNA-binding activity as being highly enriched in muscle cells, whereas others have reported it to be ubiquitous, with no apparent preference for expression in muscle. The basis for these different results is unclear, but given the multiple levels of regulation of MEF2 expression, it is perhaps not surprising that differences in cell culture or assay conditions could result in differences in MEF2 expression. Indeed, there is mounting evidence demonstrating that MEF2 expression is regulated transcriptionally, translationally, and post-translationally. This diversity of regulatory mechanisms provides multiple checkpoints to govern the functions of this family of factors during cell differentiation and growth.

Cell-Type Distribution of MEF2 Protein and mRNA

The primary mode of regulation of MEF2 expression during embryogenesis appears to be at the level of mRNA accumulation. In vertebrates and fruit flies, *mef2* transcripts are highly enriched in developing muscle cell lineages during embryogenesis. In the mouse and chick, *mef2c* is the first of the *mef2* genes to be expressed, with transcripts appearing initially in mesodermal precursors that give rise to the heart (Edmondson et al 1994). Soon thereafter, transcripts for the other *mef2* genes are expressed in the developing myocardium. *mef2* gene expression is detected in developing skeletal and smooth muscle cell lineages concomitant with activation of their differentiation programs, and this high level of transcription results in high levels of MEF2 proteins that are clearly detectable in developing muscle lineages during mammalian embryogenesis (Subramanian & Nadal-Ginard 1996). In *Xenopus* embryos, maternally derived *mef2* transcripts are present at a very low level in unfertilized eggs (Chambers et al 1992). Following gastrulation, the level of *mef2* transcripts and binding activity increases until the swimming tadpole stage, and these transcripts are confined to cells of the somitic mesoderm and later to myotomal muscle (Chambers et al 1992). Similarly, the single *mef2* gene in *Drosophila* is expressed throughout the unspecified mesoderm following gastrulation, and subsequently expression becomes restricted to the skeletal, cardiac, and visceral muscle lineages throughout embryonic and larval development (Lilly et al 1994, Nguyen et al 1994, Taylor et al 1995).

In skeletal muscle cells in culture, MEF2D has been reported to be expressed in proliferating myoblasts prior to the onset of differentiation (Breitbart et al 1993). MEF2A protein appears as cells enter the differentiation pathway, and MEF2C is expressed late in the differentiation program. The significance of these different temporal patterns of MEF2 expression is unclear.

In addition to their expression in muscle cells, members of the MEF2 family are expressed at high levels in the developing central nervous system. In vertebrates, each *mef2* gene shows a unique expression pattern in different regions of the brain (Leifer et al 1993, 1994, Lyons et al 1995, Ikeshima et al 1995, X Lin et al 1996). Expression is especially prominent in the cerebellum, cerebral cortex, and hippocampus. The timing of MEF2 expression in neural cells is consistent with a role for MEF2 factors in activation of neural differentiation, but no neural target genes have been identified to date. In *Drosophila*, D-MEF2 is also expressed at high levels in neurons within the mushroom bodies, which function as the learning center, as well as in optic neurons (Schulz et al 1996). *Drosophila* embryos lacking MEF2 die from muscle defects prior to development of the nervous system (Lilly et al 1995, Bour et al 1995, Ranganayakulu et al 1995). The functions of MEF2 in neural development in this or any other organism have not been determined.

Transcriptional Control

As discussed above, the regulation of *mef2* expression occurs primarily at the level of mRNA accumulation during embryonic development. The vertebrate *mef2* genes contain large 5′ noncoding regions with multiple alternatively spliced exons and large introns. Because of this complexity, no *cis*-acting regulatory sequences have yet been described for any vertebrate *mef2* gene. However, there has been progress toward defining the regulatory elements that control *mef2* transcription in *Drosophila*. The *D-mef2* gene contains at least a dozen independent enhancers within 12 kb upstream of the gene, each of which directs transcription in a unique temporospatial pattern during development (R Cripps, B Zhao & E Olson, unpublished data). The integration of transcriptional inputs from these different elements is required for the complete pattern of *D-mef2* expression throughout embryonic and adult muscle development.

Two *D-mef2* enhancers have been characterized in detail. A cardiac-specific enhancer, which directs transcription in cardiac precursor cells and in the heart-like organ of the embryo, known as the dorsal vessel, is located about 6 kb upstream of the gene (Gajewski et al 1997). This enhancer contains two binding sites for the cardiac homeodomain protein Tinman, which is required for *Drosophila* heart formation (Azpiazu & Frasch 1993, Bodmer 1993). *D-mef2* is the only direct in vivo target gene for Tinman identified to date (Gajewski et al 1997). Mutation of these binding sites abolishes enhancer activity, and ectopic expression of Tinman under control of a heat shock promoter results in activation of this enhancer outside the mesoderm (Gajewski et al 1997). These results suggest that part of Tinman's function in cardiac myogenesis is to activate *D-mef2* (Figure 3). It is tempting to speculate that the vertebrate *tinman* homolog *Nkx2.5* plays a similar role in cardiac muscle differentiation. *Nkx2.5* is expressed prior to *mef2* genes during development of the vertebrate heart (Lints et al 1993, Harvey 1996). It remains to be determined if a function of Nkx2.5 is to activate expression of *mef2* genes in a fashion similar to that of Tinman in the fly.

Transcription of *D-mef2* in embryonic and adult somatic muscle precursors is dependent on another enhancer located about 2 kb upstream of the gene (Cripps et al 1998). This enhancer is controlled by the basic helix-loop-helix (bHLH) transcription factor Twist, which is essential for mesodermal specification and myogenesis in *Drosophila* (Figure 3) (Baylies & Bate 1996). Twist activates this *D-mef2* enhancer directly by binding an E-box (CANNTG) that

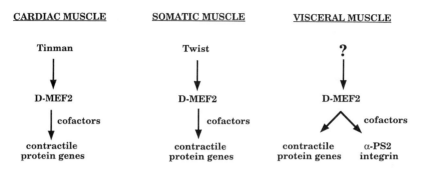

Figure 3 MEF2 in the pathways for myogenesis in *Drosophila*. The position of MEF2 in the skeletal, cardiac, and visceral muscle lineages is indicated. In the cardiac muscle lineage, Tinman directly activates *D-mef2* transcription. In the skeletal muscle lineage, Twist along with other factors not yet identified, directly activates *D-mef2*. In the visceral muscle lineage, the upstream activators of *D-mef2* transcription are not identified. In all muscle lineages, MEF2 directly switches on contractile protein genes during differentiation.

is conserved between *Drosophila melanogaster* and *D. virilis*. In *twist*-null embryos, mesoderm fails to form and *D-mef2* is not expressed (Lilly et al 1994, Nguyen et al 1994, Taylor et al 1995). By use of a temperature-sensitive mutant of Twist, Twist has been shown to be necessary for activation of this *D-mef2* enhancer in adult somatic muscle precursor cells; reduction of Twist function results in muscle phenotypes similar to those observed in flies harboring hypomorphic *D-mef2* alleles (Ranganayakulu et al 1995, Cripps et al 1998). This enhancer is also active in the early mesoderm, indicating that it regulates *D-mef2* transcription at multiple times during development. If *twist* is switched off following gastrulation, somatic muscles fail to form properly (Baylies & Bate 1996). Likewise, in the absence of D-MEF2, a similar phenotype occurs in the somatic musculature (Ranganayakulu et al 1995). The failure of somatic muscles to properly form and differentiate in the absence of Twist is likely a direct result of a failure of *D-mef2* to be activated via this enhancer (Cripps et al 1998). Since Twist is also expressed in cells in which this enhancer is inactive, additional regulatory factors must cooperate with Twist. Whether Twist regulates *mef2* gene expression during vertebrate embryogenesis remains to be determined.

Translational Control

In adult tissues, transcripts for MEF2C are restricted to skeletal muscle, brain, and spleen, whereas transcripts for the other MEF2 factors are expressed more ubiquitously (Pollock & Treisman 1991, Chambers et al 1992, Yu et al 1992, Martin et al 1993, McDermott et al 1993, Black et al 1997). Despite the widespread expression of transcripts for MEF2A, -B, and -D, several studies have reported that the corresponding proteins are largely restricted to muscle and neural cells (Yu et al 1992, Leifer et al 1993, Leifer et al 1994).

The basis for the disparity between MEF2 protein and mRNA levels has been studied in vascular smooth muscle cells, in which MEF2A protein levels dramatically increase in response to serum stimulation, without a corresponding change in mRNA levels (Suzuki et al 1995). In skeletal muscle cells, it has been shown that sequences in the 3'-untranslated region (UTR) of MEF2A transcripts play a role in translational regulation (Black et al 1997). An evolutionarily conserved sequence within the 3'-UTR of MEF2A mRNA has been shown to inhibit translation in nonmuscle cells, and this repression is released upon muscle differentiation (Black et al 1997). The level of repression observed in that study was nearly identical to the change in MEF2A protein level seen during serum stimulation in vascular smooth muscle cells, suggesting that the element within the 3'-UTR is largely responsible for the translational control of MEF2A (Suzuki et al 1995, Black et al 1997).

Although these studies indicate that translational control mechanisms play a role in regulating *mef2* gene expression, other studies suggest that MEF2 proteins, as well as transcripts, are more ubiquitously expressed following embryonic development (Dodou et al 1995, Ornatsky & McDermott 1996). These latter studies suggest that the primary mechanism of control of *mef2* gene expression is at the level of transcription. The reason for this discrepancy remains to be elucidated, but it is clear that MEF2A expression likely is regulated at multiple levels during development and differentiation. Given the role of MEF2 proteins in promoting differentiation, it would clearly benefit a cell to maintain tight control of MEF2 levels to ensure that MEF2 proteins are expressed in a precise temporospatial pattern.

Post-Translational Control

There is also evidence that the transcriptional activity of MEF2 proteins can be regulated independently of DNA binding in various cell types. It has been reported, for example, that HeLa cells and 3T3 fibroblasts contain levels of MEF2 binding activity comparable to those in C2C12 skeletal myotubes, but MEF2 lacks transcriptional activity in these nonmuscle cell types (Ornatsky & McDermott 1996). The predominant MEF2 DNA-binding complex in muscle cells is composed of MEF2A homodimers, whereas in nonmuscle cells it is made up of MEF2A:MEF2D heterodimers. These results suggest that, at least under certain conditions, MEF2D is transcriptionally silent and that the presence of MEF2A is essential for transcriptional activation. Because MEF2D contains a transcriptional activation domain, it is unclear how its activity might be repressed in nonmuscle cell types. This type of regulation could occur through the action of a negative factor in nonmuscle cells that specifically represses the activity of MEF2D. Because such a repressor would presumably be limiting, this model would also explain why overexpression of MEF2D in nonmuscle cells can activate MEF2-dependent reporter genes, since the repressor would be overcome in these types of assays.

Phosphorylation also plays an important role in the regulation of MEF2 expression. A casein kinase II (CKII) phosphorylation site is conserved in the MADS-box of all known MEF2 proteins. Phosphorylation of this site by CKII dramatically enhances the DNA-binding activity of MEF2C (Molkentin et al 1996c). This site appears to be phosphorylated constitutively in vivo with no evidence thus far for regulation. It is likely that phosphorylation of this site induces a conformational change that enhances the ability of the MADS and MEF2 domains to contact DNA (Molkentin et al 1996c). Phosphorylation of the activation domains of MEF2 factors has also been shown to have important regulatory consequences, as discussed below.

COMBINATORIAL CONTROL OF TRANSCRIPTION BY MEF2 FACTORS

Members of the MEF2 family, similar to other MADS-box proteins, interact with a variety of transcription factors to activate diverse programs of gene expression. The most extensively studied interactions of MEF2 factors are with members of the MyoD family of skeletal muscle bHLH proteins. The combinatorial associations of proteins from these two families appear to establish a transcriptional code specific for skeletal muscle gene activation.

Interactions Between MEF2 and Myogenic bHLH Proteins

The transcriptional circuitry controlling skeletal muscle development has been particularly well studied (for detailed reviews see Ludolph & Konieczny 1995, Molkentin & Olson 1996, Yun & Wold 1996). Specification and differentiation of skeletal muscle cells is controlled by members of the MyoD family of myogenic bHLH proteins, MyoD, Myf5, myogenin, and MRF4. These factors form heterodimers with a ubiquitous class of bHLH transcription factors known as E proteins and bind a consensus DNA sequence referred to as an E-box (CANNTG) in the control regions of muscle-specific genes.

Each of the myogenic bHLH factors has the ability to activate the complete program for muscle differentiation when introduced into nonmuscle cell types. The dominant muscle-inducing activity of these factors has raised the question of whether the MEF2 factors might also possess such activity. On this issue, there has been disagreement. Kaushal et al (1994) reported that MEF2 factors can activate myogenesis in transfected 10T1/2 and 3T3 fibroblasts with an efficiency comparable to that of the myogenic bHLH proteins. In contrast, Molkentin et al (1995) and others (Yu et al 1992, Ornatsky et al 1997) found that MEF2 factors were unable to activate myogenesis alone; instead, these factors cooperated with myogenic bHLH factors to activate muscle gene expression. This type of combinatorial role for MEF2 factors would appear to be more compatible with the expression pattern of these factors because it is clear they are expressed outside the skeletal muscle lineage.

A single myogenic bHLH gene in *Drosophila*, referred to as *nautilus*, is expressed in a subset of somatic muscle precursor cells and differentiated muscle fibers (Michelson et al 1990, Paterson et al 1991). There is agreement about the ability of MEF2 to activate myogenesis in the absence of *nautilus*. Ectopic expression of MEF2 in the dorsal vessel or the ectoderm, under control of various promoters, results in activation of skeletal muscle gene expression and formation of multinucleate myotubes in *Drosophila* embryos (MH Lin et al 1997). These results demonstrate that MEF2 can initiate myogenesis in certain cellular contexts, probably as a consequence of its ability to establish functional interactions with other myogenic cofactors.

Activation of muscle transcription by myogenic bHLH factors is dependent on two amino acid residues, alanine and threonine, in the core of their basic domains, along with an additional residue at the junction of the basic region and the HLH motif (Davis et al 1990, Brennan et al 1991, Weintraub et al 1991, Davis & Weintraub 1992, Winter et al 1992). These residues are specific to, and conserved in, all known myogenic bHLH proteins. If these residues from the myogenic bHLH factors are changed to asparagines, which are present at the corresponding position in the basic domains of E proteins, the myogenic bHLH factors are rendered nonmyogenic, but this type of mutant retains the ability to dimerize with E proteins and bind DNA. Based on the essential role of these specific amino acids in the basic regions of the myogenic bHLH factors for activation of myogenesis, it was proposed that these residues (and probably others) mediate interaction with an essential myogenic coregulator (Davis et al 1990, Brennan et al 1991).

Several studies suggest that MEF2 factors function as the essential myogenic coregulator required by myogenic bHLH proteins to initiate myogenesis and that members of these two families of transcription factors act through a combinatorial mechanism to control skeletal myogenesis (Kaushal et al 1994, Molkentin et al 1995, Black et al 1998). MEF2 proteins augment the myogenic activity of myogenic bHLH proteins, and this is dependent on the myogenic amino acids in the MyoD basic region (Molkentin et al 1995, Black et al 1998). This synergy also occurs on native promoters, as both the *MRF4* and *desmin* genes appear to be synergistically activated by coexpression of myogenic bHLH and MEF2 factors (Li & Capetenaki 1994, Naidu et al 1995). The role of MEF2 and myogenic bHLH proteins in synergistic activation of native promoters is apparent in the coordinate positioning of MEF2 sites and E-boxes in numerous muscle-specific control regions. Wright et al (1991) found that MEF2 sites are frequently associated with functional E-boxes bound by myogenin and that these sites are often positioned with precise spacing to allow both factors to bind DNA simultaneously, which likely promotes protein-protein interactions by these factors (Fickett 1996a).

The synergy between MEF2 and myogenic bHLH proteins is dramatized in experiments in which the bHLH region of myogenin and full-length MEF2C are expressed separately or together in transfected 10T1/2 fibroblasts. The bHLH region of myogenin can dimerize with E proteins and bind DNA, but it is devoid of myogenic activity because of the lack of a transcriptional activation domain. However, when the myogenin bHLH region is expressed with MEF2, myogenesis is efficiently activated (Molkentin et al 1995). This suggests that MEF2 contributes its transcriptional activation to the multiprotein complex with myogenin to activate downstream muscle-specific genes.

Synergy between MEF2 and myogenic bHLH factors is mediated by direct physical interaction between the MADS-box and the bHLH regions of these factors. This synergy results from physical association of MEF2 proteins with myogenic bHLH proteins that must first heterodimerize with E proteins in order to associate with MEF2 (Molkentin et al 1995, Black et al 1998). On artificial reporter genes containing either MEF2 sites or E-boxes, these factors can cooperate to activate transcription through a single DNA-binding site, without the requirement for both factors to bind DNA (Figure 4). Synergistic activation of myogenesis by MyoD and MEF2 can also be observed with MEF2 mutants that fail to bind DNA, indicating that this type of cooperativity does not require direct binding of MEF2 to DNA (Molkentin et al 1995, Black et al 1998). In contrast, the fact that myogenic bHLH proteins must bind DNA to activate myogenesis indicates that the critical in vivo targets for transcriptional activation by the MyoD/MEF2 complex must be E-box dependent (Molkentin et al 1995).

If members of the MyoD family require MEF2 proteins to activate myogenesis, how do they initiate myogenesis when expressed ectopically in nonmuscle cells without MEF2? Myogenic bHLH proteins have been shown to upregulate MEF2 expression in nonmuscle cells, and this can occur independently of activation of downstream muscle structural genes (Cserjesi & Olson 1991, Lassar et al 1991). Thus myogenic bHLH factors induce their own cofactors. Further evidence for the importance of MEF2 factors for the muscle-inducing activity of myogenic bHLH proteins comes from the observation that MyoD is incapable of initiating myogenesis in 10T1/2 fibroblasts in the presence of a dominant-negative form of MEF2A that binds DNA but lacks a transcriptional activation domain (Ornatsky & McDermott 1997).

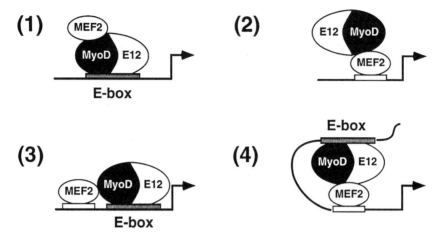

Figure 4   Potential mechanisms for activation of skeletal muscle transcription by MEF2 and myogenic bHLH factors. Transfection assays have revealed four potential mechanisms for synergistic
activation of transcription by MEF2 and myogenic bHLH proteins. (1) MEF2 can interact with
MyoD/E12 heterodimers bound to DNA. (2) MyoD/E12 heterodimers can interact with MEF2
bound to DNA. (3) MEF2 and MyoD/E12 heterodimers can bind adjacent sites to activate transcription synergistically. (4) MEF2 and MyoD/E12 heterodimers can bind non-adjacent sites and
cooperatively activate transcription through protein-protein interactions.

A Two-Step Model for Transcriptional Activation

The notion that the basic domains of myogenic bHLH factors are required to establish a myogenic transcriptional complex with MEF2 is supported by numerous studies showing that mutation or substitution of the myogenic residues in the
basic domains abolishes the ability of these factors to activate the muscle program without affecting their ability to bind to DNA (Davis et al 1990, Brennan
et al 1991, Weintraub et al 1991, Davis & Weintraub 1992, Winter et al 1992,
Black et al 1998). However, recent studies indicate that interaction of MEF2 factors and myogenic bHLH proteins alone is not sufficient to activate myogenesis
or to activate transcription synergistically (Black et al 1998). This is apparent
from studies of a class of MyoD mutants that support interaction with MEF2 but
are incapable of activating transcription and myogenesis. These studies indicate
that initiation of myogenesis requires activation signals by both MEF2 and myogenic bHLH factors to be transmitted to the transcriptional machinery through
the myogenic bHLH factor bound to DNA (Black et al 1998). These studies
suggest a two-step model for transcriptional synergy. In step one (cofactor binding), the myogenic bHLH and MEF2 proteins associate via their DNA-binding
domains. In step two (transmission of the activation signal), the transcriptional
activation domains of these factors contact the basal transcriptional machinery

to establish an active transcriptional complex. Transmission of the activation signal occurs through the DNA-bound cofactor and, in the case of the myogenic bHLH proteins, is dependent on the presence of the myogenic amino acids alanine and threonine in the basic domain (Black et al 1998). It seems likely that interaction of MEF2 results in a conformational change in the MyoD-E12 heterodimer that is dependent on interaction with MEF2 and the presence of the Ala-Thr residues in the MyoD basic domain. Such a conformational change may expose a unique binding surface or transcriptional activation domain necessary for contact with components of the basal transcriptional complex present in muscle cells and required for activation of myogenesis.

Myogenic bHLH and MEF2 Factors Establish a Mutually Reinforcing Regulatory Circuit for Myogenesis

In addition to activating the expression of downstream skeletal muscle structural genes during myogenesis, MEF2 factors play an important role in amplification and maintenance of several myogenic bHLH genes. The mouse *myogenin* and *MRF4* genes contain MEF2-binding sites in their proximal promoters that act together with adjacent E-boxes to control expression of these genes in differentiated muscle cells (Edmondson et al 1992, Cheng et al 1993, Yee & Rigby 1993, Black et al 1995, Naidu et al 1995, Malik et al 1995). The *Xenopus MyoDa* gene, which contains a MEF2 site embedded in the TATA box, is also activated by MEF2 (Leibham et al 1994, Wong et al 1994). Transcriptional activation of this gene requires binding of MEF2 and TFIID. Because TFIID binds primarily to the minor groove (Leibham et al 1994) and MEF2 to the major groove (Gossett et al 1989), it is conceivable that both factors bind simultaneously to this site although it has not been possible to demonstrate concomitant binding of both factors, possibly because the conditions for DNA binding by these factors in vitro are different.

During embryogenesis, members of the MEF2 family are not expressed in the skeletal muscle lineage until after the first myogenic bHLH gene is expressed (Edmondson et al 1994). Thus it is unlikely that MEF2 is involved in the initial activation of the myogenic bHLH genes in vivo. However, in certain skeletal muscle cell lines, it is possible that MEF2 factors are involved in the initial activation of *myogenin* transcription. The expression of MEF2D in proliferating myoblasts is consistent with this notion (Breitbart et al 1993). In addition, activation of *myogenin* transcription through the MEF2 site in differentiating skeletal myoblasts has been reported to occur in the absence of new protein synthesis, indicating that pre-existing MEF2 protein can acquire DNA binding and transcriptional activity via a post-translational mechanism (Buchberger et al 1994). Irrespective of which factor is expressed first, the ability of MEF2 and myogenic bHLH factors to regulate each other's expression provides a positive feedback mechanism for amplifying and maintaining the expression of both factors through a mutually reinforcing regulatory network.

Other MEF2-bHLH Regulatory Networks

The importance of combinatorial interactions between MEF2 and cell type-specific bHLH proteins is likely to extend beyond the skeletal muscle lineage. In neurons, for example, MASH1, a member of the achaete scute family of bHLH factors, interacts with MEF2 (Mao & Nadal-Ginard 1996, Black et al 1996). As in skeletal muscle cells, the multiprotein complex established by these factors depends on interactions between the bHLH and MADS-box and results in synergistic activation of transcription (Mao & Nadal-Ginard 1996, Black et al 1996). Because neurogenic bHLH factors do not contain the myogenic Ala-Thr residues in their basic regions, other protein determinants in MASH1 must be compatible with MEF2 interaction and subsequent transmission of activation signals to the basal transcriptional complex. The target genes for MEF2 proteins in the nervous system remain to be identified.

It has also been shown that MEF2 factors interact with the bHLH protein Twist (Spicer et al 1996). In contrast to the role of Twist as an essential activator of muscle formation in *Drosophila*, in vertebrates Twist inhibits myogenesis by interfering with the activity of myogenic bHLH factors (Hebrok et al 1994, Rohwedel et al 1995, Spicer et al 1996, Gitelman 1997). This interference is mediated by titration of limiting E protein partners for myogenic bHLH proteins and by inhibition of the transcriptional activity of MEF2 factors. Inhibition of MEF2 activity by Twist is dependent on binding of Twist to the C-terminal transcriptional activation domain of MEF2 and requires heterodimerization with E proteins. Both an intact bHLH region and C terminus are necessary for the inhibitory activity of Twist.

The molecular mechanism that mediates bHLH-MEF2 interactions may be the result of mutual interaction with the transcriptional adapter pocket proteins p300 and CBP. Both MyoD and MEF2 interact with p300 via different domains (Sartorelli et al 1997). Mutants of p300, which are incapable of supporting these interactions, ablate the ability of MyoD to activate myogenesis, suggesting that p300 is an essential component required to facilitate myogenesis by MyoD-MEF2 interactions (Sartorelli et al 1997).

Interactions with Other Transcription Factors

bHLH factors are not the only types of cofactors for MEF2. Izumo and coworkers have shown that the MADS-box of MEF2 interacts with the DNA-binding domain of the thyroid hormone receptor (TR) in vivo and in vitro and that these factors synergistically activate the α-*cardiac myosin heavy chain* gene (Lee et al

1997). There appears to be selectivity in this recognition because the steroid receptor RXR does not interact with MEF2.

Combinatorial interactions by MEF2 factors appear to play an important role in promoting muscle differentiation in multiple systems. This occurs during satellite cell differentiation in adult muscle following muscle degeneration and subsequent proliferation of satellite cells. The ets domain transcription factor, polyoma virus enhancer activator 3 (PEA3), promotes differentiation of satellite cells following degeneration, and this function is synergistically promoted in collaboration with MEF2 factors (Taylor et al 1997). Likewise, the *Drosophila* PAR domain-bZIP transcription factor PDP1 is essential for regulating differentiation of somatic muscles and activation of the *tropomyosin I* gene during embryonic muscle development, and this function is dependent upon interaction with D-MEF2 (SC Lin et al 1997).

GENETIC ANALYSIS OF MEF2 FUNCTION

The Role of MEF2 in Drosophila

Because there is only a single *mef2* gene in *Drosophila*, it has been possible to analyze the function of MEF2 in that organism without complications from possible redundancy. *Drosophila* embryos homozygous for null alleles of *D-mef2* die during embryogenesis and exhibit a complete loss of differentiation in all three muscle lineages: somatic, cardiac, and visceral (Lilly et al 1995, Bour et al 1995, Ranganayakulu et al 1995). However, myoblasts within each of these lineages are properly specified and positioned in the absence of MEF2. Consistent with the notion that myogenic bHLH factors depend on MEF2 for myogenic activity, *nautilus* is expressed normally in somatic muscle precursor cells of *D-mef2* mutant embryos, but it is unable to initiate the myogenic program. These results demonstrate that MEF2 acts late in multiple myogenic pathways to control myoblast differentiation (Figure 3). This dramatic mutant phenotype provides the first molecular evidence for a commonality in the molecular mechanisms that control differentiation of diverse muscle cell types and demonstrates that D-MEF2 is a central component of all muscle differentiation programs in *Drosophila*.

In addition to defects in muscle differentiation, *D-mef2* mutant embryos exhibit dramatic morphologic defects in the gut that resemble the defects associated with loss-of-function mutations in the α-*PS2* integrin gene (Ranganayakulu et al 1995). Indeed, α-*PS2* integrin is not expressed in *D-mef2* mutant embryos and there is a MEF2-binding site within a visceral muscle enhancer associated with the gene. Thus D-MEF2 regulates myogenesis and morphogenesis of the visceral musculature (Figure 3).

By *N*-ethylmethane sulfate mutagenesis, a series of hypomorphic *D-mef2* alleles has been generated (Ranganayakulu et al 1995). Some of these mutants lack portions of the C-terminal transcriptional activation domain, but retain the DNA-binding and dimerization domains and are partially functional. These mutant proteins are able to support partial myogenesis of somatic muscle cells but cannot activate muscle genes in cardiac or visceral muscle precursors, suggesting that activation of myogenesis in the latter muscle cell types may require a higher threshold level of MEF2 expression. A role for D-MEF2 in patterning of the somatic musculature was also revealed in embryos and adults bearing these hypomorphic alleles.

Knockouts of Mef2 Genes in Mice

The existence of four *mef2* genes with overlapping expression patterns in the mouse makes it more difficult to assess the roles of these factors in myogenesis. The functions of the vertebrate *mef2* genes are only beginning to be determined through gene inactivation studies in the mouse. The first of the *mef2* genes to be inactivated was *mef2c* (Q Lin et al 1997). Null *mef2c* embryos appear normal until about embryonic day 9, when they begin to show retarded growth and pericardial effusion, indicative of cardiac insufficiency. In contrast to normal embryos, in which the heart tube initiates rightward looping to form the right ventricular chamber beginning at about embryonic day 8.5, the heart tubes of mutant embryos do not loop and the future right ventricular region fails to form (Q Lin et al 1997).

The phenotype of *Drosophila* mutants lacking MEF2 indicates that MEF2 is required for activation of the complete program for cardiomyocyte differentiation. In *mef2c* mutant mouse embryos, several cardiac contractile protein genes are not expressed, whereas others are expressed at normal levels (Q Lin et al 1997). Because many of the muscle genes that continue to be expressed in *mef2c* mutant embryos contain essential MEF2-binding sites in their regulatory regions, it is likely that another member of the MEF2 family can support their expression in the absence of MEF2C. MEF2B is coexpressed with MEF2C during the early stages of cardiogenesis and is therefore a likely regulator of these genes (Molkentin et al 1996b). Of note, *mef2b* null mice are viable and do not display obvious muscle defects (J Molkentin & E Olson, unpublished observation). The phenotype of *mef2b/mef2c* double mutants will be especially interesting and should indicate the extent to which the functions of these genes are redundant. Because of the early lethality associated with *mef2c* mutant embryos, it will be necessary to employ conditional gene inactivation approaches to assess the in vivo functions of MEF2C in development of skeletal and smooth muscle cells and neurons.

It is interesting to note that the morphogenic defects in the hearts of *mef2c* mutant embryos are similar to those seen in mice lacking the bHLH transcription factor dHAND (Srivastava et al 1997). Whether the partial phenocopies of cardiac defects in *mef2c* and *dHAND* mutants reflect cooperative interactions between the products of these genes, as occurs between MEF2 and myogenic bHLH factors, is under investigation.

CONTROL OF GROWTH FACTOR-INDUCIBLE GENES BY MEF2 FACTORS

In addition to their role in muscle gene regulation, members of the MEF2 family have been implicated in gene activation in response to mitogenic signaling. A summary of the signaling pathways that have been shown to regulate MEF2 activity is shown in Figure 5. In several cases, MEF2 factors appear to function as endpoints for intracellular signaling pathways activated by elevation in intracellular calcium. In smooth muscle cells in the vascular wall, MEF2 expression has been shown to correlate with proliferation, but the potential

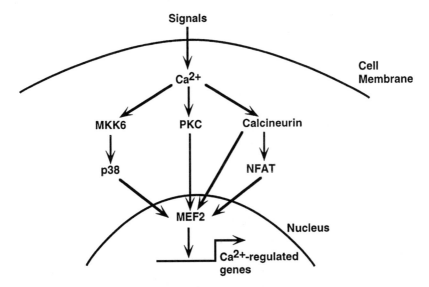

Figure 5 Signaling pathways that converge on MEF2. Each of the indicated signaling pathways has been shown to augment the transcriptional activity of MEF2 protein and to activate calcium-regulated genes. The precise mechanisms whereby these pathways activate MEF2 protein expression remain to be defined. MKK6, mitogen-activated protein (MAP) kinase kinase 6; CaMKIV, calcium-calmodulin kinase IV; NFAT, nuclear factor of activated T cells.

functions of MEF2 factors in these cells have not been addressed (Firulli et al 1996).

The Mitogen-Activated Protein (MAP) Kinase Pathway

Transcriptional activation of the *c-jun* promoter in response to serum has been shown to be mediated by MEF2D in fibroblasts (Han & Prywes 1995, Coso et al 1997). Serum responsiveness of MEF2D is dependent on the DNA-binding domain and is observed when the activation domain is replaced with that of VP16. There is no change in DNA-binding activity of MEF2D in HeLa cells treated with serum, which suggests that serum induction may regulate an essential MEF2 cofactor or a covalent modification of the DNA-binding domain.

MAP kinase signaling has also been shown to enhance the transcriptional activity of MEF2 factors in a variety of cell types. This enhancement is mediated by phosphorylation of three amino acids in the C-terminal activation domain of MEF2C by the MAP kinase family member p38 (Han et al 1997). Likewise, the MAP kinase BMK1/ERK5 is activated by exposure to serum, and this in turn phosphorylates Ser-387 in the transactivation domain of MEF2C. This phosphorylation of MEF2C results in increased transcriptional activity by MEF2C and increased transcription of the immediate-early response gene *c-jun* (Kato et al 1997). Phosphorylation of these sites does not alter the DNA-binding activity of MEF2. Thus the most likely mechanism for enhancement would be through an alteration in protein conformation or interaction with other cofactors.

MEF2 as a Target for Calcium Signaling Pathways

MEF2 factors have also been implicated in transcriptional activation in response to T cell receptor activation. Transcriptional activation of the *Nur77* gene, which encodes an orphan steroid receptor, in response to T cell activation requires two MEF2 binding sites in the promoter of the gene. There is no change in DNA-binding activity of MEF2 in activated T cells, whereas transcriptional activity of MEF2 is dramatically increased (Woronicz et al 1995). Transcriptional activation through the *Nur77* MEF2 sites is mediated by a calcium-dependent signaling pathway that is sensitive to cyclosporin A (CsA), which inhibits the calcium-calmodulin-dependent protein phosphatase, calcineurin. These results imply that calcineurin signaling must enhance MEF2 signaling by inducing a cofactor or a post-translational modification of MEF2 that potentiates transcriptional activity. It is formally possible that MEF2 is a direct substrate for calcineurin-mediated dephosphorylation, resulting in activation of its transcriptional activity. This possibility remains to be addressed.

MEF2 has also been shown to regulate the calcium-dependent lytic switch gene *BZLF1*, which is required for induction of the lytic cycle of Epstein-Barr virus (EBV) (Liu et al 1997). Transcriptional activation of the *BZLF1* gene is inhibited by CsA and another calcineurin inhibitor, FK-506, indicating that a calcineurin-dependent pathway mediates activation of the gene. CsA sensitivity of *BZLF1* transcription maps to three MEF2 sites in the *BZLF1* promoter.

In T cells, calcineurin activation leads to changes in gene expression by dephosphorylating a family of transcription factors known as nuclear factors of activated T cells (NFATs). Following dephosphorylation, NFAT proteins translocate to the nucleus and activate immune response genes (reviewed in Rao et al 1997). NFAT proteins do not bind the *BZLF1* promoter, but CsA-sensitive induction of the promoter is calcineurin and NFAT dependent. The mechanism whereby MEF2 confers responsiveness to calcineurin and NFAT signaling remains to be elucidated. Calcium-calmodulin protein kinase IV has also been shown to be a potent inducer of MEF2 activity (Liu et al 1997), but the mechanism is unknown. Whether these same types of signaling mechanisms regulate MEF2 activity in muscle cells or account for the disparity between MEF2 protein and transcriptional activity in various nonmuscle cell types warrant further investigation.

CONCLUSIONS AND FUTURE DIRECTIONS

MEF2 factors are fascinating with respect to their involvement in diverse programs of gene regulation and the multiplicity of regulatory mechanisms that control their expression and functions. While the importance of these factors as transcriptional regulators of cell growth and differentiation pathways has been clearly established, the mechanisms through which they exert their effects are only beginning to be understood. A central issue for the future will be to define the spectrum of transcriptional partners for MEF2 proteins that potentiate and inhibit their functions in diverse cell types. The confusion surrounding the cell-type distribution of MEF2 expression and function also needs to be clarified.

The apparent ability of MEF2 to control the transcription of genes involved in muscle differentiation and cell proliferation is reminiscent of the function of another MADS-box protein, SRF. A variety of muscle-specific genes contain essential SRF-binding sites in their control regions, but SRF is also required for activation of serum-inducible genes such as *c-fos*. How SRF and MEF2 mediate antagonistic programs of gene expression is an important issue for the future. Given the remarkable similarities between the functions of MEF2 and SRF, it will be of interest to determine the extent to which these factors act through similar mechanisms to control transcriptional programs for cell growth and differentiation. A likely possibility is that these factors interact with distinct sets of cofactors in proliferating and differentiating cells.

Given the common role for MEF2 factors in mediating the differentiation of skeletal, cardiac, and visceral muscles during development, another important matter will be to determine the earliest factors responsible for activation of *mef2* expression in the undifferentiated mesoderm. In this regard, significant progress has been made in *Drosophila*, where factors responsible for activation of *mef2* in the cardiac and somatic muscle lineages have been defined (Gajewski et al 1997, Cripps et al 1998). However, it is clear that numerous other factors are likely to play a role in the activation of *mef2* expression during development in *Drosophila*. What are these other factors and how do they define the common features of muscle differentiation, as well as the differences in distinct muscle lineages? What are the factors responsible for activation of *mef2* expression in vertebrates? These and other questions remain to be addressed to more fully define the diverse roles for MEF2 factors in a variety of cell types and cellular functions.

ACKNOWLEDGMENTS

We appreciate the assistance with graphics provided by Alisha Tizenor and the critical review of the manuscript by Richard Cripps. We also thank Rebekka Nicol for pointing out C-terminal sequence homologies among MEF2 factors, and members of the Olson laboratory for insights.

Work in the authors' laboratory was supported by grants from the National Institutes of Health, the Muscular Dystrophy Asssociation, the American Heart Association, the Robert A. Welch Foundation, and the Human Frontiers Science Foundation (to ENO). BLB was supported in part by a postdoctoral fellowship from the American Cancer Society.

Visit the *Annual Reviews home page* at
http://www.AnnualReviews.org

Literature Cited

Acton TB, Zhong H, Vershon AK. 1997. DNA-binding specificity of Mcm1: operator mutations that alter DNA-bending and transcriptional activities by a MADS box protein. *Mol. Cell. Biol.* 17:1881–89

Adolph EA, Subramaniam A, Cserjesi P, Olson EN, Robbins J. 1993. Role of myocyte-specific enhancer-binding factor (MEF-2) in transcriptional regulation of the alpha-cardiac myosin heavy chain gene. *J. Biol. Chem.* 268:5349–52

Amacher SL, Buskin JN, Hauschka SD. 1993. Multiple regulatory elements contribute differentially to muscle creatine kinase enhancer activity in skeletal and cardiac muscle. *Mol. Cell. Biol.* 13:2753–64

Andres V, Cervera M, Mahdavi V. 1995a. Determination of the consensus binding site for MEF2 expressed in muscle and brain reveals tissue-specific sequence constraints. *J. Biol. Chem.* 270:23246–49

Andres V, Fisher S, Wearsch P, Walsh K. 1995b. Regulation of Gax homeobox gene transcription by a combination of positive factors including myocyte-specific enhancer factor 2. *Mol. Cell. Biol.* 15:4272–81

Azpiazu N, Frasch M. 1993. *tinman* and *bagpipe*: two homeo box genes that determine cell fates in the dorsal mesoderm of *Drosophila*. *Genes Dev.* 7:1325–40

Bassel-Duby R, Hernandez MD, Gonzalez MA, Krueger JK, Williams RS. 1992. A 40-kilodalton protein binds specifically to an upstream sequence element essential for muscle-specific transcription of the human myoglobin promoter. *Mol. Cell. Biol.* 12:5024–32

Baylies MK, Bate M. 1996. *twist*: a myogenic switch in Drosophila. *Science* 272:1481–84

Black BL, Ligon KL, Zhang Y, Olson EN. 1996. Cooperative transcriptional activation by the neurogenic basic helix-loop-helix protein MASH1 and members of the myocyte enhancer factor-2 (MEF2) family. *J. Biol. Chem.* 271:26659–63

Black BL, Lu J, Olson EN. 1997. The MEF2A 3′ untranslated region functions as a *cis*-acting translational repressor. *Mol. Cell. Biol.* 17:2756–63

Black BL, Martin JF, Olson EN. 1995. The mouse MRF4 promoter is *trans*-activated directly and indirectly by muscle-specific transcription factors. *J. Biol. Chem.* 270:2889–92

Black BL, Molkentin JD, Olson EN. 1998. Multiple roles for the MyoD basic region in transmission of transcriptional activation signals and interaction with MEF2. *Mol. Cell. Biol.* 18:69–77

Bodmer R. 1993. The gene *tinman* is required for specification of the heart and visceral muscles in *Drosophila* [published erratum appears in *Development* 119(3):969]. *Development* 118:719–29

Bour BA, O'Brien MA, Lockwood WL, Goldstein ES, Bodmer R, et al. 1995. *Drosophila* MEF2, a transcription factor that is essential for myogenesis. *Genes Dev.* 9:730–41

Breitbart RE, Liang CS, Smoot LB, Laheru DA, Mahdavi V, Nadal-Ginard B. 1993. A fourth human MEF2 transcription factor, hMEF2D, is an early marker of the myogenic lineage. *Development* 118:1095–106

Brennan TJ, Chakraborty T, Olson EN. 1991. Mutagenesis of the myogenin basic region identifies an ancient protein motif critical for activation of myogenesis. *Proc. Natl. Acad. Sci. USA* 88:5675–79

Buchberger A, Ragge K, Arnold HH. 1994. The myogenin gene is activated during myocyte differentiation by pre-existing, not newly synthesized transcription factor MEF-2. *J. Biol. Chem.* 269:17289–96

Chambers AE, Kotecha S, Towers N, Mohun TJ. 1992. Muscle-specific expression of SRF-related genes in the early embryo of *Xenopus laevis*. *EMBO J.* 11:4981–91

Chambers AE, Logan M, Kotecha S, Towers N, Sparrow D, Mohun TJ. 1994. The RSRF/MEF2 protein SL1 regulates cardiac muscle-specific transcription of a myosin light-chain gene in *Xenopus* embryos. *Genes Dev.* 8:1324–34

Cheng TC, Wallace MC, Merlie JP, Olson EN. 1993. Separable regulatory elements governing myogenin transcription in mouse embryogenesis. *Science* 261:215–18

Coso OA, Montaner S, Fromm C, Lacal JC,

Prywes R, et al. 1997. Signaling from G protein-coupled receptors to the c-jun promoter involves the MEF2 transcription factor. Evidence for a novel c-jun amino-terminal kinase-independent pathway. *J. Biol. Chem.* 272:20691–97

Cripps RM, Black BL, Zhao B, Lien CL, Schulz RA, Olson EN. 1998. The myogenic regulatory gene *Mef2* is a direct target for transcriptional activation by Twist during *Drosophila* myogenesis. *Genes Dev.* 12:422–34

Cserjesi P, Lilly B, Hinkley C, Perry M, Olson EN. 1994. Homeodomain protein MHox and MADS protein myocyte enhancer-binding factor-2 converge on a common element in the muscle creatine kinase enhancer. *J. Biol. Chem.* 269:16740–5

Cserjesi P, Olson EN. 1991. Myogenin induces the myocyte-specific enhancer binding factor MEF-2 independently of other muscle-specific gene products. *Mol. Cell. Biol.* 11:4854–62

Davis RL, Cheng PF, Lassar AB, Weintraub H. 1990. The MyoD binding domain contains a recognition code for muscle-specific gene activation. *Cell* 60:733–46

Davis RL, Weintraub H. 1992. Acquisition of myogenic specificity by replacement of three amino acid residues from MyoD into E12. *Science* 256:1027–30

Dechesne CA, Wei Q, Eldridge J, Gannoun-Zaki L, Millasseau P, et al. 1994. E-box-and MEF-2-independent muscle-specific expression, positive autoregulation, and cross-activation of the chicken MyoD (CMD1) promoter reveal an indirect regulatory pathway. *Mol. Cell. Biol.* 14:5474–86

Dodou E, Sparrow DB, Mohun T, Treisman R. 1995. MEF2 proteins, including MEF2A, are expressed in both muscle and non-muscle cells. *Nucleic Acids Res.* 23:4267–74

Dodou E, Treisman R. 1997. The *Saccharomyces cerevisiae* MADS-box transcription factor Rlm1 is a target for the Mpk1 mitogen-activated protein kinase pathway. *Mol. Cell. Biol.* 17:1848–59

Edmondson DG, Cheng TC, Cserjesi P, Chakraborty T, Olson EN. 1992. Analysis of the myogenin promoter reveals an indirect pathway for positive autoregulation mediated by the muscle-specific enhancer factor MEF-2. *Mol. Cell. Biol.* 12:3665–77

Edmondson DG, Lyons GE, Martin JF, Olson EN. 1994. *Mef2* gene expression marks the cardiac and skeletal muscle lineages during mouse embryogenesis. *Development* 120:1251–63

Feo S, Antona V, Barbieri G, Passantino R, Cali L, Giallongo A. 1995. Transcription of the human beta enolase gene (*ENO-3*) is regulated by an intronic muscle-specific enhancer that binds myocyte-specific enhancer factor 2 proteins and ubiquitous G-rich-box binding factors. *Mol. Cell. Biol.* 15:5991–6002

Ferrari S, Molinari S, Melchionna R, Cusella-De Angelis MG, Battini R, et al. 1997. Absence of MEF2 binding to the A/T-rich element in the muscle creatine kinase (MCK) enhancer correlates with lack of early expression of the MCK gene in embryonic mammalian muscle. *Cell Growth Diff.* 8:23–34

Fickett JW. 1996a. Coordinate positioning of MEF2 and myogenin binding sites. *Gene* 172:GC19–32

Fickett JW. 1996b. Quantitative discrimination of MEF2 sites. *Mol. Cell. Biol.* 16:437–41

Firulli AB, Miano JM, Bi W, Johnson AD, Casscells W, et al. 1996. Myocyte enhancer binding factor-2 expression and activity in vascular smooth muscle cells. Association with the activated phenotype. *Circ. Res.* 78:196–204

Gahlmann R, Kedes L. 1993. Tissue-specific restriction of skeletal muscle troponin C gene expression *Gene Exp.* 3:11–25

Gajewski K, Kim Y, Lee YM, Olson EN, Schulz RA. 1997. D-mef2 is a target for Tinman activation during *Drosophila* heart development. *EMBO J.* 16:515–22

Gitelman I. 1997. Twist protein in mouse embryogenesis. *Dev. Biol.* 189:205–14

Gossett LA, Kelvin DJ, Sternberg EA, Olson EN. 1989. A new myocyte-specific enhancer-binding factor that recognizes a conserved element associated with multiple muscle-specific genes. *Mol. Cell. Biol.* 9:5022–33

Han J, Jiang Y, Li Z, Kravchenko VV, Ulevitch RJ. 1997. Activation of the transcription factor MEF2C by the MAP kinase p38 in inflammation. *Nature* 386:296–99

Han TH, Prywes R. 1995. Regulatory role of MEF2D in serum induction of the c-jun promoter. *Mol. Cell. Biol.* 15:2907–15

Harvey R. 1996. NK-2 homeobox genes and heart development. *Dev. Biol.* 178:203–16

Hebrok M, Wertz K, Fuchtbauer EM. 1994. M-twist is an inhibitor of muscle differentiation. *Dev. Biol.* 165:537–44

Hidaka K, Morisaki T, Byun SH, Hashido K, Toyama K, Mukai T. 1995. The MEF2B homologue differentially expressed in mouse embryonal carcinoma cells. *Biochem. Biophys. Res. Commun.* 213:555–60

Hidaka K, Yamamoto I, Arai Y, Mukai T. 1993. The MEF-3 motif is required for MEF-2-mediated skeletal muscle-specific induction of the rat aldolase A gene. *Mol. Cell. Biol.* 13:6469–78

Hobson GM, Krahe R, Garcia E, Siciliano MJ, Funanage VL. 1995. Regional chromosomal assignments for four members of the MADS domain transcription enhancer factor 2 (MEF2) gene family to human chromosomes 15q26, 19p12, 5q14, and 1q12-q23. *Genomics* 29:704–11

Ikeshima H, Imai S, Shimoda K, Hata J, Takano T. 1995. Expression of a MADS box gene, MEF2D, in neurons of the mouse central nervous system: implication of its binary function in myogenic and neurogenic cell lineages. *Neurosci. Lett.* 200:117–20

Joh K, Takano K, Mukai T, Hori K. 1991. Analysis of upstream regulatory regions required for the activities of two promoters of the rat aldolase A gene. *FEBS Lett.* 292:128–32

Kato Y, Kravchenko VV, Tapping RI, Han J, Ulevitch RJ, Lee JD. 1997. BMK1/ERK5 regulates serum-induced early gene expression through transcription factor MEF2C. *EMBO J.* 16:7054–66

Katoh Y, Loukianov E, Kopras E, Zilberman A, Periasamy M. 1994. Identification of functional promoter elements in the rabbit smooth muscle myosin heavy chain gene. *J. Biol. Chem.* 269:30538–45

Kaushal S, Schneider JW, Nadal-Ginard B, Mahdavi V. 1994. Activation of the myogenic lineage by MEF2A, a factor that induces and cooperates with MyoD. *Science* 266:1236–40

Klamut HJ, Bosnoyan-Collins LO, Worton RG, Ray PN. 1997. A muscle-specific enhancer within intron 1 of the human dystrophin gene is functionally dependent on single MEF-1/E box and MEF-2/AT-rich sequence motifs. *Nucleic Acids Res.* 25:1618–25

Kuisk IR, Li H, Tran D, Capetanaki Y. 1996. A single MEF2 site governs desmin transcription in both heart and skeletal muscle during mouse embryogenesis. *Dev. Biol.* 174:1–13

Lassar AB, Davis RL, Wright WE, Kadesch T, Murre C, et al. 1991. Functional activity of myogenic bHLH proteins requires hetero-oligomerization with E12/E47-like proteins in vivo. *Cell* 66:305–15

Lee KJ, Hickey R, Zhu H, Chien KR. 1994. Positive regulatory elements (HF-1a and HF-1b) and a novel negative regulatory element (HF-3) mediate ventricular muscle-specific expression of myosin light-chain 2-luciferase fusion genes in transgenic mice. *Mol. Cell. Biol.* 14:1220–29

Lee Y, Nadal-Ginard B, Mahdavi V, Izumo S. 1997. Myocyte-specific enhancer factor 2 and thyroid hormone receptor associate and synergistically activate the alpha-cardiac myosin heavy-chain gene. *Mol. Cell. Biol.* 17:2745–55

Leibham D, Wong MW, Cheng TC, Schroeder S, Weil PA, et al. 1994. Binding of TFIID and MEF2 to the TATA element activates transcription of the *Xenopus* MyoDa promoter. *Mol. Cell. Biol.* 14:686–99

Leifer D, Golden J, Kowall NW. 1994. Myocyte-specific enhancer binding factor 2C expression in human brain development. *Neuroscience* 63:1067–79

Leifer D, Krainc D, Yu YT, McDermott J, Breitbart RE, et al. 1993. MEF2C, a MADS/MEF2-family transcription factor expressed in a laminar distribution in cerebral cortex. *Proc. Natl. Acad. Sci. USA* 90:1546–50

Li H, Capetanaki Y. 1994. An E box in the desmin promoter cooperates with the E box and MEF-2 sites of a distal enhancer to direct muscle-specific transcription. *EMBO J.* 13:3580–89

Lilly B, Galewsky S, Firulli AB, Schulz RA, Olson EN. 1994. D-MEF2: a MADS box transcription factor expressed in differentiating mesoderm and muscle cell lineages during *Drosophila* embryogenesis. *Proc. Natl. Acad. Sci. USA* 91:5662–66

Lilly B, Zhao B, Ranganayakulu G, Paterson BM, Schulz RA, Olson EN. 1995. Requirement of MADS domain transcription factor D-MEF2 for muscle formation in *Drosophila. Science* 267:688–93

Lin MH, Bour BA, Abmayr SM, Storti RV. 1997. Ectopic expression of MEF2 in the epidermis induces epidermal expression of muscle genes and abnormal muscle development in *Drosophila. Dev. Biol.* 182:240–55

Lin MH, Nguyen HT, Dybala C, Storti RV. 1996. Myocyte-specific enhancer factor 2 acts cooperatively with a muscle activator region to regulate *Drosophila* tropomyosin gene muscle expression [published erratum appears in *Proc. Natl. Acad. Sci. USA*, 1996. 23;93(15):8152–3]. *Proc. Natl. Acad. Sci. USA* 93:4623–28

Lin Q, Schwarz J, Bucana C, Olson EN. 1997. Control of mouse cardiac morphogenesis and myogenesis by transcription factor MEF2C. *Science* 276:1404–7

Lin SC, Lin MH, Horvath P, Reddy KL, Storti RV. 1997. PDP1, a novel *Drosophila* PAR domain bZIP transcription factor expressed in developing mesoderm, endoderm and ectoderm, is a transcriptional regulator of somatic muscle genes. *Development* 124:4685–96

Lin SC, Storti RV. 1997. Developmental regulation of the *Drosophila Tropomyosin I* (*Tml*) gene is controlled by a muscle activator enhancer region that contains multiple *cis*-elements and binding sites for multiple proteins *Dev. Gen.* 20:297–306

Lin X, Shah S, Bulleit RF. 1996. The expression of MEF2 genes is implicated in CNS neuronal differentiation. *Brain Res. Mol. Brain Res.* 42:307–16

Lints TJ, Parsons LM, Hartley L, Lyons I, Harvey RP. 1993. *Nkx-2.5*: a novel murine homeobox gene expressed in early heart progenitor cells and their myogenic descendants. *Development* 119:419–31

Liu ML, Olson AL, Edgington NP, Moye-Rowley WS, Pessin JE. 1994. Myocyte enhancer factor 2 (MEF2) binding site is essential for C2C12 myotube-specific expression of the rat GLUT4/muscle-adipose facilitative glucose transporter gene. *J. Biol. Chem.* 269:28514–21

Liu S, Liu P, Borras A, Chatila T, Speck SH. 1997. Cyclosporin A-sensitive induction of the Epstein-Barr virus lytic switch is mediated via a novel pathway involving a MEF2 family member. *EMBO J.* 16:143–53

Ludolph DC, Konieczny SF. 1995. Transcription factor families: muscling in on the myogenic program. *FASEB J.* 9:1595–604

Lyons GE, Micales BK, Schwarz J, Martin JF, Olson EN. 1995. Expression of *mef2* genes in the mouse central nervous system suggests a role in neuronal maturation. *J. Neurosci.* 15:5727–38

Malik S, Huang CF, Schmidt J. 1995. The role of the CANNTG promoter element (E box) and the myocyte-enhancer-binding-factor -2 (MEF-2) site in the transcriptional regulation of the chick myogenin gene. *Eur. J. Biochem.* 230:88–96

Mao Z, Nadal-Ginard B. 1996. Functional and physical interactions between mammalian achaete-scute homolog 1 and myocyte enhancer factor 2A. *J. Biol. Chem.* 271:14371–75

Martin JF, Miano JM, Hustad CM, Copeland NG, Jenkins NA, Olson EN. 1994. A *Mef2* gene that generates a muscle-specific isoform via alternative mRNA splicing. *Mol. Cell. Biol.* 14:1647–56

Martin JF, Schwarz JJ, Olson EN. 1993. Myocyte enhancer factor (MEF) 2C: a tissue-restricted member of the MEF-2 family of transcription factors. *Proc. Natl. Acad. Sci. USA* 90:5282–86

McDermott JC, Cardoso MC, Yu YT, Andres V, Leifer D, et al. 1993. hMEF2C gene encodes skeletal muscle-and brain-specific transcription factors. *Mol. Cell. Biol.* 13:2564–77

McGrew MJ, Bogdanova N, Hasegawa K, Hughes SH, Kitsis RN, Rosenthal N. 1996. Distinct gene expression patterns in skeletal and cardiac muscle are dependent on common regulatory sequences in the MLC1/3 locus. *Mol. Cell. Biol.* 16:4524–34

Meierhans D, Sieber M, Allemann RK. 1997. High affinity binding of MEF-2C correlates with DNA bending. *Nucleic Acids Res.* 25:4537–44

Michelson A, Abmayr SM, Bate M, Martinez-Arias A, Mantiatis T. 1990. Expression of a MyoD family member prefigures muscle pattern in *Drosophila* embryos. *Genes Dev.* 4:2086–97

Molkentin JD, Black BL, Martin JF, Olson EN. 1995. Cooperative activation of muscle gene expression by MEF2 and myogenic bHLH proteins. *Cell* 83:1125–36

Molkentin JD, Black BL, Martin JF, Olson EN. 1996a. Mutational analysis of the DNA binding, dimerization, and transcriptional activation domains of MEF2C. *Mol. Cell. Biol.* 16:2627–36

Molkentin JD, Firulli AB, Black BL, Martin JF, Hustad CM, et al.1996b. MEF2B is a potent transactivator expressed in early myogenic lineages. *Mol. Cell. Biol.* 16:3814–24

Molkentin JD, Li L, Olson EN. 1996c. Phosphorylation of the MADS-box transcription factor MEF2C enhances its DNA binding activity. *J. Biol. Chem.* 271:17199–204

Molkentin JD, Markham BE. 1993. Myocyte-specific enhancer-binding factor (MEF-2) regulates alpha-cardiac myosin heavy chain gene expression in vitro and in vivo. *J. Biol. Chem.* 268:19512–20

Molkentin JD, Markham BE. 1994. An M-CAT binding factor and an RSRF-related A-rich binding factor positively regulate expression of the alpha-cardiac myosin heavy-chain gene in vivo. *Mol. Cell. Biol.* 14:5056–65

Molkentin JD, Olson EN. 1996. Combinatorial control of muscle development by basic helix-loop-helix and MADS-box transcription factors. *Proc. Natl. Acad. Sci. USA* 93:9366–73

Morisaki T, Holmes EW. 1993. Functionally distinct elements are required for expression of the AMPD1 gene in myocytes. *Mol. Cell. Biol.* 13:5854–60

Morisaki T, Sermsuvitayawong K, Byun SH, Matsuda Y, Hidaki K, et al. 1997. Mouse MEF2B gene-unique member of MEF2 gene family. *J. Biochem.* 122:939–46

Moriscot AS, Sayen MR, Hartong R, Wu P, Dillmann WH. 1997. Transcription of the rat sarcoplasmic reticulum Ca^{2+} adenosine triphosphatase gene is increased by 3,5,3′-triiodothyronine receptor isoform-specific interactions with the myocyte-specific enhancer factor-2a. *Endocrinology* 138:26–32

Muscat GE, Perry S, Prentice H, Kedes L. 1992. The human skeletal alpha-actin gene is regulated by a muscle-specific enhancer that binds three nuclear factors. *Gene Exp.* 2:111–26

Naidu PS, Ludolph DC, To RQ, Hinterberger TJ, Konieczny SF. 1995. Myogenin and MEF2 function synergistically to activate the MRF4 promoter during myogenesis. *Mol. Cell. Biol.* 15:2707–18

Nakatsuji Y, Hidaka K, Tsujino S, Yamamoto Y, Mukai T, et al. 1992. A single MEF-2 site is a major positive regulatory element required for transcription of the muscle-specific subunit of the human phosphoglycerate mutase gene in skeletal and cardiac muscle cells. *Mol. Cell. Biol.* 12:4384–90

Nakayama M, Stauffer J, Cheng J, Banerjee-Basu S, Wawrousek E, Buonanno A. 1996. Common core sequences are found in skeletal muscle slow- and fast-fiber-type-specific regulatory elements. *Mol. Cell. Biol.* 16:2408–17

Navankasattusas S, Zhu H, Garcia AV, Evans SM, Chien KR. 1992. A ubiquitous factor (HF-1a) and a distinct muscle factor (HF-1b/MEF-2) form an E-box-independent pathway for cardiac muscle gene expression. *Mol. Cell. Biol.* 12:1469–79

Nguyen HT, Bodmer R, Abmayr SM, McDermott JC, Spoerel NA. 1994. D-mef2: a *Drosophila* mesoderm-specific MADS box-containing gene with a biphasic expression profile during embryogenesis. *Proc. Natl. Acad. Sci. USA* 91:7520–24

Nishio H, Takeshima Y, Narita N, Yanagawa H, Suzuki Y, et al. 1994. Identification of a novel first exon in the human dystrophin gene and of a new promoter located more than 500 kb upstream of the nearest known promoter. *J. Clin. Invest.* 94:1037–42

Nurrish SJ, Treisman R. 1995. DNA binding specificity determinants in MADS-box transcription factors. *Mol. Cell. Biol.* 15:4076–85

Olson EN, Perry M, Schulz RA. 1995. Regulation of muscle differentiation by the MEF2 family of MADS box transcription factors. *Dev. Biol.* 172:2–14

Ornatsky OI, Andreucci JJ, McDermott JC. 1997. A dominant-negative form of transcription factor MEF2 inhibits myogenesis. *J. Biol. Chem.* 272:33271–78

Ornatsky OI, McDermott JC. 1996. MEF2 protein expression, DNA binding activity and complex composition, and transcriptional activity in muscle and non-muscle cells. *J. Biol. Chem.* 271:24927–33

Parmacek MS, Ip HS, Jung F, Shen T, Martin JF, et al. 1994. A novel myogenic regulatory circuit controls slow/cardiac troponin C gene transcription in skeletal muscle. *Mol. Cell. Biol.* 14:1870–85

Paterson BM, Walldorf U, Eldridge J, Dubendorfer A, Frasch M, Gehring W. 1991. The *Drosophila* homolog of vertebrate myogenic-determination genes encodes a transiently expressed nuclear protein marking primary myogenic cells. *Proc. Natl. Acad. Sci. USA* 88:3782–86

Pellegrini L, Tan S, Richmond TJ. 1995. Structure of serum response factor core bound to DNA. *Nature* 376:490–98

Pinney DF, de la Brousse FC, Faerman A, Shani M, Maruyama K, Emerson CP Jr. 1995. Quail myoD is regulated by a complex array of *cis*-acting control sequences. *Dev. Biol.* 170:21–38

Pollock R, Treisman R. 1991. Human SRF-related proteins: DNA-binding properties and potential regulatory targets. *Genes Dev.* 5:2327–41

Ranganayakulu G, Zhao B, Dokidis A, Molkentin JD, Olson EN, Schulz RA. 1995. A series of mutations in the D-MEF2 transcription factor reveal multiple functions in larval and adult myogenesis in *Drosophila*. *Dev. Biol.* 171:169–81

Rao A, Luo C, Hogan PG. 1997. Transcription factors of the NFAT family: regulation and function. *Annu. Rev. Immunol.* 15:707–47

Rao MV, Donoghue MJ, Merlie JP, Sanes JR. 1996. Distinct regulatory elements control muscle-specific, fiber-type-selective, and axially graded expression of a myosin light-chain gene in transgenic mice. *Mol. Cell. Biol.* 16:3909–22

Riechmann JL, Meyerowitz EM. 1997. Determination of floral organ identity by *Arabidopsis* MADS domain homeotic proteins AP1, AP3, PI, and AG is independent of their DNA-binding specificity. *Mol. Biol. Cell* 8:1243–59

Rohwedel J, Horak V, Hebrok M, Fuchtbauer EM, Wobus AM. 1995. M-*twist* expression inhibits mouse embryonic stem cell-derived myogenic differentiation in vitro. *Exp. Cell Res.* 220:92–100

Ross RS, Navankasattusas S, Harvey RP, Chien KR. 1996. An HF-1a/HF-1b/MEF-2 combinatorial element confers cardiac ventricular specificity and establishes an anterior-posterior gradient of expression. *Development* 122:1799–809

Rozek D, Pfeifer GP. 1995. In vivo protein-DNA interactions at the c-jun promoter in quiescent and serum-stimulated fibroblasts. *J. Cell. Biochem.* 57:479–87

Salminen M, Spitz F, Fiszman MY, Demignon J, Kahn A, et al. 1995. Myotube-specific activity of the human aldolase A M-promoter requires an overlapping binding site for NF1 and MEF2 factors in addition to a binding site (M1) for unknown proteins. *J. Mol. Biol.* 253:17–31

Sartorelli V, Huang J, Hamamori Y, Kedes L. 1997. Molecular mechanisms of myogenic coactivation by p300: direct interaction with the activation domain of MyoD and with the MADS box of MEF2C. *Mol. Cell. Biol.* 17:1010–26

Schulz RA, Chromey C, Lu MF, Zhao B, Olson EN. 1996. Expression of the D-MEF2 transcription factor in the *Drosophila* brain

suggests a role in neuronal cell differentiation. *Oncogene* 12:1827–31

Shore P, Sharrocks AD. 1995. The MADS-box family of transcription factors. *Eur. J. Biochem.* 229:1–13

Skopicki HA, Lyons GE, Schatteman G, Smith RC, Andres V, et al. 1997. Embryonic expression of the Gax homeodomain protein in cardiac, smooth, and skeletal muscle. *Circ. Res.* 80:452–62

Spicer DB, Rhee J, Cheung WL, Lassar AB. 1996. Inhibition of myogenic bHLH and MEF2 transcription factors by the bHLH protein Twist. *Science* 272:1476–80

Srivastava D, Thomas T, Lin Q, Kirby ML, Brown D, Olson EN. 1997. Regulation of cardiac mesodermal and neural crest development by the bHLH transcription factor, dHAND. *Nat. Genet.* 16:154–60

Subramanian SV, Nadal-Ginard B. 1996. Early expression of the different isoforms of the myocyte enhancer factor-2 (MEF2) protein in myogenic as well as non-myogenic cell lineages during mouse embryogenesis. *Mech. Dev.* 57:103–12

Suzuki E, Guo K, Kolman M, Yu YT, Walsh K. 1995. Serum induction of MEF2/RSRF expression in vascular myocytes is mediated at the level of translation. *Mol. Cell. Biol.* 15:3415–23

Suzuki E, Lowry J, Sonoda G, Testa JR, Walsh K. 1996. Structures and chromosome locations of the human MEF2A gene and a pseudogene MEF2AP. *Cytogen. Cell Gen.* 73:244–49

Taylor JM, Dupont-Versteegden EE, Davies JD, Hassell JA, Houle JD, et al. 1997. A role for the ETS domain transcription factor PEA3 in myogenic differentiation. *Mol. Cell. Biol.* 17:5550–58

Taylor MV, Beatty KE, Hunter HK, Baylies MK. 1995. *Drosophila* MEF2 is regulated by *twist* and is expressed in both the primordia and differentiated cells of the embryonic somatic, visceral and heart musculature [published erratum appears in *Mech. Dev.* 1995. 51(1):139–41] *Mech. Dev.* 50:29–41

Theissen G, Kim JT, Saedler H. 1996. Classification and phylogeny of the MADS-box multigene family suggest defined roles of MADS-box gene subfamilies in the morphological evolution of eukaryotes. *J. Mol. Evol.* 43:484–516

Theissen G, Saedler H. 1995. MADS-box genes in plant ontogeny and phylogeny: Haeckel's "biogenetic law" revisited. *Curr. Opin. Gen. Dev.* 5:628–39

Ticho BS, Stainier DY, Fishman MC, Breitbart RE. 1996. Three zebrafish MEF2 genes delineate somitic and cardiac muscle development in wild-type and mutant embryos. *Mech. Dev.* 59:205–18

Wang G, Yeh HI, Lin JJ. 1994. Characterization of *cis*-regulating elements and *trans*-activating factors of the rat cardiac troponin T gene. *J. Biol. Chem.* 269:30595–603

Weintraub H, Dwarki VJ, Verma I, Davis R, Hollenberg S, et al. 1991. Muscle-specific transcriptional activation by MyoD. *Genes Dev.* 5:1377–86

West AG, Shore P, Sharrocks AD. 1997. DNA binding by MADS-box transcription factors: a molecular mechanism for differential DNA bending. *Mol. Cell. Biol.* 17:2876–87

Winter B, Braun T, Arnold HH. 1992. Cooperativity of functional domains in the muscle-specific transcription factor Myf-5. *EMBO J.* 11:1843–55

Woronicz JD, Lina A, Calnan BJ, Szychowski S, Cheng L, Winoto A. 1995. Regulation of Nur77 orphan steroid receptor in activation-induced apoptosis. *Mol. Cell. Biol.* 15:6364–76

Wong MW, Pisegna M, Lu MF, Leibham D, Perry M. 1994. Activation of *Xenopus* MyoD transcription by members of the MEF2 protein family. *Dev. Biol.* 166:683–95

Wright WE, Binder M, Funk W. 1991. Cyclic amplification and selection of targets (CASTing) for the myogenin consensus binding site. *Mol. Cell. Biol.* 11:4104–10

Yee SP, Rigby PW. 1993. The regulation of myogenin gene expression during the embryonic development of the mouse. *Genes Dev.* 7:1277–89

Yu YT. 1996. Distinct domains of myocyte enhancer binding factor-2A determining nuclear localization and cell type-specific transcriptional activity. *J. Biol. Chem.* 271:24675–83

Yu YT, Breitbart RE, Smoot LB, Lee Y, Mahdavi V, Nadal-Ginard B. 1992. Human myocyte-specific enhancer factor 2 comprises a group of tissue-restricted MADS box transcription factors. *Genes Dev.* 6:1783–98

Yun K, Wold B. 1996. Skeletal muscle determination and differentiation: story of a core regulatory network and its context. *Curr. Opin. Cell Biol.* 8:877–89

Annu. Rev. Cell Dev. Biol. 1998. 14:197–230
Copyright © 1998 by Annual Reviews. All rights reserved

BIOLUMINESCENCE

Thérèse Wilson and J. Woodland Hastings

Department of Molecular and Cellular Biology, Harvard University, Cambridge,
Massachusetts 02138; e-mail: woody@hastingslab.harvard.edu;
wilson@biosan.harvard.edu

KEY WORDS: luciferase, autoinducer, quorum sensing, GFP, symbiosis

ABSTRACT

Bioluminescence has evolved independently many times; thus the responsible
genes are unrelated in bacteria, unicellular algae, coelenterates, beetles, fishes,
and others. Chemically, all involve exergonic reactions of molecular oxygen with
different substrates (luciferins) and enzymes (luciferases), resulting in photons of
visible light ($\approx$50 kcal). In addition to the structure of luciferan, several factors
determine the color of the emissions, such as the amino acid sequence of the
luciferase (as in beetles, for example) or the presence of accessory proteins,
notably GFP, discovered in coelenterates and now used as a reporter of gene
expression and a cellular marker. The mechanisms used to control the intensity
and kinetics of luminescence, often emitted as flashes, also vary. Bioluminescence
is credited with the discovery of how some bacteria, luminous or not, sense
their density and regulate specific genes by chemical communication, as in the
fascinating example of symbiosis between luminous bacteria and squid.

CONTENTS

197

INTRODUCTION

Basic research on bioluminescence, often carried out for the pleasure of uncovering how organisms manage the feat of converting chemical energy into light, can now be credited with remarkable advances in fields unrelated to bioluminescence. An important example stems from the study of bacterial luminescence, where the discovery of autoinduction led to the notion of "quorum sensing," and thus of chemical communication between bacteria, which is throwing light on processes ranging from pathogenesis to symbiosis. Another example is the green fluorescent protein (GFP), discovered decades ago as an accessory emitter in coelenterate bioluminescence and now used extensively as a reporter protein.

Throughout evolution, bioluminescence has been reinvented many times; some 30 different independent systems are still extant. The enzymes (luciferases) catalyzing the light-emitting reactions of fireflies, coelenterates, and bacteria, for example, show no homology to each other, and the substrates (luciferins) of these reactions are unrelated chemically. There is, however, one common thread tying together different systems at the molecular level: All bioluminescences (with fungal luminescence a possible exception) are luciferase-catalyzed reactions of molecular oxygen with the luciferins. All involve a luciferase-bound peroxy-luciferin intermediate, the breakdown of which provides energy for excitation.[1]

Several factors affect the color of a bioluminescence. In the simplest case, the emission matches the fluorescence of an excited luciferase-bound product of the reaction. The luciferase structure can itself alter the color, as in the firefly, where single amino acid substitutions in the luciferase result in significant shifts in the emission spectrum. In bacteria and coelenterates, the chromophores of accessory proteins associated with a luciferase may serve as alternate emitters, such as the yellow fluorescent protein (YFP) in bacteria and GFP in coelenterates.

---

[1]The terms luciferin and luciferase are generic, referring to the substrate and enzyme in a bioluminescent reaction irrespective of their structures, so they must be qualified by specifying the organism. Luciferase genes from different groups of organisms are typically not homologous and may be distinguished by their different abbreviations: *lux* (bacterial), *luc* (firefly), and *lcf* (dinoflagellate).

The cell biology and regulation of bioluminescence differ among groups. While bacteria and some other systems emit light continuously, in many the luminescence occurs as flashes, typically of 0.1–1 s duration. These require a rapid turn on and off of an enzymatic reaction, with reagents sequestered appropriately and subject to quick mobilization. Luminescent organelles in scale worms and fireflies represent modifications of endoplasmic reticulum and peroxisomes, respectively. Dinoflagellate organelles (scintillons) are novel cytoplasmic structures whose flash is triggered by a rapid pH change within the organelle. In coelenterates, flashing is caused by calcium entry, and the calcium sites on the relevant proteins have homologies with calmodulin, whereas in fireflies, the triggering agent is unknown, although oxygen is a candidate.

Progress in the fundamental knowledge of bioluminescence has also led to numerous gene-reporting techniques and very sensitive analytical methods; these are not reviewed here, even though thanks to them new basic knowledge is now acquired in many areas of biology and medicine.

Work on bioluminescence is actively pursued at all levels, from the perspective of the naturalist to that of the photochemist. Although the last Annual Review article on this subject dates back thirty years (Hastings 1968), many aspects of bioluminescence have been the objects of selective reviews in recent years, and these are cited here. The present account combines a broad overview of the chemistry and cellular control of bioluminescence with deeper discussions of selected topics, in the hope of conveying the interest and importance of bioluminescence to a reader unfamiliar with the field.

DIVERSITY OF CHEMISTRIES

How Is Light Generated?

Each time a photon of visible light is emitted at room temperature, by a living organism or chemicals in a test tube, the reaction responsible for the creation of the excited state, and thus for the emission, must be a very exergonic process, because a photon of green light ($\approx$500 nm), for example, corresponds to $\approx$60 kcal per mole (or about eight times the energy released by the hydrolysis of ATP to ADP). It must also happen in one step because the pooling of the energy of two or more exothermic reaction steps can occur only in rare conditions not encountered here. The actual emission of chemiluminescence or bioluminescence (which is a chemiluminescence that requires an enzyme) is the extremely rapid final process of a usually multistep reaction, in which the penultimate step is the generation of a molecule in an electronically excited state, P*. The excited state of the emitter has a very short lifetime. It holds the reaction energy for no more than a few nanoseconds before releasing it in the form of a photon, and it cannot be distinguished from the excited singlet state (thus fluorescence) created by the absorption of a photon by P, as shown by a *vertical arrow* below (for example, see Turro 1978; for a brief review, see Wilson 1995).

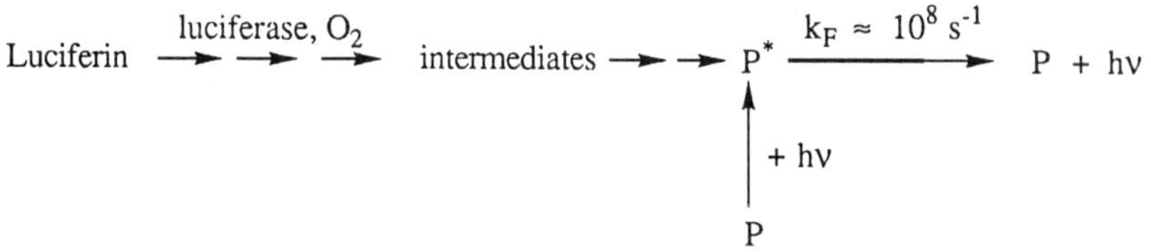

$$\text{Luciferin} \xrightarrow{\quad\text{luciferase, } O_2\quad} \text{intermediates} \longrightarrow \longrightarrow P^* \xrightarrow{\quad k_F \approx 10^8 \text{ s}^{-1}\quad} P + h\nu$$

$$\uparrow \; + h\nu$$

$$P$$

Therefore, in principle, the spectrum of a bio- or chemiluminescence matches the fluorescence spectrum of the reaction product P, and this should provide a clue as to the identity of this product. As a corollary, there cannot be an efficient bioluminescence if the emitter has a low fluorescence efficiency. In an in vitro luciferase/luciferin reaction, kinetic events happening on a time scale longer than nanoseconds reflect processes preceding the formation of the excited emitter, not its very fast radiative deactivation.

Among the simplest model systems studied chemically, the decomposition of four-membered ring dioxetanones are especially relevant to bioluminescence (Shimomura 1982). These strained and energy-rich peroxides decompose to form CO_2 and an often-excited carbonyl compound, releasing a large reaction energy at the small initial cost of breaking the comparatively weak O-O bond.

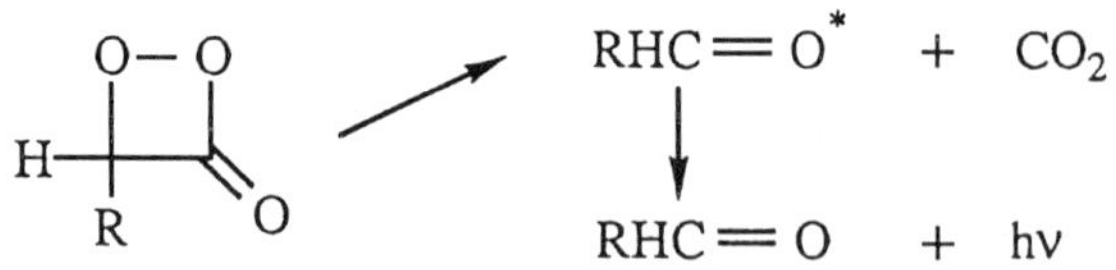

$$RHC{=}O^* + CO_2$$
$$\downarrow$$
$$RHC{=}O + h\nu$$

The cleavage of a dioxetanone, formed in the oxidation of a luciferin, may be catalyzed by an internal electron transfer to the O-O bond from the R moiety if its oxidation potential is appropriately low; the consequence is a fast cascade of processes terminating in the generation of the excited state of RHC=O, possibly via a final charge-annihilation process. Though yet unproven, even in model systems, this proposal of a chemically induced electron-exchange luminescence, or CIEEL, is often invoked and discussed in the bioluminescence literature, notably in the firefly and coelenterate cases, as well as in the bacterial luciferase reaction, which does not involve a dioxetanone intermediate (see below) (Schuster 1979, Catalani & Wilson 1989, McCapra 1997).

The expectation that the bioluminescence should match spectrally the fluorescence of the reaction product may not be realized for several reasons. One is that the emission may originate from an enzyme-bound intermediate or product; the intensity and spectrum may then differ from that of the free excited product. The firefly system best illustrates this case. Another possibility is that a second fluorophore (F, scheme below) such as GFP is present, to which the energy carried by the primary excited species (P*) is transferred, thereby causing this accessory fluorophore to become excited and emit its own fluorescence.

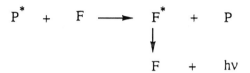

$$P^* \; + \; F \; \longrightarrow \; F^* \; + \; P$$
$$\downarrow$$
$$F \; + \; h\nu$$

Electronic energy can, in fact, be transferred from one molecule to another in several ways (Lamola 1969, Turro 1978). One way is trivial; the accessory fluorophore simply absorbs the light emitted by the primary excited state and re-emits it as its own fluorescence. In contrast to this radiative process, radiationless energy transfer can happen by either of two mechanisms. If there is very close contact between energy donor and acceptor, electrons can jump between orbitals on donor and acceptor, resulting in so-called electron-exchange (or Dexter) energy transfer. Alternatively, if there is a good overlap between the absorption spectrum of the second fluorophore and the emission spectrum of the primary emitter, energy transfer can take place at distances much greater than molecular diameters, via so-called Förster resonance energy transfer (FRET) (Wu & Brand 1994). The rate is an inverse function of r^6, where r is the distance between donor and acceptor, and strongly depends on their mutual orientation. In favorable situations, resonance transfer remains efficient over tens of Å. The green emission of coelenterates is considered to be the result of radiationless energy transfer to GFP (see below).

In still another situation, an accessory fluorophore may actually participate in the reaction, by binding to an enzyme-substrate intermediate and influencing the kinetics of the reaction. The fluorophore, then, may acquire its excitation energy in a different way, i.e. bypassing excitation of the primary emitter. The bacterial accessory emitters (YFP and LumP) may function in this way (see below). The complexities of this aspect of bioluminescence at the mechanistic and molecular levels will be obvious in the discussion of specific examples below.

Bacteria

Bacterial bioluminescence is the foremost example of a bioluminescence that does not appear to involve the intermediacy of a dioxetanone. Luciferase catalyses a mixed function oxidation of a long chain aldehyde and reduced flavin mononucleotide, $FMNH_2$ (Lee et al 1991, Baldwin & Ziegler 1992, Meighen 1994, Tu & Mager 1995). Once bound to the enzyme, $FMNH_2$ is protected against autoxidation, which is faster than the enzymatic reaction. The first step of the catalytic reaction is the formation of an unusually stable, chromatographically purifiable, luciferase-bound flavin hydroperoxide (Hastings et al 1973, Vervoort et al 1986). In a second step, aldehyde reacts to form a postulated peroxyhemiacetal, $E \cdot FOOA$, spectrally tracked but not yet isolated (Macheroux et al 1993). In spite of indications that there are many steps involved (Abu-Soud et al 1993), it is the lifetime of $E \cdot FOOA$ that determines the rate of the reaction. The emitter is the enzyme-bound 4a-hydroxyflavin, identified by its emission spectrum (Kurfürst et al 1987). The quantum yield is ≈ 0.3 hν per reacting $FMNH_2$ molecule (Figure 1).

Electrochemical studies (Mager & Tu 1995) and the correlation of the reaction rate with the oxidation potentials of substituents in the 8-position (Eckstein et al 1993) suggest that the rate-determining step is an electron transfer (or charge redistribution) from the dihydroflavin moiety to the especially weak peroxide bond within the peroxyhemiacetal, thereby causing the O-O bond cleavage. The excitation step is regarded as a charge annihilation between two radical-ion centers, occurring within the constraints of the enzyme pocket. Since none of these postulated reaction intermediates is stable apart from the enzyme, the mechanism remains perforce hypothetical. Up to now, the chemiluminescence efficiencies of non-enzymatic model systems have been so disappointingly low that they inform poorly on the enzymatic reaction (Merenyi et al 1992).

Luciferases from all bioluminescent bacteria studied are heterodimers of α (≈ 40 kDa) and β (≈ 35 kDa) subunits. The *luxA* and *luxB* genes encoding the α- and β-subunits are adjacent in the *lux* operon, which also contains, among others, three genes (*luxC, D*, and *E*) encoding proteins that make up the fatty acid reductase complex (for aldehyde synthesis). *LuxA* and *B* have been cloned and expressed heterologously and extensively used as molecular reporters. There is a higher degree of similarity among α-subunits of different strains than between the β-subunits; the α and β of each strain are themselves quite similar (32% identity); β probably evolved by gene duplication. The organization of the complete *lux* regulon is of special interest (Baldwin & Ziegler 1992, Meighen 1994) and is discussed further below.

---→

Figure 1   Bacterial and dinoflagellate bioluminescence. (*A*) In the bacterial reaction, the breakdown of the enzyme-bound peroxyhemiacetal $E \cdot FOOA$ is considered to involve electron transfer followed by charge annihilation resulting in the generation of the excited state (Eckstein et al 1993). (*B*) The structures of dinoflagellate luciferin and reaction products are known, but the reaction mechanism is not (Nakamura et al 1989).

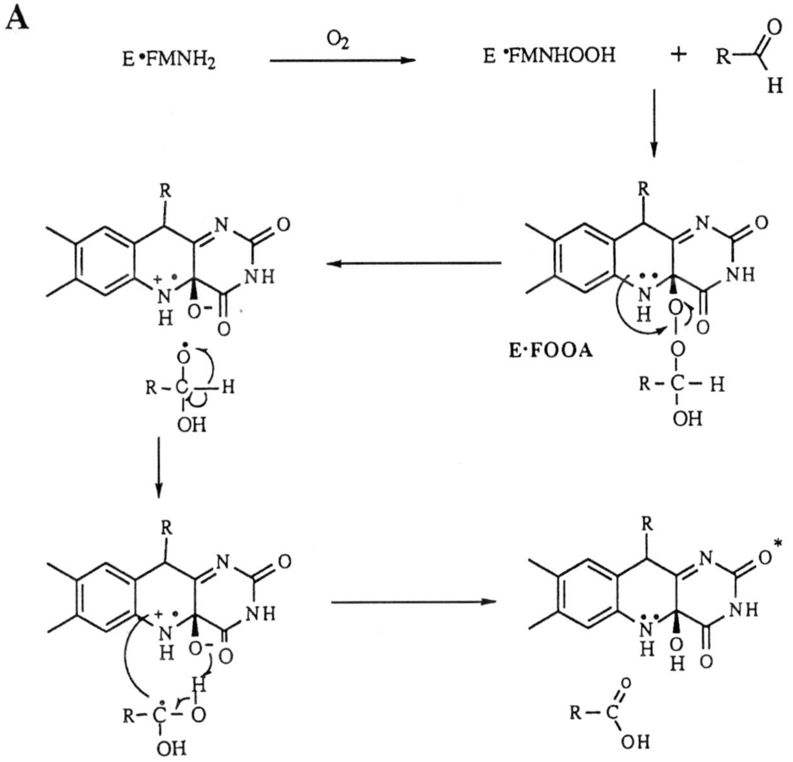
A
E •FMNH2
O2
E •FMNHOOH
E·FOOA

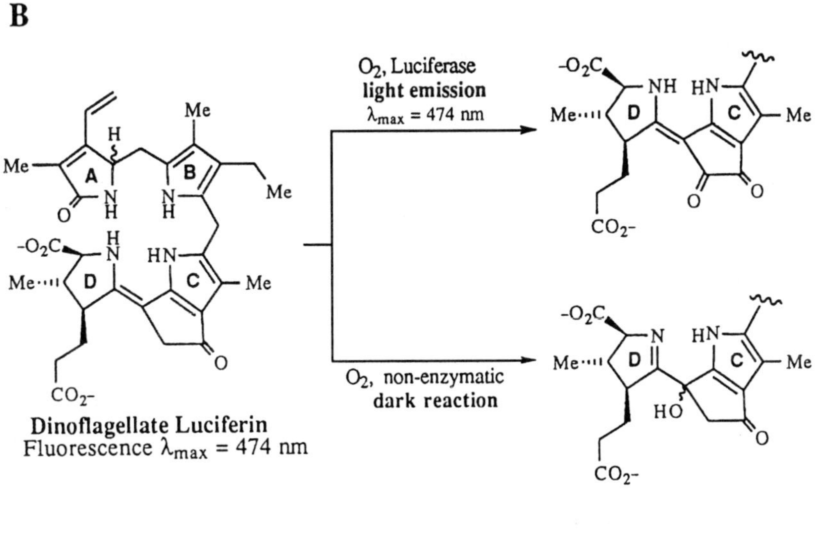
B
O2, Luciferase
light emission
λmax = 474 nm
O2, non-enzymatic
dark reaction
Dinoflagellate Luciferin
Fluorescence λmax = 474 nm

The crystal structure of *Vibrio harveyi* luciferase has been determined at both 2.4 and 1.5 Å resolution, but only in the absence of substrates. A deep pocket on the α-subunit extending to the β-subunit may be the catalytic site (Fisher et al 1995, 1996).

Cnidaria (Coelenterates) and Ctenophores

Many coelenterates and ctenophores, such as the sea pansy *Renilla*, the jelly-fish *Aequorea*, the hydroid *Obelia*, and the ctenophore *Mnemiopsis* are bio-luminescent. The emission is triggered by calcium, albeit by different mech-anisms at the cellular and molecular levels. Within the coelenterates, recent findings indicate that the bioluminescent systems of the related hydrozoan and anthozoan classes may be quite different, even though they use the same lu-ciferin, coelenterazine. Coelenterazine is an imidazolopyrazine, which occurs widely in luminous and non-luminous marine organisms (Shimomura et al 1980, Shimomura 1987, Thomson et al 1997). The luciferin of the crustacean *Vargula* is also an imidazolopyrazine, albeit with different substituents (Inouye et al 1992, Mager & Tu 1995).

In *Renilla*, the anthozoan in which the biochemistry has been most studied, four proteins are involved (Cormier 1978). The first, a sulfokinase, removes a sulfate from the precursor (storage form?) of coelenterazine. The freed coelen-terazine binds to a protein (luciferin-binding protein, 18.5 kDa, with three Ca^{2+} binding sites) and is released in the presence of calcium. Its oxidation is then catalyzed by *Renilla* luciferase (35 kDa); the reaction involves the formation of a dioxetanone intermediate, which breaks down to give CO_2 and oxidized luciferin (coelenteramide) in the excited state (Hart et al 1978) (Figure 2). The fourth protein is the green fluorescent protein, *Renilla* GFP, which (like the first two proteins) is not needed for the light-emitting reaction as such and, indeed, is not present in all anthozoans. In the absence of GFP, luciferase-bound ex-cited coelenteramide emits blue light ($\lambda_{max} \approx 480$ nm). In its presence, the light emitted is green ($\lambda_{max} \approx 509$ nm).

When first isolated, the hydrozoan *Aequorea* system appeared not to have the classic luciferase/luciferin system, nor to require oxygen (Shimomura et al 1962). In the presence of a calcium chelator, one can isolate and pu-rify a photoprotein, aequorin, which requires only calcium for light production. It is now clear that the photoprotein is simply a stable luciferase reaction inter-mediate to which an oxygenated form of the coelenterazine is already bound,

→

Figure 2 The bioluminescence reactions of both coelenterazine (*A*) and firefly luciferin (*B*) have been shown to involve the intermediacy of dioxetanone (Shimomura 1982). The hypothetical in-tramolecular electron transfer pathway is indicated in the firefly case (Koo et al 1978).

A

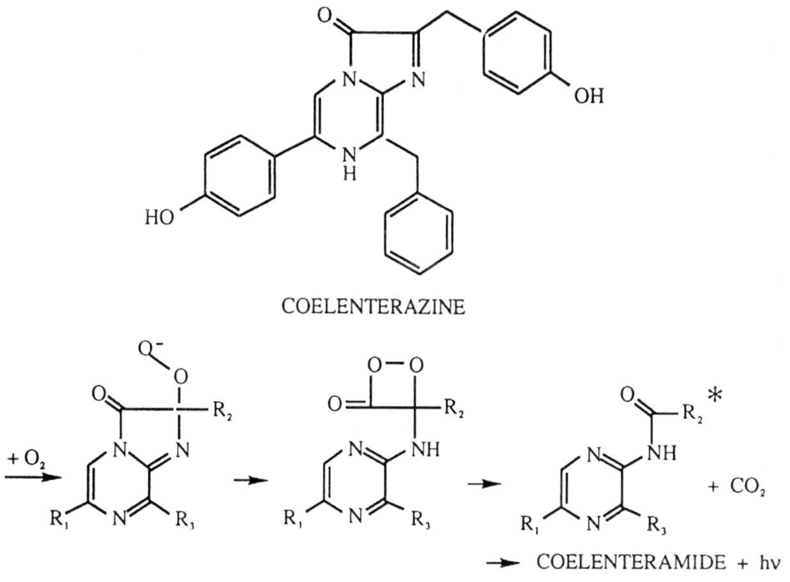
COELENTERAZINE
+ O2
R1
R2
R3
NH
+ CO2
COELENTERAMIDE + hν

B

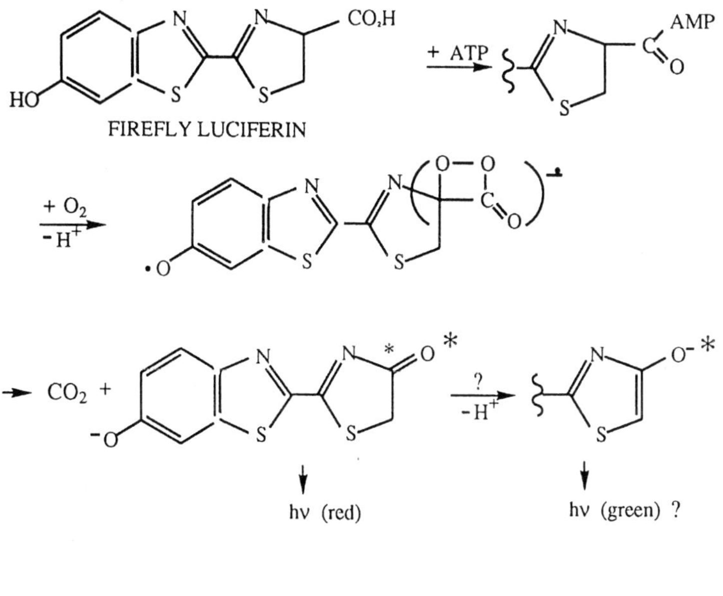
CO2H
FIREFLY LUCIFERIN
+ ATP
AMP
+ O2
- H+
CO2 +
?
- H+
hν (red)
hν (green) ?

probably as a hydroperoxide. Calcium, for which the protein has three binding sites, triggers the flash by allowing the reaction to go to completion via the dioxetanone intermediate. Thus instead of triggering at the stage of luciferin availability, calcium acts here on a reaction intermediate.

As in the case of *Renilla*, the emission is blue (486 nm) when the *Aequorea* reaction is carried out in vitro, whereas the bioluminescence from the living organism is green (508 nm) because of the presence of the soluble green fluorescent protein, *Aequorea* GFP (Johnson et al 1962, Morin & Hastings 1971). This scenario is quite general: in coelenterates that emit in the green fluorescence band of GFP in vivo, the emission in extracts is in blue. Although the *Renilla* and *Aequorea* bioluminescence systems are similar, in fact they differ at the molecular level. Both utilize coelenterazine as luciferin (as do diverse organisms in distant phyla), and both make use of a GFP as a secondary emitter, but neither their luciferases nor their GFPs appear to be closely related evolutionarily (C Szent Gyorgyi, personal communication).

The three (12 amino acid long) Ca^{2+}-binding sites of aequorin, obelin (from the hydrozoan *Obelia*), and *Renilla* luciferin-binding protein are homologous to the Ca^{2+}-binding sites of other calcium-binding proteins such as calmodulin. Calmodulin has four such sites, where the spacing between sites 3 and 4 is the same as that between sites 2 and 3 of the three bioluminescence proteins. It is speculated that these genes had a common ancestor and that site 2 in calmodulin might have become the luciferin-binding site in the coelenterates' proteins (Tsuji et al 1995).

The involvement of energy transfer was first inferred in the case of *Obelia*, where, in extracts, photoprotein and GFP are found together in granules (Morin & Hastings 1971). If the cells are mechanically ruptured in sea water containing $MgCl_2$ (a Ca^{2+} antagonist), then centrifuged lightly to remove large cell debris, the supernatant contains both intact granules and the soluble "photoprotein" (i.e. the luciferase/luciferin hydroperoxide, Ca-triggerable system). If calcium is added to the supernatant, it causes a flash of blue light by reacting with the photoprotein. If water is now added, the granules osmotically rupture, and green light is produced as the photoprotein and its associated GFP come in contact with calcium. However, if the order of additions is reversed, first water, then calcium, only blue light is emitted, because the photoprotein-GFP complex has dissociated in dilute solution, thus preventing energy transfer.

Later experiments with *Renilla* showed that energy transfer still takes place quite efficiently in reaction mixtures containing as little as 0.1 μM GFP (Ward & Cormier 1976). At such a low concentration, energy transfer could take place only if the two proteins were pre-associated, because the average distance between non-associated proteins would be an order of magnitude too large to allow for radiationless transfer. Indeed, chromatography showed that one luciferase molecule complexes with one GFP homodimer (Ward & Cormier 1978).

The study of coelenterate bioluminescence brought two remarkable benefits: GFP and aequorin. GFP is a uniquely valuable reporter of gene expression (see below), whereas aequorin provides a highly sensitive and rapid assay for intracellular calcium. The clone for apoaequorin has been expressed in different cells and can be visualized with added coelenterazine (e.g. Johnson et al 1995). *Renilla* luciferase is also used as a reporter (Lorenz et al 1991, 1996, Mayerhofer et al 1995).

Fireflies

Most bioluminescent insects are beetles (Coleoptera), in the families of Elateridae (such as click beetles), Phengodidae (the railroad worm with its red and green lanterns is a spectacular example) (Viviani & Bechara 1997), and Lampyridae, the fireflies. The reaction chemistry is presumably the same or similar for all beetles because their luciferases all react and give light with firefly luciferin (Wood 1995). This is not the case in bioluminescent Dipterae (such as the New Zealand glow worm), which are not discussed here.

Firefly luciferin is a benzothiazoyl-thiazole, an altogether different substrate from coelenterate luciferin, but again a dioxetanone is the critical energy-rich intermediate in the reaction. Luciferase first catalyzes the condensation of luciferin with ATP in the presence of Mg^{2+}, followed by the reaction of the adenylate with oxygen and cyclization of the peroxide; ATP provides the good leaving group AMP. The breakdown of the dioxetanone (rather than the hydrolysis of the adenylate) releases the energy, $\approx$50 kcal/mole, necessary to generate the excited state of oxyluciferin and CO_2 (Figure 2), with an overall efficiency reportedly close to 1 photon per oxidized luciferin (McCapra & Perring 1985, McElroy & DeLuca 1985). Even though the luciferin is the same in all beetles, their emissions span a wide-wavelength range, from green to orange (and even red in the railroad worm; note that the difference in energy between 560 and 630 nm photons is only $\approx$6 kcal/mol). Emission likely originates from the enzyme-bound mono-anion of oxyluciferin in its keto form, and the energy of its excited state, hence the color of the emission, probably depends on the tertiary stucture at the catalytic site (McCapra et al 1994; see below). The instability of free oxyluciferin in aqueous solution makes definitive assignments difficult.

Firefly luciferase is a 62 kDa monomeric protein with no prosthetic group. Its cDNA and that of several other beetle luciferases have been cloned and expressed in *Escherichia coli* and many eukaryotes (De Wet et al 1987, Masuda et al 1989, Wood et al 1989, Devine et al 1993). There is 40–50% sequence identity at the amino acid level between all luciferases of beetles belonging to the same family. Since the first step of the reaction is substrate activation by formation of an adenylate, it is not surprising that firefly luciferase shows sequence similarity with other enzymes that also activate the carboxyl group of their substrates via adenylation. For example, 4-coumarate:CoA ligases and luciferase have 17% sequence identity, although they probably diverged more than a billion years ago (Schroder 1989, Wood 1995).

The crystal structure of firefly luciferase shows two distinct domains, a large N-terminal domain and a small C-terminal domain linked by a flexible, four-residue loop (Conti et al 1996). There is a cleft exposed to water between these two distinct domains. The residues that are most conserved among all beetle luciferases and the other ATP-activating enzymes are located on the surfaces facing this cleft and on the loop connecting the domains. The active site may be located in this region. However, the cleft is too wide to allow both surfaces to interact simultaneously with luciferin. On binding ATP or the adenylate, a conformation change probably occurs, water is excluded (the active site of luciferase is reported to be very hydrophobic; DeLuca 1969), and the substrate gets pinched in the cleft. Unfortunately, firefly luciferase is the only ATP-activating enzyme superfamily for which the crystal structure has been determined. Whether a further conformation change to utilize a new active site is required for the second function of luciferase, that of catalyzing the light-emitting reaction of the adenylated substrate with oxygen, is impossible to anticipate.

Dinoflagellates

The most studied of the many bioluminescent dinoflagellates, which are the unicellular algae responsible for much of the so-called phosphorescence of the sea, is *Gonyaulax polyedra*. Because its luciferin reacts with the luciferases of all dinoflagellates tested so far, it is likely to be representative of the group at large. The structure of dinoflagellate luciferin, determined from *Pyrocystis lunula*, shows no similarity to any other luciferin (Nakamura et al 1989). It is a linear tetrapyrrole probably derived from chlorophyll and very sensitive to autoxidation. The site of oxidation on the chromophore depends on whether the reaction is luciferase-catalyzed, and luminescence accompanies only the enzymatic reaction (Figure 1*B*).

The reaction product is not fluorescent, in contrast to unoxidized luciferin, which fluoresces brightly with a spectrum matching that of the bioluminescence ($\lambda_{max} \approx 470$ nm) (Hastings 1978). This paradox is not yet resolved. One possibility is that the bioluminescence is emitted by an excited transient intermediate, as in the bacterial reaction. Another is that an excited state formed in the reaction transfers its energy to still unreacted luciferin. However, studies indicate that only one luciferin molecule is required for light emission and the bioluminescence intensity in the in vitro reaction decays monoexponentially.

Two proteins are involved in *Gonyaulax* bioluminescence. One is a luciferin-binding protein (LBP), a dimer of two identical 75.5 kDa subunits, which sequesters luciferin at a physiological pH, protecting it from autoxidation, and releases it as the pH drops to 6 (Morse et al 1989b, Mittag et al 1997). The other, a luciferase (LCF) (137 kDa), is inactive at pH 8 and becomes active exactly in the pH range at which the LBP makes luciferin available for the reaction. The two proteins and luciferin are tightly packaged in special cytoplasmic organelles, the scintillons (Nicolas et al 1991, Desjardins & Morse 1993). The full-length cDNA of LBP and LCF have been cloned and sequenced (Lee et al 1993, Bae & Hastings 1994, Li & Hastings 1998). Both genes are present in many copies and neither has introns. They show no sequence homology with other proteins in the data bases, except for their N-terminal domains, which have a 50% sequence identity over a stretch of ≈100 residues. Interestingly, the luciferase contains three homologous and contiguous repeat sequences of 377 amino acids, and each of these sequences expresses a catalytically active peptide (Li et al 1997). In vivo, bioluminescence is emitted both as brief flashes (≈100 ms) and as a low intensity glow. The mechanisms involved in the control of emission at the biochemical, cellular, and circadian levels are discussed below.

WHAT DETERMINES THE EMISSION SPECTRUM?

The simplest scenario, which calls for the bioluminescence to be spectrally identical to the fluorescence of the reaction product (the oxidized substrate), fits the cases of coelenterates and ctenophores, such as *Mnemiopsis*, which do not have GFP, and the crustacean *Vargula*, which also uses an imidazolopyrazine as luciferin and oxidizes it via a dioxetanone. But more often than not this simple script is not followed, sometimes because of the presence of accessory proteins (see below). Another complication may arise if the immediate reaction product, is chemically unstable after emission. In that case, the emission corresponds to the fluorescence of an intermediate. As mentioned above, this occurs in bacterial bioluminescence and could well be taking place in dinoflagellate and firefly bioluminescence; nevertheless, in these cases it is still a chromophore directly formed in the excited state that emits the bioluminescence, even if it is not the final reaction product. The emission spectrum may also be affected by the protein environment, since the emitter is typically luciferase-bound.

The Enzyme: Firefly Luciferase

Mutagenesis of the luciferase cDNA of the Japanese firefly (*Luciola cruciata*) resulted in emissions ranging from the green to the red, as a consequence, in each case, of single amino acid substitutions (Kajiyama & Nakano 1991). For example, the substitution H433Y shifted the peak of emission from 562 nm to 612 nm, while the emission bandwidth remained unchanged. Four of the five residues that singly caused color shifts upon substitution are located along the second half of the sequence in the large N-terminal domain, and the fifth is in the C-terminal domain. In the case of click beetle luciferase isozymes, expression in *E. coli* of four different cDNAs coding for proteins differing in only a few amino acids resulted in peak emissions ranging from green to orange; these substitutions were all in a short region of the the N-terminal domain (Wood et al 1989).

To understand how the substitution of a single residue can radically affect the emission spectrum would require knowing, besides the exact location of these residues vis-à-vis the active site, the chemical identity of the excited reaction product. It is assumed that the excited mono-anion of the keto form of oxyluciferin emits red light (Wood 1995). It had been thought that the wild-type yellow emission resulted from enolization during the lifetime of the excited state, at physiological pH 8. Indeed, the 5,5'-dimethyl analog of luciferin, which cannot enolize, emits only red light. It was also thought that low pH ($\approx$6) results in red light because of more extended conjugation. Oxyluciferin is so extremely unstable that it is practically impossible to confirm experimentally these conclusions (White & Roswell 1991).

The previous work had thus focused on the identity of two discrete emitters, one emitting yellow light, the other red. But the observation that naturally occurring and mutant luciferases emitted in a whole range of colors, each with an emission spectrum consisting of a narrow, shoulderless band, cannot be accounted for by the superposition of the spectra of these two emitters. In fact, the effect of protein environment on the color of emission may be due to restriction on the conformation of luciferin (McCapra et al 1994, McCapra 1997). While the molecule is probably quite insensitive in the ground state to the angle of twist between the two rings around the C2-C2' axis, in the excited state the energy minimum is estimated to correspond to a structure with the rings at a 90° angle. When a twisted excited oxyluciferin anion emits, it ends up in a twisted ground state because conformation changes are too slow to compete with emission of a photon; the energy of the electronic transition will then correspond to photons toward the red end of the spectrum. But if the luciferin intermediate is constrained by luciferase to be nearly planar, the energy of the emitted photon will be larger, i.e. blue-shifted. Thus the degree of twist might determine a continuum of emission colors.

Accessory Proteins: GFP

In some systems, the bioluminescence spectrum may not match the fluorescence of the luciferase reaction product because of the presence in vivo of an accessory fluorophore. The most famous of such "antenna" proteins is coelenterate GFP.

The GFP proteins turn out to be remarkably interesting. Their most unusual (and valuable) feature is that the chromophore is covalently bound. In *Aequorea* GFP, it results from the post-translational cyclization, dehydration, and oxidation of residues Ser65-Tyr66-Gly67 in the 238 amino acids protein (Heim et al 1994). The cloning of a cDNA of this GFP (Prasher et al 1992), and the demonstration that its expression in prokaryotic or eukaryotic cells produces a fluorescent protein, thus without the need for any coelenterate-specific enzymes, opened the gates to innumerable applications of GFP as a reporter gene and a marker of cellular localization (Chalfie et al 1994).

GFP chromophore

Even though the GFP peptides of *Aequorea* and *Renilla* are not strongly homologous (Cubitt et al 1995; C Szent Gyorgyi, personal communication), their imidazolinone chromophores are identical, and the fluorescence spectra of both consist of a narrow band at 509 nm. However, the absorption spectrum of wild-type *Aequorea* GFP shows two bands, a major peak at 395 nm and a minor one at 475 nm, whereas that of *Renilla* GFP consists of a single peak at 498 nm, fivefold more intense than the 395 nm peak of *Aequorea* GFP. This in itself demonstrates, as for the visual pigments, how much the protein environment of a chromophore may influence its spectral properties. The numerous mutants of *Aequorea* GFP have now made this abundantly clear, while making available custom-made GFP of specially desirable spectroscopic properties (Heim & Tsien 1996). Mutations in GFP far removed from the chromophore can affect the absorption and fluorescence spectra, but the near-full-length gene is essential: Only one amino acid can be deleted at the N terminus and at most 15 at the C terminus without loss of fluorescence (Cubitt et al 1995).

Within the chromophore itself, mutations of either Ser65 or Tyr66 yield fluorescent proteins displaying only one absorption band. In the case of Ser65 mutants, the short-wavelength band is lost with little spectral shift of either the 475 nm band or the emission maximum; the properties of this particularly useful S65T mutant are very close to those of *Renilla* GFP. In mutants of Tyr66, the 475 nm band is lost, while the fluorescence is shifted to the blue by as much as 60 nm in T66H. In contrast, Gly67 cannot be substituted without complete loss of fluorescence.

The biosynthesis of the chromophore can be looked upon as requiring successive steps: proper folding of the peptide chain so as to bring residues 65 and 67 to the geometry appropriate for cyclization, dehydration, and finally oxidation to form a C=C double bond on the phenolic side chain of tyrosine and thus create the 4-hydroxycinnamyl part of the chromophore. If GFP is expressed in anaerobically grown *E. coli*, the correct molecular weight protein is produced, but it is not fluorescent. The subsequent appearance of fluorescence requires only the admission of oxygen and will occur in extracts; it develops relatively slowly, in a matter of hours (Heim et al 1994). The mechanism of this slow oxidation step is unknown, other than that it requires no enzyme since it occurs even in very dilute lysates. It deserves particular mention because it limits the use of GFP as a fast reporter of gene expression.

The kinetics of chromophore formation in mutant S65T expressed in *E. coli* was studied by comparing soluble mature GFP, where the chromophore is already formed, with the nonfluorescent GFP extracted from inclusion bodies, where improper folding prevents cyclization of the chromophore (Reid & Flynn 1997). Neither of these proteins is fluorescent after denaturation. Upon renaturation, the soluble protein reacquires its fluorescence in a matter of minutes since its chromophore is preformed. In contrast, the GFP extracted from inclusion bodies requires hours, because after protein folding and cyclization of Thr65 and Gly67, the slow oxidation step must still take place. The rate of protein folding seems to be the same in these two GFPs, as shown by the same rate of acquisition of resistance to proteolysis following denaturation/renaturation.

Many of the properties of GFP, such as its thermal stability and remarkable resistance to proteolysis, derive from its unique structure. The crystal structures of WT GFP (Yang et al 1996, Brejc et al 1997) and mutants S65T (Ormö et al 1996) and Y65H/Y145F (Wachter et al 1997) show the chromophores located at the center of a protein cylinder, dubbed a β-can. The S65T crystals are monomeric, whereas WT GFP forms monomeric or dimeric crystals made of two parallel cans (30 × 40 Å), each with its central chromophore protected by 11 β-strands cylindrically wrapped around it. Solvent access to the inside cavity in these "lanterns" is blocked on top and bottom by short segments of α-helices, although some water molecules are immobilized inside; there is clearly no room for an enzyme to catalyse chromophore formation. The GFP dimers seen in the crystal result from hydrophilic interactions between three of the β-strands resulting in many hydrogen bonds. There is also a small hydrophobic patch that may play a role in the interaction of GFP and aequorin. The state of association of aequorin and GFP in vivo is unclear. In solution, the association depends on both concentration and ionic strength. It is reported that GFP and aequorin may form a heterotetramer (Cutler & Ward 1997).

Surprisingly, the aequorin-GFP system seems less than ideal for energy transfer. Of the two absorption bands of WT GFP, at 395 and 475 nm, only the weaker long-wavelength band overlaps significantly with the emission band of aequorin. The situation is more favorable in *Renilla*, and it has inspired the constructions of pairs of *Aequorea* GFP mutants with spectral properties specifically suited to their use as donor-acceptor tags in studies of protein-protein interactions in vivo. In two ingenious fluorescence experiments mimicking in vivo aggregation, donor and acceptor pairs, each made of a blue- and a green-shifted GFP mutant, were linked together by flexible chains of 20 or 25 amino acids, which included a protease-sensitive site. After addition of the specific protease, the fluorescence gradually shifted from green to blue as the two GFPs separated and resonance energy transfer became less efficient (Heim & Tsien 1996, Mitra et al 1996).

The photophysics of *Aequorea* GFP are complex and interesting. The intensity ratio of its two absorption bands depends on pH, ionic strength, and temperature. They originate from the ground states of two different forms of the chromophore, which can photoconvert (during the course of hours under laser irradiation). Excitation in the high-energy band (<400 nm) results in its bleaching, with a concomitant increase of absorbance in the lower energy band and an isosbestic point at 425 nm. This process is only partially and slowly reversible (days) in the dark. The two forms differ by their state of ionization associated with the network of hydrogen bonds tying the chromophore to the rest of the protein. The presence of the threonine methyl in S65T is sufficient to keep the chromophore permanently in its ionized form and prevent photoisomerization (Chattoraj et al 1996, Brejc et al 1997).

Accessory Proteins: YFP and BFP

It is not known whether the association of aequorin and GFP, which modifies the color of the emission, also alters the kinetics of the reaction, indicative of a chemical interaction prior to excitation. Such interactions do occur in the case of two accessory proteins in bioluminescent bacteria, where in contrast to GFP, the chromophores are not covalently bound. While in vitro emission from the bacterial luciferase-catalyzed reaction peaks at ≈495 nm, the in vivo emission is blue shifted to ≈475 nm in *Photobacterium phosphoreum* and *P. leiognathi*. This is due to the presence of a protein (LumP, 21 kDa) in which the fluorophore is 6,7-dimethyl-8-(1'-D-ribityl)lumazine, a precursor of riboflavin (Koka & Lee 1979). A yellow fluorescence protein (YFP, 28 kDa), with FMN as chromophore, causes a strain (Y-1) of *Vibrio fischeri* to emit yellow light ($\lambda_{max} \approx 540$ nm) (Daubner et al 1987, Macheroux et al 1987).

In vitro, these two functionally analogous proteins shift the emission peaks of the corresponding luciferase reactions in a concentration-dependent manner. LumP and YFP are homologous (O'Kane et al 1991) and also share homology with riboflavin synthase, which binds two molecules of lumazine (O'Kane & Prasher 1992). YFP and LumP do not simply acquire their excitation energy by energy transfer from the luciferase-hydroxyflavin, the normal emitter, but influence the enzymatic reaction at an earlier stage. YFP, for example, accelerates up to 10-fold the rate of intensity of decay of the in vitro reaction of *V. fischeri* luciferase, in a concentration-dependent manner (Eckstein et al 1990). LumP has a similar but smaller effect on the reaction of *P. phosphoreum* and *P. leiognathi* luciferases (Petushkov et al 1996a,b). Neither the apoproteins nor the chromophores alone are effective, nor do YFP or LumP associate with luciferase itself. Therefore, the fluorescence proteins must interact with and destabilize an enzyme-bound intermediate, such as the peroxyhemiacetal, and deviate the reaction course.

In the case of LumP, the luciferase-bound emitter it thought to be generated in its excited state while complexed with LumP, the excited state of which is created by energy transfer, resulting in blue emission. However, the effects of LumP and YFP on the rate of intensity decay, described above, are not entirely consistent with this mechanism. For YFP there is a further observation. If there were a single primary emitter of nanoseconds lifetime and it either emitted blue light or transferred its energy to YFP, the time courses of blue and yellow emissions should be identical on the experimental time scale of seconds (in the single-turnover standard assay). This, however, is not observed: In the presence of YFP, the onset kinetics of blue emission (from the luciferase-bound hydroxyflavin emitter) and yellow emission (from YFP) are clearly different. Thus a single kinetic pathway and primary emitter with an ultimate energy transfer process to YFP can definitely not account for the results (Eckstein et al 1990). The blue emission must originate from that fraction of peroxyhemiacetal that has not reacted with YFP, whereas yellow emission originates from the complex, via an intra-complex energy transfer process.

The effect of aldehyde chain length on the reaction rate, with or without YFP, supports the assumption that the critical intermediate with which YFP (and presumably LumP) interacts is the peroxyhemiacetal. If a fast rate of intensity decay, as with dodecanal and tetradecanal, reflects a short lifetime for this intermediate, then the chances of its interception by YFP will be the poorest. Indeed, at a given concentration, YFP is relatively more effective with aldehydes of shorter chain length (Sirokmán & Hastings 1997).

The effect of YFP is prominent at 4°C and virtually absent at 20°C. One possibility is that a dimeric inactive form of YFP is favored by higher temperature. Another is that a change in YFP conformation could affect its ability to attain a critical geometry at the active site (Sirokmán et al 1995).

Finally, the case of YFP illustrates, once again, how much a protein can alter the emission spectrum of its noncovalently bound chromophore, in this case FMN. The λ_{max} of free FMN fluorescence is 525 nm, whereas in YFP it is red-shifted to 540 nm, possibly by the conformation changes in the isoalloxazine moiety imposed by protein binding (Karatani & Hastings 1993).

CELL BIOLOGY AND CELLULAR CONTROL OF LUMINESCENCE

As the biochemistry of different luminescent systems differs, so do the structural and regulatory aspects at the cellular level (Hastings & Morin 1991). In some cases, the luciferase system appears to be distributed throughout the cytoplasm, whereas in others the cells (photocytes) specialized for bioluminescence possess organelles responsible for light emission. Still other systems remain uninvestigated.

Bacteria

Bacteria emit light continuously, and their small size would seem to argue against any subcellular localization of the light-emitting system; this has been confirmed by immunogold labeling (Colepicolo et al 1989b). Reports that bacteria emit light in pulses (Berzhanskaya et al 1975) were intriguing because bacterial luciferase constitutes a shunt of the electron transport pathway, which could involve some kind of feedback regulation with cyclic bursts. However, careful measurements of emission from a single bacterium established that the light emission is indeed continuous (Haas 1980).

Cnidaria

Cnidarian photocytes may be clustered or widely scattered, most often located in or near the endoderm. In *Obelia*, action potentials in the conducting epithelium result in the release of calcium in the photocytes, which triggers flashing. An inward calcium current occurs in depolarized support cells, not the photocytes, and gap junctions between the two provide channels for calcium entry to the photocytes (Dunlap et al 1987). In extracts of hydrozoan and anthozoan, luminescence activity occurs in both particulate and soluble fractions (see above; Morin & Hastings 1971), suggesting that an organelle is involved. Although some evidence supported this possibility (Anderson & Cormier 1973, Spurlock & Cormier 1975), further studies did not (Case & Strause 1978). The particles might represent cytoplasmic vesicles formed from endoplasmic reticulum during extraction.

Fireflies

Adult firefly lanterns are comprised of stacked units in which the photocytes are arranged in rosettes, with a central cylinder through which run branches of the lantern nerve and tracheae that carry oxygen to the cells (Case & Strause 1978). The lantern itself comprises a series of such rosettes, stacked side-by-side in many dorso-ventral columns. Based on immunochemical labeling, organelles containing luciferase in the photocytes of the American firefly were identified as peroxisomes (Hanna et al 1976). Indeed, the C-terminal tripeptide SKL peroxisomal targeting sequence is present in luciferase (Gould et al 1989), and when the gene is expressed in yeast or mammalian cells, luciferase localizes to peroxisomes (Keller et al 1987, Aflalo 1990, Soto et al 1993). The SKL sequence is absent in the Japanese firefly luciferase (Masuda et al 1989).

Although flashing is initiated by a nerve impulse, the nerve terminals in the light organ are not on photocytes but on tracheolar cells, which may regulate the supply of oxygen, suggesting that this controls the flash (Ghiradella 1977). However, the rapid kinetics and bunched flashes, complex wave forms, and high-frequency flickering all seem unlikely to be regulated by access to oxygen. Equally baffling is how a membrane-bound cytoplasmic organelle could be linked to an excitatory process, be it transmitted via a membrane or a diffusible reagent. A novel discovery may be in store.

Dinoflagellates

Bioluminescence in dinoflagellates is emitted from many ($\approx$400 per cell) small ($\approx$0.4 μm) organelles, the scintillons. It has been studied extensively in only one species, *G. polyedra*; the ultrastructure and flash control mechanism are fascinating and novel. Scintillon luminescence, visualized by image intensification, colocalizes with the fluorescence of luciferin (Johnson et al 1985). Identified by immunolabeling (Nicolas et al 1987a), scintillons are spherical vesicles projecting into the cell vacuole. This preserves the continuity of the vacuolar membrane conducting the triggering action potential (Eckert 1965), which is postulated to open proton channels. This causes a transient pH change in the scintillons, the activation of the reaction, and a flash (Hastings & Dunlap 1986).

The two major proteins, luciferase (LCF) and luciferin-binding protein (LBP), are localized to the scintillons (Nicolas et al 1991). Upon cell extraction at pH 8, activity can be obtained from both soluble and particulate fractions. The latter is attributed to scintillons that seal off at the neck to form closed vesicles, which can be purified by density gradient centrifugation. Upon a shift to pH 6, they emit flashes closely mimicking the in vivo flash, with kinetics independent of concentration. These vesicles can be recharged in vitro by incubating with luciferin. The soluble fraction contains luciferase and the luciferin-LBP complex, but emits light only upon a shift to pH 6, which activates the luciferase-catalyzed oxidation of the released luciferin; in this case, the kinetics of the luminescence depends upon luciferase concentration (Hastings 1978). The components of all luminous dinoflagellates studied cross-react biochemically, and all have scintillons, as judged by in vitro assays in extracts (Schmitter et al 1976) and immunocytochemical labeling (Nicolas et al 1987b). One significant difference between species is the the absence of lucifern-binding protein in *Pyrocystis*, yet flashing is still tightly controlled (Colepicolo et al 1993).

Luminescence in *G. polyedra* and other dinoflagellates is regulated by an endogenous circadian clock, and is maximum during the dark (night) phase (Johnson & Hastings 1986). Remarkably, both luciferase and luciferin-binding protein in *G. polyedra* are destroyed at the end of the night phase and then synthesized again in the next cycle. Moreover, the scintillons themselves are broken down and reformed each day (Fritz et al 1990); the circadian cycle may actually be viewed as a daily differentiation of certain cellular processes.

The synthesis of the two luminescence proteins LCF and LBP of *Gonyaulax* is regulated translationally; their mRNA levels and translatabilities remain constant over the circadian cycle (Morse et al 1989a, Mittag et al 1998). A protein of ≈45 kDa has been demonstrated to bind to the 3'UTR of the *lbp* mRNA at an unusual 22 nt sequence containing seven U(U)G repeats (Mittag et al 1994) and is hypothesized to regulate 5' initiation (Mittag et al 1997). The circadian mechanism and how it regulates cellular processes remains one of the real enigmas in biology. Synthesis and destruction is not the only mode of regulation, even in dinoflagellates. For example, in *Pyrocystis*, the amount of luciferase remains constant over the cycle (Knaust et al 1998), but its cellular location and responsiveness change from night to day (Widder & Case 1982).

Polynoid Scale Worms

Scale worms are marine annelids possessing two rows of scales covering the dorsal surface of the animal. In luminous species the cells of the ventral epithelial layer of the scales are photocytes. When attacked by a predator, the scales first emit rapid flashes so as to frighten and deter, but they may then be shed in the water while the animals themselves escape, leaving the now glowing scales as luminous decoys. Little is known of the biochemistry. A fluorescence attributed to flavin develops in proportion to the amount of light emitted (Bassot & Bilbaut 1977) and a photoprotein (≈500 kDa), which emits light upon the addition of superoxide radicals, can be extracted from the cells (Nicolas et al 1982, Colepicolo et al 1990).

Within each photocyte are some 30 to 50 luminous organelles (1 to 5 μm in diameter) called photosomes, arranged in concentric rows around the central nucleus (Pavans de Ceccatty et al 1977). The photosomes are made of tubules of endoplasmic reticulum, 20 nm in diameter, structured as regular paracrystalline arrays. Flashes (≈100 ms) are triggered by calcium entry accompanying epithelial action potentials; conduction is facilitated by numerous gap junctions. A striking feature is that in isolated scales, repetitive stimuli (e.g. 1 Hz) result in progressive increases in flash intensity, attributed to the recruitment of more and more photosomes. This results from the rapid (ms) formation of new dyad junctions, thereby coupling additional photosomes to the excitatory plasma membrane (Bilbaut & Bassot 1977, Bassot 1987). The recruitment may be observed photometrically by luminescence and fluorescence of individual photosomes. After many (20–30) stimuli, fatigue occurs and flash intensity decreases. A single strong stimulus can evoke a similar train of flashes with a similar pattern of increasing then declining intensities. Paracrystalline arrays structurally similar to photosomes are also found in photoreceptors (Eakin & Brandenburger 1975, Bassot & Nicolas 1978).

REGULATION OF BACTERIAL BIOLUMINESCENCE

Autoinduction, Intercellular Chemical Signaling, and Quorum Sensing by Bacteria

We owe to bioluminescent bacteria the discovery of a clever way of intercellular communication. Why would isolated bacteria, free-living at sea, spend energy to emit light? The answer is, they do not, because the relevant genes are never turned on. We now know that luminescent, as well as a variety of non-luminescent, bacteria start the specific transcription of some genes only when the cell density is high enough for the products of these genes to have an impact on the environment. In culture, V. harveyi and V. fischeri first grow without synthesizing luciferase (and therefore without luminescing) until mid or late exponential phase is attained and a cell density threshold is crossed, after which luciferase is expressed and the cells luminesce. A not-yet luminescing, low density culture can indeed be activated to synthesize luciferase and luminesce by the addition of medium from a late culture (Nealson et al 1970). This medium contains a freely diffusible pheromone, the autoinducer, which is synthesized by the bacteria and accumulates in the medium as the cells grow. Thus by sensing the level of autoinducer, the cells are able to estimate their density and to initiate the energetically costly synthesis of luciferase (and the whole bioluminescence system) only when they are numerous enough to be seen, as when cultured in the light organ of a host such as a fish or a squid (Boettcher & Ruby 1995).

In V. fischeri, the autoinducer (VAI) is an N-acyl-homoserine lactone (Eberhard et al 1981).

VAI

Its regulon, which has been cloned and expressed in *E. coli*, contains two regulatory genes, *luxI* and *luxR*, in two divergent operons (Meighen 1994, Ulitzur & Dunlap 1995, Fuqua et al 1996). The product of *luxI* on the rightward operon (which contains *luxA* and *luxB* for the two luciferase subunits, as well as *luxC*, *D*, and *E* for aldedyde synthesis) synthesizes the autoinducer from S-adenosylmethionine and an acyl-acyl carrier protein (Moré et al 1996, Hanzelka & Greenberg 1996, Schaefer et al 1996). The *luxR* gene on the leftward operon codes for the LuxR protein, whose N-terminal domain binds the autoinducer (Hanzelka & Greenberg 1995); this causes the LuxR C-terminal domain to act as a transcriptional regulator, by binding DNA in synergy with RNA polymerase at a palindromic sequence located upstream of the transcription start of the rightward *lux* operon (Stevens & Greenberg 1997).

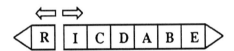

When the concentration of VAI in the medium (and therefore within the cell) is below a threshold, transcription of the rightward operon goes on at a steady but low level, allowing for the build up of autoinducer concentration to the point where VAI associates with *luxR* and activates transcription of both operons in an autocatalytic feedback loop (Eberhard et al 1991, Dunlap 1992). Some apparent contradictions remain, possibly because most studies have been done with the *lux* regulon cloned in *E. coli*, which may be lacking some elements important for the specificity of the autoinducer (Sitnikov et al 1995).

A growing list of other gram-negative, non-bioluminescent bacteria are now known to utilize a signaling system based on various homoserine lactones and homologs of LuxI- LuxR-type proteins, although often more complex than the autoinduction scheme of *V. fischeri* outlined above (Swift et al 1996). Among these are *Pseudomonas aeruginosa*, in which two systems, LasI-LasR and RhlI-RhlR, control the generation of several virulence factors, notably in the lungs of cystic fibrosis patients; *Agrobacterium tumefaciens*, a plant pathogen, in which TraI-TraR regulates the conjugate transfer of oncogenic plasmids into cell nuclei; and *Erwinia carotovora*, utilizing ExpR-ExpI to activate the synthesis of antibiotics and of plant cell-wall degrading exoenzymes in plants. Remarkably, in all these bacteria the signaling pheromones are also N-acyl homoserine lactones, differing from the *V. fischeri* autoinducer only by the structure of the acyl groups. It is therefore not surprising, for example, that there is a significant degree of homology between LuxI, LasI, TraI, and ExpI. The R proteins are also homologous but to a lesser degree. Although the purple bacterium *Rhodobacter sphaeroides* is not known to associate with a eukaryotic host, a homoserine lactone autoinducer has recently been shown to prevent aggregation (Puskas et al 1997), adding to the remarkable generality of this mode of transcriptional regulation.

This summary grossly oversimplifies the complexities of quorum sensing as now understood. For instance, there is evidence that *V. fischeri* responds to more than one autoinducer, and this is certainly the case in the other most studied bioluminescent *Vibrio* species, *V. harveyi*, in which autoinduction was first discovered (Nealson et al 1970). One of its autoinducers, HAI, is a N-acyl-homoserine lactone (Moré et al 1996), a close analog of VAI, yet the genes in *V. harveyi* serving the functions of *luxR* and *luxI* are not a part of the *lux* operon,

HAI

are not homologous to *luxR* and *luxI*, and VAI and HAI do not cross react (Bassler et al 1993). In contrast, the same N-acyl-homoserine lactone may be utilized by a number of different species. For example, VAI is a signaling molecule not only in *V. fischeri*, but also in *E. carotovora* and several other bacteria. This apparent lack of specificity may relate to interactions between species. Bacteria may, for example, have the ability and an advantage in monitoring the population of other species, as well as in sensing their own density (Fuqua et al 1996).

Among non-luminous bacteria utilizing a homoserine lactone as autoinducer, the insect pathogen *Xenorhabdus nematophilus* is of special interest (Dunphy et al 1997). These bacteria live in the gut tract of a parasitic nematode, which invades the hemocoel of insect larvae, where the bacteria are released and then grow, killing the insect. It was recently shown, by comparison of the virulent and an avirulent mutant of *X. nematophilus*, that virulence is regulated by HAI, the *V. harveyi* autoinducer; the avirulent mutant becomes virulent if injected in an insect together with HAI. In contrast, the regulation of luminescence of a very similar bacterial symbiont of nematodes (also an insect pathogen), *Photorhabdus* (formerly *Xenorhabdus*) *luminescens*, exhibits an autoinduction-like pattern but appears not to involve an autoinducer; it is speculated that regulation occurs post-transcriptionally (Hosseini & Nealson 1995). Another strain of *P. luminescens* has been isolated from human wounds; it also appears to autoinduce its luminescence, but nothing is known of the mechanism involved (Colepicolo et al 1989a).

What Can Luminous Bacteria Teach Us About Symbiosis?

The complexities of the association of *P. luminescens* and its nematode host were recently reviewed (Forst & Nealson 1996). They bring up the basic questions posed by symbiosis in the case of bioluminescent bacterial symbionts and their hosts. Several of these are addressed in a beautiful system particularly well suited to studies at the molecular, cellular, and morphological levels, the sepiolid squid *Eupryma scolopes*.

Its light organ hosts contains a dense culture ($>10^{10}$ cells/ml) of a specific strain of *V. fischeri* bacteria (Ruby & McFall-Ngai 1992, Ruby 1996). Both host and symbiont can be cultured in the laboratory, and the mutual benefits they derive from the association are easily understood: The squid is provided with a behaviorally useful light source, and the bacteria are given room and board and disseminated. The light organ of newly hatched offspring is bacteria-free and must therefore acquire symbionts from the surrounding seawater, in the only case where this mode of initiation of symbiosis has been unambiguously established.

In a young, still symbiont-free squid exposed to seawater containing *V. fischeri* cells, a special ciliated microvillous epithelium moves the sea water past pores leading to the empty crypts of the organ, presumably to facilitate entry of the bacteria. This induces development programs in both the organ and the symbionts; exposure to a very few bacteria for only a few hours is enough to start this colonization process. The crypts grow, the cells of the ciliated microvillous structure undergo alterations, then regress, and after 4 days die by bacteria-induced apoptosis (McFall-Ngai & Ruby 1991, Montgomery & McFall-Ngai 1994). None of these developments occur if the new organ is not exposed to competent bacteria. As for the bacteria, they immediately start proliferating rapidly, but after 12–24 h their growth rate declines, their size decreases, and they lose their flagella (Ruby & Asato 1993). Every morning the squid expels up to 90% of the bacteria from its organ (Boettcher et al 1996), which is repopulated by bacterial growth, while the expelled bacteria are viable and regrow flagella.

Of the thousands of bacteria from which to choose, many of which are luminous, how is the specific species and strain selected? There is as yet no answer to this fundamental question, but one speculation is that luminous bacteria are selected because the luciferase system detoxifies harmful reactive oxygen species (ROS), which may be generated in abundance by the host's light organ. Indeed, tissues lining the organ are rich ($\approx$250-fold richer than other squid tissues) in a peroxidase homologous to human myeloperoxidase (Weis et al 1996), which catalyzes the reaction of H_2O_2 and Cl^- to produce the more potent bactericidal agents HOCl and singlet oxygen (Steinbeck et al 1992). A role for luciferase is indicated by the fact that while mutants lacking *luxA* are capable of colonizing the light organ, their population soon drops to 10% of normal. Mutants defective in either *luxI* or *luxR* behave in a similar way. They colonize the light organ normally, although with a significantly reduced light output, but 48 h later their population is down to 10%. However, this does not explain how the selection of a particular luminescent strain is achieved. Another possibility is that the ROS induce the specific transcription of resistance genes (Khan & Wilson 1995) present only in the competent symbiont strain, meaning that the host peroxidase is part of a signaling system important in the establishment of the symbiosis.

Different strains of a given luminous species may differ in competence. As noted earlier, the *E. scolopes* organ can be colonized only by *V. fischeri*, including strains isolated as symbionts from fishes or other squids. Interestingly, if newly hatched squid are exposed separately to either of two strains of *V. fischeri* found in the Hawaiian coastal waters, where the squid lives, both are able to successfully colonize the light organ. However, if they are exposed to a mixture of the two, the *V. fischeri* strain normally found in the squid's organ—and paradoxically the far less luminescent of the two in laboratory cultures—soon outcompetes the other and becomes completely dominant, leading to a monoculture (Lee & Ruby 1994).

Recent work illustrates the importance of studies of the *V. fischeri-E. scolopes* symbiosis and their probable significance in the general field of pathogenicity. *V. fischeri* was found to have a gene homologous to the *Vibrio cholerae* transcription activator *toxR*, which regulates the production of the cholera toxin. *V. fischeri* also secretes an enzyme, halovibrin, which, like cholera toxin, has ADP-ribosyltransferase activity. However, halovibrin and cholera toxin share no sequence similarity (Reich & Schoolnik 1996). This is an intriguing finding, especially with regard to the pathogenic role of enzymes with ADP-ribosyltransferase activity.

Lastly, the case of the *V. fischeri-E. scolopes* association answers a general question in symbiosis: How is the symbiont population maintained within acceptable limits, so as not to overgrow the host? The daily dumping of 90% of the bacteria from the light organ appears to be the answer here.

In contrast to *V. fischeri*, *P. leiognathi*, and *P. phosphoreum*, which also colonize the light organs of fishes and squids, *V. harveyi* has never been found as a light organ symbiont. As a marine enterobacterium, it occurs in the gut of fishes and invertebrates. By attracting organisms to ingest fecal pellets that would otherwise sediment to the bottom, its luminescence may serve to aid in the dispersion and propagation of the bacteria, a rather unglamorous return for the cost of emitting light.

PERSPECTIVES

Evolutionary aspects of bioluminescence remain among the most intriguing of the unknowns. Based on the number of different extant systems, it has been estimated that light emission originated independently at least 30 times, from bacteria, fungi, and algae all the way to squid and fish (Hastings 1983). Furthermore, it is reasonable to assume that even more bioluminescence systems might have evolved but did not survive, for light emission is not essential for life. While in some cases, such as fungi, the function of bioluminescence is not obvious, nor is its mechanism (Shimomura et al 1993), in others it is clear that light is meant to be seen and used for various different functions, such as courtship or to repel predators or attract prey.

That bioluminescence is not found in higher vertebrates or plants, where it could also be functionally important, suggests that some barrier to the de novo creation of bioluminescence came into play. This might be regarded as in keeping with the great preponderance of luminescence in marine organisms. Bioluminescence is indeed abundantly present among fishes: Some have light organs harboring luminous bacteria, others have photophores utilizing coelenterazine or *Vargula* luciferin (which they may acquire nutritionally).

Through what circumstances did luminous bacteria become uniquely successful as symbionts in higher organisms? Since non-bioluminescent dinoflagellates engage in symbiotic associations with higher organisms such as clams and corals (which harness them for photosynthesis), why have bioluminescent species not been co-opted to provide light? What are the traits critical to a symbiont-host relationship? Some of these questions are being asked in the case of the squid.

An old idea, that bioluminescence did not first evolve for the production of light, but as a mechanism of detoxifying an atmosphere becoming dangerously aerobic (McElroy & Seliger 1962), keeps resurfacing in various forms (Seliger 1975, Seliger 1987, Barros & Bechara 1998). The finding that coelenterazine, widespread in luminous and non-luminous marine organisms, is a potent antioxidant suggests that protection against reactive oxygen species could have been its primary role (Rees et al 1998). Enzymes that would rapidly channel the energy liberated by the oxidation of coelenterazine into harmless photons might then have been selected. In another example, bacterial luciferase expressed in *E. coli* acts as a source of superoxide in the absence of the bioluminescence substrate decanal, not in its presence (Gonzalez-Flecha & Demple 1994).

The chemistry of all known bioluminescence reactions remains punctuated with question marks. There is no definitive picture yet of the elementary steps that culminate in the release of the large reaction energy ($\approx$50 kcal) as light. This is not surprising, considering that the mechanism of only a few of the simplest reactions is understood at the molecular level. In chemiluminescence and bioluminescence, the involvement of electron and charge transfer processes remains an area of discussion, with no definitive answers. Progress will require the development of more responsive model systems and more incisive techniques. Because chemi- and bioluminescence are, by definition, triggered chemically rather than by light, they are not amenable to the panoply of ultrafast laser-based photophysical methods now used to probe photochemical processes.

One can anticipate from the diversity of luciferins and luciferases that common characteristics will emerge that will help elucidate the critical features of chemiexcitation. In any case, the mechanistic uncertainties do not detract from the uniqueness of bioluminescence as a non-invasive and immediately responsive probe of a reaction or molecular marker. The extreme sensitivity of light-detecting systems brings analytical methods down to better than the femtomole level.

ACKNOWLEDGMENTS

We thank Drs. Anatol Eberhard, Tom Fagan, Pete Greenberg, Margaret McFall-Ngai, Jim Morin, David Morse, Deb Robertson, and Ned Ruby for critical reviews of the text and helpful and enjoyable discussions, and the National Science Foundation for support of research in this area.

Visit the *Annual Reviews home page* at
http://www.AnnualReviews.org

Literature Cited

Abu-Soud HM, Clark AC, Francisco WA, Baldwin TO, Raushel FM. 1993. Kinetic destabilization of the hydroperoxy flavin intermediate by site-directed modification of the reactive thiol in bacterial luciferase. *J. Biol. Chem.* 268:7699–706

Aflalo C. 1990. Targeting of cloned firefly luciferase to yeast mitochondria. *Biochemistry* 29:4758–66

Anderson JM, Cormier MJ. 1973. Lumisomes, the cellular site of bioluminescence in coelenterates. *J. Biol. Chem.* 248:2937–43

Bae YM, Hastings JW. 1994. Cloning, sequencing and expression of dinoflagellate luciferase DNA from a marine alga, *Gonyaulax polyedra. Biochim. Biophys. Acta* 1219:449–56

Baldwin TO, Ziegler MM. 1992. The biochemistry and molecular biology of bacterial luminescence. In *Chemistry and Biochemistry* of *Flavoenzymes*, ed. F Muller, pp. 467–530. Boca Raton: CRC Press

Barros MB, Bechara EJH. 1998. Bioluminescence as a possible auxiliary oxygen detoxifying mechanism in Elaterid larvae. *Free Radic. Biol. Med.* 24:767–77

Bassler BL, Wright M, Showalter RE, Silverman MR. 1993. Intercellular signalling in *Vibrio harveyi*: sequence and function of genes regulating expression of luminescence. *Mol. Microbiol.* 9:773–86

Bassot J-M. 1987. A transient intracellular coupling explains the facilitation of responses in the bioluminescent system of scale-worms. *J. Cell Biol.* 105:2235–43

Bassot J-M, Bilbaut A. 1977. Bioluminescence des elytres d'Acholoe IV. Luminescence et fluorescence des photosomes. *Biol. Cell.* 28:163–68

Bassot J-M, Nicolas M-T. 1978. Similar paracrystals of endoplasmic reticulum in the photoemitters and the photoreceptors of scale worms. *Experientia* 34:726–28

Berzhanskaya LY, Gitelson II, Fish AM, Chumakova RI. 1975. Pulsed nature of bacterial luminescence. *Ser. Biol. Dokl. Akad. Nauk. SSSR* 222:1220–22

Bilbaut A, Bassot J-M. 1977. Bioluminescence des elytres d'Acholoe II. Donnees photometriques. *Biol. Cell.* 28:145–54

Boettcher KJ, Ruby EG. 1995. Detection and quantification of *Vibrio fischeri* autoinducer from symbiotic squid light organs. *J. Bacteriol.* 1995:1053–58

Boettcher KJ, Ruby EG, McFall-Ngai MJ. 1996. Bioluminescence in the symbiotic squid *Euprymna scolopes* is controlled by a daily biological rhythm. *J. Comp. Physiol. A* 179:65–73

Brejc K, Sixma TK, Kitts PA, Kain SR, Tsien RY, et al. 1997. Structural basis for dual excitation and photoisomerization of the *Aequorea victoria* green fluorescent protein. *Proc. Natl. Acad. Sci. USA* 94:2306–11

Case JF, Strause LG. 1978. Neurally controlled luminescent systems. In *Bioluminescence in Action*, ed. PJ Herring, pp. 331–66. London: Academic

Catalani LH, Wilson T. 1989. Electron transfer and chemiluminescence. Two inefficient systems: 1,4-dimethoxy-9,10-diphenylanthracene peroxide and diphenoyl peroxide. *J. Am. Chem. Soc.* 111:2633–39

Chalfie M, Tu Y, Euskirchen G, Ward WW, Prasher DC. 1994. Green fluorescent protein as a marker for gene expression. *Science* 263:802–5

Chattoraj M, King BA, Bublitz GU, Boxer SG. 1996. Ultra-fast excited state dynamics in green fluorescent protein: multiple states and proton transfer. *Proc. Natl. Acad. Sci. USA* 93:8362–67

Colepicolo P, Camarero VCCP, Karnovsky ML, Nicolas M-T, Bassot J-M, Hastings JW. 1990. A sensitive and specific assay for superoxide anion released by neutrophils and macrophages, based on polynoidin bioluminescence. *Anal. Biochem.* 184:369–74

Colepicolo P, Cho KW, Poinar GO, Hastings JW. 1989a. Growth and luminescence of the bacterium *Xenorhabdus luminescens* from a human wound. *Appl. Environ. Microbiol.* 55:2601–6

Colepicolo P, Nicolas M-T, Bassot J-M, Hastings JW. 1989b. Expression and localization of bacterial luciferase determined by immunogold labeling. *Arch. Microbiol.* 152:72–76

Colepicolo P, Roenneberg T, Morse DM, Taylor WR, Hastings JW. 1993. Circadian regulation of bioluminescence in the dinoflagellate *Pyrocystis lunula*. *J. Phycol.* 29:173–79

Conti E, Franks NP, Brick P. 1996. Crystal structure of firefly luciferase throws light on a superfamily of adenylate-forming enzymes. *Structure* 4:287–98

Cormier MJ. 1978. Comparative biochemistry of animal systems. In *Bioluminescence in Action*, ed. PJ Herring, pp. 75–108. London: Academic

Cubitt AB, Heim R, Adams SR, Boyd AE, Gross LA, Tsien RY. 1995. Understanding, improving and using green fluorescent proteins. *Trends Biochem. Sci.* 20:448–55

Cutler MW, Ward WW. 1997. Spectral analysis and proposed model for GFP dimerization. In *Bioluminescence and Chemiluminescence*, ed. JW Hastings, LJ Kricka, PE Stanley, pp. 403–6. Chichester: Wiley & Sons

Daubner SC, Astorga AM, Leisman GB, Baldwin TO. 1987. Yellow light emission of *Vibrio fischeri* strain Y-1: purification and characterization of the energy-accepting yellow fluorescent protein. *Proc. Natl. Acad. Sci. USA* 84:8912–16

DeLuca M. 1969. Hydrophobic nature of the active site of firefly luciferase. *Biochemistry* 8:160–66

Desjardins M, Morse D. 1993. The polypeptide components of scintillons, the bioluminescence organelles of the dinoflagellate *Gonyaulax polyedra*. *Biochem. Cell Biol.* 71:176–82

Devine JH, Kutuzova GD, Green VA, Ugarova NN, Baldwin TO. 1993. Luciferase from the East European firefly *Luciola mingrelica*: cloning and nucleotide sequence of the cDNA, overexpression in *Escherichia coli* and purification of the enzyme. *Biochim. Biophys. Acta* 1173:121–32

De Wet JR, Wood KV, DeLuca M, Helinski DR,

Subramani S. 1987. Firefly luciferase gene: structure and expression in mammalian cells. *Mol. Cell. Biol.* 7:725–37

Dunlap K, Takeda K, Brehm P. 1987. Activation of a calcium-dependent photoprotein by chemical signalling through gap junctions. *Nature* 325:60–62

Dunlap PV. 1992. Mechanism for iron control of the *Vibrio fischeri* luminescence system: involvement of cyclic AMP and cyclic AMP receptor protein and modulation of DNA level. *J. Biolum. Chemilum.* 7:203–14

Dunphy G, Miyamoto C, Meighen E. 1997. A homoserine lactone autoinducer regulates virulence of an insect-pathogenic bacterium, *Xenorhabdus nematophilus* (Enterobacteriaceae). *J. Bacteriol.* 179:5288–91

Eakin RM, Brandenburger JL. 1975. Retinal differences between light-tolerant and light avoiding slugs. *J. Ultrastruct. Res.* 53:382–94

Eberhard A, Burlingame AL, Eberhard C, Kenyon GL, Nealson KH, Oppenheimer NJ. 1981. Structural identification of autoinducer of *Photobacterium fischeri* luciferase. *Biochemistry* 20:2444–49

Eberhard A, Longin T, Widrig CA, Stranick SJ. 1991. Synthesis of the *lux* gene autoinducer in *Vibrio fischeri* is positively autoregulated. *Arch. Microbiol.* 155:294–97

Eckert R. 1965. Bioelectric control of bioluminescence in the dinoflagellate *Noctiluca*. *Science* 147:1140–45

Eckstein JW, Cho KW, Colepicolo P, Ghisla S, Hastings JW, Wilson T. 1990. A time-dependent bacterial bioluminescence emission spectrum in an in vitro single turnover system: Energy transfer alone cannot account for the yellow emission of *Vibrio fischeri* Y-1. *Proc. Natl. Acad. Sci. USA* 87:1466–70

Eckstein JW, Hastings JW, Ghisla S. 1993. Mechanism of bacterial bioluminescence: 4a,5-dihydroflavin analogs as models for luciferase hydroperoxide intermediates and the effect of substituents at the 8-position of flavin on luciferase kinetics. *Biochemistry* 32:404–11

Fisher AJ, Raushel FM, Baldwin TO, Rayment L. 1995. Three-dimensional structure of bacterial luciferase from *Vibrio harveyi* at 2.4 Å resolution. *Biochemistry* 34:6581–86

Fisher AJ, Thompson TB, Thoden JB, Baldwin TO, Rayment I. 1996. The 1.5-Å resolution crystal structure of bacterial luciferase in low salt conditions. *J. Biol. Chem.* 271:21956–68

Forst S, Nealson KH. 1996. Molecular biology of the symbiotic-pathogenic bacteria *Xenorhabdus* spp. and *Photorhabdus* spp. *Microbiol. Rev.* 60:21–43

Fritz L, Morse D, Hastings JW. 1990. The circadian bioluminescence rhythm of *Gonyaulax* is related to daily variations in the number of light emitting organelles. *J. Cell Sci.* 95:321–28

Fuqua C, Winans SC, Greenberg EP. 1996. Census and consensus in bacterial ecosystems: the LuxR-LuxI family of quorum-sensing transcriptional regulators. *Annu. Rev. Microbiol.* 50:727–51

Ghiradella H. 1977. Fine structure of the tracheoles of the lantern of a photurid firefly. *J. Morphol.* 153:187–204

Gonzalez-Flecha B, Demple B. 1994. Intracellular generation of superoxide as a byproduct of *Vibrio harveyi* luciferase expressed in *Escherichia coli*. *J. Bacteriol.* 176:2293–99

Gould SJ, Keller G-A, Hosken N, Wilkinson J, Subramani S. 1989. A conserved tripeptide sorts proteins to peroxisomes. *J. Cell Biol.* 108:1657–64

Haas E. 1980. Bioluminescence from single bacterial cells exhibits no oscillation. *Biophys. J.* 31:301–12

Hanna CH, Hopkins TA, Buck J. 1976. Peroxisomes of the firefly lantern. *J. Ultrastruct. Res.* 57:150–62

Hanzelka BL, Greenberg EP. 1995. Evidence that the N-terminal region of the *Vibrio fischeri* LuxR protein constitutes an autoinducer-binding domain. *J. Bacteriol.* 177:815–17

Hanzelka BL, Greenberg EP. 1996. Quorum sensing in *Vibrio fischeri*: evidence that S-adenosylmethionine is the amino acid substrate for autoinducer synthesis. *J. Bacteriol.* 178:5291–94

Hart RC, Stempel KE, Boyer PD, Cormier MJ. 1978. Mechanism of the enzyme-catalyzed bioluminescent oxidation of coelenterate-type luciferin. *Biochem. Biophys. Res. Commun.* 81:980–86

Hastings JW. 1968. Bioluminescence. *Annu. Rev. Biochem.* 37:597–630

Hastings JW. 1978. Bacterial and dinoflagellate luminescent systems. In *Bioluminescence in Action*, ed. PJ Herring, pp. 129–170. London: Academic

Hastings JW. 1983. Biological diversity, chemical mechanisms, and the evolutionary origins of bioluminescent systems. *J. Mol. Evol.* 19:309–21

Hastings JW, Balny C, Le Peuch C, Douzou P. 1973. Spectral properties of an oxygenated luciferase-flavin intermediate isolated by low-temperature chromatography. *Proc. Natl. Acad. Sci. USA* 70:3468–72

Hastings JW, Dunlap JC. 1986. Cell-free components in dinoflagellate bioluminescence. The particulate activity: scintillons; the soluble components: luciferase, luciferin, and luciferin-binding protein. *Meth. Enzymol.* 133:307–23

Hastings JW, Morin JG. 1991. Bioluminescence. In *Neural and Integrative Animal Physiology*, ed. CL Prosser, pp. 131–70. New York: Wiley Intersci.

Heim R, Prasher DC, Tsien RY. 1994. Wavelength mutations and posttranslational autoxidation of green fluorescent protein. *Proc. Natl. Acad. Sci. USA* 91:12501–4

Heim R, Tsien RY. 1996. Engineering green fluorescent protein for improved brightness, longer wavelengths and fluorescence resonance energy transfer. *Curr. Biol.* 6:178–82

Herring PJ, ed. 1978. *Bioluminescence in Action.* London: Academic. 570 pp.

Hosseini PK, Nealson KH. 1995. Symbiotic luminous soil bacteria: unusual regulation for an unusual niche. *Photochem. Photobiol.* 62:633–40

Inouye S, Ohmiya Y, Toya Y, Tsuji FI. 1992. Imaging of luciferase secretion from transformed Chinese hamster ovary cells. *Proc. Natl. Acad. Sci. USA* 89:9584–87

Johnson CH, Hastings JW. 1986. The elusive mechanism of the circadian clock. *Am. Sci.* 74:29–36

Johnson CH, Inoue S, Flint A, Hastings JW. 1985. Compartmentalization of algal bioluminescence: autofluorescence of bioluminescent particles in the dinoflagellate *Gonyaulax* as studied with image-intensified video microscopy and flow cytometry. *J. Cell Biol.* 100:1435–46

Johnson CH, Knight MR, Kondo T, Masson P, Sedbrook J, et al. 1995. Circadian oscillations of cytosolic and chloroplastic free calcium in plants. *Science* 259:1863–65

Johnson FH, Shimomura O, Saiga Y, Gershman G, Reynolds GT, Waters JR. 1962. Quantum efficiency of *Cypridina* luminescence with a note on that of *Aequorea. J. Cell. Comp. Physiol.* 60:85–103

Kajiyama N, Nakano E. 1991. Isolation and characterization of mutants of firefly luciferase which produce different colors of light. *Protein Eng.* 4:691–93

Karatani H, Hastings JW. 1993. Two active forms of the accessory yellow fluorescence protein of the luminous bacterium *Vibrio fischeri* strain Y1. *Photochem. Photobiol.* 18:227–32

Keller G-A, Gould SJ, DeLuca M, Subramani S. 1987. Firefly luciferase is targeted to peroxisomes in mammalian cells. *Proc. Natl. Acad. Sci. USA* 84:3264–68

Khan AU, Wilson T. 1995. Reactive oxygen species as cellular messengers. *Chem. Biol.* 2:437–45

Knaust R, Urbig T, Li L, Taylor W, Hastings JW. 1998. The circadian rhythm of biolumi-

nescence in *Pyrocystis* is not due to differences in the amount of luciferase: a comparative study of three bioluminescent marine dinoflagellates. *J. Phycol.* 34:167–72

Koka P, Lee J. 1979. Separation and structure of the prosthetic group of the blue fluorescence protein from the bioluminescent bacterium *Photobacterium phosphoreum. Proc. Natl. Acad. Sci. USA* 76:3068

Koo J-Y, Schmidt SP, Schuster GB. 1978. Bioluminescence of the firefly: key steps in the formation of the electronically excited state for model systems. *Proc. Natl. Acad. Sci. USA* 75:30–33

Kurfürst M, Macheroux P, Ghisla S, Hastings JW. 1987. Isolation and characterization of the transient, luciferase-bound flavin-4a-hydroxide in the bacterial luciferase reaction. *Biochim. Biophys. Acta* 924:104–10

Lamola AA. 1969. *Energy Transfer and Organic Photochemistry.* New York: Interscience. 374 pp.

Lee D-H, Mittag M, Sczekan S, Morse D, Hastings JW. 1993. Molecular cloning and genomic organization of a gene for luciferin-binding protein from the dinoflagellate *Gonyaulax polyedra. J. Biol. Chem.* 268:8842–50

Lee J, Matheson IBC, Muller F, O'Kane DJ, Vervoort J, Visser AJWG. 1991. The mechanism of bacterial bioluminescence. In *Chemistry and Biochemistry of Flavoenzymes*, ed. F Muller, pp. 109–51. Orlando: CRC Press

Lee K-H, Ruby EG. 1994. Competition between *Vibrio fischeri* strains during initiation and maintenance of a light organ symbiosis. *J. Bacteriol.* 176:1985–91

Li L, Hastings JW. 1998. The structure and organization of the luciferase gene in the photosynthetic dinoflagellate *Gonyaulax polyedra. Plant Mol. Biol.* 36:275–84

Li L, Hong R, Hastings JW. 1997. Three functional luciferase domains in a single polypeptide chain. *Proc. Natl. Acad. Sci. USA* 94:8954–58

Lorenz WW, Cormier MJ, O'Kane DJ, Hua D, Escher AA, Szalay AA. 1996. Expression of the *Renilla reniformis* luciferase gene in mammalian cells. *J. Biolumin. Chemilumin.* 11:31–37

Lorenz WW, McCann RO, Longiaru M, Cormier MJ. 1991. Isolation and expression of a cDNA encoding *Renilla reniformis* luciferase. *Proc. Natl. Acad. Sci. USA* 88:4438–42

Macheroux P, Ghisla S, Hastings JW. 1993. Spectral detection of an intermediate preceding the excited state in the bacterial luciferase reaction. *Biochemistry* 32:14183–86

Macheroux P, Schmidt KU, Steinerstauch P,

Ghisla S, Colepicolo P, et al. 1987. Purification of the yellow fluorescent protein from *Vibrio fischeri* and identity of the flavin chromophore. *Biochem. Biophys. Res. Commun.* 146:101–6

Mager IX, Tu S-C. 1995. Chemical aspects of bioluminescence. *Photochem. Photobiol.* 62:607–14

Masuda T, Tatsumi H, Nakano E. 1989. Cloning and sequence analysis of cDNA for luciferase of a Japanese firefly, *Luciola cruciata*. *Gene* 77:265–70

Mayerhofer R, Langridge WHR, Cormier MJ, Szalay AA. 1995. Expression of recombinant *Renilla* luciferase in transgenic plants results in high levels of light emission. *Plant J.* 7:1031–38

McCapra F. 1997. Mechanisms in chemiluminescence and bioluminescence—unfinished business. In *Bioluminescence and Chemiluminescence*, ed. JW Hastings, LJ Kricka, PE Stanley, pp. 7–15. Chichester: Wiley & Sons

McCapra F, Gilfoyle DJ, Young DW, Church NJ, Spencer P. 1994. The chemical origin of colour differences in beetle bioluminescence. In *Bioluminescence and Chemiluminescence*, ed. AK Campbell, LJ Kricka, PE Stanley, pp. 387–91. Chichester: Wiley & Sons

McCapra FM, Perring KD. 1985. Luciferin bioluminescence. In *Chemi- and Bioluminescence*, ed. JG Burr, pp. 359–86. New York: Dekker

McElroy WD, DeLuca M. 1985. Firefly luminescence. In *Chemi- and Bioluminescence*, ed. JG Burr, pp. 387–99. New York: Dekker

McElroy WD, Seliger HH. 1962. Origin and evolution of bioluminescence. In *Horizons in Biochemistry*, ed. M Kasha & B Pullman, pp. 91–101. New York: Academic

McFall-Ngai MJ, Ruby EG. 1991. Symbiont recognition and subsequent morphogenesis as early events in an animal-bacterial mutualism. *Science* 254:1491–94

Meighen EA. 1994. Genetics of bacterial bioluminescence. *Annu. Rev. Genet.* 28:117–39

Merenyi G, Lind J, Mager HIX, Tu S-C. 1992. Properties of 4a-hydroxy-4a,5-dihydroflavin radicals in relation to bacterial bioluminescence. *J. Phys. Chem.* 96:10528–33

Mitra RD, Silva CM, Youvan DC. 1996. Fluorescence resonance energy transfer between blue-emitting and red-shifted excitation derivatives of the green fluorescent protein. *Gene* 173:13–17

Mittag M, Eckerskorn C, Strupat K, Hastings JW. 1997. Differential translational initiation of *lbp* mRNA is caused by a small 5' open reading frame. *FEBS Lett.* 411:245–50

Mittag M, Lee D-H, Hastings JW. 1994. Circadian expression of the luciferin-binding protein correlates with the binding of a protein to its 3' untranslated region. *Proc. Natl. Acad. Sci. USA* 91:5257–61

Mittag M, Li L, Hastings JW. 1998. The mRNA level of the circadian regulated *Gonyaulax* luciferase remains constant over the cycle. *Chronobiol. Int.* 15:93–98

Montgomery MK, McFall-Ngai MJ. 1994. Bacterial symbionts induce host organ morphogenesis during early postembryonic development of the squid *Euprymna scolopes*. *Development* 120:1719–29

Moré MI, Finger LD, Stryker JL, Fuqua C, Eberhard A, Winans SC. 1996. Enzymatic synthesis of a quorum-sensing autoinducer through use of defined substrates. *Science* 272:1655–58

Morin JG, Hastings JW. 1971. Energy transfer in a bioluminescent system. *J. Cell. Physiol.* 77:313–18

Morse D, Milos PM, Roux E, Hastings JW. 1989a. Circadian regulation of bioluminescence in *Gonyaulax* involves translational control. *Proc. Natl. Acad. Sci. USA* 86:172–76

Morse D, Pappenheimer AM, Hastings JW. 1989b. Role of a luciferin binding protein in the circadian bioluminescent reaction of *G. polyedra*. *J. Biol. Chem.* 264:11822–26

Nakamura H, Kishi Y, Shimomura O, Morse D, Hastings JW. 1989. Structure of dinoflagellate luciferin and its enzymatic and nonenzymatic air-oxidation products. *J. Am. Chem. Soc.* 111:7607–11

Nealson KH, Platt T, Hastings JW. 1970. The cellular control of the synthesis and activity of the bacterial luminescent system. *J. Bacteriol.* 104:313–22

Nicolas M-T, Bassot J-M, Shimomura O. 1982. Polynoidin: a membrane photoprotein isolated from the bioluminescent system of scale-worms. *Photochem. Photobiol.* 35:201–7

Nicolas M-T, Morse D, Bassot J-M, Hastings JW. 1991. Colocalization of luciferin binding protein and luciferase to the scintillons of *Gonyaulax polyedra* revealed by double immunolabeling after fast-freeze fixation. *Protoplasma* 160:159–66

Nicolas M-T, Nicolas G, Johnson CH, Bassot J-M, Hastings JW. 1987a. Characterization of the bioluminescent organelles in *Gonyaulax polyedra* (dinoflagellates) after fast-freeze fixation and antiluciferase immunogold staining. *J. Cell Biol.* 105:723–35

Nicolas M-T, Sweeney BM, Hastings JW. 1987b. The ultrastructural localization of luciferase in three bioluminescent dinoflagellates, two species of *Pyrocystis*, and *Noctiluca*, using anti-luciferase and immunogold labeling. *J. Cell Sci.* 87:189–96

O'Kane DJ, Prasher DC. 1992. Evolutionary

origins of bacterial bioluminescence. *Mol. Microbiol.* 6:443–49

O'Kane DJ, Woodward B, Lee J, Prasher DC. 1991. Borrowed proteins in bacterial bioluminescence. *Proc. Natl. Acad. Sci. USA* 88:1100–4

Ormö M, Cubitt AB, Kallio K, Gross LA, Tsien RY, Remington SJ. 1996. Crystal structure of the Aequorea victoria green fluorescent protein. *Science* 273:1392–95

Prasher DC, Eckenrode VK, Ward WW, Prendergast FG, Cormier MJ. 1992. Primary structure of the *Aequorea victoria* greenfluorescent protein. *Gene* 111:292–93

Petushkov VN, Gibson BG, Lee J. 1996a. Direct measure of excitation transfer in the protein complex of bacterial luciferase hydroxyflavin and the associated yellow fluorescence proteins from *Vibrio fischeri* Y1. *Biochemistry* 35:8413–18

Petushkov VN, Ketelaars M, Gibson BG, Lee J. 1996b. Interaction of *Photobacterium leiognathi* and *Vibrio fischeri* Y1 luciferases with fluorescent (antenna) proteins: bioluminescence effects of the aliphatic additive. *Biochemistry* 35:12086–93

Puskas A, Greenberg EP, Kaplan S, Schaefer AL. 1997. A quorum-sensing system in the free-living photosynthetic bacterium *Rhodobacter sphaeroides*. *J. Bacteriol.* 179:7530–37

Rees J-F, De Wergifosse B, Noiset O, Dubuisson M, Janssens B, Thompson EM. 1998. The origins of marine bioluminescence: turning oxygen defence mechanisms into deep-sea communication tools. *J. Exp. Biol.* 201:1211–21

Reich KA, Schoolnik GK. 1996. Halovibrin, secreted from the light organ symbiont *Vibrio fischeri*, is a member of a new class of ADP-ribosyltransferases. *J. Bacteriol.* 178:209–15

Reid BG, Flynn GC. 1997. Chromophore formation in green fluorescent protein. *Biochemistry* 36:6786–91

Ruby EG. 1996. Lessons from a cooperative, bacterial-animal association: the *Vibrio fischeri—Euprymna scolopes* light organ symbiosis. *Annu. Rev. Microbiol.* 50:591–624

Ruby EG, Asato LM. 1993. Growth and flagellation of *Vibrio fischeri* during initiation of the sepiolid squid light organ symbiosis. *Arch. Microbiol.* 159:160–67

Ruby EG, McFall-Ngai MJ. 1992. A squid that glows in the night: development of an animal-bacterial mutualism. *J. Bacteriol.* 174:4865–70

Schaefer AL, Val DL, Hanzelka BL, Cronan JE, Greenberg EP. 1996. Generation of cell-to-cell signals in quorum sensing: acyl homoserine lactone synthase activity of a purified *Vibrio fischeri* LuxI protein. *Proc. Natl. Acad. Sci. USA* 93:9505–9

Schmitter RE, Njus D, Sulzman FM, Gooch VD, Hastings JW. 1976. Dinoflagellate bioluminescence: a comparative study of in vitro components. *J. Cell. Physiol.* 87:123–34

Schroder J. 1989. Protein sequence homology between plant 4-coumarate:CoA ligase and firefly luciferase. *Nucleic Acids Res.* 17:460

Schuster GB. 1979. Chemiluminescence of organic peroxides. Conversion of ground-state reactants to excited-state products by the chemically initiated electron-exchange luminescence mechanism. *Acc. Chem. Res.* 12:366–73

Seliger HH. 1975. The origin of bioluminescence. *Photochem. Photobiol.* 21:355–61

Seliger HH. 1987. The evolution of bioluminescence in bacteria. *Photochem. Photobiol.* 45:291–97

Shimomura O. 1982. Mechanism of bioluminescence. In *Chemical and Biological Generation of Excited States*, ed. W Adam, G Cilento, pp. 249–76. New York: Academic

Shimomura O. 1987. Presence of coelenterazine in non-bioluminescent marine organisms. *Comp. Biochem. Physiol.* 86B:361–63

Shimomura O, Inoue S, Johnson FH, Haneda Y. 1980. Widespread occurrence of coelenterazine in marine bioluminescence. *Comp. Biochem. Physiol.* 65B:435–37

Shimomura O, Johnson FH, Saiga Y. 1962. Extraction, purification and properties of aequorin, a bioluminescent protein from the luminous hydromedusan, *Aequorea*. *J. Cell. Comp. Physiol.* 59:223–40

Shimomura O, Satoh S, Kishi Y. 1993. Structure and non-enzymatic light emission of two luciferin precursors isolated from the luminous mushroom *Panellus-stipticus*. *J. Biolum. Chemilum.* 8:201–5

Sirokmán G, Hastings JW. 1997. Effectiveness of the accessory yellow fluorescent protein in the bacterial luciferase reaction correlates with the lifetime of the peroxyhemiacetal intermediate: the stereochemistry of the reaction. *Photochem. Photobiol.* 66:198–203

Sirokmán G, Wilson T, Hastings JW. 1995. A bacterial luciferase reaction with a negative temperature coefficient attributable to protein-protein interaction. *Biochemistry* 34:13074–81

Sitnikov DM, Schineller JB, Baldwin TO. 1995. Transcriptional regulation of bioluminescence genes from *Vibrio fischeri*. *J. Bacteriol.* 17:801–12

Soto U, Pepperkok R, Ansorge W, Just WW. 1993. Import of firefly luciferase into mammalian peroxisomes in vivo requires nucleoside triphosphates. *Exp. Cell Res.* 205:66–75

Spurlock BO, Cormier MJ. 1975. A fine structure study of the anthocodium in Renilla mülleri. Evidence for the existence of a bioluminescent organelle, the luminelle. *J. Cell. Biol.* 64:15–28

Steinbeck MJ, Khan AU, Karnovsky MJ. 1992. Intracellular singlet oxygen generation by phagocytosing neutrophils in response to particles coated with a chemical trap. *J. Biol. Chem.* 267:13425–33

Stevens AM, Greenberg EP. 1997. Quorum sensing in *Vibrio fischeri:* essential elements for activation of the luminescence genes. *J. Bacteriol.* 179:557–62

Swift S, Throup JP, Williams P, Salmond GPC, Stewart GSAB. 1996. Quorum sensing: a population-density component in the determination of bacterial phenotype. *Trends Biochem. Sci.* 21:214–19

Thomson CM, Herring PJ, Campbell AK. 1997. The widespread occurrence and tissue distribution of the imidazolopyrazine luciferins. *J. Biolum. Chemilum.* 12:87–91

Tsuji FI, Ohmiya Y, Fagan TF, Toh H, Inouye S. 1995. Molecular evolution of the Ca^{2+}-binding photoproteins of the Hydrozoa. *Photochem. Photobiol.* 62:657–61

Tu S-C, Mager HIX. 1995. Biochemistry of bacterial bioluminescence. *Photochem. Photobiol.* 62:615–24

Turro NJ. 1978. *Modern Molecular Photochemistry.* Menlo Park: Benjamin/Cummings. 628 pp.

Ulitzur S, Dunlap PV. 1995. Regulatory circuitry controlling luminescence autoinduction in *Vibrio fischeri. Photochem. Photobiol.* 62:625–32

Vervoort J, Muller F, Lee J, van den Berg WAM, Moonen CTW. 1986. Identification of the true carbon-13 nuclear magnetic resonance spectrum of the stable intermediate II in bacterial luciferase. *Biochemistry* 25:8062–67

Viviani VR, Bechara EJH. 1997. Bioluminescence and biological aspects of Brazilian railroad worms (Coleoptera: Phengodidae). *Ann. Entomol. Soc. Am.* 90:389–98

Wachter RM, King BA, Heim R, Kallio K, Tsien RY, et al. 1997. Crystal structure and photodynamic behavior of the blue emission variant Y66H/Y145F of green fluorescent protein. *Biochemistry* 36:9759–66

Ward WW, Cormier MJ. 1976. In vitro energy transfer in *Renilla* bioluminescence. *J. Phys. Chem.* 80:2289–91

Ward WW, Cormier MJ. 1978. Energy transfer via protein-protein interaction in *Renilla* bioluminescence. *Photochem. Photobiol.* 27:389–96

Weis VM, Small AL, McFall-Ngai MJ. 1996. A peroxidase related to the mammalian antimicrobial protein myeloperoxidase in the *Euprymna-Vibrio* mutualism. *Proc. Natl. Acad. Sci. USA* 93:13683–88

White EH, Roswell DF. 1991. Analogs and derivatives of firefly oxyluciferin, the light emitter in firefly bioluminescence. *Photochem. Photobiol.* 53:131–36

Widder EA, Case JF. 1982. Distribution of subcellular bioluminescence sources in a dinoflagellate, *Pyrocystis fusiformis. Biol. Bull.* 162:423–48

Wilson T. 1995. Comments on the mechanisms of chemi- and bioluminescence. *Photochem. Photobiol.* 62:601–6

Wood KV. 1995. The chemical mechanism and evolutionary development of beetle bioluminescence. *Photochem. Photobiol.* 62:662–73

Wood KV, Lam YA, Seliger HH, McElroy WD. 1989. Complementary DNA coding click beetle luciferases can elicit bioluminescence of different colors. *Science* 244:700–2

Wu P, Brand L. 1994. Resonance energy transfer: methods and applications. *Analyt. Biochem.* 218:1–13

Yang F, Moss LG, Phillips GN Jr. 1996. The molecular structure of green fluorescent protein. *Nat. Biotechnol.* 14:1246–51

Annu. Rev. Cell Dev. Biol. 1998. 14:231–64

PHOSPHOINOSITIDE LIPIDS AS SIGNALING MOLECULES: Common Themes for Signal Transduction, Cytoskeletal Regulation, and Membrane Trafficking

T. F. J. Martin

Department of Biochemistry, University of Wisconsin, 420 Henry Mall, Madison, Wisconsin 53706; e-mail: tfmartin@facstaff.wisc.edu

KEY WORDS: phosphatidylinositol phosphates, lipid kinases, phosphoinositide-binding proteins, protein phosphorylation, actin assembly, membrane budding, membrane fusion

---

ABSTRACT

Signaling roles for phosphoinositides that involve their regulated hydrolysis to generate second messengers have been well characterized. Recent work has revealed additional signaling roles for phosphoinositides that do not involve their hydrolysis. PtdIns 3-P, PtdIns 3,4,5-P_3, and PtdIns 4,5-P_2 function as site-specific signals on membranes that recruit and/or activate proteins for the assembly of spatially localized functional complexes. A large number of phosphoinositide-binding proteins have been identified as the potential effectors for phosphoinositide signals. Common themes of localized signal generation and the spatially localized recruitment of effector proteins appear to underlie mechanisms employed in signal transduction, cytoskeletal, and membrane trafficking events.

CONTENTS

CRITERIA FOR PHOSPHOINOSITIDE SIGNALING

A signaling role for inositol phospholipids was established in the 1980s when it became clear that phospholipase C-mediated hydrolysis of PtdIns 4,5-P_2 generates the intracellular signals Ins 1,4,5-P_3 and diacylglycerol for regulating Ca^{2+} mobilization and protein phosphorylation mechanisms, respectively (Berridge & Irvine 1984). More recently the inositol phospholipids have been found to have signaling roles that do not require their hydrolysis. In this role, phosphoinositides serve as site-specific signals on membranes that recruit and regulate protein complexes at the interface with the cytosol. Phosphoinositide signals are used in this way for signal transduction, cytoskeletal assembly, and membrane budding and fusion processes that are spatially restricted to specific membrane domains.

The concept of phosphoinositides as spatially localized membrane signals is relatively recent, and there remain many gaps in our understanding of the detailed mechanisms involved. There are considerable obstacles to establishing the full outline of membrane-based signaling processes. Many of the phospholipids are in low abundance in cells but at high local concentrations in membrane domains that are not readily detected by conventional biochemical approaches. Establishing the identity of the effector proteins regulated by phosphoinositide binding is also challenging because of the difficulty of extending in vitro findings into the intracellular environment. As was true for cytosol-based signaling pathways, it is useful to describe criteria for establishing a signaling role for phosphoinositides in a cellular process.

Firstly, it is essential to establish the nature of the lipid involved in the cellular process (e.g. PtdIns 3,4,5-P_3, PtdIns 4,5-P_2, or others). In some cases it may be possible to detect changes in the levels of the phosphoinositide in response to cellular activation. In other cases, it may be necessary to use techniques for detecting localized phosphoinositides in membrane domains (e.g. immunocytochemistry with phosphoinositide antibodies; Voorhout et al 1992, Tran et al 1993). For some cellular processes, phosphoinositides may be essential constitutively produced cofactors rather than regulated signals whose levels change. The introduction of phosphoinositide phosphatases (Zhang et al 1998) and phospholipases (Rhee & Bae 1997) of defined specificity or of phosphoinositide-specific antibodies (Fukami et al 1988) and phosphoinositide-binding peptides (Hartwig et al 1995) into cells should inhibit cellular responses mediated by phosphoinositide signals and help to establish the identity of the lipid involved. Cell-permeant lipid kinase inhibitors with better specificities than those currently available will simplify this identification.

Secondly, overexpressing wild-type or constitutively active phosphoinositide kinases of defined substrate specificity (Shibasaki et al 1997) or sometimes even introducing the phosphoinositide itself (Franke et al 1997) should mimic the effects of cellular activation or enhance a phosphoinositide-dependent process. With the increasingly complete characterization of lipid kinases, the identification of their upstream activators, and the elucidation of the targeting mechanisms responsible for their membrane localization, a fuller repertoire of methods to selectively increase phosphoinositide levels will become available.

Lastly, it is important to identify the effector apparatus that is regulated by the phosphoinositide signal and is responsible for mediating changes in cellular events. Numerous phosphoinositide-binding proteins have been identified as candidate effector proteins for phosphoinositide signals (see below). An improved understanding of the molecular basis for phosphoinositide-protein interactions will facilitate the generation of mutations that abrogate effector-phosphoinositide binding to critically assess the role of such interactions in cellular events (Salim et al 1996). The possibility that localized phosphoinositide synthesis directly imparts new properties to the membrane leaflet (such as curvature for budding) will require testing by reconstituting cellular processes in artificial membranes.

In only a limited number of cases has the nature of the lipid, the role of its regulated synthesis by a defined lipid kinase, and the identity of a physiological downstream effector for the lipid been characterized for a cellular process. This article reviews the diversity of known phosphoinositide signals, the lipid kinases responsible for their synthesis, and the potential effectors of the phosphoinositide signals involved in signal transduction, cytoskeletal and membrane trafficking events. For related reviews of these topics see DeCamilli et al 1996 and Martin 1997.

A DIVERSITY OF SIGNALING MOLECULES
IS GENERATED BY LIPID PHOSPHORYLATION

The dynamic phosphorylation at the D3, D4, and D5 hydroxyls of the inositol headgroup generates a diverse array of phosphoinositides that are well suited for signaling roles. Classical work (Grado & Ballou 1960) that characterized PtdIns 4-P and PtdIns 4,5-P_2 (referred to here as D4 phosphoinositides) provided the first view of the interconvertible diversity of these phospholipids. The discovery of phosphorylation at the D3 hydroxyl of the inositol headgroup (Whitman et al 1988) leading to the generation of PtdIns 3-P, PtdIns 3,4-P_2 and PtdIns 3,4,5-P_3 (referred to here as D3 phosphoinositides) increased this diversity. Recent findings have uncovered additional phosphoinositides generated by novel kinase reactions, and it is likely that the complete cellular complement remains to be be characterized.

A summary of the synthetic pathways for the seven polyphosphoinositides identified as of 1998 derived by the phosphorylation of PtdIns is shown in Figure 1. The classical D4 phosphoinositides are primarily synthesized by the sequential phosphorylation of PtdIns by PtdIns 4-kinase and PtdIns 4-P 5-kinase

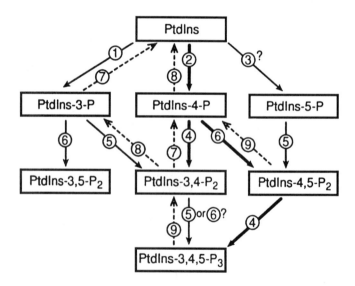

Figure 1 Synthetic pathways for phosphoinositides. *Solid arrows* represent kinase reactions with major pathways indicated by *bold arrows*. *Dotted arrows* represent phosphatase reactions. Numbers correspond to individual enzyme-catalyzed reactions: 1, PtdIns 3-kinase (type III); 2, PtdIns 4-kinase; 3, PtdIns 5-kinase (conjectured); 4, PtdIns 3-kinase (type I or II); 5, PtdIns 5-P 4-kinase; 6, PtdIns 4-P 5-kinase; 7, 3-phosphatase; 8, 4-phosphatase; 9, 5-phosphatase.

(2 followed by 4 in Figure 1). An alternative pathway for the synthesis of PtdIns $4,5$-P_2 (3 followed by 5 in Figure 1) is suggested by the finding that the type II isoform of PtdIns 4-P 5-kinase may be a PtdIns 5-P 4-kinase (Rameh et al 1997b). PtdIns 5-P, which had not been previously identified, was found to be a minor lipid present in mammalian cells (Rameh et al 1997b), which suggests the existence of a yet-uncharacterized PtdIns 5-kinase (3 in Figure 1). The recent discovery of PtdIns $3,5$-P_2 in yeast and mammalian cells (Whiteford et al 1997, Dove et al 1997) and the finding that the type I PtdIns 4-P 5-kinase also utilizes PtdIns 3-P as a substrate (Rameh et al 1997b) indicate an additional novel phosphoinositide synthesis pathway (1 followed by 6 in Figure 1). This work will undoubtedly be followed by efforts to elucidate the cellular role of PtdIns $3,5$-P_2, whose levels change in response to osmotic stress (Dove et al 1997).

Synthesis of D3 phosphoinositides is catalyzed by several classes of PtdIns 3-kinases (see below) that phosphorylate PtdIns to form PtdIns 3-P (1 in Figure 1) or PtdIns 4-P and PtdIns $4,5$-P_2 to form PtdIns $3,4$-P_2 and PtdIns $3,4,5$-P_3, respectively (4 in Figure 1). Recent work (Rameh et al 1997b, Zhang et al 1997) reveals that the type II PtdInsP kinase, now characterized as a PtdIns 5-P 4-kinase, also employs PtdIns 3-P as a substrate providing an alternative pathway for PtdIns $3,4$-P_2 synthesis from a PtdIns 3-P precursor (Rameh et al 1997b, Zhang et al 1997) (1 followed by 5 in Figure 1). Novel dual substrate specificities for the PtdInsP kinases were recently reported (Zhang et al 1997), which would allow the sequential phosphorylation of PtdIns 3-P at the D4 and D5 hydroxyls by PtdInsP kinases to form PtdIns $3,4,5$-P_3 (from 1 to 5 to 5/6 in Figure 1).

LIPID KINASES AND THEIR REGULATION

Because the major pathways for D3 and D4 phosphoinositide synthesis proceed through 4-phosphorylation of PtdIns (Figure 1), the distribution of PtdIns 4-kinase in membranes will largely dictate where localized D3 and D4 phosphoinositide synthesis can occur. PtdIns 4-kinase activity is principally membrane associated and localized to plasma membrane, nuclear membrane, lysosomes, Golgi, endoplasmic reticulum and constitutive secretory vesicles (Carpenter & Cantley 1990, Pike 1992, Olsson et al 1995) depending upon the tissue. In secretory tissues, PtdIns 4-kinase activity is present on glucose transporter vesicles, chromaffin granules, mast cell granules, coated vesicles, and in neural synaptosomes (Pike 1992). Biochemical studies characterized type II and type III forms of the enzyme that differed in sensitivity to adenosine and detergent activation (Carpenter & Cantley 1990, Pike 1992), but this classification is somewhat blurred by recent molecular cloning. cDNAs corresponding to two isoforms of PtdIns 4-kinase, an α isoform (Wong & Cantley 1994) and a β

isoform (Meyers & Cantley 1997), have been characterized. The α isoform, homologous to a yeast STT4 enzyme, exists as long ($\approx$200 kDa) and short ($\approx$100 kDa) forms derived from alternative splicing (Wong & Cantley 1994, Nakagawa et al 1996a, Gehrmann et al 1996, Balla et al 1997). The β isoform ($\approx$100 kDa), homologous to the yeast PIK1 enzyme (Nakagawa et al 1996b, Meyers & Cantley 1997, Balla et al 1997), is inhibited by both wortmannin and LY294002 (Downing et al 1996), which were previously thought to be diagnostic for certain PtdIns 3-kinase enzymes (Carpenter & Cantley 1996).

Wortmannin inhibits the synthesis of PtdIns 4-P that is required for hormone receptor-mediated phosphoinositide turnover, which initially suggested that the wortmannin-sensitive β isoform of PtdIns 4-kinase had a dedicated role in phosphoinositide synthesis for signal transduction (Downing et al 1996). Recent studies, however, found that splicing isoforms of the type α PtdIns 4-kinase are also inhibited by wortmannin (Nakagawa et al 1996a, Balla et al 1997). Nonetheless, it is likely that the α and β isoforms play distinct cellular roles because they exhibit distinct intracellular distributions (Wong et al 1997). Additional isoforms of PtdIns 4-kinase, possibly with dedicated membrane trafficking roles, will likely be characterized. Neither the α nor β cDNAs encode the enzyme classified as the type II enzyme, a 55 kDa protein with a kinase activity inhibited by the 4C5G antibody (Carpenter & Cantley 1990). A 4C5G-sensitive PtdIns 4-kinase, a resident of glucose transporter vesicles (Del Vecchio & Pilch 1991), is involved in the phosphoinositide synthesis essential for ARF activation of phospholipase D (Liscovitch et al 1994) and differs in membrane localization and wortmannin-insensitivity from α and β isoforms (Wong et al 1997).

The characterized cDNAs for PtdIns 4-kinases encode hydrophilic proteins that lack transmembrane domains. The basis for the membrane association and targeting of PtdIns 4-kinase isoforms to specific membranes is poorly understood although several potential mechanisms for localization have emerged. The α isoform contains a PH domain that could mediate its membrane association (Wong & Cantley 1994, Nakagawa et al 1996a). β isoforms associate with the cytoplasmic domains of several transmembrane and receptor proteins (Kauffmann-Zeh et al 1994, Pertile & Cantley 1995, Berditchevski et al 1997). Additional studies are needed to determine the basis for the membrane recruitment of the PtdIns 4-kinases in order to understand how localized membrane domains of D3 and D4 phosphoinositides are formed.

PtdIns 4-P 5-kinase activity is principally cytosolic and is enriched in neural synaptosomes (Stubbs et al 1988). Two isoforms of PtdIns 4-P 5-kinase that are related in sequence and differ from members of the phosphoinositide 3- and 4-kinase families have been characterized (Boronenkov & Anderson 1995, Loijens & Anderson 1996, Ishihara et al 1996). The type I isoform (Loijens

& Anderson 1996, Ishihara et al 1996) is a true PtdIns 4-P 5-kinase and also phosphorylates the D5 hydroxyl of PtdIns 3-P (Rameh et al 1997b). The type II isoform, a PtdInsP 4-kinase, phosphorylates the D4 hydroxyl of PtdIns 5-P and PtdIns 3-P (Zhang et al 1997, Rameh et al 1997b). Although the type I isoform is likely to be a bona fide constituent in the classical biosynthetic pathway for formation of PtdIns 4,5-P_2 from PtdIns 4-P, the type II isoform may catalyze an alternative route of PtdIns 4,5-P_2 synthesis from PtdIns 5-P or catalyze PtdIns 3,4-P_2 synthesis from PtdIns 3-P (see Figure 1).

The central importance of PtdIns 4-P 5-kinase for the synthesis of PtdIns 4,5-P_2 and PtdIns 3,4,5-P_3 in specific membrane compartments implies that regulatory and targeting mechanisms can operate on this enzyme, but only preliminary accounts of this have been reported. The type II isoform contains a proline-rich domain that may be an SH3-binding site and thus able to mediate the coupling of type I PtdIns 3-kinases for the channeled synthesis of PtdIns 3,4,5-P_3 (Boronenkov & Anderson 1995, Zhang et al 1997). A splicing isoform of the type II enzyme associates with a TNF receptor (Castellino et al 1997). The bona fide PtdIns 4-P 5-kinase (type I) is uniquely stimulated by phosphatidic acid (Jenkins et al 1994), which is speculated to be an important element of a positive feedback circuit with PLD (phospholipase D) that generates increased PtdIns 4,5-P_2 and may operate in membrane budding or fusion events (Liscovitch & Cantley 1995) (see below). Nonhydrolyzable guanine nucleotides stimulate PtdIns 4-P phosphorylation, implying a G protein regulation of 5-kinase activity (Smith & Chang 1989). Rho stimulates PtdIns 4-P 5-kinase activity in cell lysates (Chong et al 1994) and associates with a type I enzyme, although this association may be indirect (Ren et al 1996). Rac1 also associates directly or indirectly with the type I PtdIns 4-P 5-kinase (Tolias et al 1995). It will be important to further characterize Rac/Rho protein regulation of the type I PtdIns 4-P 5-kinase because of the role of phosphoinositides and Rho family members in the regulation of the actin cytoskeleton (see below).

The characteristics of PtdIns 3-kinases have been discussed in several recent reviews (Carpenter & Cantley 1996, Vanhaesebroeck et al 1997, Domin & Waterfield 1997). These enzymes are classified into three groups according to structure and activity. Class I enzymes are heterodimers of catalytic and adaptor subunits that utilize PtdIns, PtdIns 4-P, and PtdIns 4,5-P_2 as substrates. The adaptor subunits of these enzymes contain SH2 domains that mediate recruitment to phosphotyrosine residues on the cytoplasmic domains of receptors, which results in activation of the 3-kinase. Class II enzymes preferentially phosphorylate PtdIns and PtdIns 4-P but not PtdIns 4,5-P_2 in vitro and contain C2 domains that could mediate membrane interactions. Class III enzymes, which phosphorylate only PtdIns in vitro, consist of heterodimers of a catalytic subunit (such as yeast Vps34p) associated with a serine/threonine protein kinase adaptor subunit (such as yeast Vps15p) that is required for membrane recruitment (Stack et al 1993).

PHOSPHOINOSITIDE-BINDING PROTEINS: EFFECTORS FOR PHOSPHOINOSITIDE SIGNALS

The identification of protein constituents that exhibit stereoselective interactions with phosphoinositides is an important step toward defining proteins with effector roles in phosphoinositide-dependent signaling pathways. Proteins with characterized phosphoinositide-binding activities are summarized in Table 1.

Table 1   Phosphoinositide-binding proteins

Category	Example	Binding specificity[a]	Binding site[b]	Reference[c]
Protein kinases and phospholipases	PKB/Akt	D3	PH	Franke et al 1997
	PDK1	D3	PH	Stokoe et al 1997
	βARK	D3	PH	Rameh et al 1997a
	BTK	D3	PH	Rameh et al 1997a
	PLCγ_1	D4	PH	Garcia et al 1995
Cytoskeletal proteins	Gelsolin	D3	KR	Hartwig et al 1996
	Profilin	D3	KR	Lu et al 1996
	Cofilin	nd	KR	Yonezawa et al 1991
	α-actinin	nd	KR/PH	Fukami et al 1996
	Vinculin	nd	KR	Gilmore & Burridge 1996
	Spectrin	nd	PH	Hyvonen et al 1995
	CapZ	D4	nd	Schafer et al 1996
GTPases and accessory proteins	Dynamin	D4	PH	Salim et al 1996
	ARF	nd	nd	Randazzo 1997
	ARF GEFs	D3	PH	Klarlund et al 1998
	ARF GAPs	D3	PH	Tanaka et al 1997
	PLD	D3 = D4	nd	Hammond et al 1997
	Rac/Rho GEFs	D3	PH	Rameh et al 1997a
Membrane trafficking proteins	Clathrin adaptors	D3	KR	Hao et al 1997
	EEA1	PI3P	nd	Patki et al 1997
	CAPS	D4	PH	Loyet et al 1998
	Synaptotagmin	D3	KR	Schiavo et al 1996
	Mint	nd	PTB	Okamoto & Sudhof 1997

[a]Binding preference for either D3 or D4 phosphoinositides if tested; not determined (nd) indicates PtdIns 4,5,-P$_2$ binding without testing D3 phosphoinositide binding.

[b]Characterized binding sites consisting of PH (or PTB) domain or (KR) lysine/arginine-rich region (see text) or not determined (nd).

[c]Representative reference for each protein; consult text for additional references.

Until recently, only D4 phosphoinositides were employed in protein binding studies (Janmey 1994) but the availability of D3 phosphoinositides has led to the characterization of phosphoinositide-binding specificity for a number of proteins. Many proteins exhibit a binding specificity that favors D3 over D4 phosphoinositides (Table 1). Proteins in this category are potential effectors that function downstream of PtdIns 3-kinases and may mediate the effects of PtdIns 3,4-P_2 and PtdIns 3,4,5-P_3 on protein phosphorylation, cytoskeletal regulation, GTP exchange reactions, and membrane coat recruitment. Proteins that bind PtdIns 3-P that may act downstream of type III PtdIns 3-kinase involved in membrane trafficking have recently been identified, such as AP-2 and EEA1 (Rapoport et al 1997, Patki et al 1997). A small group of proteins exhibit a specificity for binding D4 phosphoinositides in preference to D3 phosphoinositides (Table 1). This group includes proteins that function in cytoskeletal regulation, exocytosis, and endocytosis and are the potential effectors for the cellular roles of D4 phosphoinositides.

MOLECULAR BASIS FOR PROTEIN-PHOSPHOINOSITIDE INTERACTIONS

Basic and Hydrophobic Sequences

Two general classes of binding sites for the stereoselective interaction of phosphoinositides with proteins have been identified: The first consists of short ($\approx$10–20 residues) colinear sequences that are rich in basic and hydrophobic residues, and the second consists of longer sequences ($\approx$120 residues) that share a well-defined tertiary structure of the PH domain. Studies on gelsolin (Yu et al 1992) resulted in the assignment of phosphoinositide binding to two separate regions near the N terminus (CKSGLKYKKGGVASGF and KHVVP-NEVVVQRLFQVKGRR). Peptides corresponding to these sequences exhibit PtdIns 4,5-P_2–binding similar to that of gelsolin (Janmey et al 1992). The first of these lysine/arginine-rich sequences was suggested to constitute a motif (K/RXXXXKXK/RK/R) that was present in other phosphoinositide-binding cytoskeletal proteins such as gCap39, villin, cofilin, and profilin (Yu et al 1992). A simple electrostatic interaction between lysine/arginine and phosphoinositol phosphates cannot fully account for the phosphoinositide-binding properties of gelsolin, which does not bind deacylated or deacylated/deglycerinated phosphoinositides (Janmey 1994). However, these short sequences contain a high percentage of hydrophobic amino acids that may form the part of the binding site that interacts with the diacylglycerol moiety.

The phosphoinositide-binding sites for several other actin-associated proteins are not homologous to those of gelsolin. It was suggested that a short peptide sequence (FSMDLRTKST) in profilin was responsible for phosphoinositide binding (Sohn et al 1995). A 12 residue sequence (WAPECAPLKSKM) of cofilin was reported to bind PtdIns 4,5-P_2 (Yonezawa et al 1991). A linear sequence in α-actinin (TAPYRNVNIQNFHLSWK) accounted for PtdIns 4,5-P_2 binding, which was eliminated by mutagenesis of the two arginine and lysine residues (Fukami et al 1996). Although a diverse array of nonhomologous sequences constitute phosphoinositide-binding sites in cytoskeletal proteins, each contains at least two basic residues in the context of a high percentage ($\approx$50%) of hydrophobic residues. These short sequences may provide hydrophobic contacts with phospholipid acyl chains as well as charge interactions between the basic residues and the phosphate groups on the inositol headgroup. A hexadecapeptide from neurogranin exhibiting these hallmark features (WAAK-IQASFRGHMARKK) interacts with high affinity and specificity with phosphoinositides preferring PtdIns 3,4,5-P_3 over other phospholipids, and acquires a structure upon binding to phosphoinositides (Lu & Chen 1997).

Several coat proteins have been isolated in an effort to identify inositol polyphosphate-binding proteins. Clathrin adaptor proteins AP-2 and AP-3, as well as coatomer protein, interact with inositol phosphates and with phosphoinositides (Beck & Keen 1991, Fleischer et al 1994, Ye et al 1995, Norris et al 1995). Phosphoinositide interactions with AP-2 are mediated by N-terminal sequences of the α subunit (Beck & Keen 1991, Gaidarov et al 1996) and the phosphoinositide-binding site of a homologous subunit of AP-3 was suggested to consist of PKKKHLDYLIQATNE (Ye et al 1995, Hao et al 1997), a sequence also rich in basic and hydrophobic residues.

Several inositol phosphate-binding proteins such as centaurin-α and synaptotagmin II were purified based on inositol polyphosphate-binding (Fukuda et al 1994, Cullen et al 1995, Theibert et al 1997). However, phosphoinositides are probably the natural ligands for these proteins (Hammonds-Odie et al 1996, Schiavo et al 1996, Mehrotra et al 1997). The inositol phosphate-binding domain on synaptotagmin consists of the highly basic sequence GKRLKKKK-TTVKKK in the C2B domain (Fukuda et al 1994, 1995a). This portion of the C2 domain is disordered (Sutton et al 1995) but adopts an ordered structure upon binding inositol phosphates (Mehrotra et al 1997). Phosphoinositides bind to the same or an overlapping site in the C2B domain (Schiavo et al 1996). These lysine-rich sequences probably represent the inositol phosphate-binding portions of larger phosphoinositide-binding domains. In synaptotagmin, this basic sequence is flanked by regions rich in hydrophobic residues that could mediate acyl chain interactions.

PH Domains

PH (and related PTB) domains are the best-characterized and possibly most widespread of phosphoinositide-binding motifs. PH domains, termed pleckstrin homology from the sequences initially identified in the platelet protein kinase C substrate pleckstrin, comprise $\approx$120 amino acid colinear regions identified by sequence comparison in nearly 100 proteins (Musacchio et al 1993, Gibson et al 1994). PH domains are present in cytoskeletal components (spectrin, α-actinin), guanine nucleotide exchange proteins or GTPase-regulating proteins (Ras-GRF, Dbl, VAV, cdc24, SOS, Ras-GAP, Tiam-1, ARNO, GRP1/cytohesin-1) and GTPases (dynamin), phosphoinositide-regulated protein kinases (Akt/PKB, PDK1), other protein kinases (BTK, βARK), and phospholipases (PLC). Although not well conserved at the primary sequence level, NMR and X-ray diffraction studies reveal a remarkable similarity between the structures for PH domains from pleckstrin, spectrin, PLCδ_1, and dynamin (Yoon et al 1994, Macias et al 1994, Hyvonen et al 1995, Ferguson et al 1995, Zheng et al 1996a, Salim et al 1996). The PH domain consists of two nearly orthogonal β sheets of three or four strands that form a β sandwich closed off near its C terminus by an amphipathic α helix.

Harlan et al (1994) originally reported that the PH domains of pleckstrin, ras-GAP, βARK, and T cell kinase interacted with PtdIns-4,5-P_2. Subsequent studies confirmed that PH domains from a large number of proteins (PLCδ_1, spectrin, dynamin, BTK, SOS, Tiam-1, OSBP, Akt/PKB, SOS, GRP1/cytohesin-1, ARNO) bind phosphoinositides but with different affinities and specificities (Zheng et al 1996a, Salim et al 1996, Rameh et al 1997b, Frech et al 1997, Franke et al 1997, Kubiseski et al 1997, Klarlund et al 1997, Paris et al 1997). A study of six PH domains (Rameh et al 1997a) found that four exhibit a selectivity for PtdIns 3,4,5-P_3 over other phosphoinositides, whereas two others bound PtdIns 3,4,5-P_3 and PtdIns-4,5-P_2 with similar affinities. The PH domain of Akt/PKB has a high affinity and specificity for PtdIns 3,4-P_2 over PtdIns 4,5-P_2 and PtdIns 3,4,5-P_3 (Franke et al 1997, Klippel et al 1997, Frech et al 1997), whereas the PH domain of a kinase that phosphorylates PKB/Akt, PDK1, prefers PtdIns 3,4,5-P_3 over PtdIns 3,4-P_2 (Stokoe et al 1997). A similar preferential selectivity for binding PtdIns 3,4,5-P_3 was characterized for a number of PH domains including ARF nucleotide exchange factors and GTPase-activating proteins (Tanaka et al 1997, Klarlund et al 1998). The PH domains of PLCδ, CAPS, and dynamin are distinct in preferentially binding PtdIns 4,5-P_2 rather than D3 phosphoinositides (Salim et al 1996, Loyet et al 1998). The majority of PH domains where binding specificity has been determined have characteristics expected for effector proteins for PtdIns 3-kinase signaling.

Phosphoinositide binding to PH domains occurs at an electrostatically polarized (basic) face of the domain with critical residues residing on the loops between the β sheets (Lemmon et al 1996, 1997). This is a highly variable region between individual PH domains, which accounts for the diversity of phosphoinositide-binding specificity and affinity. For the PH domain of PLCδ_1, which exhibits the highest affinity for phosphoinositides among the PH domains, binding is mediated by a network of interactions between the 4 and 5 position phosphates of the inositol headgroup and amino acid side chains, mainly lysine and arginine, of the variable loops of the PH domain (Ferguson et al 1995). Weaker binding of phosphoinositides to other PH domains corresponds to a more superficial interaction of the inositol headgroup with PH domain loops establishing many fewer interactions (Lemmon et al 1997).

There is evidence that phosphoinositides are physiological ligands for the PH domains of some of the above proteins. Mutation of critical loop residues required for phosphoinositide binding by the BTK PH domain results in a loss-of-function agammaglobinaemia phenotype (Salim et al 1996). Increasing evidence implicates D3 phosphoinositides as physiological regulators of Akt/PKB activity (see below). Mutagenesis studies on many of the other phosphoinositide-binding proteins will be required to convincingly establish the role of such interactions in cell function. Whether phosphoinositides constitute the sole ligands for all PH domains is an unresolved issue. The fact that the structurally homologous PTB domain (Lemmon et al 1996) interacts with phosphotyrosyl peptides via a binding site that overlaps with that for phosphoinositides (Rameh et al 1997a) suggests that phosphoamino acid peptides could be the ligands, or co-ligands, for some PH domains. For certain PH domains, cooperative interactions with multiple ligands may occur such as for βARK, where phosphoinositides and $\beta\gamma$ subunits exhibit a synergism in binding (Pitcher et al 1995). The ability of the dynamin-1 PH domain, but not other PH domains including that of PLCδ_1, to interfere with rapid endocytosis in chromaffin cells (Artalejo et al 1997) suggests that phosphoinositides are not the endogenous ligand for this PH domain despite the fact that direct phosphoinositide binding (Salim et al 1996) as well as phosphoinositide activation of the dynamin GTPase (Lin & Gilman 1996) have been demonstrated.

PH domains are essential for the membrane recruitment of several proteins that contain them, such as PKB/Akt (Andjelkovic et al 1997), GAP1[IP4BP] (Lockyer et al 1997), Dbl (Zheng et al 1996b), and βARK (Pitcher et al 1995). It is possible that other phospholipids, including minor novel phosphoinositides such as PtdIns 3,5-P_2, are the ligands that mediate membrane recruitment of PH domain-containing proteins found to bind D3 or D4 phosphoinositides only weakly. The active pace of research on the PH domain will soon clarify the general role of this motif and lead to the identification of additional physiological ligands that mediate membrane recruitment. At present, the concept of the PH domain as a signal-dependent membrane adapter that functions in the focal assembly of protein complexes at the membrane interface is very useful (Hemmings 1997). The fact that PH domains are frequently accompanied by other motifs (SH2, SH3, proline-rich, GTP exchange) in proteins is consistent with the notion that the recruitment of the PH domain protein would nucleate sites on the membrane for protein complex assembly.

MEMBRANE MICRODOMAINS OF PHOSPHOINOSITIDES AND SITE-SPECIFIC PROTEIN COMPLEX ASSEMBLY

It is likely that phosphoinositides and the proteins they recruit are spatially localized at focal sites in specific membranes. Phosphoinositides and the phosphoinositide kinases are not uniformly distributed in cellular membranes (Pike 1992), and the phosphoinositides are metabolically compartmentalized (Monaco & Gershengorn 1992). Biochemical evidence for membrane domains enriched in receptor-regulated pools of PtdIns $4,5$-P_2 and enzymes has been reported (Pike & Casey 1996, Hope & Pike 1996). Studies employing fluorescent PtdIns $4,5$-P_2 in liposomes revealed that phosphoinositide-binding peptides can stabilize membrane microdomains in which both protein and phospholipid constituents are segregated (Glaser et al 1996).

Immunocytochemical studies with phosphoinositide-specific antibodies provide a preview of what may be a general concept of spatially localized domains of phosphoinositides in cellular membranes. PtdIns $4,5$-P_2 colocalizes with α-actinin in focal contacts and membrane ruffles (Fukami et al 1994). A localized synthesis of PtdIns $4,5$-P_2 on dense-core vesicles in neuroendocrine cells during a priming step for exocytosis can be detected by immunocytochemistry (K Loyet, personal communication). Spatially segregated membrane domains enriched for polyphosphoinositides would exhibit a positive membrane curvature (Chernomordik 1996) that could contribute to the remodeling of the bilayer for events such as membrane budding and fusion. The recruitment of phosphoinositide-binding proteins to such sites could allow for the assembly of signal transduction complexes, cytoskeletal-membrane attachments, coated membrane domains for bud formation, and scaffolds for membrane fusion reactions. Current efforts to define such mechanisms involving phosphoinositide-binding effector proteins are discussed below and summarized in Figure 2.

PROTEIN KINASES AS EFFECTORS FOR PHOSPHOINOSITIDES IN SIGNAL TRANSDUCTION

PtdIns $3,4,5$-P_3 serves an essential signaling role in mediating the effects of a wide range of extracellular stimuli on cell proliferation, cell survival, and metabolism (Toker & Cantley 1997). Recent studies elucidated an important effector pathway that involves D3 phosphoinositide-mediated membrane recruitment and activation of several protein kinases (Figure 2a). The PKB/Akt

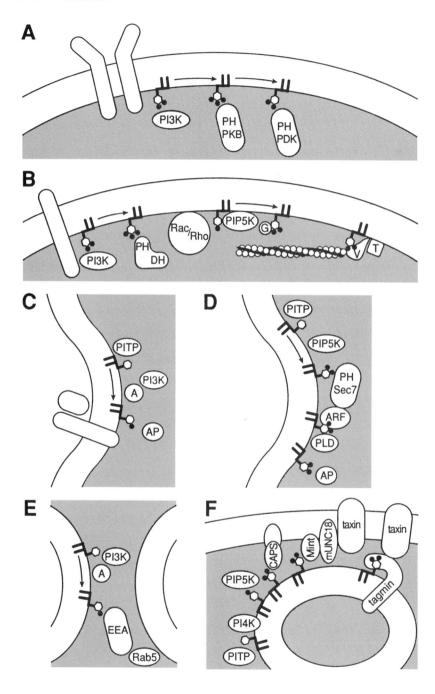

kinase is activated downstream of receptor-regulated PtdIns 3-kinase in part by direct interaction of PtdIns 3,4-P_2 with its PH domain (Franke et al 1997, Klippel et al 1997, Frech et al 1997, Cohen et al 1997). Recruitment of PKB/Akt to the membrane requires its PH domain (Andejkovic et al 1997), and possible dimerization of PKB/Akt at the membrane has been suggested (Franke et al 1997). PKB/Akt undergoes phosphorylation and activation by additional phosphoinositide-dependent protein kinases such as PDK1 (Alessi et al 1997, Stephens et al 1998). The phosphorylation of PKB/Akt by PDK1 requires D3 phosphoinositide binding to the PH domain of PKB/Akt (Stokoe et al 1997, Cohen et al 1997). PDK1 also contains a PH domain that binds PtdIns 3,4,5-P_3; however, its kinase activity may be constitutive, and phosphoinositide binding may serve to recruit PDK1 to a membrane site near its membrane bound substrate (Alessi et al 1997). This system represents the clearest example of phosphoinositide signaling where the identity of the lipid(s) involved, the basis of its regulated synthesis by a defined kinase, and the role of a physiologically relevant phosphoinositide-binding effector are relatively well defined (Figure 2a).

Several substrates of PKB/Akt that act downstream in signaling pathways regulating metabolism (Cohen et al 1997) and cell survival (del Peso et al 1997) have been identified. Expression of a constitutively active PtdIns 3-kinase

←——

Figure 2   Common themes in phosphoinositide signaling involving site-specific membrane recruitment. (*A*) Signal transduction mechanism employing receptor-regulated PtdIns 3-kinase (PI3K) to form D3 phosphoinositides for the recruitment of PH domain-containing kinases, PKB and PDK. (*B*) Cytoskeleton assembly mechanisms employing receptor-regulated PtdIns 3-kinase to form D3 phosphoinositides for the activation of PH domain-containing Dbl family members that promote guanine nucleotide exchange on Rho family members. Rho/Rac are depicted as potential activators of PtdIns 4-P 5-kinase (PIP5K) to form PtdIns 4,5-P_2, which uncaps gelsolin (G) from actin to allow filament elongation, or promotes a conformational change in vinculin (V) to allow it to tether actin to talin (T). (*C*) Golgi membrane-budding reaction is depicted to proceed through cargo receptor activation of a PtdIns 3-kinase (PI3K) containing an adaptor (A) subunit. PtdIns transfer protein (PITP) enhances PtdIns 3-kinase-catalyzed phosphorylation to form PtdIns 3-P, which promotes the binding of clathrin adaptor proteins (AP) to cargo receptor tail. (*D*) Golgi membrane-budding reaction is depicted as proceeding through PITP enhancement of PtdIns 4-kinase phosphorylation along with PIP5K to form PtdIns 4,5-P_2. This phosphoinositide recruits and activates the PH domain and Sec7 homology-containing exchange factors that promote guanine nucleotide exchange on ARF. ARF activates phospholipase D, which promotes further synthesis of PtdIns 4,5-P_2 via phosphatidic acid stimulation of PIP5K. Adaptor proteins (AP) are shown binding to acidic phospholipids. (*E*) Endosome fusion mechanism is depicted to proceed through activation of an adaptor-containing PtdIns 3-kinase (A and PI3K) that forms PtdIns 3-P, which recruits EEA for binding to Rab5. (*F*) Exocytotic fusion mechanism is depicted to involve PITP, PtdIns 4-kinase (PI4K), and PIP5K to promote formation of PtdIns 4,5-P_2 on the vesicle membrane. Potential effectors of this phosphoinositide are CAPS, Mint-mUNC18 complexes, and synaptotagmin (tagmin). Potential interactions of mUNC18 and tagmin with syntaxin (taxin) are depicted.

(Martin et al 1996, Frevert & Kahn 1997) or a PKB/Akt (Kohn et al 1996) enhances Glut4 translocation to the plasma membrane of 3T3-L1 adipocytes, suggesting that the PKB/Akt-catalyzed phosphorylation of an unidentified protein substrate regulates an aspect of the exocytotic pathway of glucose transporter vesicles. Delineation of this downstream pathway will provide interesting insights into the regulation of membrane trafficking by phosphoinositide-dependent protein phosphorylation.

PROTEIN EFFECTORS FOR CYTOSKELETAL REGULATION

Phosphoinositides have been implicated in the regulation of actin cytoskeleton assembly at several levels. Extensive connections between phosphoinositides and the Rho family of GTP-binding proteins, which mediate extracellular signal regulation of cytoskeletal rearrangements, have been identified (Hall 1998). A large family of Rho guanine nucleotide exchange factors has been characterized whose members contain Dbl homology (DH) domain as well as a PH domain that mediates the targeting of these proteins to the membrane (Cerione & Zheng 1996, Zheng et al 1996b). Constitutively active PtdIns 3-kinase activates Rac-dependent lamellipodia and Rho-dependent stress fiber assembly in fibroblasts (Reif et al 1996). The PH domain of some Dbl family members exhibits selectivity for binding D3 phosphoinositides (Rameh et al 1997a). This indicates that D3 phosphoinositide synthesis could promote recruitment of exchange factors to specific sites on the membrane for activation of Rho family GTPases (Carpenter et al 1997) (Figure 2*b*).

With the identification of numerous Rho/Rac-binding proteins (Tapon & Hall 1997), there are many options for downstream signaling to the cytoskeleton. One pathway for the Rho-dependent induction of stress fiber formation involves the activation of a Rho kinase (ROK) that phosphorylates both myosin light chain (Amano et al 1996) and myosin phosphatase (Kimura et al 1996), which leads to increased binding of myosin and the bundling of actin filaments. Another mechanism that promotes de novo actin polymerization involves D4 phosphoinositides as mediators of Rho/Rac regulation of the cytoskeleton (Figure 2*b*). In platelets, Rac activation results in increased actin polymerization for lamellae formation, which arises from an increase in the number of free actin barbed-ends available for filament elongation (Hartwig et al 1995). Rac activation causes an increased synthesis of PtdIns 4,5-P_2, which may be mediated by Rac stimulation of a type I PtdIns 4-P 5-kinase. The downstream effector proteins in this system are gelsolin and other capping proteins whose actin barbed-end capping activities are inhibited by phosphoinositides (Janmey 1994, Schafer et al 1996) (Figure 2*b*).

There are other potential downstream effectors among the phosphoinositide-binding proteins that regulate actin assembly (Table 1) (Janmey 1994). Poly-phosphoinositides induce conformational changes in vinculin that allow vinculin to mediate the cross-linking of talin to actin, which plays a role in focal adhesion assembly (Gilmore & Burridge 1996) (Figure 2b). Consistent with a role for vinculin or other phosphoinositide-binding cytoskeletal proteins as important effectors, the Rho-dependent stimulation of focal adhesion formation in fibroblasts is blocked by microinjection of antibodies to PtdIns 4,5-P_2 (Gilmore & Burridge 1996).

In related efforts to assess physiological roles for phosphoinositides in regulating actin assembly, overexpression of the type I PtdIns 4-P 5-kinase in COS-7 cells was found to cause a dramatic increase in the assembly of short actin filaments (Shibasaki et al 1997). This depends upon a functional kinase domain and is counteracted by coexpression of a type II 5-phosphatase that decreases cellular PtdIns 4,5-P_2 levels (Zhang et al 1995). Conversely, overexpression of a type II 5-phosphatase in COS-7 cells reduces the number of actin stress fibers (Sakasaki et al 1997). Expression of a dominant-negative form of RhoA fails to suppress the formation of actin filaments induced by 5-kinase overexpression, consistent with a role for PtdIns 4-P 5-kinase downstream of Rho (Shibasaki et al 1997). These studies to alter cellular levels of polyphosphoinositides in cells provide an important link between in vitro studies of phosphoinositide-binding by cytoskeletal proteins and the regulation of actin assembly in vivo. Additional studies are required to determine which of the many candidate cytoskeletal proteins (Table 1) serve as essential effectors for phosphoinositide signaling in cytoskeletal rearrangements.

PROTEIN EFFECTORS FOR MEMBRANE COAT FORMATION AND BUDDING REACTIONS

Many intracellular transport events require the assembly of vesicle coats at specific sites on the membrane during budding (Rothman & Wieland 1996). Coat components bind to the cytoplasmic tails of transmembrane proteins that associate with transported cargo in the lumen of the budding vesicle, which serves to concentrate and sort cargo for transport (Kirchhausen et al 1997). Non-clathrin COPII- and COPI-coated vesicles mediate transport between the endoplasmic reticulum and Golgi and within the Golgi, respectively (Schekman & Orci 1996). Clathrin-coated vesicles mediate the endocytic trafficking of proteins to early endosomes and the trafficking of proteins from the *trans*-Golgi network to late endosomes. Clathrin assembly at the site of vesicle budding utilizes adaptor proteins, AP-1 for the Golgi and AP-2/AP-3 for the plasma membrane (Robinson 1997). Protein sorting at the *trans*-Golgi network to multiple destinations involves the generation of numerous distinct transport vesicles for which coats and mechanisms of assembly have yet to be fully characterized (Traub & Kornfeld 1997).

As for other spatially localized, membrane-associated events requiring protein recruitment, there is evidence for an essential role for phosphoinositides in the assembly of vesicle coats. It remains to be determined whether phosphoinositides are required as constitutive cofactors for assembly or whether they act as regulatory signals that specify the site and timing of assembly. Within the variety of budding processes examined, coat components and adaptor proteins, as well as the enzyme PLD, have suggested roles as phosphoinositide effectors.

The initial indication that D3 phosphoinositides were critical for aspects of membrane trafficking was the discovery that a yeast vacuolar protein sorting gene *VPS34* encoded a PtdIns 3-kinase (Schu et al 1993). The *VPS34* gene product phosphorylates PtdIns, but not other phosphoinositides, and mammalian homologues exhibit a similar substrate specificity (Volinia et al 1995). Loss-of-function mutants of *VPS34* exhibit a defect in sorting newly synthesized proteins, as well as endocytosed proteins, to the vacuole, and it was suggested that the Vps34p protein executes a function essential for the formation of vesicles in the Golgi or their subsequent trafficking (Stack et al 1995). A serine/threonine-specific protein kinase (VPS15p) mediates the membrane recruitment and activation of the Vps34p lipid kinase (Stack et al 1993). The Vps15p/Vps34p complex has been suggested to be regulated by cargo receptors for vacuolar hydrolases (Marcusson et al 1994). In this model, cargo accumulation would specify the timing and location of budding by stimulating PtdIns 3-P formation (Horazdovsky et al 1995).

The immediate downstream effector for PtdIns 3-P remains to be identified. PtdIns 3-P could alter the structure of the bilayer to facilitate budding, recruit coat proteins or adaptors to the site of budding, or function as a vesicle membrane component essential for subsequent docking or fusion reactions (Stack et al 1995). The role of a dynamin homologue (Vps1p) in vacuolar sorting suggests that clathrin coat proteins may be involved (Conibear & Stevens 1995), and the sorting defects of conditional clathrin mutants are consistent with this (Stack et al 1995). Whether PtdIns 3-P functions to recruit clathrin adaptor proteins for bud formation remains to be determined.

In yeasts, PtdIns $3,5$-P$_2$ synthesis was found to be dependent upon the Vps34p PtdIns 3-kinase (Dove et al 1997). This could indicate that the role of PtdIns 3-P in vacuolar sorting is to serve as a precursor to PtdIns $3,5$-P$_2$. The loss-of-function phenotype for *FAB1*, which encodes one of two yeast PtdInsP 5-kinases (Yamamoto et al 1995, Loijens & Anderson 1996), includes a vacuolar morphology defect, which suggests a role for a 5-phosphorylated inositide in aspects of vacuole membrane cycling. Genetic studies, however, did not reveal the epistatic interaction between *VPS34* and *FAB1* alleles that is anticipated for a conversion of PtdIns 3-P to PtdIns 3,5-P_2 as essential for vacuolar targeting (Yamamoto et al 1995).

To investigate potential roles for the products of PtdIns 3-kinases in membrane trafficking in mammalian cells, extensive use has been made of wortmannin, a characterized irreversible inhibitor of some but not all PtdIns 3-kinases (Carpenter & Cantley 1996). The Vps34p lipid kinase is relatively insensitive to wortmannin (Stack & Emr 1994), whereas mammalian class III PtdIns 3-kinases that include Vps34p homologues exhibit a range of sensitivities to the drug (Stephens et al 1994, Volinia et al 1995). Wortmannin is not highly specific and is known to inhibit myosin light chain kinase, several phospholipases, and several PtdIns 4-kinases, albeit at higher concentrations (Cross et al 1995, Wong et al 1997). A chemically distinct inhibitor of PtdIns 3-kinases LY290042 (Vlahos et al 1994) is also used in membrane trafficking studies. Several mammalian PtdIns 3-kinase isoforms are inhibited by LY290042, but unfortunately so are isoforms of PtdIns 4-kinase. Thus studies that rely exclusively on wortmannin and LY294002 are difficult to interpret, and it is necessary to employ other methods such as dominant-negative mutants to assess the role of PtdIns 3-kinase in membrane trafficking reactions (Haruta et al 1995).

Wortmannin treatment of mammalian cells results in a limited repertoire of membrane trafficking defects that is restricted to the late Golgi-lysosomal-endosomal pathway (Brown et al 1995, Clague et al 1995, Davidson 1995, Reaves et al 1996, Shpetner et al 1996). Wortmannin treatment causes a striking swelling of late endosomal-prelysosomal compartments (Brown et al 1995, Reaves et al 1996); the inhibition of transport of endocytosed receptors from late endosomes to lysosomes (Shpetner et al 1996); the mis-sorting of cathepsin D, a lysosomal protease that is sorted via the mannose 6-phosphate receptor in the *trans*-Golgi (Brown et al 1995, Davidson 1995); an inhibition of transferrin receptor recycling (Shepherd et al 1996); the inhibition of GLUT4 transporter recycling (Yang et al 1996); and a partial inhibition of fluid phase endocytosis (G Li et al 1995).

In vitro reconstitution studies in mammalian systems of vesicle biogenesis from the *trans*-Golgi have identified several molecular requirements for budding and have begun to elucidate the role of phosphoinositides in budding reactions (Figure 2c,d). The formation of constitutive and regulated vesicles from the *trans*-Golgi of neuroendocrine cells in vitro depends upon at least two cytosolic protein fractions as well as ATP (Ohashi et al 1995). One of the required cytosolic factors is PtdIns transfer protein, which binds and transports PtdIns and PtdChol in vitro (Wirtz 1997). Mammalian PtdIns transfer proteins accelerate the phosphorylation of PtdIns through 4-phosphorylation and

3-phosphorylation reactions by providing PtdIns to PtdIns 4-kinase and PtdIns 3-kinase (Martin 1995, Wirtz 1997). A requirement for PtdIns transfer protein in Golgi budding reactions likely indicates a role for phosphoinositides in some aspect of vesicle formation.

In vitro reactions in which the formation of constitutive exocytic vesicles containing TGN38 are formed are inhibited by high concentrations of wortmannin, which correspond to the range that inhibits a Golgi-associated PtdIns 3-kinase (Jones et al 1993, Jones & Howell 1997). The PtdIns 3-kinase resembles the VPS34 lipid kinase in substrate specificity and low sensitivity to wortmannin, which led to the suggestion of a required role for PtdIns 3-P in vesicle formation (Jones & Howell 1997; see also Hickinson et al 1997). The enzyme resides in a membrane-bound complex with an adaptor protein (p62) that is related to, but immunologically distinct from, the p85a subunit of a type I PtdIns 3-kinase. Rab6 and several unidentified GTP-binding proteins co-reside in the complex in association with the cytoplasmic domain of TGN38 (Jones et al 1993, Jones & Howell 1997). The properties of a membrane and cytosolic p62-containing complex suggest a model in which a p62-Rab6 complex is recruited to TGN38 in the Golgi, thereby mediating the binding of PtdIns 3-kinase for the essential formation of PtdIns 3-P (Figure 2c). The effector system for PtdIns 3-P remains to be identified for this Golgi budding reaction, but may involve the p200 lace-like coats described for these vesicles (Ladinsky et al 1994).

Other experimental work on the biogenesis of vesicles in the *trans*-Golgi and the formation of COPI-coated vesicles within the Golgi suggests alternative or additional roles for the phosphoinositides (PtdIns $4,5$-P_2 or PtdIns $3,4,5$-P_3) in budding reactions (Figure 2d). ADP ribosylation factors (ARFs) comprise a family of proteins that play essential roles in Golgi membrane traffic by mediating the recruitment of coat proteins to the membrane (Rothman & Wieland 1996). COPI vesicle formation can be reconstituted in vitro with ARF and coatomer as the sole cytosolic factors (Orci et al 1993). An ARF guanine nucleotide exchange factor (ARF GEF) catalyzes GTP binding to ARF, and ARF-GTP promotes coatomer binding. An ARF GTPase-activating factor (ARF GAP) catalyzes uncoating prior to fusion of vesicles with an acceptor membrane. The recruitment of AP-1 clathrin adaptors to the Golgi membrane (Stamness & Rothman 1993) is ARF dependent, as is recruitment of AP-1 to immature secretory granules (Dittie et al 1996) and AP-2 to endosomal membranes (West et al 1997).

A potential key role for phosphoinositides in coat protein recruitment mediated by ARF is indicated by the dependence of ARF regulators and effectors on the presence of phosphoinositides in the membrane. ARF GEFs that contain Sec7 homology domains and PH domains that mediate phosphoinositide-stimulated exchange activity have been characterized (Paris et al 1997, Klarlund et al 1997, 1998). ARF itself interacts with polyphosphoinositides (Randazzo 1997), which promote its nucleotide exchange (Terui et al 1994, Paris et al 1997) and its interaction with ARF GAP (Randazzo 1997). ARF GAPs also contain PH domains and exhibit phosphoinositide-regulated activity (Tanaka et al 1997). These observations suggest that phosphoinositides could play a central role as cofactors or regulators in recruiting ARF to the membrane and regulating its cycle of activity by affecting ARF GEFs and GAPs. Consistent with an essential role for phosphoinositides in membrane-coating reactions, the charged antibiotic neomycin, which binds polyphosphoinositides, inhibits *trans*-Golgi budding of regulated secretory granules and the membrane recruitment of AP-2 in vitro (Ohashi et al 1995, West et al 1997).

The finding that ARF is a GTP-dependent activator of PLD (Brown et al 1993, Cockcroft et al 1994) led to the suggestion that PLD functions as an effector for ARF in coat protein recruitment (Ktistakis et al 1996, Roth & Sternweis 1997). For COPI vesicle formation from the Golgi (Ktistakis et al 1996), for the budding of regulated secretory granules from the *trans*-Golgi involving an AP-1 adaptor (Chen et al 1996, 1997), and for AP-2 adaptor recruitment to endosomal membranes (West et al 1997), the ARF requirement can be bypassed by direct provision of PLD to the in vitro budding reaction. Diverting endogenous PLD catalysis with primary alcohols inhibits budding (Ktistakis et al 1996, Bi et al 1997, Chen et al 1997). The data are consistent with the possibility that PLD serves an essential effector role for ARF in budding.

PLD itself is an additional potential effector for phosphoinositides in membrane budding reactions because PLD activity and its stimulation by ARF stringently require polyphosphoinositides (Brown et al 1993, Liscovitch et al 1994). Either D4 or D3 polyphosphoinositides function equally effectively as cofactors for PLD. The phosphoinositide dependence of enzyme activity is mediated by direct interactions with the PLD, although the phosphoinositide-binding site on the enzyme has not been identified (Hammond et al 1997). The basis for an autocatalytic cycle for the ARF-dependent activation of PLD has been proposed (Liscovitch & Cantley 1995), which suggests that production of phosphatidic acid by PLD could result in the enhanced production of PtdIns $4,5-P_2$ by activation of the type I PtdIns 4-P 5-kinase (Jenkins et al 1994). The PtdIns $4,5-P_2$ formed would further enhance PLD activity, as well as ARF activation by ARF GEFs. Termination of this cycle might occur by deactivation of ARF through phosphoinositide stimulation of an ARF-GAP or by a phosphoinositide 5-phosphatase (Chung et al 1997). This mechanism encompasses some of the known in vitro properties of participant proteins and provides a basis for generating a spatially restricted membrane budding site (Figure 2d). The requirement for phosphoinositides in all aspects of the ARF activation/deactivation cycle and for PLD activation suggests a critical role for phosphoinositides in Golgi budding and membrane coat recruitment; however, there is presently no evidence for this role in vivo and future work will need to address this.

The precise steps in late Golgi trafficking that are affected by wortmannin and presumed to require D3 phosphoinositides are uncertain. Such steps may involve sorting of proteins to appropriate vesicles, the formation of vesicles and the exit of a sorted protein from the *trans*-Golgi, the fusion of transport vesicles with endosomal intermediates, or recycling of sorted proteins back to the *trans*-Golgi. A recent study reported that wortmannin did not affect the recycling of the mannose 6-phosphate receptor to the *trans*-Golgi (Nakajima & Pfeffer 1997). However, there is evidence that wortmannin affects the sorting in the *trans*-Golgi of pro-cathepsin D by the mannose 6-phosphate receptor to clathrin-coated post-Golgi vesicles (Gaffet et al 1997). Wortmannin had little effect on levels of clathrin-coated vesicles; however, the vesicles from drug-treated cells exhibited reduced levels of the mannose 6-phosphate receptor, suggesting that cargo sorting rather than budding was being affected by wortmannin (Gaffet et al 1997).

A mechanism by which 3-phosphorylated inosites could regulate the sorting of cargo in the endosomal/lysosomal pathway was suggested by the observation that PtdIns 3-P enhances the affinity of the adaptor protein AP-2 complex for binding tyrosine-based signals present on membrane receptor cytoplasmic tails (Rapoport et al 1997, Kirchhausen et al 1997) (Figure 2*c*). In this mechanism, PtdIns 3-P would be a co-ligand in a protein complex that would modulate an interaction. By affecting the affinity of cytoplasmic tail interactions with adaptor proteins AP-1 and AP-2, D3 phosphoinositides could influence the routing of internalized proteins to recycling endosomes or to late endosomes and lysosomes (Marks et al 1997).

PROTEIN EFFECTORS FOR MEMBRANE FUSION AND RETRIEVAL

In addition to budding and membrane coat recruitment, phosphoinositides have been implicated in membrane fusion reactions. D3 and D4 phosphoinositides appear to be involved in endosome and exocytotic membrane fusion reactions, respectively. The nature of the effector proteins that mediate the requirement for phosphoinositides in fusion are beginning to be identified.

There is evidence for additional steps in the endosomal pathway at which PtdIns 3-kinases are required. Wortmannin and LY294002 inhibit the homotypic fusion between early endosomes that can be reconstituted in vitro (Jones & Clague 1995, G Li et al 1995). A clue to the underlying mechanism was provided by the observation that a constitutively active but not wild-type Rab5 reversed the inhibition by wortmannin (G Li et al 1995). A constitutively active PtdIns 3-kinase also stimulated in vitro endosome fusion. These studies provide a convincing link between early endosome fusion and PtdIns 3-kinase activity and suggest that lipid kinases or their D3 phosphoinositide products function upstream of a fusion mechanism that involves activation of Rab5 (G Li et al 1995). An indication for a direct effect of D3 phosphoinositides and a tangible clue on a potential effector for D3 phosphoinositide regulation of Rab5 function were provided by the identification of EEA1 (early endosomal antigen) as a PtdIns 3-P-binding protein that resides in part on endosomes (Patki et al 1997). Treatment of cells with wortmannin caused a translocation of EEA1 from an endosomal to cytosolic distribution. Moreover, EEA1 was found to bind liposomes that contain PtdIns-3-P (Patki et al 1997), although its specificity for binding other D3 and D4 phosphoinositides is unknown. The sequence of the protein is homologous to that of Vps19p and contains a Zn^{2+}-binding domain that mediates interactions with Rab5 (Mu et al 1995). This work provides a model (Figure 2e) for the mechanism of action of D3 phosphoinositides in membrane fusion acting as a signal that recruits EEA1 to endosomes. EEA1 would then recruit or bind resident Rab5 to promote fusion. A number of components of the membrane-bound machinery that interact with activated Rab5, such as nucleotide exchange factors and effectors, have been identified (Horiuchi et al 1997), and this complex may constitute a protein scaffold that, acting with EEA1, allows membrane ligation and fusion.

That phosphoinositides are essential for exocytic fusion reactions was suggested by the discovery that PtdIns transfer protein is required for the reconstitution of Ca^{2+}-dependent neurotransmitter secretion in permeable PC12 cells (Hay & Martin 1993). PtdIns transfer protein was purified as one of three cytosolic factors required for an ATP-dependent priming step that precedes a Ca^{2+}-triggered membrane fusion step (Hay & Martin 1993). The ATP-dependence of priming and the role of PtdIns transfer protein were clarified by the finding that a type I PtdIns 4-P 5-kinase was one of the other cytosolic priming factors (Hay et al 1995) and that these two proteins synergistically stimulate priming. These results indicate a role for phosphoinositide phosphorylation in some aspect of regulated exocytic membrane fusion, which had been suggested by earlier studies of Holz and coworkers (Eberhard et al 1990). PtdIns 4-kinase is a resident on secretory vesicles from adrenal chromaffin, mast, and pancreatic β cells (Pike 1992), and this enzyme was shown to be essential for priming exocytosis (Wiedemann et al 1996). Priming is a reversible process, and the reversal of priming appears to be catalyzed by a phosphoinositide 5-phosphatase (Martin et al 1997).

These results indicate that synthesis of PtdIns 4,5-P_2 during priming is essential for regulated exocytosis. That additional phosphorylation by a PtdIns 3-kinase is not involved in priming was suggested by the failure of wortmannin and LY294002 to interfere with priming (Martin et al 1997) and by the ability of phospholipase Cδ to inhibit exocytosis from ATP-primed cells (Hay et al 1995). In addition, introduction of PtdIns 4,5-P_2 but not PtdIns 3,4,5-P_3 micelles into permeable cells selectively interfered with regulated exocytosis presumably by competing with endogenous effectors for the phosphoinositides (Martin et al 1997). The essential role of the intact PtdIns 4,5-P_2 lipid, rather than a derived metabolite, was suggested by the failure of all potential metabolites tested to significantly alter exocytosis in the absence or presence of Ca^{2+} (Hay et al 1995, Martin et al 1997) and the ability of a PtdIns 4,5-P_2 antibody to inhibit exocytosis from ATP-primed cells (Hay et al 1995).

A requirement for PtdIns 4,5-P_2 in regulated exocytosis raises a number of questions concerning the identity of the membrane where critical pools of phosphoinositides are generated and the function of these phosphoinositides in exocytosis. Recent immunocytochemical studies with PtdIns 4,5-P_2 specific antibodies conducted with permeable PC12 cells indicate that high concentrations of PtdIns 4,5-P_2 are synthesized on secretory granule membranes during ATP-dependent priming (K Loyet, personal communication). There have been few direct studies of the biophysical effects of PtdIns 4,5-P_2 in membrane bilayers, but it is likely that the highly charged hydrophilic headgroup would confer properties on a membrane that are antagonistic to fusion. The strong positive curvature imparted to the membrane might destabilize a stalk intermediate envisioned for bilayer fusion (Chernomordik 1996). It is likely that PtdIns 4,5-P_2 in the granule membrane would need to be segregated into domains in order to allow fusion to proceed. Such segregation could be mediated by protein binding to PtdIns 4,5-P_2, as was demonstrated for a lysine-rich peptide in liposomes (Glaser et al 1996). An analogous process on the secretory granule could recruit a PtdIns 4,5-P_2-binding protein to the membrane that is essential for subsequent Ca^{2+}-triggered fusion events.

A small number of proteins, including dynamin, CapZ, and CAPS, have been characterized that exhibit a specificity for binding D4 phosphoinositides over D3 phosphoinositides (Table 1). The CAPS protein was discovered as a factor that reconstitutes regulated secretion in permeable PC12 cells at the Ca^{2+}-dependent fusion step that follows ATP-dependent priming (Walent et al 1992, Ann et al 1997). Liposome binding and proteolysis studies indicate that CAPS interacts with D4 but not D3 phosphoinositides and that binding of PtdIns 4,5-P_2 promotes a conformational change (Loyet et al 1998). These observations suggest that CAPS may be an effector for PtdIns 4,5-P_2 in regulated exocytosis in neural and endocrine cells. CAPS copurifies with dense-core vesicles and plasma membrane from brain tissue (Berwin et al 1998). A model in which CAPS on vesicles and plasma membrane undergoes a conformational change in response to PtdIns 4,5-P_2 synthesis on the vesicle has been proposed (Loyet et al

1998). This could serve the purpose of segregating PtdIns 4,5-P_2 on the vesicle and promoting the close apposition of the vesicle to the plasma membrane for fusion (Figure 2*f*).

PtdIns 4,5-P_2 functions in the regulated exocytosis of granules in cells of hemapoietic origin as well. GTPγS-stimulated hexosaminidase secretion in permeable HL60 cells requires the cytosolic factors ARF and PtdIns transfer protein (Fensome et al 1996). It was suggested that the synthesis of PtdIns 4,5-P_2, either activated by PtdIns transfer protein through a PtdIns 4-kinase/PtdIns 4-P 5-kinase pathway, or by ARF via PLD production of phosphatidic acid and stimulation of PtdIns 4-P 5-kinase, was the common factor essential for exocytosis. Phosphoinositide-binding proteins that mediate the essential role of PtdIns 4,5-P_2 in regulated exocytosis in hemapoietic cells, which do not express CAPS, have not been identified.

Based on in vitro phosphoinositide-binding studies, additional potential effectors for PtdIns 4,5-P_2 in regulated exocytosis have been suggested. Genetic and biochemical evidence indicates that synaptotagmin I, an abundant secretory vesicle protein, is an essential component of the Ca^{2+}-sensing mechanism in the regulated exocytosis of synaptic vesicles in nerve cells (Sudhof 1995). Synaptotagmin I interacts with phosphoinositides via its membrane distal C2B domain, and Ca^{2+} increases binding to PtdIns 4,5-P_2 but decreases binding to PtdIns 3,4,5-P_3 (Schiavo et al 1996). It was suggested that the Ca^{2+}-dependent switching of synaptotagmin from a preference for binding PtdIns 3,4,5-P_3 to binding PtdIns 4,5-P_2 may be part of a vesicle docking mechanism that is activated by Ca^{2+} at concentrations below those required for fusion (Schiavo et al 1996). The distribution of PtdIns 3,4,5-P_3 and PtdIns 4,5-P_2 in synaptic terminals will need to be established to evaluate this model. If synaptic vesicles, like dense-core vesicles, synthesize high concentrations of PtdIns 4,5-P_2, the effect of Ca^{2+} may be to promote the association of the membrane distal C2B domain of synaptotagmin with the vesicle membrane (Figure 2*f*). This folding of synaptotagmin might unmask the C2A domain for Ca^{2+}-dependent interactions that occur with the presynaptic membrane proteins syntaxin and SNAP-25, which may be essential for fusion (Chapman et al 1995, C Li et al 1995, Schiavo et al 1997). The effects of InsP6 indicate an important role for the C2B domain of synaptotagmin in evoked neurotransmitter release. InsP6 inhibits evoked neurotransmitter release, but this can be prevented by C2B domain antibodies (Fukuda et al 1995b, Ohara-Imaizumi et al 1997). Synaptotagmin I binds InsP6 via its C2B domain (Fukuda et al 1994, 1995b) and InsP6 competitively inhibits C2B domain interactions with phosphoinositides (Schiavo et al 1996). It is possible that InsP6 inhibits evoked neurotransmitter release by interfering with synaptotagmin-phosphoinositide interactions.

An additional component of the exocytotic apparatus suggested to interact with phosphoinositides are the Mint proteins (Okamoto & Sudhof 1997). mUNC18 is a major soluble syntaxin-interacting protein required for neurotransmitter secretion. mUNC18-interacting proteins termed Mints, identified by yeast two-hybrid screening, contain a PTB domain that interacts with PtdIns 4,5-P_2. It was proposed that Mint complexed with mUNC18 may mediate vesicle docking through the binding of Mint to PtdIns 4,5-P_2 on the vesicle and of mUNC18 with syntaxin on the plasma membrane (Figure 2f).

PtdIns 4,5-P_2 formed on secretory vesicles during priming in neuroendocrine cells may also play a role in the endocytic retrieval of the vesicle membrane. The clathrin adaptors AP-2 and AP-3 and dynamin bind polyphosphoinositides (Beck & Keen 1991, Ye et al 1995, Norris et al 1995, Salim et al 1996, Gaidarov et al 1996, Hao et al 1997). Synaptojanin, a phosphoinositide 5-phosphatase, has been suggested to function in endocytosis but its role is unclear (Cremona & DeCamilli 1997). The dynamin GTPase is stimulated by PtdIns 4,5-P_2 binding (Lin & Gilman 1996), suggesting that phosphoinositide hydrolysis might occur following clathrin coating and scission of the coated vesicle by dynamin. Alternatively, because phosphoinositide binding to AP-2 and AP-3 inhibits adaptor-mediated clathrin coat assembly (Beck & Keen 1991, Ye et al 1995, Norris et al 1995), dephosphorylation of phosphoinositides could be a positive signal for clathrin recruitment if it occurred following AP-2 or AP-3 recruitment to the membrane. At present there is no direct evidence for either of these models, and additional studies are required to clarify the roles of phosphoinositides in endocytosis.

PERSPECTIVES

There are now many examples where phosphoinositides have been implicated as essential cofactors or regulators involved in signal transduction, cytoskeletal, and membrane trafficking events. A theme common to each is the role of phosphoinositides as site-specific signals that recruit and/or activate protein effectors to assemble a spatially localized machinery on the membrane that alters a cellular function. Critical gaps in our knowledge, particularly for membrane trafficking events, concern the mechanisms that activate phosphoinositide kinases that specify the site and timing of phosphoinositide signals. Cellular localization studies need to be undertaken to reveal what is predicted to be the highly localized properties of phosphoinositide signaling mechanisms. In vitro studies of protein-phosphoinositide binding and membrane-associated reactions have contributed heavily to our current view of phosphoinositides as site-specific membrane signals, and the major future challenge is to test the validity of these models on the role of phosphoinositides in vivo. Particularly important will be the determination of whether phosphoinositide binding is critical for the function of numerous effector proteins that are proposed to function downstream of phosphoinositide kinase reactions.

Visit the *Annual Reviews* home page at
http://www.AnnualReviews.org

Literature Cited

Alessi DR, Deak M, Casamyor A, Caudwell FB, Morrice N, et al. 1997. 3-phosphoinositide-dependent protein kinase-1 (PDK1): structural and functional homology with the *Drosophila* DSTPK61 kinase. *Curr. Biol.* 7:776–89

Amano M, Ito M, Kimura K, Fukata Y, Chihara K, et al. 1996. Phosphorylation and activation of myosin by Rho-associated kinase. *J. Biol. Chem.* 271:20246–49

Andjelkovic M, Alessi DR, Meier R, Fernandez A, Lamb NJC, et al. 1997. Role of translocation in the activation and function of protein kinase B. *J. Biol. Chem.* 272:31515–24

Ann K, Kowalchyk JA, Loyet KM, Martin TFJ. 1997. Novel Ca^{2+}-binding protein (CAPS) related to UNC-31 required for Ca^{2+}-activated exocytosis. *J. Biol. Chem.* 272:19637–40

Artalejo CR, Lemmon MA, Schlessinger J, Palfrey HC. 1997. Specific role for the PH domain of dynamin 1 in the regulation of rapid endocytosis in adrenal chromaffin cells. *EMBO J.* 16:1565–74

Balla T, Downing GJ, Jaffe H, Kim S, Zolyomi A, Catt KJ. 1997. Isolation and molecular cloning of wortmannin-sensitive bovine type III phosphatidylinositol 4-kinases. *J. Biol. Chem.* 272:18358–66

Beck KA, Keen JH. 1991. Interaction of phosphoinositide cycle intermediates with the plasma membrane-associated clathrin assembly protein AP-2. *J. Biol. Chem.* 266:4442–47

Berditchevski F, Tolias KF, Wong K, Carpenter CL, Hemler ME. 1997. A novel link between integrins, transmembrane 4 superfamily proteins and phosphatidylinositol 4-kinase. *J. Biol. Chem.* 272:2595–98

Berridge MJ, Irvine RF. 1984. Inositol trisphosphate, a novel second messenger in cellular signal transduction. *Nature* 312:315–21

Berwin B, Floor E, Martin TFJ. 1998. CAPS (mammalian UNC-31) protein localizes to membranes involved in dense-core vesicle exocytosis. *Neuron.* In press

Bi K, Roth MG, Ktistakis NT. 1997. Phosphatidic acid formation by phospholipase D is required for transport from the endoplasmic reticulum to the Golgi complex. *Curr. Biol.* 7:301–7

Boronenkov IV, Anderson RA. 1995. The sequence of phosphatidylinositol 4-phosphate 5-kinase defines a novel family of lipid kinases. *J. Biol. Chem.* 270:2881–84

Brown HA, Gutowski S, Moomaw CR, Slaughter C, Sternweis PC. 1993. ADP-ribosylation factor, a small GTP-dependent regulatory protein, stimulates phospholipase D activity. *Cell* 75:1137–44

Brown WJ, DeWald DB, Emr SD, Plutner H, Balch WE. 1995. Role for phosphatidylinositol 3-kinase in the sorting and transport of newly synthesized lysosomal enzymes in mammalian cells. *J. Cell Biol.* 130:781–96

Carpenter CL, Cantley LC. 1990. Phosphoinositide kinases. *Biochemistry* 29:11147–56

Carpenter CL, Cantley LC. 1996. Phosphoinositide kinases. *Curr. Opin. Cell Biol.* 8:153–58

Carpenter CL, Tolias KF, Couvillon AC, Hartwig JH. 1997. Signal transduction pathways involving the small G proteins Rac and Cdc42 and phosphoinositide kinases. *Adv. Enzyme Regul.* 37:377–90

Castellino AM, Parker GJ, Boronenkov IV, Anderson RA, Chao MV. 1997. A novel interaction between the juxtamembrane region of the p55 tumor necrosis factor receptor and phosphatidylinositol 4-phosphate 5-kinase. *J. Biol. Chem.* 272:5861–70

Cerione RA, Zheng Y. 1996. The Dbl family of oncogenes. *Curr. Opin. Cell Biol.* 8:216–22

Chapman ER, Hanson PI, An S, Jahn R. 1995. Ca^{2+} regulates the interaction between synaptotagmin and syntaxin I. *J. Biol. Chem.* 270:23667–71

Chen Y-G, Shields D. 1996. ADP-ribosylation factor-1 stimulates formation of nascent secretory vesicles from the *trans*-Golgi network of endocrine cells. *J. Biol. Chem.* 271:5297–300

Chen Y-G, Siddhanta A, Austin CD, Hammond SM, Sung T-C, et al. 1997. Phospholipase D stimulates release of nascent secretory vesicles from the *trans*-Golgi network. *J. Cell Biol.* 138:495–504

Chernomordik L. 1996. Non-bilayer lipids and

biological fusion intermediates. *Chem. Phys. Lipids* 81:203–13

Chong LD, Traynor-Kaplan A, Bokoch GM, Schwartz MA. 1994. The small GTP-binding protein rho regulates a phosphatidylinositol 4-phosphate 5-kinase in mammalian cells. *Cell* 79:507–13

Chung J-K, Sekiya F, Kang H-S, Lee C, Han J-S, et al. 1997. Synaptotagmin inhibition of phospholipase D activity by hydrolysis of phosphatidylinositol 4,5-bisphosphate. *J. Biol. Chem.* 272:15980–85

Clague MJ, Thorpe C, Jones AT. 1995. Phosphatidylinositol 3-kinase regulation of fluid phase endocytosis. *FEBS Lett.* 367:272–74

Cockcroft S, Thomas GM, Fensome A, Geny B, Cunningham E, et al. 1994. Phospholipase D: a downstream effector of ARF in granulocytes. *Science* 263:523–26

Cohen P, Alessi DR, Cross DAE. 1997. PDK1, one of the missing links in insulin signal transduction? *FEBS Lett.* 410:3–10

Conibear E, Stevens TH. 1995. Vacuolar biogenesis in yeast: sorting out the sorting proteins. *Cell* 83:513–16

Cullen PJ, Hsuan JJ, Truong O, Letcher AJ, Jackson TR, et al. 1995. Identification of a specific Ins(1,3,4,5)P_4-binding protein as a member of the GAP1 family. *Nature* 376:527–30

Cremona O, DeCamilli P. 1997. Synaptic vesicle endocytosis. *Curr. Opin. Neurobiol.* 7:323–30

Cross MJ, Stewart A, Hodgkin MN, Kerr DJ, Wakelam MJO. 1995. Wortmannin and its structural analogue demethoxviridin inhibit stimulated phospholipase A2 activity in Swiss 3T3 cells. *J. Biol. Chem.* 270:25352–55

Davidson HW. 1995. Wortmannin causes mistargeting of procathepsin D. Evidence for the involvement of a phosphatidylinositol 3-kinase in vesicular transport to lysosomes. *J. Cell Biol.* 130:797–805

DeCamilli P, Emr SD, McPherson PS, Novick P. 1996. Phosphoinositides as regulators in membrane traffic. *Science* 271:1533–39

del Peso L, Gonzales-Garcia M, Page C, Herrera R, Nunez G. 1997. Interleukin 3-induced phosphorylation of BAD through the protein kinase Akt. *Science* 278:687–89

Del Vecchio RL, Pilch PF. 1991. Phosphatidylinositol 4-kinase is a component of glucose transporter (GLUT 4)-containing vesicles. *J. Biol. Chem.* 266:13278–83

Dittie AS, Hajibagheri N, Tooze SA. 1996. The AP-1 adaptor complex binds to immature secretory granules from PC12 cells and is regulated by ADP-ribosylation factor. *J. Cell Biol.* 132:523–36

Domin J, Waterfield MD. 1997. Using structure to define the function of phosphoinositide 3-kinase family members. *FEBS Lett.* 410:91–95

Dove SK, Cooke FT, Douglas MR, Sayers LG, Parker PJ, Michell RH. 1997. Osmotic stress activates phosphatidylinositol 3,5-bisphosphate synthesis. *Nature* 390:187–92

Downing GJ, Kim S, Nakanishi S, Catt KJ, Balla T. 1996. Characterization of a soluble adrenal phosphatidylinositol 4-kinase reveals wortmannin sensitivity of type III phosphatidylinositol kinases. *Biochemistry* 35:3587–94

Eberhard DA, Cooper CL, Low MG, Holz RW. 1990. Evidence that the inositol phospholipids are necessary for exocytosis. *Biochem. J.* 268:15–25

Fensome A, Cunningham E, Prosser S, Tan SK, Swigart P, et al. 1996. ARF and PITP restore GTPγS-stimulated protein secretion from granulocytic HL60 cells depleted of cytosol by promoting PIP2 synthesis. *Curr. Biol.* 6:730–38

Ferguson KM, Lemmon MA, Schlessinger J, Sigler PB. 1995. Structure of the high affinity complex of inositol trisphosphate with a phospholipase C pleckstrin homology domain. *Cell* 83:1037–46

Fleischer B, Xie J, Mayrleitner M, Shears SB, Palmer DJ, et al. 1994. Golgi coatomer binds and forms K^+-selective channels gated by inositol polyphosphates. *J. Biol. Chem.* 269:17826–32

Franke TF, Kaplan DR, Cantley LC, Toker A. 1997. Direct regulation of the Akt proto-oncogene product by phosphatidylinositol-3,4-bisphosphate. *Science* 275:665–68

Frech M, Andjelkovic M, Ingley E, Reddy KK, Falck JR, Hemmings BA. 1997. High affinity binding of inositol phosphates and phosphoinositides to the pleckstrin homology domain of RAC/protein kinase B and their influence on kinase activity. *J. Biol. Chem.* 272:8474–81

Frevert EU, Kahn BB. 1997. Differential effects of constitutively active PI 3-kinase on glucose transport, glycogen synthase activity and DNA synthesis in 3T3-L1 adipocytes. *Mol. Cell. Biol.* 17:190–98

Fukami K, Endo T, Imamura M, Takenawa T. 1994. α-actinin and vinculin are PIP2-binding proteins involved in signaling by tyrosine kinase. *J. Biol. Chem.* 269:1518–22

Fukami K, Matsuoka K, Nakanishi O, Yamakawa A, Kawai S, Takenawa T. 1988. Antibody to phosphatidylinositol 4,5-bisphosphate inhibits oncogene-induced mitogenesis. *Proc. Natl. Acad. Sci. USA* 85:9057–61

Fukami K, Sawada N, Endo T, Takenawa T. 1996. Identification of a phosphatidylinositol 4,5-bisphosphate binding site in chicken skeletal muscle α-actinin. *J. Biol. Chem.* 271: 2646–50

Fukuda M, Aruga J, Niinobe M, Aimoto S, Mikoshiba K. 1994. Inositol 1,3,4,5-tetrakisphosphate binding to C2B domain of IP4BP/synaptotagmin II. *J. Biol. Chem.* 269:29206–11

Fukuda M, Kojima T, Aruga J, Niinobe M, Mikoshiba K. 1995a. Functional diversity of C2 domains of synaptotagmin family. *J. Biol. Chem.* 270:26523–27

Fukuda M, Moreira JE, Lewis FMT, Sugimori M, Niinobe M, et al. 1995b. Role of the C2B domain of synaptotagmin in vesicular release and recycling as determined by specific antibody injection into the squid giant synapse preterminal. *Proc. Natl. Acad. Sci. USA* 92:10708–12

Gaffet P, Jones AT, Clague MJ. 1997. Inhibition of calcium-independent mannose 6-phosphate receptor incorporation into *trans*-Golgi network-derived clathrin-coated vesicles by wortmannin. *J. Biol. Chem.* 272: 24170–75

Gaidarov I, Chen Q, Falck JR, Reddy KK, Keen JH. 1996. A functional phosphatidylinositol 3,4,5-trisphosphate/phosphoinositide-binding domain in the clathrin adaptor AP-2 α subunit. *J. Biol. Chem.* 271:20922–9

Garcia P, Gupta R, Shah S, Morris AJ, Rudge SA, et al. 1995. The pleckstrin homology domain of phospholipase C-δ₁ binds with high affinity to phosphatidylinositol 4,5-bisphosphate in bilayer membranes. *Biochemistry* 34:16228–34

Gehrmann T, Vereb G, Schmidt M, Klix D, Meyer HE, et al. 1996. Identification of a 200 kD polypeptide as type 3 phosphatidylinositol 4-kinase from bovine brain by partial protein and cDNA sequencing. *Biochim. Biophys. Acta* 1311:53–63

Gibson TJ, Hyvonen M, Musacchio A, Saraste M, Birney E. 1994. PH domain: the first anniversary. *Trends Biochem. Sci.* 19:349–53

Gilmore AP, Burridge K. 1996. Regulation of vinculin binding to talin and actin by phosphatidylinositol 4,5-bisphosphate. *Nature* 381:531–35

Glaser M, Wanaski S, Buser CA, Boguslavsky V, Rashidzada W, et al. 1996. Myristoylated alanine-rich C kinase substrate (MARCKS) produces reversible inhibition of phospholipase C by sequestering phosphatidylinositol 4,5-bisphosphate in lateral domains. *J. Biol. Chem.* 271:26187–93

Grado C, Ballou CE. 1960. Myo-inositol phosphates from beef brain phosphoinositide. *J. Biol. Chem.* 235:PC23–24

Hall A. 1998. Rho GTPases and the actin cytoskeleton. *Science* 279:509–14

Hammond SM, Jenco JM, Nakashima S, Cadwallader K, Gu Q, et al. 1997. Characterization of two alternatively spliced forms of phospholipase D1. *J. Biol. Chem.* 272:3860–68

Hammonds-Odie LP, Jackson TR, Profit AA, Blader IJ, Turck CW, et al. 1996. Identification and cloning of centaurin-α. *J. Biol. Chem.* 271:18859–68

Hao W, Tan Z, Prasad K, Reddy KK, Chen J, et al. 1997. Regulation of AP-3 function by inositides. Identification of phosphatidylinositol 3,4,5-trisphosphate as a potent ligand. *J. Biol. Chem.* 272:6393–98

Harlan JE, Hajduk PJ, Yoon HS, Fesik SW. 1994. Pleckstrin homology domains bind to phosphatidylinositol 4,5-bisphosphate. *Nature* 371:168–70

Hartwig JH, Bokoch GM, Carpenter CL, Janmey PA, Taylor LA, et al. 1995. Thrombin receptor ligation and activated Rac uncap actin filament barbed ends through phosphoinositide synthesis in permeabilized human platelets. *Cell* 82:643–53

Hartwig JH, Kung S, Kovacsovics T, Janmey PA, Cantley LC, et al. 1996. D3 phosphoinositides and outside-in integrin signaling by glycoprotein IIb-IIIa mediate platelet actin assembly and filopodial extension induced by phorbol 12-myristate 13-acetate. *J. Biol. Chem.* 271:32986–93

Haruta T, Morris AJ, Rose DW, Nelson JG, Meuckler M, Olefsky JM. 1995. Insulin-stimulated GLUT4 translocation is mediated by a divergent intracellular signaling pathway. *J. Biol. Chem.* 270:27991–94

Hay JC, Fisette PL, Jenkin GH, Fukami K, Takenawa T. 1995. ATP-dependent inositide phosphorylation is required for Ca²⁺-activated exocytosis. *Nature* 374:173–77

Hay JC, Martin TFJ. 1992. Resolution of regulated secretion into sequential MgATP-dependent and calcium-dependent stages mediated by distinct cytosolic proteins. *J. Cell Biol.* 119:139–51

Hay JC, Martin TFJ. 1993. Phosphatidylinositol transfer protein required for ATP-dependent priming of Ca²⁺-activated secretion. *Nature* 366:572–75

Hemmings BA. 1997. PH domains-a universal membrane adapter. *Science* 275:1899

Hickinson DM, Lucocq JM, Towler MC, Clough S, James J, et al. 1997. Association of a phosphatidylinositol-specific 3-kinase with a human *trans*-Golgi network resident protein. *Curr. Biol.* 7:987–90

Hope HR, Pike LJ. 1996. Phosphoinositides and phosphoinositide-utilizing enzymes in detergent-insoluble lipid domains. *Mol. Biol. Cell* 7:843–51

Horazdovsky BF, DeWald DB, Emr SD. 1995.

Protein transport to the yeast vacuole. *Curr. Opin. Cell Biol.* 7:544–51

Horiuchi H, Lippe R, McBride HM, Rubino M, Woodman P, et al. 1997. A novel Rab5 GDP/GTP exchange factor complexed to Rabaptin-5 links nucleotide exchange to effector recruitment and function. *Cell* 90:1149–59

Hyvonen M, Macias MJ, Nilges M, Oschkinat H, Saraste M, et al. 1995. Structure of the binding site for inositol phosphates in a PH domain. *EMBO J.* 14:4676–85

Ishihari H, Shibasaki Y, Kizuki N, Katagiri H, Yazaki Y, et al. 1996. Cloning of cDNAs encoding two isoforms of 68 kD type I phosphatidylinositol 4-phosphate 5-kinase. *J. Biol. Chem.* 271:23611–64

Janmey PA. 1994. Phosphoinositides and calcium as regulators of cellular actin assembly and disassembly. *Annu. Rev. Physiol.* 56:169–91

Janmey PA, Lamb J, Allen PG, Matsudaira PT. 1992. Phosphoinositide-binding peptides derived from the sequences of gelsolin and villin. *J. Biol. Chem.* 267:11818–23

Jenkins GH, Fisette PL, Anderson RA. 1994. Type I phosphatidylinositol 4-phosphate 5-kinase isoforms are specifically stimulated by phosphatidic acid. *J. Biol. Chem.* 269:11547–54

Jones AT, Clague MJ. 1995. Phosphatidylinositol 3-kinase activity is required for early endosome fusion. *Biochem. J.* 311:31–34

Jones SM, Crosby JR, Salamero J, Howell KE. 1993. A cytosolic complex of p62 and rab6 associates with TGN38/41 and is involved in budding of exocytic vesicles from the *trans*-Golgi network. *J. Cell Biol.* 122:775–88

Jones SM, Howell KE. 1997. Phosphatidylinositol 3-kinase is required for the formation of constitutive transport vesicles from the TGN. *J. Cell Biol.* 139:339–49

Kauffmann-Zeh A, Klinger R, Endemann G, Waterfield MD, Wetzker R, et al. 1994. Regulation of human type II phosphatidylinositol kinase activity by epidermal growth factor-dependent phosphorylation and receptor association. *J. Biol. Chem.* 269:31243–51

Kimura K, Ito M, Amano M, Chihara K, Fukata Y, et al. 1996. Regulation of myosin phosphatase by Rho and Rho-associated kinase. *Science* 273:245–48

Kirchhausen T, Bonifacino JS, Riezman H. 1997. Linking cargo to vesicle formation: receptor tail interactions with coat proteins. *Curr. Opin. Cell Biol.* 9:488–95

Klarlund JK, Guilherme A, Holik JJ, Virbasius JV, Chawla A, Czech MP. 1997. Signaling by phosphoinositide 3,4,5-trisphosphate through proteins containing pleckstrin and Sec7 homology domains. *Science* 275:1927–30

Klarlund JK, Rameh LE, Cantley LC, Buxton JM, Holik JJ. 1998. Regulation of GRP1-catalyzed ADP ribosylation factor guanine nucleotide exchange by phosphatidylinositol 3,4,5-trisphosphate. *J. Biol. Chem.* 273:1859–62

Klippel A, Kavanaugh WM, Pot D, Williams LT. 1997. A specific product of phosphatidylinositol 3-kinase directly activates the protein kinase Akt through its pleckstrin homology domain. *Mol. Cell. Biol.* 17:338–44

Kohn AD, Summers SA, Birnbaum MJ, Roth RA. 1996. Expression of a constitutively active Akt Ser/Thr kinase in 3T3-L1 adipocytes stimulates glucose uptake and glucose transporter 4 translocation. *J. Biol. Chem.* 271:31372–78

Ktistakis NT, Brown HA, Waters MG, Sternweis PC, Roth MG. 1996. Evidence that phospholipase D mediates ADP ribosylation factor-dependent formation of Golgi coated vesicles. *J. Cell Biol.* 134:295–306

Kubiseski TJ, Chook YM, Parris WE, Rozakis-Adcock M, Pawson T. 1997. High affinity binding of the pleckstrin homology domain of mSos1 to phosphatidylinositol 4,5-bisphosphate. *J. Biol. Chem.* 272:1799–804

Ladinsky MS, Kremer JR, Furcinitti PS, McIntosh JR, Howell KE. 1994. HVEM tomography of the *trans*-Golgi network: structural insights and identification of a lace-like vesicle coat. *J. Cell Biol.* 127:29–38

Lemmon MA, Falsca M, Ferguson KM, Schlessinger J. 1997. Regulatory recruitment of signalling molecules to the cell membrane by pleckstrin-homology domains. *Trends Cell Biol.* 7:237–42

Lemmon MA, Ferguson KM, Schlessinger J. 1996. PH domains: diverse sequences with a common fold recruit signaling molecules to the cell surface. *Cell* 85:621–24

Li C, Ullrich B, Zhang JZ, Anderson RGW, Borse N, Sudhof TC. 1995a. Ca^{2+}-dependent and -independent activities of neural and non-neural synaptotagmins. *Nature* 375:594–99

Li G, D'Souza-Schorey C, Barbieri MA, Roberts RL, Klippel A, et al. 1995b. Evidence for phosphatidylinositol 3-kinase as a regulator of endocytosis via activation of Rab5. *Proc. Natl. Acad. Sci. USA* 92:10207–11

Lin HC, Gilman AG. 1996. Regulation of dynamin I GTPase activity by G protein $\beta\gamma$ subunits and phosphatidylinositol 4,5-bisphosphate. *J. Biol. Chem.* 271:27979–82

Liscovitch M, Cantley LC. 1995. Signal transduction and membrane traffic: the PITP/phosphoinositide connection. *Cell* 81:659–62

Liscovitch M, Chalifa V, Pertile P, Chen C-S, Cantley LC. 1994. Novel functions of phosphatidylinositol 4,5-bisphosphate as a cofactor for brain membrane phospholipase D. *J. Biol. Chem.* 269:21403–6

Lockyer PJ, Bottomley JR, Reynolds JS, McNulty TJ, Venkateswarlu K, et al. 1997. Distinct subcellular localizations of the putative inositol 1,3,4,5-tetrakisphosphate receptors GAP1^{IP4BP} and GAP1^m result from the GAP1^{IP4BP} PH domain directing plasma membrane targeting. *Curr. Biol.* 7:1007–10

Loijens JC, Anderson RA. 1996. Type I phosphatidylinositol 4-phosphate 5-kinases are distinct members of this novel lipid kinase family. *J. Biol. Chem.* 271:32937–43

Loyet KM, Kowalchyk JA, Chaudhary A, Chen J, Prestwich GD, Martin TFJ. 1998. Specific binding of phosphatidylinositol 4,5-bisphosphate to CAPS, a potential phosphoinositide effector protein for regulated exocytosis. *J. Biol. Chem.* 273:8337–43

Lu P-J, Chen C-S. 1997. Selective recognition of phosphatidylinositol 3,4,5-trisphosphate by a synthetic peptide. *J. Biol. Chem.* 272: 466–72

Lu P-J, Shieh W-R, Rhee SG, Yin HL, Chen C-S. 1996. Lipid products of phosphoinositide 3-kinase bind human profilin with high affinity. *Biochemistry* 35:14027–34

Macias MJ, Musacchio A, Ponstingl H, Nilges M, Saraste M, et al. 1994. Structure of the pleckstrin homology domain from β-spectrin. *Nature* 369:675–77

Marcusson EG, Horazdovsky BF, Cereghino JL, Gharakhanian E, Emr SD. 1994. The sorting receptor for yeast vacuolar carboxypeptidase Y is encoded by the VPS10 gene. *Cell* 77:579–86

Marks MS, Ohno H, Kirchhausen T, Bonifacino JS. 1997. Protein sorting by tyrosine-based signals: adapting to the Ys and wherefores. *Trends Cell Biol.* 7:124–28

Martin SS, Haruta A, Morris AJ, Klippel A, Williams LT, Olefsky JM. 1996. Activated phosphatidylinositol 3-kinase is sufficient to mediate actin rearrangement and GLUT4 translocation in adipocytes. *J. Biol. Chem.* 271:17605–8

Martin TFJ. 1995. New directions for phosphatidylinositol transfer. *Curr. Biol.* 5:990–92

Martin TFJ. 1997. Phosphoinositides as spatial regulators of membrane traffic. *Curr. Opin. Neurobiol.* 7:331–38

Martin TFJ, Loyet KM, Barry VA, Kowalchyk JA. 1997. The role of PtdIns 4,5-bisphosphate in exocytotic membrane fusion. *Biochem. Soc. Trans.* 25:1137–41

Mehrotra B, Elliott JT, Chen J, Olszewski JD, Profit AA, et al. 1997. Selective photoaffinity labeling of the inositol polyphosphate binding C2B domains of synaptotagmins. *J. Biol. Chem.* 272:4237–44

Meyers R, Cantley LC. 1997. Cloning and characterization of a wortmannin-sensitive human phosphatidylinositol 4-kinase. *J. Biol. Chem.* 272:4384–90

Monaco ME, Gershengorn MC. 1992. Subcellular organization of receptor-mediated phosphoinositide turnover. *Endocr. Rev.* 13:707–18

Mu F-T, Callaghan JM, Steele-Mortimer O, Stenmark H, Parton RG, et al. 1995. EEA1, an early endosome-associated protein. *J. Biol. Chem.* 270:13503–11

Musacchio A, Gibson T, Rice P, Thompson J, Saraste M. 1993. The PH domain: a common piece in the structural patchwork of signalling proteins. *Trends Biochem. Sci.* 18:343–48

Nakagawa T, Goto K, Kondo H. 1996a. Cloning, expression and localization of 230 kD phosphatidylinositol 4-kinase. *J. Biol. Chem.* 271: 12088–94

Nakagawa T, Goto K, Kondo H. 1996b. Cloning and characterization of a 92 kD soluble phosphatidylinositol 4-kinase. *Biochem. J.* 320:643–49

Nakajima Y, Pfeffer SR. 1997. Phosphatidylinositol 3-kinase is not required for recycling of mannose 6-phosphate receptors from late endosomes to the *trans*-Golgi network. *Mol. Biol. Cell* 8:577–82

Norris FA, Ungewickell E, Majerus PW. 1995. Inositol hexakisphosphate binds to clathrin assembly protein 3 and inhibits clathrin cage assembly in vitro. *J. Biol. Chem.* 270:214–17

Ohara-Imaizumi M, Fukuda M, Niinobe M, Misonou H, Ikeda K, et al. 1997. Distinct roles of C2A and C2B domains of synaptotagmin in the regulation of exocytosis in adrenal chromaffin cells. *Proc. Natl. Acad. Sci. USA* 94:287–91

Ohashi M, DeVries KJ, Frank R, Snoek GT, Bankaitis VA, et al. 1995. A role for the phosphatidylinositol transfer protein in secretory vesicle formation. *Nature* 377:544–47

Okamoto M, Sudhof TC. 1997. Mints, Munc18-interacting proteins in synaptic vesicle exocytosis. *J. Biol. Chem.* 272:31459–64

Olsson H, Martinez-Arias W, Drobak BK, Jergil B. 1995. Presence of a novel form of phosphatidylinositol 4-kinase in rat liver. *FEBS Lett.* 361:282–86

Orci L, Palmer DJ, Amherdt M, Rothman JE. 1993. Coated vesicle assembly in the Golgi requires only coatomer and ARF proteins from the cytosol. *Nature* 364:732–34

Paris S, Beraud-Dufour S, Robineau S, Bigay J, Antonny B, et al. 1997. Role of protein-phospholipid interactions in the activation of

ARF1 by the guanine nucleotide exchange factor Arno. *J. Biol. Chem.* 272:22221–26

Patki V, Virbasius J, Lane WS, Toh BH, Shpetner HS, Corvera S. 1997. Identification of an early endosomal protein regulated by phosphatidylinositol 3-kinase. *Proc. Natl. Acad. Sci. USA* 94:7326–30

Pertile P, Cantley LC. 1995. Type 2 phosphatidylinositol 4-kinase is recruited to CD4 in response to CD4 cross-linking. *Biochim. Biophys. Acta* 1248:129–40

Pike L. 1992. Phosphatidylinositol 4-kinases and the role of polyphosphoinositides in cellular regulation. *Endocr. Rev.* 13:692–706

Pike LJ, Casey L. 1996. Localization and turnover of phosphatidylinositol 4,5-bisphosphate in caveolin-enriched membrane domains. *J. Biol. Chem.* 271:26453–56

Pitcher JA, Touhara K, Payne ES, Lefkowitz RJ. 1995. Pleckstrin homology domain-mediated membrane association and activation of the β-adrenergic receptor kinase requires coordinate interaction with the G βγ subunits and lipid. *J. Biol. Chem.* 270:11707–10

Rameh LE, Arvidsson A, Carraway KL, Couvillon AD, Rathbun G, et al. 1997a. A comparative analysis of the phosphoinositide binding specificity of pleckstrin homology domains. *J. Biol. Chem.* 272:22059–66

Rameh LE, Tolias KF, Duckworth BC, Cantley LC. 1997b. A new pathway for synthesis of phosphatidylinositol 4,5-bisphosphate. *Nature* 390:192–96

Randazzo PA. 1997. Functional interaction of ADP-ribosylation factor 1 with phosphatidylinositol 4,5-bisphosphate. *J. Biol. Chem.* 272:7688–92

Rapoport I, Miyazaki M, Boll W, Duckworth B, Cantley LC, et al. 1997. Regulatory interactions in the recognition of endocytic sorting signals by AP-2 complexes. *EMBO J.* 16:2240–50

Reaves B, Bright N, Mullock B, Luzio J. 1996. The effect of wortmannin on the localization of lysosomal type I integral membrane glycoproteins suggests a role for phosphoinositide 3-kinase activity in regulating membrane traffic late in the endocytic pathway. *J. Cell Sci.* 109:749–62

Reif K, Nobes CD, Thomas G, Hall A, Cantrell DA. 1996. Phosphatidylinositol 3-kinase signals activate a selective subset of Rac/Rho-dependent effector pathways. *Curr. Biol.* 6:1445–55

Ren X-D, Bokoch GM, Traynor-Kaplan A, Jenkins GH, Anderson RA, et al. 1996. Physical association of the small GTPase rho with a 68 kD phosphatidylinositol 4-phosphate 5-kinase in Swiss 3T3 cells. *Mol. Biol. Cell.* 7:435–42

Rhee SG, Bae YS. 1997. Regulation of phosphoinositide-specific phospholipase C isozymes. *J. Biol. Chem.* 272:15045–48

Robinson MS. 1997. Coats and vesicle budding. *Trends Cell Biol.* 7:99–102

Roth MG, Sternweis PC. 1997. The role of lipid signaling in constitutive membrane traffic. *Curr. Opin. Cell Biol.* 9:519–26

Rothman JE, Wieland FT. 1996. Protein sorting by transport vesicles. *Science* 272:227–34

Sakisaka T, Itoh T, Miura K, Takenawa T. 1997. Phosphatidylinositol 4,5-bisphosphate phosphatase regulates the rearrangement of actin filaments. *Mol. Cell. Biol.* 17:3841–49

Salim K, Bottomley MJ, Querfurth E, Zvelebil MJ, Gout I, et al. 1996. Distinct specificity in the recognition of phosphoinositides by the pleckstrin homology domains of dynamin and Bruton's tyrosine kinase. *EMBO J.* 15:6241–50

Schafer DA, Jennings PB, Cooper JA. 1996. Dynamics of capping protein and actin assembly in vitro: uncapping barbed ends by polyphosphoinositides. *J. Cell Biol.* 135:169–79

Schekman R, Orci L. 1996. Coat proteins and vesicle budding. *Science* 271:1526–33

Schiavo G, Gu Q-M, Prestwich GD, Sollner TH, Rothman JE. 1996. Calcium-dependent switching of the specificity of phosphoinositide binding to synaptotagmin. *Proc. Natl. Acad. Sci. USA* 93:13327–32

Schiavo G, Stenbeck G, Rothman JE, Sollner TH. 1997. Binding of the synaptic vesicle v-SNARE, synaptotagmin, to the plasma membrane t-SNARE, SNAP-25, can explain docked vesicles at neurotoxin-treated synapses. *Proc. Natl. Acad. Sci. USA* 94:997–1001

Schu PV, Takegawa K, Fry MJ, Stack JH, Waterfield MD, Emr SD. 1993. Phosphatidylinositol 3-kinase encoded by a yeast Vps34 gene essential for protein sorting. *Science* 260:88–91

Shepherd PR, Reaves BJ, Davidson HW. 1996. Phosphoinositide 3-kinases and membrane traffic. *Trends Cell Biol.* 6:92–97

Shibasaki Y, Ishihara H, Kizuki N, Asano T, Oka Y, Yazaki Y. 1997. Massive actin polymerization induced by phosphatidylinositol-4-phosphate 5-kinase in vivo. *J. Biol. Chem.* 272:7578–81

Shpetner H, Joly M, Hartley D, Corvera S. 1996. Potential sites of PI-3 kinase function in the endocytic pathway revealed by the PI-3 kinase inhibitor wortmannin. *J. Cell Biol.* 132:595–605

Smith CD, Chang KJ. 1989. Regulation of brain phosphatidylinositol 4-phosphate kinase by GTP analogues. *J. Biol. Chem.* 264:320–10

Sohn RH, Chen J, Koblan KS, Bray PF,

Goldschmidt-Clermont PJ. 1995. Localization of a binding site for phosphatidylinositol 4,5-bisphosphate on human profilin. *J. Biol. Chem.* 270:2114–20

Stack JH, Emr SD. 1994. Vps34p required for yeast vacuolar protein sorting is a multiple specificity kinase that exhibits both protein kinase and phosphatidylinositol-specific PI 3-kinase activities. *J. Biol. Chem.* 269:31552–62

Stack JH, Herman PK, Schu PV, Emr SD. 1993. A membrane-associated complex containing the Vps15 protein kinase and the Vps34 PI 3-kinase is essential for protein sorting to the yeast lysosome-like vacuole. *EMBO J.* 12:2195–204

Stack JH, Horazdovsky B, Emr SD. 1995. Receptor-mediated protein sorting to the vacuole in yeast. *Annu. Rev. Cell Dev. Biol.* 11:1–33

Stamnes MA, Rothman JE. 1993. The binding of AP-1 clathrin adaptor particles to Golgi membranes requires ADP-ribosylation factor, a small GTP-binding protein. *Cell* 73:999–1005

Stephens L, Anderson K, Stokoe D, Erdjument-Bromage H, Painter GF, et al. 1998. Protein kinase B kinases that mediate phosphatidylinositol 3,4,5-trisphosphate-dependent activation of protein kinase B. *Science* 279:710–14

Stephens L, Cooke FT, Walters R, Jackson T, Volinia S, et al. 1994. Characterization of a phosphatidylinositol-specific phosphoinositide 3-kinase from mammalian cells. *Curr. Biol.* 4:203–14

Stokoe D, Stephens LR, Copeland T, Gaffney PRJ, Reese CB, et al. 1997. Dual role of phosphatidylinositol-3,4,5-trisphosphate in the activation of protein kinase B. *Science* 277:567–70

Stubbs EB, Kelleher JA, Sun GY. 1988. Phosphatidylinositol kinase, phosphatidylinositol 4-phosphate kinase and diacylglycerol kinase activities in rat brain subcellular fractions. *Biochim. Biophys. Acta* 958:247–54

Sudhof TC. 1995. The synaptic vesicle cycle: a cascade of protein-protein interactions. *Nature* 375:645–53

Sutton RB, Davletov BA, Berghuis AM, Sudhof TC, Sprang SR. 1995. Structure of the first C2 domain of synaptotagmin I: a novel Ca^{2+}/phospholipid-binding fold. *Cell* 80:929–38

Tanaka K, Imajoh-Ohmi S, Sawada T, Shirai R, Hashimoto Y. et al. 1997. A target of phosphatidylinositol 3,4,5-trisphosphate with a zinc finger motif similar to that of the ADP-ribosylation-factor GTPase-activating protein and two pleckstrin homology domains. *Eur. J. Biochem.* 245:512–19

Tapon N, Hall A. 1997. Rho, rac and Cdc42 GTPases regulate the organization of the actin cytoskeleton. *Curr. Opin. Cell Biol.* 9:86–92

Terui T, Kahn RA, Randazzo PA. 1994. Effects of acid phospholipids on nucleotide exchange properties of ADP-ribosylation factor 1. *J. Biol. Chem.* 269:28130–35

Theibert AB, Prestwich GD, Jackson TR, Hammonds-Odie LP. 1997. The purification and assay of inositide-binding proteins. In *Signalling by Inositides: A Practical Approach*, ed. S Shears, pp. 117–50. New York: Oxford Univ. Press

Toker A, Cantley LC. 1997. Signaling through the lipid products of phosphoinositide-3-kinase. *Nature* 387:673–76

Tolias KF, Cantley LC, Carpenter CL. 1995. Rho family GTPases bind to phosphoinositide kinases. *J. Biol. Chem.* 270:17656–59

Tran D, Gascard P, Berthon B, Fukami K, Takenawa T, et al. 1993. Cellular distribution of polyphosphoinositides in rat hepatocytes. *Cell. Signal.* 5:565–81

Traub LM, Kornfeld S. 1997. The *trans*-Golgi network: a late secretory sorting station. *Curr. Opin. Cell Biol.* 9:527–33

Vanhaesebroeck B, Leevers SJ, Panayotou G, Waterfield MD. 1997. Phosphoinositide 3-kinases: a conserved family of signal transducers. *Trends Biochem. Sci.* 22:267–72

Vlahos CJ, Matter WF, Hui KY, Brown RF. 1994. A specific inhibitor of phosphatidylinositol 3-kinase, 2-(4-morpholinyl)-8-phenyl-4-H-1-benzopyran-4-one (LY294002). *J. Biol. Chem.* 269:5241–48

Volinia S, Dhand R, Vanhaesebroeck B, MacDougall LK, Stein R, et al. 1995. A human phosphatidylinositol 3-kinase complex related to the yeast Vps34p-Vps15p protein sorting system. *EMBO J.* 14:3339–48

Voorhout WF, van Genderen IL, Yoshioka T, Fukami K, Geuze HJ, van Meer G. 1992. Subcellular localization of glycolipids as revealed by immuno-electronmicroscopy. *Trends Glycosci. Glycotechnol.* 4:533–46

Walent JH, Porter BW, Martin TFJ. 1992. A novel 145 kd brain cytosolic protein reconstitutes Ca^{2+}-regulated secretion in permeable neuroendocrine cells. *Cell* 70:765–75

West MA, Bright NA, Robinson MS. 1997. The role of ADP-ribosylation factor and phospholipase D in adaptor recruitment. *J. Cell Biol.* 138:1239–54

Whiteford CC, Brearly CA, Ulug ET. 1997. Phosphatidylinositol 3,5-bisphosphate defines a novel PI 3-kinase pathway in resting mouse fibroblasts. *Biochem. J.* 323:597–601

Whitman M, Downes CP, Keeler M, Keller T, Cantley LC. 1988. Type I phosphatidylinositol kinase makes a novel inositol phospholipid, phosphatidylinositol 3-phosphate. *Nature* 332:644–46

Wiedemann C, Schafer T, Burger MM. 1996. Chromaffin granule-associated phosphatidylinositol 4-kinase is required for stimulated secretion. *EMBO J.* 15:2094–101

Wirtz KWA. 1997. Phospholipid transfer proteins revisited. *Biochem. J.* 324:353–60

Wong K, Cantley LC. 1994. Cloning and characterization of a human phosphatidylinositol 4-kinase. *J. Biol. Chem.* 269:28878–84

Wong K, Meyers R, Cantley LC. 1997. Subcellular locations of phosphatidylinositol 4-kinase isoforms. *J. Biol. Chem.* 272:13236–41

Yamamoto A, DeWald DB, Boronenkov IV, Anderson RA, Emr SD, et al. 1995. Novel PI(4)P 5-kinase homologue, Fab1p, essential for normal vacuole function and morphology in yeast. *Mol. Biol. Cell* 6:525–39

Yang J, Clarke JF, Ester CJ, Young PW, Kasuga M, Holman GD. 1996. Phosphatidylinositol 3-kinase acts at an intracellular membrane site to enhance GLUT4 exocytosis in 3T3-L1 cells. *Biochem. J.* 313:125–31

Ye W, Ali N, Bembenek ME, Shears SB, Lafer EM. 1995. Inhibition of clathrin assembly by high affinity binding of specific inositol phosphates to the synapse-specific clathrin assembly protein AP-3. *J. Biol. Chem.* 270:1564–68

Yonezawa N, Homma Y, Yahara I, Sakai H, Nishida E. 1991. A short sequence responsible for both phosphoinositide binding and actin binding activities of cofilin. *J. Biol. Chem.* 266:17218–21

Yoon HS, Hajduk PJ, Petros AM, Olejniczak ET, Meadows RP, et al. 1994. Solution structure of a pleckstrin-homology domain. *Nature* 369:672–75

Yu F-X, Sun H-Q, Janmey PA, Yin HL. 1992. Identification of a polyphosphoinositide-binding sequence in an actin monomer-binding domain of gelsolin. *J. Biol. Chem.* 267:14616–21

Zhang X, Jefferson AB, Auethavekiat V, Majerus P. 1995. The protein deficient in Lowe syndrome is a phosphatidylinositol 4,5-bisphosphate 5-phosphatase. *Proc. Natl. Acad. Sci. USA* 92:4853–56

Zhang X, Hartz PA, Philip E, Racusen LC, Majerus PW. 1998. Cell lines from kidney proximal tubules of a patient with Lowe syndrome lack OCRL inositol polyphosphate 5-phosphatase and accumulate phosphatidylinositol 4,5-bisphosphate. *J. Biol. Chem.* 273:1574–82

Zhang X, Loijens JC, Boronenkov IV, Parker GJ, Norris FA, et al. 1997. Phosphatidylinositol-4-phosphate 5-kinase isozymes catalyze the synthesis of 3-phosphate-containing phosphatidylinositol signaling molecules. *J. Biol. Chem.* 272:17756–61

Zheng J, Cahill SM, Lemmon MA, Fushman D, Schlessinger J, Cowburn D. 1996a. Identification of the binding site for acidic phospholipids on the PH domain of dynamin: implications for stimulation of GTPase activity. *J. Mol. Biol.* 255:14–21

Zheng Y, Glaven JA, Wu WJ, Cerione RA. 1996b. Phosphatidylinositol 4,5-bisphosphate provides an alternative to guanine nucleotide exchange factors by stimulating the dissociation of GDP from Cdc42Hs. *J. Biol. Chem.* 271:23815–19

Annu. Rev. Cell Dev. Biol. 1998. 14:265–303
Copyright © 1998 by Annual Reviews. All rights reserved

MITOCHONDRIAL DYNAMICS IN YEAST

Greg J. Hermann and Janet M. Shaw

Department of Biology, University of Utah, Salt Lake City, Utah 84112;
e-mail: shaw@bioscience.utah.edu

KEY WORDS: organelle inheritance, membrane morphology, fusion, cytoskeleton, GTPase

ABSTRACT

Proteins that control mitochondrial dynamics in yeast are being identified at a rapid pace. These proteins include cytoskeletal elements that regulate organelle distribution and inheritance and several outer membrane proteins that are required to maintain the branched, mitochondrial reticulum. Interestingly, three of the high molecular weight GTPases encoded by the yeast genome are required for mitochondrial integrity and are potential regulators of mitochondrial branching, distribution, and membrane fusion. The recent finding that mtDNA mixing is restricted in the mitochondrial matrix has stimulated the hunt for the molecular machinery that anchors mitochondrial nucleoids in the organelle. Considering that many aspects of mitochondrial structure and behavior are strikingly similar in different cell types, the functional analyses of these yeast proteins should provide general insights into the mechanisms governing mitochondrial dynamics in all eukaryotes.

CONTENTS

265

1081-0706/98/1115-0265$08.00

INTRODUCTION

The mitochondrion is a complex organelle with a double membrane, its own genome, and a separate protein synthetic machinery. A variety of important cellular functions are carried out by the mitochondrial compartment including reactions of the tricarboxylic acid (TCA) cycle, oxidative phosphorylation and ATP production, and the biosynthesis of cellular metabolites including some amino acids and lipids (Attardi & Schatz 1988). Because these organelles cannot be synthesized de novo, pre-existing mitochondria must grow continuously throughout the cell cycle and be inherited by daughter cells during division (Birky 1983, Palade 1983, Yaffe 1991, Berger & Yaffe 1996, Warren & Wickner 1996). Several decades of research have established that mitochondrial growth requires the import of nuclear-encoded proteins from the cytoplasm and the synthesis of polypeptides encoded by the organelle genome. The incorporation of lipids and the replication of mtDNA are also essential features of mitochondrial biogenesis. Detailed information on the ultrastructure and biogenesis of mitochondria can be found in a number of excellent reviews (Tandler & Hoppel 1972, Stevens 1981, Wolstenholme & Fauron 1995, Lill & Neupert 1996, Nunnari & Walter 1996, Schatz 1996, Neupert 1997), and chapters on this topic are a standard feature of most cell biology textbooks. In contrast, investigators have only recently begun to analyze the molecular basis of mitochondrial dynamics in cells, specifically, mitochondrial shape and cellular distribution, mitochondrial division and fusion, and mitochondrial inheritance during cell division.

The morphology and distribution of mitochondria are usually tailored to meet the specialized energy needs of a cell. In textbooks, mitochondria are commonly depicted as static, sausage-shaped structures scattered throughout the cytoplasm. However, in living cells the organelles often form a tubular network that changes shape and size frequently due to fission and fusion events (Bereiter-Hahn 1990, Bereiter-Hahn & Voth 1994). In some organisms, these fusion events are developmentally regulated and serve to remodel the mitochondrial compartment as cells differentiate. One of the most dramatic examples occurs during spermatogenesis in insects where mitochondrial fusion generates two giant organelles that are tightly wrapped around the base of the rapidly beating flagellum (Fuller 1993). Mitochondria in other cell types are also localized near structures that consume large amounts of ATP. In muscle cells, for example, mitochondria stacked in columns between actin-myosin bundles generate the energy required for muscle contraction (Bakeeva et al 1978). Similarly, nerve cell mitochondria are found clustered at the presynaptic membrane where they provide the ATP required for neurotransmitter release and neurosecretory vesicle recycling and reloading (Landau & Kwanbunbumpen 1969). The cytoskeleton plays a key role in determining these different mitochondrial morphologies and distributions and is also required for polarized mitochondrial movements and mitochondrial inheritance in most cell types (Bereiter-Hahn & Voth 1994, Hollenbeck 1996, Simon & Pon 1996).

Due to its many experimental advantages, the budding yeast *Saccharomyces cerevisiae* has emerged as a favorite model system to study mitochondrial dynamics. Interest has been fueled by the growing awareness that many aspects of mitochondrial behavior in yeast are similar to those observed in other cell types. Genetic screens carried out by a number of groups have identified a set of proteins required for mitochondrial morphology maintenance and mitochondrial inheritance during mitotic division. In addition, in vitro assays that reconstitute aspects of mitochondrial motility have been developed, setting the stage for a biochemical dissection of this process. This review summarizes what has been learned recently about the molecular components that play a role in yeast mitochondrial dynamics.

MITOCHONDRIAL MORPHOLOGY AND DISTRIBUTION THROUGHOUT THE YEAST LIFE CYCLE

Detailed descriptions of the *S. cerevisiae* life cycle and mitochondrial ultrastructure have been published elsewhere (Stevens 1981, Pon & Schatz 1991). Below we review the relevant features of mitochondrial morphology and behavior in yeast during mitosis, mating and meiosis, and sporulation.

Mitosis

The electron microscope was used in early studies to examine yeast mitochondrial ultrastructure and morphology after fixation and thin sectioning (Stevens 1977, 1981). More recently, investigators have begun to use a number of vital dyes that preferentially accumulate in actively respiring organelles as well as targeted forms of the green fluorescent protein (GFP) (Bereiter-Hahn 1976, 1990, Johnson et al 1980, Chen 1989, Koning et al 1993, Nunnari et al 1997). In mitotically dividing cells, actively respiring mitochondria appear as a highly branched, tubular network located near the cell periphery (Hoffman & Avers 1973, Stevens 1981). Within this network, mitochondrial DNA (mtDNA nucleoids) stained with the DNA-specific dye DAPI (Williamson & Fennell 1979), are visualized as bright spots distributed at widely spaced intervals. Although it sometimes appears as if there is a single, continuous mitochondrial compartment in yeast cells, the actual number of mitochondria can range from one to ten because the organelles frequently fuse and divide (Stevens 1981, Koning et al 1993, Nunnari et al 1997).

Yeast cells can survive without their mtDNA, which encodes gene products required for mitochondrial protein synthesis, electron transport, and oxidative phosphorylation. However, other metabolic functions that occur in the mitochondrial compartment such as reactions of the TCA cycle and amino acid and lipid biosynthesis are essential (Kovacova et al 1968, Gbelska et al 1983, Yaffe & Schatz 1984). As a consequence, yeast buds can only survive if they inherit part of the mitochondrial network from the mother cell during division. Mitochondrial inheritance begins early in the cell cycle (late G1/early S phase) when a portion of the network extends into the developing daughter cell or bud (Figure 1A) (Stevens 1981, McConnell et al 1990, Simon et al 1997). As the bud grows (S/G2 phase), additional mitochondrial membranes are transferred in from the mother cell. Mitochondria are reported to move in a linear and polarized fashion during this period (Simon et al 1995, 1997). A transient clustering of mitochondria at the bud tip is also observed (Simon et al 1997), suggesting that mitochondria can be captured and immobilized immediately after transfer to prevent their accidental return to the mother cell. Prior to cytokinesis, these immobilized mitochondria are redistributed throughout the bud.

Mating

Haploid yeast cells exposed to mating pheromone develop mating projections, adhere to one another, and ultimately fuse to form a dumbbell-shaped zygote (Figure 1B) (Sprague & Thorner 1994). Prior to (or concomitant with) nuclear

A Mitosis

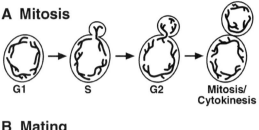

G1   S   G2   Mitosis/
                            Cytokinesis

B Mating

G1 Arrest/   Cell Fusion/   Nuclear Fusion
Schmooing   Mitochondrial Fusion

C Meiosis/Sporulation

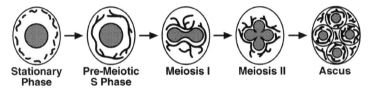

Stationary   Pre-Meiotic   Meiosis I   Meiosis II   Ascus
Phase   S Phase

Figure 1   Mitochondrial dynamics during the life cycle of *S. cerevisiae*. (*A*) Mitochondrial morphology and inheritance during mitotic cell division. Mitochondria are located near the cortex of
the cell as a branched tubular network. They are partitioned continuously from the mother cell into
the bud from early in S phase until cytokinesis. (*B*) Mitochondrial fusion during mating. Haploid
yeast cells of different mating types form a diploid zygote by cellular and nuclear fusion. Prior
to nuclear fusion, the parental mitochondrial networks in the zygote fuse to form one intercon-
nected organelle. (*C*) Mitochondrial morphology and inheritance during meiosis and sporulation.
Meiosis and sporulation in diploid yeast produces four haploid daughter cells enclosed within the
mother cell (an ascus). Individual mitochondrial compartments in pre-meiotic stationary phase are
dispersed at the cell cortex. In pre-meiotic S phase, these individual mitochondria fuse to form
one large branched network. During meiotic nuclear divisions, the mitochondrial membrane remains closely associated with the nucleus. This association leads to the incorporation of part of the
mitochondrial network into newly formed spores.

fusion, mitochondrial compartments derived from each parent rapidly fuse in the
zygote, creating a single, continuous network (Azpiroz & Butow 1993, Nunnari
et al 1997). This mitochondrial fusion is accompanied by the complete mixing
and redistribution of most mitochondrial components throughout the network.
As a consequence of this mitochondrial fusion and compartment mixing, buds
produced from any position on the zygote inherit mitochondrial networks of
fairly uniform membrane and protein composition.

Meiosis and Sporulation

The most dramatic changes in mitochondrial distribution and morphology occur during meiosis and sporulation in *S. cerevisiae* (Figure 1*C*). Mitochondria in pre-meiotic cells appear as punctate structures dispersed at the cell cortex (Miyakawa et al 1984, Smith et al 1995). By early prophase, these discrete units have fused to form a tubular reticulum. The mtDNA nucleoids within this reticulum are highly condensed and resemble a series of beads on a string when stained with DAPI (Miyakawa et al 1984). The mitochondrial reticulum next migrates to the cell center where it remains associated with the nuclear membrane during the first and second meiotic divisions. At the end of meiosis II, four discrete mitochondrial tubules remain, each one located near an individual nuclear lobe. This intimate association of the mitochondrial and nuclear membranes ensures that mitochondria are included when each nuclear lobe is enclosed by the prospore cell membrane.

APPROACHES TO THE STUDY OF MITOCHONDRIAL DYNAMICS

Morphological screens are being used very successfully to identify genes required for Mitochondrial Distribution and Morphology (MDM) and Mitochondrial Morphology Maintenance (MMM) (McConnell et al 1990, Burgess et al 1994, Hermann et al 1997). By shifting temperature-sensitive yeast strains to 37°C and staining with fluorescent dyes to visualize the mitochondrial compartment, mutations have been isolated that fall into several different classes including (*a*) mutations that block mitochondrial inheritance but do not affect mitochondrial morphology, (*b*) mutations that alter mitochondrial morphology and block mitochondrial inheritance, and (*c*) mutations that alter mitochondrial morphology but do not block mitochondrial inheritance. The defects in most of the mutants appear to be specific for mitochondria and do not affect the morphology or inheritance of other cytoplasmic organelles that have been examined (e.g. nuclei and vacuoles). Independent selections for genes affecting Mitochondrial Genome Maintenance (MGM) (Jones & Fangman 1992) and Yeast Mitochondrial Escape (YME) (Thorsness & Fox 1993) have also yielded genes required for the maintenance of mitochondrial morphology and inheritance. Table 1 lists the published genes identified by the approaches cited above that are discussed in this review.

Cell-free assays that recapitulate mitochondrial behaviors in vivo are also being used to understand the mechanisms regulating yeast mitochondrial dynamics. To date, these assays focus exclusively on the interactions of yeast mitochondria with actin filaments and actin-based mitochondrial motility (see below).

ROLE OF THE CYTOSKELETON IN MITOCHONDRIAL DISTRIBUTION AND INHERITANCE

Studies in a wide variety of cell types indicate that mitochondria colocalize with microtubules (Heggeness et al 1978, Ball & Singer 1982, Summerhayes et al 1983), actin microfilaments (Drubin et al 1993), and intermediate filaments (Hirokawa 1982, Mose-Larsen et al 1982, Summerhayes et al 1983, Stromer & Bendayan 1990) and are transported through the cytoplasm using both microtubule-based (Nangaku et al 1994, Morris & Hollenbeck 1995, Pereira et al 1997, Hirokawa 1998) and actin-based (Kuznetsov et al 1992, Morris & Hollenbeck 1995, Simon et al 1995, Bearer et al 1996, Hollenbeck 1996) motor activities. To date, only the actin and intermediate filament cytoskeletons have been implicated in mitochondrial distribution and inheritance in *S. cerevisiae*. Current work focuses on understanding how these two cytoskeletal systems function at the molecular level to control different mitochondrial behaviors.

Microtubules

Although microtubules play a direct role in organelle motility and distribution in many eukaryotic cell types, they do not appear to participate in mitochondrial dynamics in *S. cerevisiae*. Disruption of the yeast microtubule network with mutations in β tubulin (Huffaker et al 1987) or with microtubule destabilizing drugs (Jacobs et al 1988) has no effect on mitochondrial morphology or mitochondrial transmission to daughter cells. These results are not surprising given that *S. cerevisiae* lacks an extensive cytoplasmic microtubule array and that mitochondria do not colocalize with microtubules in budding yeast (Adams & Pringle 1984, Kilmartin & Adams 1984). Microtubules also appear to be dispensable for mitochondrial movements in the filamentous fungi *Aspergillus nidulans* (Oakley & Reinhart 1985).

Cytoplasmic microtubules are required, however, for mitochondrial distribution in the fission yeast *Schizosaccharomyces pombe* (Yaffe et al 1996). Fission yeast contain a cortical network of tubular mitochondria similar to that observed in budding yeast (Davison & Garland 1977). Disruption of the *S. pombe* microtubule cytoskeleton with mutations in α or β tubulin, or with drugs that destabilize microtubules, results in clumped and unequally distributed mitochondria (Yaffe et al 1996). This effect on mitochondrial morphology is likely to be direct, since mitochondria partially colocalize with cytoplasmic microtubules throughout interphase in *S. pombe* cells. Kinesin-like motors that transport mitochondria on microtubules and/or regulate mitochondrial distribution in vivo have been identified in mammals and flies (Nangaku et al 1994, Pereira et al 1997). Thus the molecular mechanisms controlling mitochondrial distribution

Table 1 Genes involved in mitochondrial inheritance and morphology in yeast

Gene	Amino acids	Mutant phenotype	Properties	Reference
ACT1	375 aa (42 kDa)	Some mutant alleles have clumped mitochondria and exhibit defects in mitochondrial transfer to buds	Conventional actin	(Drubin et al 1993) (Lazzarino et al 1994)
CLU1	1277 aa (145 kDa)	Partial collapse of mitochondrial reticulum	Homologous to *cluA* in *Dictyostelium*	(Zhu et al 1997) (Fields et al 1998)
DNM1/ MDM29	757 aa (85 kDa)	Mitochondria collapse into one large elongated structure	Dynamin-like GTPase; localized to punctate structures along mitochondria	(Gammie et al 1995) (D Otsuga et al, submitted)
FZO1	855 aa (98 kDa)	Collapsed mitochondria; loss of mtDNA	Predicted GTPase; outer mitochondrial membrane protein required for mitochondrial fusion	(Hales & Fuller 1997) (GJ Hermann et al, submitted)
MDM1	443 aa (51 kDa)	Fragmented mitochondrion; defective transfer of mitochondria and/or nuclei into buds	Vimentin-like protein; forms 10-nm filaments in vitro; protein is localized to punctate spots in the cytoplasm	(McConnell et al 1990) (McConnell & Yaffe 1992) (McConnell & Yaffe 1993) (Fisk & Yaffe 1997)
MDM10	493 aa (56 kDa)	Large spherical mitochondria; defective transfer of mitochondria into buds; increased loss of mtDNA	Novel outer mitochondrial membrane protein	(Sogo & Yaffe 1994)
MDM12	271 aa (31 kDa)	Large spherical mitochondria; defective transfer of mitochondria into buds; increased loss of mtDNA	Novel outer mitochondrial membrane protein	(Berger et al 1997)

Gene	Size	Phenotype	Protein	References
MDM20	796 aa (93 kDa)	Normal mitochondrial morphology; defective transfer of mitochondria into buds; loss of actin cables	Novel protein; potential heptad repeats	(Hermann et al 1997)
MGM1/ MDM17	912 aa (101 kDa)	Aggregated mitochondria; defective transfer of mitochondria into buds; loss of mtDNA	Dynamin-like GTPase; outer mitochondrial membrane protein	(Jones & Fangman 1992) (Guan et al 1993) (KA Shephard & MP Yaffe, unpublished data) (SW Gorsich & JS Shaw, unpublished data)
MMM1/ YME6	426 aa (49 kDa)	Large spherical mitochondria; defective transfer of mitochondria into buds; loss of mtDNA	Novel outer mitochondrial membrane protein	(Burgess et al 1994) (Thorsness & Weber 1996)
OLE1/ MDM2	510 aa (58 kDa)	Aggregated mitochondria; defective transfer of mitochondria into buds	Δ9 fatty acid desaturase	(Stukey et al 1990) (Stewart & Yaffe 1991) (Kohlwein et al 1997)
PTC1/ MDM28	281 aa (32 kDa)	Delayed transfer of mitochondria into buds	Serine/threonine phosphatase	(van Zyl et al 1989) (Maeda et al 1993) (Roeder et al 1998)
YME1	747 aa (82 kDa)	Clumped and swollen mitochondria; increased escape of mtDNA to the nucleus	ATP and zinc-dependent protease; inner mitochondrial membrane protein	(Thorsness et al 1993) (Campbell et al 1994) (Weber et al 1996)

in *S. pombe* may be more similar to those found in mammals and flies than in other fungi. To resolve this issue, it will be important to determine whether the actin and intermediate filament cytoskeletons also contribute to mitochondrial positioning, morphology, and motility in *S. pombe* as they do in *S. cerevisiae*.

Intermediate Filaments

MDM1   Genetic evidence that intermediate filaments are required for mitochondrial morphology and inheritance comes from studies of the *S. cerevisiae MDM1* gene (McConnell et al 1990). Mutations in *MDM1* cause temperature-sensitive growth defects, abnormal mitochondrial morphology (fragmentation and clumping), and block the transfer of both mitochondria and nuclei into growing buds. The *mdm1* effect on nuclear migration (the result of a misoriented mitotic spindle) is interesting because other mutations that prevent nuclear migration and division do not disrupt mitochondrial partitioning (Thomas & Botstein 1986, Huffaker et al 1988).

MDM1 encodes a protein with limited similarity to two mammalian intermediate filament proteins, keratin and vimentin (McConnell & Yaffe 1992). Like other intermediate filament proteins, the purified Mdm1 protein (Mdm1p) will self-assemble into 10-nm filaments in vitro (McConnell & Yaffe 1993). However, Mdm1p does not form a recognizable network of cytoplasmic filaments in vivo. Instead, Mdm1p is found in abundant punctate structures distributed throughout the mother and bud cytoplasms (McConnell & Yaffe 1992). These structures are distinct from actin microfilaments and microtubules and do not exclusively colocalize with mitochondria, nuclei, or any other cytoplasmic organelle in wild-type cells. Nevertheless, defects in mitochondrial and nuclear inheritance are correlated with the loss of these Mdm1p structures at the restrictive temperature in the conditional *mdm1-1* mutant. Although the organization of these Mdm1p structures looks substantially different from intermediate filament networks found in other cell types, all the available evidence suggests that Mdm1p is a bona fide intermediate filament protein. For the purposes of this discussion, we refer to these yeast Mdm1p structures as the Mdm1p cytoskeleton.

Fisk & Yaffe recently isolated additional mutant alleles of *mdm1* that retain cytoplasmic Mdm1p cytoskeletons at all temperatures (Fisk & Yaffe 1997). These *mdm1* alleles can be grouped into different phenotypic classes, which demonstrate that the Mdm1p cytoskeleton performs separate functions in mitochondrial dynamics and nuclear segregation. Class I mutations disrupt both mitochondrial inheritance and nuclear segregation, class II mutations block only mitochondrial inheritance, and class III mutations block only nuclear segregation. These data are consistent with the idea that Mdm1p forms an intermediate filament cytoskeleton that binds multiple cytoplasmic structures. All the mutants defective in mitochondrial inheritance contain small, round, clumped mitochondria instead of the tubular membrane reticulum found in wild-type cells. Thus it is unclear whether Mdm1p's primary role is in maintaining mitochondrial morphology, directing mitochondrial inheritance, or both. The mutations in *MDM1* affecting nuclear segregation fall into two categories: (*a*) those that do not segregate nuclei into daughter cells and (*b*) those that partition all of the nuclear DNA into the bud. The nuclear defects in these *mdm1* alleles resemble those reported for mutations that affect mitotic spindle positioning and may reveal a role for the Mdm1p network in binding and orienting spindle pole bodies (SPBs). Finally, when the different *mdm1* mutant alleles are combined, complex genetic interactions including synthetic effects, intragenic complementation, and intragenic suppression are observed. These results support the notion that Mdm1p functions in vivo in an oligomeric state.

Based on the similarity of the Mdm1p amino acid sequence to intermediate filament proteins, the ability of Mdm1p to form 10-nm filaments in vitro, and the effects of *mdm1* mutations on the distribution of two different cellular organelles, it seems likely that the Mdm1p spots visualized by indirect immunofluorescence experiments form a cytoskeletal framework distributed throughout the yeast cytoplasm. SPB binding to this Mdm1p cytoskeleton (directly or indirectly) could act to orient the mitotic spindle during cell division. Similarly, mitochondrial morphology and positioning in cells could be regulated by anchoring mitochondrial membranes or membrane-associated proteins to this Mdm1p cytoskeleton. It seems unlikely that the transport of mitochondria into daughter cells is mediated by a conventional motor protein that moves along Mdm1p filaments because intermediate filaments contain no intrinsic polarity, a feature required for directed motor movements along cytoskeletal structures (Fuchs & Weber 1994). In fact, intermediate filament-dependent motor proteins have not been identified in any cell type. Yaffe and colleagues have proposed an alternative model for Mdm1p-mediated mitochondrial motility that involves the sequential binding and release of mitochondria to generate a crawling or amoeboid-like movement along Mdm1p filament tracks (Berger & Yaffe 1996). A better understanding of Mdm1p network architecture in cells and of the nature of Mdm1p-organelle interactions should help to determine whether Mdm1p functions as a scaffold for mitochondrial binding or as a cytoskeletal track for mitochondrial movement.

Actin

The actin cytoskeleton has been shown to control mitochondrial positioning in a variety of cell types (Drubin et al 1993, Bereiter-Hahn & Voth 1994, Hollenbeck 1996), and it is now clear that mitochondria are transported along filamentous actin tracks in neuronal axons (Kuznetsov et al 1992, Morris & Hollenbeck

1995) and insect cells (Bradley & Satir 1979, Sturmer et al 1995). In yeast, genetic and biochemical studies suggest that the actin cytoskeleton mediates both mitochondrial positioning and mitochondrial transport.

ACT1   *S. cerevisiae* contains a single essential actin gene, *ACT1*, that participates in a wide variety of cellular processes (Shortle et al 1982, Botstein et al 1997, Winsor & Schiebel 1997). In vivo, filamentous actin (F-actin) is organized into cables (bundles of F-actin) and cortical patches (associated with the plasma membrane) that undergo cell cycle–regulated changes in distribution (Adams & Pringle 1984, Kilmartin & Adams 1984, Welch et al 1994). In mitotically dividing cells, actin cables are oriented parallel to the mother-bud axis and are well positioned to deliver membrane-bound organelles, such as mitochondria, to the daughter cell. In fact, indirect immunofluorescence studies have revealed a striking colocalization of elongated mitochondrial tubules along these actin cables throughout the mitotic cell cycle (Drubin et al 1993, Lazzarino et al 1994, Simon et al 1997, Roeder et al 1998).

Although mutations in the *ACT1* gene cause a variety of cellular phenotypes (Botstein et al 1997), only a subset of *act1* mutants display defects in mitochondrial morphology and inheritance. Drubin and coworkers first showed that certain *act1* mutants contain clumped and disorganized mitochondrial networks (Drubin et al 1993). Similar mitochondrial morphology defects, as well as mitochondrial inheritance defects, are observed in *act1-3* mutant cells (Lazzarino et al 1994). The mitochondrial inheritance defect in *act1-3* has been correlated with a lack of normal mitochondrial motility in time-lapse video microscopy studies (Simon et al 1995). *act1* mutants also alter mitochondrial morphology and motility during meiotic division in yeast (Smith et al 1995). Finally, defects in mitochondrial behavior have also been reported in wild-type yeast cells treated with the actin depolymerizing drug latrunculin A (Lat-A). Within minutes of Lat-A treatment, wild-type mitochondrial networks fragment and long-distance mitochondrial movements slow down and become less polarized (Boldogh et al 1998). When combined with the observation that yeast mitochondria align along actin cables in vivo, these results strongly suggest that actin cables provide a scaffold for the attachment and movement of mitochondrial membranes in yeast cells.

MITOCHONDRIAL MOTILITY AND ACTIN-DEPENDENT MOTORS   Drubin and colleagues noted that the majority of *act1* mutants with amino acid substitutions under or near the myosin foot print exhibited defects in mitochondrial organization (Drubin et al 1993). This result was very exciting because it suggested that a myosin-like motor activity bound to the outer mitochondrial membrane might be responsible for transporting the organelle along actin filaments or cables. Two assays developed by Pon and coworkers indicate that such actin-mitochondrial interactions can occur in vitro. The first is a sedimentation assay that reconstitutes the binding of isolated yeast mitochondria to phalloidin stabilized yeast F-actin (Lazzarino et al 1994). Mitochondrial binding to F-actin is saturable, ATP dependent, and reversible and requires at least two mitochondrial components: (a) a peripheral mitochondrial membrane protein(s) with ATP-sensitive actin-binding activity (called mitochondrial actin binding protein or mABP) and (b) an integral membrane protein component required for docking of mABP (Lazzarino et al 1994, Boldogh et al 1998). Two integral outer membrane proteins shown to control mitochondrial morphology in vivo, Mmm1p and Mdm10p (Burgess et al 1994, Sogo & Yaffe 1994), are required to dock mABP on the outer mitochondrial membrane (Boldogh et al 1998). These results have led to the suggestion that Mdm10p and Mmm1p act as mitochondrial receptors for mABP, which can, in turn, act as an adaptor to indirectly attach mitochondria to F-actin.

The second assay reconstitutes ATP-dependent, actin-filament sliding on the surface of immobilized yeast mitochondria (Simon et al 1995). In this assay, both the concentration of ATP required and the rate of actin filament sliding are consistent with the presence of a myosin-like motor activity on the outer mitochondrial surface. The *S. cerevisiae* genome encodes five genes, *MYO1–MYO5*, that exhibit sequence similarity to the myosin superfamily in the motor domain. Surprisingly, this myosin-like motor activity does not appear to be encoded by any of the five *S. cerevisiae* myosin genes; mitochondrial motility is unaffected in the single *myo1*, *myo2*, *myo3*, *myo4*, and *myo5* mutants and in double *myo2-myo4* and *myo3-myo5* mutants (Simon et al 1995, Goodson et al 1996). Although all combinations of myosin mutations have not been tested, these results raise the possibility that a novel type of actin-dependent motor mediates mitochondrial motility in yeast. It will be interesting to see whether the mABP activity identified in the mitochondrial sedimentation assay is responsible for this motor activity or if it contributes to the motor activity in some fashion.

MDM20   Additional genetic evidence that actin is required for mitochondrial inheritance in yeast comes from studies of the *mdm20* mutant (Hermann et al 1997). Cells lacking *MDM20* exhibit severe defects in mitochondrial inheritance but retain normal mitochondrial morphology. Although cortical actin patches are still present in *mdm20* cells, actin cables aligned along the mother bud axis cannot be detected in rhodamine-phalloidin staining experiments. Significantly, both the actin organization defects and the mitochondrial inheritance defects in *mdm20* can be suppressed by increasing the dose of *TPM1* or *TPM2*. *TPM1* and *TPM2* encode two different yeast tropomyosins that bind directly to F-actin and promote the assembly and/or stabilization of actin filaments (Liu & Bretscher 1989, 1992, Drees et al 1995). In the *mdm20* mutant, extra copies of *TPM1* and *TPM2* suppress mitochondrial inheritance defects by partially restoring actin cables in the cytoplasm (Hermann et al 1997). When combined with the observations that mitochondria bind to actin filaments and move along actin filaments in vitro, these genetic studies strongly suggest that mitochondria are transported into yeast buds along actin filaments or cables in vivo.

Mutations in the *TPM1* gene also disrupt actin cables but not cortical actin patches (Liu & Bretscher 1989). Surprisingly, mitochondrial inheritance is not blocked when *TPM1* is disrupted in the strain background used for the *MDM20* studies (Hermann et al 1997). It is important to note that cells lacking actin cables may still contain individual actin filaments that are not detected by conventional staining methods. Thus cells lacking the Tpm1 protein might still contain unbundled actin filaments that are capable of supporting mitochondrial movement. In fact, Pon and coworkers have shown that the velocity of mitochondrial movement is normal in the *tpm1* mutant strain (Simon et al 1997). However, long-distance mitochondrial movement in *tpm1* cells is less linear and polarized and, as a consequence, the organelles appear to move more randomly and sometimes enter buds late. The nonlinear mitochondrial movement observed in these cells suggests that actin filaments are present in the *tpm1* mutant but are not completely polarized along the mother-bud axis.

If disorganized actin arrays can support mitochondrial inheritance in the *tpm1* mutant strain, why don't similar actin arrays support mitochondrial inheritance in the *mdm20* mutant? One attractive model is that actin filaments required for mitochondrial inheritance may be present in the *tpm1* mutant but absent in the *mdm20* mutant. According to this scenario, the *MDM20* gene product somehow acts in vivo to define actin-containing structures that participate in mitochondrial transport. Although the Mdm20 protein localizes to the cytoplasm, it does not contain any functional domains or structural motifs implicated in actin assembly or regulation (Hermann et al 1997). Additional studies are required to determine the biochemical activity of this novel protein and its role in regulating actin organization and mitochondrial transport.

COORDINATING MITOCHONDRIAL INHERITANCE WITH BUD EMERGENCE

PTC1/MDM28

Transfer of the mitochondrial network in wild-type yeast always begins immediately after bud emergence, suggesting that mitochondrial inheritance is tightly linked to the cell cycle (Stevens et al 1981, McConnell et al 1990, Simon et al 1997). This cell cycle coordination is disrupted in the *mdm28* mutant resulting in a striking delay in mitochondrial inheritance (Roeder et al 1998). When mitochondrial distribution is examined in synchronized cultures after α-factor release, networks are not detected in new *mdm28* buds until they are greater than half the diameter of the mother cell. In contrast, mitochondrial networks are always detected in wild-type buds regardless of bud size. Surprisingly, the mitochondrial inheritance delay in *mdm28* does not cause a significant change in growth rate relative to wild-type on rich medium. This last observation suggests that the timing of mitochondrial inheritance in yeast is not critical as long as buds receive mitochondria prior to cytokinesis.

MDM28 is identical to *PTC1*, a gene encoding a serine/threonine phosphatase in the High Osmolarity Glycerol response (HOG) pathway (van Zyl et al 1989, Maeda et al 1993, 1994). The HOG pathway plays an important role in the yeast osmostress response and is composed of a signal transducer and a MAP kinase cascade that terminates with the Pbs2p and Hog1p kinases (Morgan et al 1995, Schultz et al 1995, Posas et al 1996). An increase in extracellular osmolarity results in the activation of the HOG kinase cascade and induces yeast to accumulate glycerol (Brewster et al 1993, Maeda et al 1994). Genetic evidence suggests that Ptc1p acts as a negative regulator of the Pbs2p and Hog1p kinases in this pathway (Maeda et al 1993, 1994). Consequently, cells lacking *PTC1* contain hyperactive Pbs2p and Hog1p kinases and accumulate elevated levels of intracellular glycerol (Jiang et al 1995).

Increasing the cytoplasmic glycerol concentration in wild-type cells does not cause a mitochondrial inheritance delay and thus is not responsible for the mitochondrial phenotype observed in the *ptc1* mutant (Roeder et al 1998). Although an increase in intracellular glycerol concentration can be accompanied by the transient disassembly and reassembly of the yeast actin cytoskeleton (Chowdhury et al 1992), actin organization appears wild-type in the *ptc1* mutant and is not responsible for the mitochondrial inheritance delay observed in these cells (Roeder et al 1998). In addition, epistasis experiments with *ptc1* and mutations in the HOG pathway kinases suggest that *PTC1* is not acting through the HOG pathway to control the timing of mitochondrial inheritance. These observations have led to the suggestion that *PTC1* acts either directly or through a different signaling pathway to affect the mitochondrial segregation machinery in the cell. Identification of the downstream targets of Ptc1p may reveal how the timing of mitochondrial inheritance is regulated.

Yeast cells may rely on more than one mechanism to coordinate mitochondrial inheritance with bud emergence. First, the molecular machinery that transports mitochondrial membranes into buds could be activated at (or immediately prior to) the onset of bud formation. According to this model, late activation of the transport machinery would account for the mitochondrial inheritance delay observed in the *ptc1* mutant. Second, a portion of the mitochondrial network could attach to the incipient bud site in a cell cycle–regulated manner and be passively pulled into the expanding bud. In support of this model, mitochondria are reported to converge on the ring of actin patches that mark the incipient bud site (Simon et al 1997), although a physical attachment to this site has not been demonstrated. The observation that mitochondria can move into *ptc1* buds long after they first emerge (Roeder et al 1998) suggests that mitochondrial inheritance does not strictly require a physical link between the organelle and the incipient bud site.

Although *PTC1* is the first gene demonstrated to control the timing of mitochondrial transport to buds, a similar phenotype is reported for a strain carrying mutations in two different genes (*BRO1* and *CAF1*) (Nickas & Yaffe 1996). *BRO1* also encodes a component of a yeast signal transduction pathway (the PKC pathway), although its exact function in this pathway is not understood. A detailed analysis of mitochondrial behavior in the *BRO1* and *CAF1* single and double mutants should provide useful information regarding the link between the PKC signaling pathway and the temporal control of mitochondrial inheritance.

Mitochondrial Inheritance and Cell Cycle Checkpoint Controls

In all the mitochondrial inheritance and morphology mutants described to date, daughter cells that fail to receive a mitochondrial compartment do not separate from the mother cell (McConnell et al 1990, Burgess et al 1994, Sogo & Yaffe 1994, Berger et al 1997, Hermann et al 1997). This is somewhat surprising because in many cases a complete septum appears to form between the mother and bud, and buds can be released from the mother cell by digesting with enzymes that break down the cell wall (MP Yaffe, personal communication). This defect in bud separation does not block progression through the cell cycle, and mitochondrial inheritance mutants often accumulate multiple attached daughter cells, all lacking the organelle. Although it has been suggested that these cell separation defects represent a cytokinesis checkpoint that prevents bud release in the absence of mitochondrial inheritance, this model has not been tested by showing that the cytokinesis block is absent in mutants that abolish checkpoint control (Hartwell & Weinert 1989).

GENES REQUIRED FOR MITOCHONDRIAL MORPHOLOGY MAINTENANCE

The formation of the yeast mitochondrial reticulum is an amazing architectural feat. The compartment must be shaped into a series of elongated tubules that

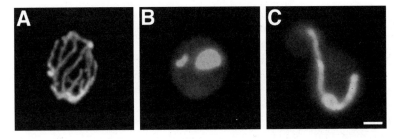

Figure 2 Mitochondrial morphology in wild-type and mutant *S. cerevisiae* cells. Mitochondrial morphology in (*A*) wild-type, (*B*) *mdm12*, and (*C*) *dnm1* cells was visualized using a matrix-targeted form of the green fluorescent protein. The cells shown in (*A*) and (*B*) are unbudded. In (*C*), the bud is in the upper left. Bar = 2 μm.

have the capacity to divide and fuse with one another. In addition, the entire structure must be localized to the peripheral cytoplasm and must be distributed evenly around the circumference of the cell (see Figure 2*A*). As described below, the analysis of mutants with defective mitochondrial morphology has begun to identify molecules required to maintain this extended reticulum. These studies indicate that changes in wild-type mitochondrial morphology can have dramatic affects on the motility and inheritance of the organelle and on mitochondrial genome maintenance.

MMM1

Jensen and coworkers identified the *MMM1* gene in a morphological screen for temperature-sensitive mutations affecting mitochondrial morphology (Burgess et al 1994). In strains harboring the *mmm1-1* allele, a shift to the nonpermissive temperature rapidly (and reversibly) transforms the mitochondrial network into one or a few large, spherical organelles (similar to those shown in Figure 2*B*). Despite their abnormal morphology, the *mmm1* mitochondrial spheres retain typical features of organelle ultrastructure including an outer membrane and an inner membrane, with deep invaginations or cristae. Defects in *mmm1* mitochondrial function occur only after prolonged incubation at the nonpermissive temperature and appear to be a secondary consequence of the change in mitochondrial morphology.

   MMM1 encodes a mitochondrial outer membrane protein with a single transmembrane domain and a large, C-terminal domain facing the cytoplasm (Burgess et al 1994). Cells lacking this protein contain large, spherical mitochondria at all temperatures, grow slowly on the fermentable carbon source glucose, and are inviable on nonfermentable carbon sources such as glycerol. These growth phenotypes appear to result from a severe defect in mitochondrial inheritance. Jensen and coworkers suggested that this mitochondrial inheritance defect results from the inability of giant *mmm1* mitochondria to fit through the mother-bud neck, effectively preventing their delivery to daughter cells (Burgess et al 1994). Although the inheritance of these large mitochondria is also blocked in glucose-grown *mmm1* cells, these cells survive because they also contain a number of small mitochondrial compartments that are efficiently transmitted to buds.

MDM10

MDM10 was identified by Yaffe and coworkers in a screen for mitochondrial distribution and morphology mutants (Sogo & Yaffe 1994). The novel protein encoded by this gene is also anchored in the mitochondrial outer membrane. Null mutations in *MDM10* result in temperature-sensitive growth on glucose, collapse of the mitochondrial network to form giant spheres, and defects in mitochondrial inheritance at all temperatures. In addition, *mdm10* null strains exhibit an increased frequency of petite generation, which is usually associated with deletions in mtDNA or its loss (Berger et al 1997). Unlike *mmm1* mutant strains, *mdm10* null cells do grow, albeit extremely slowly, on nonfermentable carbon sources (Sogo & Yaffe 1994). The ability of *mdm10* cells to proliferate under some conditions is presumably due to the inheritance of smaller mitochondrial compartments, which are also observed in these cells.

A *MDM10* homologue was recently identified in the filamentous fungi *Podospora anserina* (*PaMDM10*, 35.9% identity) (Jamet-Vierny et al 1997). *P. anserina* has captured the interest of scientists studying cellular aging because it undergoes a programmed senescence correlated with changes in the structure of the mitochondrial genome. Like the *mdm10* mutation in budding yeast, a mutation in *PaMDM10* converts most of the normal tubular mitochondria into giant spherical, oval, or tadpole-shaped organelles (Jamet-Vierny et al 1997). The change in mitochondrial morphology is associated with increased thermosensitivity and a mating type-specific decrease in lifespan. In addition, two deleted forms of the *P. anserina* mtDNA reproducibly accumulate during the senescence program of the *PaMDM10* mutant strain. The similar phenotypes observed for *mdm10* mutations in budding yeast and filamentous fungi underscore the importance of mitochondrial compartment integrity to mitochondrial genome stability.

MDM12

MDM12 encodes a third mitochondrial outer membrane protein required for mitochondrial morphology maintenance and mitochondrial inheritance (Berger et al 1997). Cells lacking this protein are temperature-sensitive for growth and contain giant mitochondrial spheres similar to those observed in the *mdm10* and *mmm1* mutant strains (Figure 2*B*).

The fission yeast *S. pombe* contains a *MDM12* homologue (32% identity) whose function in mitochondrial dynamics is at least partially conserved (Berger et al 1997). Although the *S. pombe MDM12* does not rescue mitochondrial phenotypes in the *S. cerevisiae mdm12* mutant, it does induce dominant mitochondrial morphology and inheritance defects in wild-type *S. cerevisiae* cells that are similar to those observed in the *S. cerevisiae mdm12* mutant. Thus proteins required for mitochondrial morphology and inheritance may be conserved between fission and budding yeast even though different cytoskeletal structures may control mitochondrial behavior in the two species.

As described above, the *mmm1*, *mdm10*, and *mdm12* strains all survive under certain growth conditions, suggesting that some mitochondrial inheritance is occurring in these strains. This inheritance is restricted to very small mitochondrial compartments that appear to bud from the giant organelles found in these cells (Burgess et al 1994). The simplest explanation for these results is that it is the size, and not the molecular composition, of giant mitochondria that prevents their transfer to daughter cells. A mutation in a suppressor designated *SOT1* (suppressor of *mdm10/mdm12*; *SOT1* is dominant) restores wild-type mitochondrial morphology and mitochondrial inheritance in *mdm10* and *mdm12* mutant cells (Berger et al 1997). Because *SOT1* does not exhibit any mitochondrial phenotype on its own, the mechanism by which it suppresses *mdm10* and *mdm12* phenotypes is uncertain. *SOT1* may act solely to restore a mitochondrial shape that is competent to interact with the inheritance machinery and thin enough to fit through the mother-bud neck. Alternatively, *SOT1* could activate or be part of a redundant cellular pathway that also transmits mitochondria to buds. Why such a bypass mechanism would also restore mitochondrial morphology is not clear.

Models for the functions of Mdm10p, Mdm12p, and Mmm1p are still highly speculative. It is possible that these proteins act within the organelle to maintain mitochondrial integrity and establish mitochondrial shape. In this case, defects in mitochondrial movement and inheritance would be an indirect consequence of changes in mitochondrial morphology. Alternatively, the cytoplasmic domains of Mdm10p, Mdm12p, and Mmm1p could act individually or in concert to mediate mitochondrial attachment to cytoplasmic structures including the cytoskeletal components Mdm1p and actin. Such interactions could be responsible for generating the elongated mitochondrial tubules and the directed mitochondrial movements observed in wild-type cells. Although an interaction between these outer membrane proteins and Mdm1p has not been demonstrated, a recent study indicates that a peripheral membrane component required for F-actin binding to mitochondria fails to assemble onto mitochondria isolated from *mmm1* and *mdm10* mutant cells (Boldogh et al 1998). Identification of protein-binding partners and/or the specific biochemical activities of

Mdm10p, Mdm12p, and Mmm1p should lead to a better understanding of their functions.

DNM1/MDM29

The mitochondrial morphology defect caused by the *mdm29* mutation is strikingly different from that observed in *mmm1*, *mdm10*, and *mdm12*. In the *mdm29* strain, the mitochondrial reticulum collapses to one side of the cell and forms an elongated structure that appears to function normally and is inherited by daughter cells during division (D Otsuga, BR Keegan, GJ Hermann, E Brisch, W Bleazard, JM Shaw, submitted) (Figure 2*C*). Unlike other mitochondrial distribution and morphology mutants that affect cell growth, *mdm29* null cells grow as well as wild-type at all temperatures and on all carbon sources.

MDM29 is identical to *DNM1* (Gammie et al 1995) and encodes one of three dynamin-related proteins in yeast. The dynamins are a family of high molecular weight GTPases implicated in membrane transport and remodeling events at distinct cellular locations (De Camilli et al 1995, Warnock & Schmid 1996, Schmid 1997, Urrutia et al 1997; A van der Bliek, submitted). Mammalian dynamin is the best characterized of the family members and has been shown to assemble into collars around the base of clathrin-coated pits (Hinshaw & Schmid 1995, Takei et al 1995). Subsequent GTP hydrolysis by dynamin in these collars stimulates a "pinchase" that releases endocytic vesicles (Sweitzer & Hinshaw 1998). Previous studies showed that mutations in *dnm1* do not block endocytosis in yeast (Gammie et al 1995). More recently, Shaw and coworkers showed that the controlled depletion of Dnm1p causes the gradual collapse of the mitochondrial network to one side of the cell, while re-expression of Dnm1p quickly restores wild-type mitochondrial distribution and morphology (D Otsuga, BR Keegan, GJ Hermann, E Brisch, W Bleazard, JM Shaw, submitted). These data strongly suggest that Dnm1p functions to spread the mitochondrial reticulum evenly around the cell periphery. Consistent with this model, the Dnm1 protein is found in punctate structures at the cell cortex that colocalize with the tips and sides of mitochondrial tubules and branchpoints in the mitochondrial network. Dnm1p appears to be bound either directly or indirectly to the mitochondrial compartment and remains associated with the collapsed, spherical mitochondria found in the *mdm10* and *mdm12* mutants.

Like other members of the dynamin family, the N-terminal domain of Dnm1p contains a conserved, tripartite GTP-binding motif (Gammie et al 1995). GTP binding and/or hydrolysis appears to be required for Dnm1p function in vivo because Dnm1 proteins containing mutations in this region fail to rescue mitochondrial distribution and morphology defects in the *dnm1* mutant (D Otsuga, BR Keegan, GJ Hermann, E Brisch, W Bleazard, JM Shaw, submitted). These mutant Dnm1 proteins also induce dominant mitochondrial distribution and morphology defects in wild-type cells that can be rescued by overexpressing the wild-type Dnm1 protein. This last observation suggests that, like mammalian dynamin, Dnm1p associates with itself and/or with additional cellular components that help to establish mitochondrial distribution and morphology.

Exactly how the Dnm1 GTPase acts to control mitochondrial morphology and distribution is unclear. Dnm1p assembly on the mitochondrial membrane might regulate the formation of tubules or branches that are required to elaborate the network at the cell surface. Alternatively, Dnm1p could simply be part of a structure that anchors portions of the mitochondrial reticulum at the cell cortex.

MGM1/MDM17

MGM1 encodes a second dynamin-like GTPase implicated in mitochondrial dynamics (Jones & Fangman 1992, Guan et al 1993). Although this gene was first identified in a screen for mutations affecting mitochondrial genome maintenance (Jones & Fangman 1992), it was recently re-isolated as *MDM17* by Shepard & Yaffe (KA Shepard, MP Yaffe, submitted). Mitochondrial membranes in an *mgm1* disruption strain aggregate (Guan et al 1993) and are not efficiently transferred to buds (KA Shepard, MP Yaffe, submitted). The loss of mtDNA observed in this mutant strain appears to be a secondary consequence of the change in mitochondrial morphology (KA Shepard, MP Yaffe, submitted). In wild-type cells, the Mgm1 protein localizes to the mitochondrial compartment where it uniformly associates with the cytoplasmic face of the outer membrane (KA Shepard, MP Yaffe, submitted; SW Gorsich, JM Shaw, unpublished observations). Antibodies specific for Mgm1p recognize two forms of the protein present in equimolar amounts: a 100-kDa species that behaves as an integral membrane protein and a 90-kDa form that peripherally associates with the organelle (KA Shepard, MP Yaffe, submitted). Pulse-chase studies suggest that there is not a precursor/product relationship between these two Mgm1 polypeptides. The ability of the larger and smaller Mgm1p species to complement mitochondrial morphology and mtDNA-loss phenotypes will have to be assessed by independently expressing the two forms of the protein in *mgm1* cells. Studies are under way to determine whether the Mgm1p GTPase domain is required for function in vivo and whether Mgm1 assembles into rings on or near the mitochondrial outer membrane. Given how little we currently know about the biochemical activity of Mgm1p, roles for this protein in mitochondrial positioning, inheritance, branching, fission, and fusion are equally feasible.

CLU1

The story of *Saccharomyces CLU1* begins with the isolation of a novel, 150-kDa protein from *Dictyostelium* called CluA (Zhu et al 1997). CluA was initially identified based on its cross-reactivity with antibodies generated against an unconventional myosin. However, analysis of the purified CluA protein and the polypeptide sequence predicted from the CluA gene revealed no myosin-like activities or structural features. Further analysis showed that CluA was required for mitochondrial positioning. Mitochondria in *Dictyostelium* cells are normally found dispersed uniformly throughout the cytoplasm. In *cluA⁻* cells, all the mitochondria were found clustered in the cell center. An increased frequency of multinucleate cells was also observed, suggesting that cytokinesis was defective in the *cluA⁻* mutant. Despite its obvious role in mitochondrial distribution, CluA behaved like a soluble protein and was not enriched in mitochondrial fractions.

The yeast *CLU1* gene encodes a functional homologue of the *Dictyostelium* CluA gene and can restore mitochondrial distribution in the *cluA⁻* mutant (Fields et al 1998). Genetic studies indicate that *CLU1* is also required for wild-type mitochondrial distribution in yeast. In *clu1* null cells, the mitochondrial reticulum appears less branched and is sometimes confined to one half of the cell cortex. Despite this change in distribution, *clu1* mitochondria appear to function normally and are inherited by buds during division. Although the partially collapsed mitochondrial morphology in *clu1* cells is not as severe as that observed in the *dnm1* mutant, the *clu1* and *dnm1* mitochondrial phenotypes are similar, suggesting that these two genes may act in a common pathway to control mitochondrial distribution and shape. The ability of Clu1p to complement mitochondrial distribution defects in the *Dictyostelium cluA⁻* mutant and the similarity of the yeast *clu1* and *Dictyostelium cluA⁻* mitochondrial phenotypes provide a striking demonstration of the degree to which cellular mechanisms governing mitochondrial dynamics have been conserved between species.

Maintenance of a Branched Mitochondrial Network

There is never a time during mitotic growth when mitochondrial morphology has to be established de novo. Nevertheless, the mutant mitochondrial morphologies described above suggest that a number of independent events are required to generate and/or maintain the yeast mitochondrial reticulum. A simple and highly speculative diagram of these events is shown in Figure 3. Mitochondria that have lost important cellular interactions (e.g. cytoskeletal attachment) collapse into spherical organelles, which can be viewed as the ground state (*mdm10, mdm12,* and *mmm1* strains). Attachment of these spherical organelles to cytoplasmic structures serves to stretch out or elongate the membranes and anchor them to the cell cortex. Candidates for these cytoplasmic attachment sites include cytoskeletal filaments composed of actin and the intermediate filament-like protein Mdm1. At some point before, during, or after these events, the mitochondrial double membrane must be shaped into long tubules that are joined to form a branched network or reticulum. Although our current understanding of this

**Ground
State**　　　　**Cortical Localization
Tubule Formation**　　　　**Peripheral
Distribution**

Figure 3 A highly speculative model for the maintenance of a branched mitochondrial network in *S. cerevisiae*. From mutant mitochondrial morphologies that have been observed, a number of independent events required to generate the mitochondrial reticulum can be envisioned. (*Left*) Mitochondria that have lost important cellular attachments collapse into giant spheres (ground state). (*Center*) Attachment of these organelles to cytoplasmic structures anchors them to the cortex and elongates the membranes. (*Right*) The branched reticulum (formed by an unknown mechanism) is distributed evenly around the cell periphery.

process is murky at best, it probably requires regulated membrane fission and fusion, as well as the activities of membrane-remodeling proteins (for example, Mgm1p and Dnm1p). Once the mitochondrial reticulum is formed, it must be distributed evenly in the peripheral cytoplasm. This could be accomplished by attaching the reticulum to Dnm1p-containing complexes, which appear to have the correct cellular distribution for this function. It is also possible that mitochondrial reticulum formation and peripheral distribution are obligatorily coupled. Although aspects of this model may prove to be incorrect, it includes a number of testable features and should provide a useful framework for the molecular, genetic, and biochemical analysis of mitochondrial architecture.

ROLE OF THE MITOCHONDRIAL MEMBRANE

OLE1/MDM2

Although it seems obvious that the lipid composition of the mitochondrial membrane is critical for organelle integrity and behavior, only one mutant, *mdm2*, reveals an essential role for lipids in mitochondrial dynamics. The *mdm2* mutant causes abnormal mitochondrial aggregation and defective mitochondrial inheritance (Stewart & Yaffe 1991). *MDM2* is allelic to *OLE1*, a gene previously shown to encode a Δ9 fatty acid desaturase (Stukey et al 1989, 1990). Mutations in *OLE1/MDM2* are thought to cause defects in mitochondrial morphology and inheritance by altering the level of unsaturated fatty acids in, and thus the physical properties of, mitochondrial membranes (Stewart & Yaffe 1991). Shifting the *mdm2-1* strain to the nonpermissive temperature results in a 2.5-fold decrease in unsaturated fatty acid levels and the fragmentation of the mitochondrial network into smaller vesicles that aggregate within the mother cell (Kohlwein et al 1997). These mitochondrial fragments retain normal organellar ultrastructure and can still be labeled with potential-dependent dyes, suggesting that the integrity of the inner mitochondrial membrane is not grossly compromised (Stewart & Yaffe 1991). The mitochondrial phenotypes and the conditional growth defect in *ole1/mdm2* can be rescued by adding oleic acid to the growth medium, suggesting that it is the change in fatty acid levels and not some additional activity of the desaturase that is responsible for these phenotypes (Stewart & Yaffe 1991). Although fatty acids are important for membrane integrity throughout the cell, the membrane defect caused by *ole1/mdm2* has not been reported to affect the morphology or segregation of other cytoplasmic organelles.

Because cardiolipin is an abundant inner membrane component rich in unsaturated fatty acids (Hoch 1992, Kent 1995), it initially seemed possible that cardiolipin was the major lipid affected in *ole1/mdm2*. However, several groups have now reported the surprising finding that yeast cells lacking cardiolipin are viable on both fermentable and nonfermentable carbon sources (Jiang et al 1997, Tuller et al 1998). Based on these results, it seems likely that defects in a different mitochondrial lipid, or multiple classes of mitochondrial lipids, are responsible for the phenotypes observed in the *ole1/mdm2* mutant.

What is the role of unsaturated fatty acids in mitochondrial dynamics? One possibility is that changes in unsaturated fatty acid levels affect the activities of integral membrane proteins, which depend on specific lipid modifications or a specific bilayer composition. An alternative model proposed by Schneiter & Kohlwein is that changes in membrane composition lead to alterations in membrane curvature that are required to regulate fission and fusion (Schneiter & Kohlwein 1997). Tests of these models will require further in vivo analyses as well as in vitro assays that reconstitute various mitochondrial membrane-dependent behaviors.

MAINTENANCE OF MITOCHONDRIAL DNA

The *S. cerevisiae* mitochondrial genome encodes RNAs and proteins essential for mitochondrial translation, electron transport, and ATP synthesis (Dujon 1981, Pon & Schatz 1991). Yeast cells contain 50–100 copies of mtDNA, which are packaged together with proteins into structures referred to as nucleoids (Williamson & Fennell 1979). Although yeast buds inherit mtDNA along with the mitochondrial compartment during mitosis, mtDNA segregation does not occur randomly. Instead, it is hypothesized that a segregation apparatus controls the movement of mtDNA nucleoids relative to other mitochondrial constituents (Azpiroz & Butow 1993, Nunnari et al 1997).

Early studies of zygotic first buds (pedigree analysis) indicated that mtDNA movement was restricted in yeast. When haploid cells containing genetically marked mtDNAs were mated, recombinant mitochondrial genomes were found exclusively in buds produced from the zygote neck (heteroplasmic buds) (Birky et al 1978, Strausberg & Perlman 1978, Zinn et al 1987). In contrast, buds produced from the ends of the zygote usually contained only one type of mtDNA derived from the closest parent (homoplasmic buds). These results suggested that mitochondrial fusion and genome mixing occurred during mating, but that mtDNA mixing was limited to the medial portion of the zygote. This non-random mtDNA segregation pattern was also apparent under conditions where other mitochondrial matrix components, specifically the soluble matrix enzyme citrate synthase 1 (CS1), redistributed freely in the zygote (Azpiroz & Butow 1993). A demonstration of restricted mtDNA movement was recently provided by Nunnari and coworkers who devised a method of labeling the mtDNA of one haploid parent with 5-bromodeoxyuridine (Nunnari et al 1997). After mating, these labeled mitochondrial nucleoids remained in one half of the zygote even after mitochondrial fusion and matrix component mixing had occurred. This result provided a direct explanation for the nonrandom mtDNA inheritance patterns observed in yeast zygotes and suggested that mtDNA nucleoids are (*a*) anchored in the mitochondrial matrix (perhaps to the inner membrane) and (*b*) actively segregated during division. Interestingly, mtDNA movement in zygotes does not appear to be restricted under all conditions. When haploid parents with (rho⁺) and without (rho°) mtDNA are mated, 100% of the progeny inherit mtDNA (Dujon 1981). Azpiroz & Butow showed that this mtDNA inheritance results because mitochondrial nucleoids can equilibrate freely throughout zygotes formed by mating rho⁺ and rho° cells (rho⁺ × rho°) (Azpiroz & Butow 1993). Although the mechanisms responsible for mtDNA segregation in wild-type and non-wild-type matings are not understood, the search for the molecular components that mediate this process is now under way.

Studies of altered mtDNA segregation patterns suggest that specific nucleotide sequences in mtDNA can promote mitochondrial genome inheritance. In rho⁻ strains, the majority of the mtDNA is deleted and the remaining mtDNA (usually a single short mtDNA sequence) is amplified, resulting in a mass of DNA equivalent to that observed in a rho⁺ strain (Dujon 1981). Some of these amplified rho⁻ mtDNAs have been termed hypersuppressive because they are preferentially inherited (95% of the time) by zygotic buds in matings with rho⁺ strains (Dujon 1981, Piskur 1994). Hypersuppressive rho⁻ mtDNAs usually contain tandem repeats of one of several 300-bp stretches called *rep* sequences (Blanc & Dujon 1980, De Zamaroczy et al 1981). The enhanced inheritance of rho⁻ mtDNAs in crosses indicates that these *rep* sequences may be preferentially replicated or segregated into daughter cells.

A number of nuclear genes required for the stable maintenance of mtDNA have been identified. Mutations in some of these genes lead to defects in mitochondrial morphology (*FZO1, MDM10, MDM12, MGM1*) and, in some cases, it has been shown that the loss of mtDNA nucleoids in these strains is a secondary consequence of changes in mitochondrial shape (GJ Hermann, JW Thatcher, JP Mills, KG Hales, MT Fuller, J Nunnari, JM Shaw, submitted; KA Shepard, MP Yaffe, submitted). Other genes are required for mtDNA replication, repair, and recombination, or for mitochondrial genome expression (Costanzo & Fox 1990, Schmitt & Clayton 1993, Fox 1996, Shadel & Clayton 1997). Two genes, *MGT1* and *ABF2*, are of particular interest because their roles in mtDNA segregation have been explored in some detail.

MGT1

The *MGT1* (Mitochondrial Genome Transmission) gene was identified in a screen for mutations that restored normal mtDNA segregation patterns in crosses between rho$^+$ and hypersuppressive rho$^-$ strains (Zweifel & Fangman 1991). *MGT1* encodes a mitochondrial endonuclease that specifically cleaves Holliday junctions formed during recombination (Kleff et al 1992, Lockshon et al 1995). Although these Holliday junctions are not easily detected in the mtDNA of wild-type strains, cells lacking *MGT1* have elevated levels of these unresolved recombination intermediates (Lockshon et al 1995). The increased physical linkage between mitochondrial genomes in *mgt1* mutants causes the mtDNA to aggregate into fewer and larger nucleoids that, because of their decreased number, are less likely to be transmitted to daughter cells. In *mgt1*Δ hypersuppressive strains, rho$^-$ mtDNAs with tandemly repeated *rep* sequences undergo homologous recombination more frequently than rho$^+$ mtDNAs and, as a result, suffer a greater degree of genome crosslinking and aggregation. Thus the ability of *mgt1* mutations to restore normal mtDNA segregation patterns in crosses between rho$^+$ and hypersuppressive rho$^-$ strains is due to the fact that these aggregated rho$^-$ mtDNAs are inherited less efficiently. These results indicate that the nucleoid is the segregating unit in mitochondria and support the idea that recombination among mtDNAs plays an important role in the segregation of mitochondrial genomes.

ABF2

The abundant Abf2 protein is a member of the high mobility group (HMG) family of DNA-binding proteins and is associated with mtDNA nucleoids in vivo (Caron et al 1979; Diffley & Stillman 1991, 1992; Megraw & Chae 1993). Studies indicate that changes in Abf2p levels affect a variety of mtDNA phenotypes including mtDNA organization, maintenance, copy number, and recombination.

In *abf2* null cells, mtDNA nucleoids have altered protein profiles and increased DNase I sensitivities, indicating that Abf2p is important for mtDNA organization (Newman et al 1996). The level of Abf2p expression in cells has also been shown to be important for mtDNA stability. High levels of Abf2p expression result in mitochondrial genome loss (Megraw & Chae 1993, Zelenaya-Troitskaya et al 1998), and cells lacking Abf2p exhibit an increased frequency of mtDNA nucleoid loss when grown on the fermentable carbon source glucose at 30°C (Diffley & Stillman 1991, Megraw & Chae 1993). In contrast, *abf2* null cells can maintain mitochondrial genomes on the nonfermentable carbon source glycerol at 30°C, indicating that Abf2p is not essential for mtDNA replication, gene expression, or transmission to buds. However, when cells are grown on glycerol at elevated temperatures (37°C), Abf2p is essential for viability (Megraw & Chae 1993). Alterations in Abf2p levels also appear to affect mtDNA copy number; the mtDNA content is reduced by approximately 50% in *abf2* null cells maintained on glycerol and increased by 50 to 150% (relative to wild type) in cells containing several extra copies of the *ABF2* gene (Zelenaya-Troitskaya et al 1998). Finally, both the distribution of mtDNA nucleoids and the efficiency of mtDNA recombination are severely affected in crosses between parental strains lacking Abf2p (Zelenaya-Troitskaya et al 1998).

How does Abf2p affect mtDNA maintenance, copy number, and recombination in vivo? One possibility is that Abf2p serves a histone-like function in cells, and the loss of this protein causes pleiotropic defects in mtDNA-related behaviors. The abundance of Abf2p in mitochondria (approximately 1 molecule of Abf2p per 30 base pairs of mtDNA) (Diffley & Stillman 1992) and the observation that Abf2p has supercoiling activity (Caron et al 1979, Diffley & Stillman 1992) are consistent with this model. An alternative explanation is suggested by the recent reports that mtDNA replication may be a recombination-dependent process in yeast (Lockshon et al 1995, Bendich 1996). It is possible that altered Abf2p levels cause defects in mtDNA recombination that lead to secondary defects in mtDNA replication and genome maintenance. Several observations suggest a role for Abf2p in recombination. First, Abf2p is a HMG family member, and other HMG proteins have been shown to bind preferentially to cruciform DNA, which resembles Holliday junction intermediates formed during replication (Teo et al 1995). Second, a recent study showed that Abf2p promotes the formation or stabilization of Holliday recombination junctions in wild-type mtDNA (MacAlpine et al 1998). The level of these recombination intermediates appears to decrease in cells lacking Abf2p and to increase in cells overproducing Abf2p. Thus mitochondrial genome copy number and maintenance may depend on the formation of recombination structures that prime mtDNA replication.

ESCAPE OF MITOCHONDRIAL DNA
TO THE NUCLEUS

Thorsness & Fox have isolated a number of mutations that increase the rate at which DNA is lost from the mitochondrion and transferred to the nucleus in yeast (Thorsness & Fox 1993). Three of these *YME* genes encode mitochondrial proteins and appear to be important for mitochondrial genome maintenance and/or mitochondrial integrity.

Mutations in *YME1* increase the rate of mtDNA escape and cause temperature-sensitive growth defects on both fermentable and nonfermentable carbon sources (Thorsness et al 1993). *YME1* encodes an ATP and zinc-dependent protease that is tightly associated with the inner mitochondrial membrane (Thorsness et al 1993, Weber et al 1996). The proteolytic domain of Yme1p is located in the intermembrane space and is required for the turnover of mitochondrial inner membrane proteins (Nakai et al 1995, Pearce & Sherman 1995, Leonhard et al 1996, Weber et al 1996). *yme1* mutant cells also contain fragmented, clumped, and swollen mitochondria that appear to be associated with proteolytic vacuoles (Campbell et al 1994). A second gene, *YME2*, also encodes a mitochondrial inner membrane protein exposed to the intermembrane space (Hanekamp & Thorsness 1996). Mutations in *YME2* can suppress the cold-sensitive growth defect of the *yme1* mutant and exhibit synthetic growth defects with *yme1* on nonfermentable carbon sources. A third gene, *YME6* (Thorsness & Weber 1996), is identical to the previously characterized mitochondrial morphology gene *MMM1* (see above) (Burgess et al 1994).

All three *YME* genes described above encode proteins localized to the mitochondrial compartment, and mutations in two of these genes appear to cause severe defects in mitochondrial morphology. Thus the increased rate of mtDNA loss/escape observed in these *yme* mutants may result from breaches in the mitochondrial compartment introduced by these morphology changes or by degradative processes that turn over defective mitochondria in these cells (Thorsness & Weber 1996). Regardless of the mechanism of DNA escape, the studies of yeast mitochondrial morphology mutants and these *yme* mutants indicate that mitochondrial genome maintenance depends heavily on the integrity of the mitochondrial compartment.

MITOCHONDRIAL FISSION AND FUSION

Over the past two decades, researchers have identified many of the molecules that regulate heterotypic fusion reactions (between unlike membranes) and homotypic fusion reactions (between like membranes) in yeast, mammalian cells, and neurons. These include the NSF (NEM sensitive factor) ATPase and its related family members, SNAPs (soluble NSF attachment proteins); the cognate membrane-docking proteins called v-SNAREs and t-SNAREs (SNAP receptors); proteins such as Sec1p that regulate SNARE availability; and the Rab family of small GTPases, which contribute to the specificity and efficiency of the fusion reaction (Pfeffer 1996, Rothman 1996, Hay & Scheller 1997, Novick & Zerial 1997). In addition, there is now evidence that the dynamin GTPase regulates membrane division or fission at the cell surface (Sweitzer & Hinshaw 1998). Surprisingly, none of these molecules has been shown to control the fission or fusion of mitochondria in any cell type. Mitochondria are one of the few cellular organelles that have two distinct membranes. The dispensability of these molecules for mitochondrial membrane dynamics may indicate that a different type of molecular machinery is required to coordinate the behavior of these two membranes during division and fusion. Although we are far from understanding the molecular basis of these events, a potential regulator of mitochondrial fusion in flies and yeast was recently described, and two of the proteins implicated in yeast mitochondrial morphology maintenance share molecular features with the membrane fission protein dynamin.

Fission

In *S. cerevisiae*, mitochondrial fission events at branchpoints or within tubules generate new ends in the reticular network (Nunnari et al 1997). Membrane division or fission is also required to separate the mother and daughter mitochondrial networks during cytokinesis. Although division might be accomplished by simply pulling on opposite ends of a mitochondrial tubule, an alternative possibility is that a protein (or proteins) assembled on the cytoplasmic face of the mitochondrion constricts and pinches the compartment into two pieces. This is the mechanism by which the dynamin GTPase catalyzes the release of clathrin-coated vesicles from the plasma membrane (Sweitzer & Hinshaw 1998). The yeast *MGM1* and *DNM1* genes (described above) encode predicted GTPases that are structurally related to dynamin. Although mutations in these genes cause dramatic changes in mitochondrial morphology, it is not known if these changes result from defects in membrane fission or division. More work is required to determine the activities and topologies of the Dnm1 and Mgm1 proteins. In addition, other unidentified molecules may act from inside or outside the organelle to control mitochondrial division.

Fusion

Time-lapse analyses of fluorescently labeled mitochondrial networks suggest that membrane fission events are balanced by frequent fusion events (Nunnari et al 1997). As in other cell types, mitochondrial fusion in yeast appears to occur when a free mitochondrial end or tip encounters another mitochondrial end or a tubule side (Bereiter-Hahn & Voth 1994, Nunnari et al 1997). These observations have led to the idea that components of the fusion machinery are either concentrated at, or specifically activated at, mitochondrial tips (Nunnari et al 1997). In both yeast and mammalian cells, fusion has been proposed to initiate at stable contact sites between the inner and outer mitochondrial membranes (Bereiter-Hahn & Voth 1994).

Studies of mitochondrial dynamics during yeast mating provide a clear demonstration of mitochondrial fusion. As described above, early genetic studies indicated that marked mtDNAs derived from different haploid parents recombined in yeast zygotes (Thomas & Wilkie 1968, Dujon 1981). This recombination could occur only if mitochondria from each parent fused in the zygote to allow mitochondrial genome mixing. Using indirect immunofluorescence techniques, Azpirov & Butow (1993) demonstrated that a matrix component present in one parent quickly redistributed throughout the diploid zygote. This result indicated that mitochondria derived from each parent were mixing in the zygote, but did not confirm that the two populations of mitochondria were actually fusing with one another. In a later study, Nunnari and colleagues (1997) used fluorescent tags of different colors to visualize the mitochondria of both haploid parents in living cells. After mating, these two mitochondrial markers rapidly redistributed and colocalized throughout zygotes, indicating that mitochondrial fusion had occurred. Because one of the fluorescent markers used in this study was localized to the mitochondrial matrix, mixing could only result if both the inner and outer mitochondrial membranes fused.

In crosses between wild-type yeast cells, the rate at which different mitochondrial constituents mix after fusion can vary depending on the type of molecule and its location in the organelle. As described above, soluble matrix proteins equilibrate rapidly throughout the zygote after mitochondrial fusion (Azpiroz & Butow 1993, Nunnari et al 1997). Butow and coworkers have examined the redistribution of GFP-tagged inner and outer mitochondrial membrane proteins in zygotes and find that these proteins equilibrate at a slower rate than matrix proteins throughout the fused mitochondrial network (Okamoto et al 1997). In contrast, mtDNA genomes behave as if they are anchored within the organelle and do not mix extensively in the zygote (Nunnari et al 1997). Interestingly, the sorting patterns of mitochondrial nucleoids and proteins can change dramatically when matings are performed with rho$^-$ or rho^0 cells (Azpiroz & Butow 1993). The molecular basis for these changes in sorting patterns is not understood.

FZO1   The cloning by Hales & Fuller (1997) of the *Drosophila fuzzy onions* (*fzo*) gene represents a major leap forward for the mitochondrial fusion field. This gene encodes the first protein known to play a role in mitochondrial fusion in any system. The Fzo protein defines a family of related molecules, one of which is clearly required for mitochondrial dynamics in *S. cerevisiae*.

During *Drosophila* spermatogenesis, mitochondria aggregate and fuse to form two giant organelles that are tightly coiled around one another, like the layers of an onion (Fuller 1993). In *fzo* mutant males, the individual mito-chondria aggregate normally but fail to fuse, giving rise to structures that look more like fuzzy onions when viewed in cross section with the electron micro-scope (Hales & Fuller 1997). The *fzo* gene encodes an 81.5-kDa protein with a predicted GTPase domain near the N terminus, two closely spaced potential membrane spanning domains near the C terminus, and three predicted heptad repeats. The Fzo protein appears on spermatid mitochondria just as fusion be-gins and disappears soon after fusion is complete. The correlation between the timing of mitochondrial fusion and Fzo expression is striking and suggests that this protein could be the actual mediator of membrane fusion. The fly Fzo protein has homologues in yeast and nematodes and is ubiquitously expressed in mammalian tissues. Thus Fzo defines a new family of GTPases that may play a general role in regulating mitochondrial fusion, and/or other mitochondrial behaviors in cells. Recent studies of the yeast *fzo* homologue suggest that this is indeed the case.

The *S. cerevisiae fzo* gene, called yeast *FZO1* (y*FZO1*; 19% identity to *fzo*), also performs an essential role in mitochondrial fusion. Yeast cells lacking the Fzo1 protein contain multiple spherical or slightly elongated mitochondrial compartments that are inherited normally by buds but lose their mtDNA nu-cleoids (GJ Hermann, JW Thatcher, JP Mills, KG Hales, MT Fuller, J Nunnari, JM Shaw, submitted). Fzo1p depletion studies indicate that this defect in mi-tochondrial genome maintenance is a secondary consequence of changes in mitochondrial morphology. A conditional mutation in *FZO1* causes fragmen-tation of the mitochondrial network and blocks mitochondrial fusion during mating. These results indicate that the mitochondrial morphology changes in *fzo1* null cells result from defects in mitochondrial fusion. Like the fly Fzo protein, yeast Fzo1p is distributed over the length of the mitochondrion and behaves like an integral membrane protein. However, unlike *Drosophila* Fzo, which is expressed in a very narrow developmental window when mitochon-drial fusion is occurring (Hales & Fuller 1997), yeast Fzo1p is present on mitochondria at relatively constant levels throughout the yeast life cycle (GJ Hermann, JW Thatcher, JP Mills, KG Hales, MT Fuller, J Nunnari, JM Shaw, submitted). This may explain why mitochondrial fusion events appear to occur continuously during mitotic growth. Protease protection studies indicate that the N-terminal GTPase domain of yeast Fzo1p is exposed to the cytoplasm where it is available to interact with other proteins and cellular structures that could regulate its activity and the behavior of the mitochondrial compartment.

The similarities between the fly and yeast Fzo proteins leave no doubt that the Fzo family of transmembrane GTPases plays an essential and conserved role in regulating mitochondrial dynamics.

Although the nucleotide hydrolyzing activities and binding preferences of fly and yeast Fzo have not been tested, mutations expected to alter these properties have been generated in the predicted GTPase domains of both proteins. These mutant proteins localize to mitochondrial membranes in their respective organisms, but fail to support mitochondrial fusion in *Drosophila* or rescue mitochondrial morphology defects in yeast (Hales & Fuller 1997; GJ Hermann, JW Thatcher, JP Mills, KG Hales, MT Fuller, J Nunnari, JM Shaw, submitted). Unlike the equivalent mutations in proteins of the ras and dynamin superfamilies, the yeast and fly *fzo* mutations do not produce dominant interfering phenotypes in vivo (Hales & Fuller 1997; GJ Hermann, JW Thatcher, JP Mills, KG Hales, MT Fuller, J Nunnari, JM Shaw, submitted). The latter result suggests that the mechanism of Fzo function may differ from that of other characterized GTPases.

The behavior of yeast mitochondria in vivo suggests that components of the fusion machinery are localized or activated at mitochondrial ends (Nunnari et al 1997). Yet, fusion of free ends often occurs with the sides of mitochondrial tubules, indicating that molecules mediating fusion are distributed throughout the organelle. Yeast Fzo1p covers the mitochondrial outer membrane with its predicted GTPase domain facing the cytoplasm (GJ Hermann, JW Thatcher, JP Mills, KG Hales, MT Fuller, J Nunnari, JM Shaw, submitted) and, as proposed by Hales & Fuller (1997), could perform a SNARE-like function to control mitochondrial-mitochondrial docking prior to fusion. In this context, GTP binding and/or hydrolysis by yeast Fzo1p might act to regulate mitochondrial docking just as Rab GTPase family members facilitate SNARE complex formation in other intracellular transport reactions (Pfeffer 1996, Novick & Zerial 1997). Alternatively, Fzo1p might be required for the fusion of mitochondrial membranes after docking has already occurred. Other roles for Fzo1p have not been excluded. For example, Fzo1p might regulate mitochondrial morphology in yeast by interacting with cytoskeletal components in the cytoplasm, or other mitochondrial membrane proteins. Both in vivo and in vitro studies are now under way to distinguish between these models for Fzo1 protein function.

PERSPECTIVES AND FUTURE DIRECTIONS

It is clear that mitochondrial morphology and inheritance are regulated in most cell types. In the past eight years, *S. cerevisiae* has emerged as a powerful experimental system to study different mitochondrial behaviors. Although we know the identities of several genes that control mitochondrial shape and inheritance, additional genes and proteins will almost certainly be involved. Now that the sequence of the yeast genome is complete, the identification of these additional components should proceed quickly.

As is usually the case, what we have learned about mitochondrial dynamics has raised many new questions. What is the relationship between mitochondrial morphology and mitochondrial inheritance? What are the exact roles of the actin- and Mdm1-based cytoskeletons in maintaining mitochondrial morphology and directing mitochondrial partitioning? What is the identity of the myosin-like motor on the mitochondrial surface and is this the molecule that provides the force for directed mitochondrial movements during cell division? How are the distribution and copy number of mtDNA nucleoids maintained, and how are their movements restricted in the mitochondrial matrix? What are the molecular mechanisms that control mitochondrial membrane fission and fusion, and how are these processes regulated? Identifying the protein players involved in these events is a necessary first step but cannot provide all the answers. We will also need to develop in vitro assays that reconstitute different mitochondrial behaviors (similar to the assays for mitochondrial-actin interactions) if we hope to understand the precise molecular mechanisms by which these molecules work. There are many excellent opportunities for geneticists, cell biologists, and biochemists in this field, and we can look forward to new developments and insights in the next few years.

ACKNOWLEDGMENTS

We thank the past and present members of the Shaw laboratory who contributed to this review including William Bleazard, Ellen Brisch, Noelle Fukushima, Steve Gorsich, Brian Keegan, Denichiro Otsuga, Amy Roeder, and John Thatcher. Denichiro Otsuga and Brian Keegan contributed the confocal images in Figure 2. We also thank Ronald Butow, Margaret Clarke, Margaret Fuller, Rob Jensen, Sepp Kohlwein, Jodi Nunnari, Philip Perlman, Liza Pon, Peter Thorsness, and Michael Yaffe for sending reprints and for communicating results prior to publication. We are grateful to Jodi Nunnari and Joe Dickinson for many helpful discussions and critical reading of the manuscript. Work in the Shaw laboratory is supported by grants from the National Institutes of Health (GM53466), the American Cancer Society (RPG 940 3504 CSM), and the University of Utah Huntsman Cancer Institute. G Hermann was supported by a National Institutes of Health Predoctoral Genetics Training Grant (5 T32 GM07464) and a University of Utah Graduate Research Fellowship.

Visit the *Annual Reviews home page* at
http://www.AnnualReviews.org

Literature Cited

Adams AEM, Pringle JR. 1984. Relationship of actin and tubulin distribution in wild-type and morphogenic mutant *Saccharomyces cerevisiae*. *J. Cell Biol.* 98:934–45

Attardi G, Schatz G. 1988. Biogenesis of mitochondria. *Annu. Rev. Cell Biol.* 4:289–333

Azpiroz R, Butow RA. 1993. Patterns of mitochondrial sorting in yeast zygotes. *Mol. Biol. Cell* 4:21–36

Bakeeva LE, Chentsov YS, Skulachev VP. 1978. Mitochondrial framework (reticulum mitochondriale) in rat diaphragm muscle. *Biochim. Biophys. Acta* 501:349–69

Ball EH, Singer SJ. 1982. Mitochondria are associated with microtubules and not with intermediate filaments in cultured fibroblasts. *Proc. Natl. Acad. Sci. USA* 79:123–26

Bearer EL, DeGiorgis JA, Medeiros NA, Reese TS. 1996. Actin-based motility of isolated axoplasmic organelles. *Cell Motil. Cytoskelet.* 33:106–14

Bendich AJ. 1996. Structural analysis of mitochondrial DNA molecules from fungi and plants using moving pictures and pulse-field gel electrophoresis. *J. Mol. Biol.* 255:564–88

Bereiter-Hahn J. 1976. Dimethylaminostyrylmethylpyribiniumiodine (DASPMI) as a fluorescent probe for mitochondria in situ. *Biochim. Biophys. Acta* 423:1–14

Bereiter-Hahn J. 1990. Behavior of mitochondria in the living cell. *Int. Rev. Cytol.* 122:1–63

Bereiter-Hahn J, Voth M. 1994. Dynamics of mitochondria in living cells: shape changes, dislocations, fusion, and fission of mitochondria. *Microsc. Res.* 27:198–219

Berger KH, Sogo LF, Yaffe MP. 1997. Mdm12p, a component required for mitochondrial inheritance that is conserved between budding and fission yeast. *J. Cell Biol.* 136:545–53

Berger KH, Yaffe MP. 1996. Mitochondrial distribution and inheritance. *Experientia* 52:1111–16

Birky CW. 1983. The partitioning of cytoplasmic organelles at cell division. *Int. Rev. Cytol.* 15:49–89

Birky CW, Demko CA, Perlman PS, Strausberg R. 1978. Uniparental inheritance of mitochondrial genes in yeast: dependence on the input bias of mitochondrial DNA and preliminary investigations of the mechanism. *Genetics* 89:615–51

Blanc H, Dujon B. 1980. Replicator regions of the yeast mitochondrial DNA responsible for suppressiveness. *Proc. Natl. Acad. Sci. USA* 77:3942–46

Boldogh I, Vojtov N, Karmons S, Pon LA. 1998. Interaction between mitochondria and the actin cytoskeleton in budding yeast requires two integral mitochondrial outer membrane proteins, Mmm1p and Mdm10p. *J. Cell Biol.* 141:1371–81

Botstein D, Amberg D, Mulholland J, Huffaker T, Adams A, et al. 1997. The yeast cytoskeleton. In *The Molecular Biology of the Yeast Saccharomyces*, ed. JR Pringle, JR Broach, EW Jones. pp. 1–90. Cold Spring Harbor, NY: Cold Spring Harbor Lab. Press

Bradley TJ, Satir P. 1979. Evidence of microfilament-associated mitochondrial movement. *J. Supramol. Struct.* 12:165–75

Brewster JL, de Valoir T, Dwyer ND, Winter E, Gustin MC. 1993. An osmosensing signal transduction pathway in yeast. *Science* 259:1760–63

Burgess SM, Delannoy M, Jensen RE. 1994. *MMM1* encodes a mitochondrial outer membrane protein essential for establishing and maintaining the structure of yeast mitochondria. *J. Cell Biol.* 126:1375–91

Campbell CL, Tanaka N, White KH, Thorsness PE. 1994. Mitochondrial morphology and functional defects in yeast caused by *yme1* are suppressed by mutation of a 26S protease subunit homologue. *Mol. Biol. Cell* 5:899–905

Caron F, Jacq C, Rouviere-Yaniv J. 1979. Characterization of a histone-like protein extracted from yeast mitochondria. *Proc. Natl. Acad. Sci. USA* 76:4265–69

Chen LB. 1989. Fluorescent labeling of mitochondria. *Methods Cell Biol.* 29:103–23

Chowdhury S, Smith KW, Gustin MC. 1992. Osmotic stress and the yeast cytoskelton: phenotype-specific suppression of an actin mutation. *J. Cell Biol.* 118:561–71

Costanzo MC, Fox TD. 1990. Control of mitochondrial gene expression in *Saccharomyces cerevisiae*. *Annu. Rev. Genet.* 24:91–113

Davison MT, Garland PB. 1977. Structure of mitochondria and vacuoles of *Candida utilis* and *Schizosaccharomyces pombe* studied by electron microscopy of serial thin sections and model building. *J. Gen. Microbiol.* 98:147–53

De Camilli P, Takei K, McPherson PS. 1995. The function of dynamin in endocytosis. *Curr. Opin. Neurobiol.* 5:559–65

De Zamaroczy M, Marotta R, Faugeron-Fonty G, Goursot R, Mangin M, et al. 1981. The origin of replication of the yeast mitochondrial genome and the phenomenon of suppressivity. *Nature* 292:75–78

Diffley JF, Stillman B. 1991. A close relative of the nuclear, chromosomal high-mobility group protein HMG1 in yeast mitochondria. *Proc. Natl. Acad. Sci. USA* 88:7864–68

Diffley JF, Stillman B. 1992. DNA binding

properties of an HMG1-related protein from yeast mitochondria. *J. Biol. Chem.* 267: 3368–74

Drees B, Brown C, Barrell BG, Bretscher A. 1995. Tropomyosin is essential in yeast, yet the *TPM1* and *TPM2* products perform distinct functions. *J. Cell Biol.* 128:383–92

Drubin DG, Jones HD, Wertman KF. 1993. Actin structure and function: roles in mitochondrial organization and morphogenesis in budding yeast and identification of the phalloidin-binding site. *Mol. Biol. Cell* 4: 1277–94

Dujon B. 1981. Mitochondrial genetics and functions. In *Molecular Biology of the Yeast Saccharomyces*, ed. JM Strathern, EW Jones, JR Broach, pp. 505–635. Cold Spring Harbor, NY: Cold Spring Harbor Lab. Press

Fields SD, Conrad MN, Clarke M. 1998. The *S. cerevisiae CLU1* and *D. discoideum cluA* genes are functional homologues that influence mitochondrial morphology and distribution. *J. Cell Sci.* 111:1717–27

Fisk HA, Yaffe MP. 1997. Mutational analysis of Mdm1p function in nuclear and mitochondrial inheritance. *J. Cell Biol.* 138:485–94

Fox TD. 1996. Genetic strategies for identification of mitochondrial translation factors in *Saccharomyces cerevisiae*. *Methods Enzymol.* 264:228–37

Fuchs E, Weber K. 1994. Intermediate filaments: structure, dynamics, function, and disease. *Annu. Rev. Biochem.* 63:345–82

Fuller MT. 1993. Spermatogenesis. In *The Development of Drosophila melanogaster*, ed. M Bate, A Martinez-Arias, pp. 71–147. Cold Spring Harbor, NY: Cold Spring Harbor Lab. Press

Gammie AE, Kurihara LJ, Vallee RB, Rose MD. 1995. *DNM1*, a dynamin-related gene, participates in endosomal trafficking in yeast. *J. Cell Biol.* 130:553–66

Gbelska Y, Subik J, Goffeau A, Kovac L. 1983. Intramitochondrial ATP and cell functions: Yeast cells depleted of intramitochondrial ATP lose the ability to grow and multiply. *Eur. J. Biochem.* 130:281–86

Goodson HV, Anderson BL, Warrick HM, Pon L, Spudich JA. 1996. Synthetic lethality screen identifies a novel yeast myosin I gene (*MYO5*): Myosin I proteins are required for polarization of the actin cytoskeleton. *J. Cell Biol.* 133:1277–91

Guan K, Farh L, Marshall TK, Deschenes RJ. 1993. Normal mitochondrial structure and genome maintenance in yeast requires the dynamin-like product of the *MGM1* gene. *Curr. Genet.* 24:141–48

Hales KG, Fuller MT. 1997. Developmentally regulated mitochondrial fusion mediated by a conserved, novel, predicted GTPase. *Cell* 90:121–29

Hanekamp T, Thorsness PE. 1996. Inactivation of *YME2/RNA12*, which encodes an integral inner mitochondrial membrane protein, causes increased escape of DNA from mitochondria to the nucleus in *Saccharomyces cerevisiae*. *Mol. Cell Biol.* 16:2764–71

Hartwell LH, Weinert TA. 1989. Checkpoints: controls that ensure the order of cell cycle events. *Science* 246:629–34

Hay JC, Scheller RH. 1997. SNAREs and NSF in targeted membrane fusion. *Curr. Opin. Cell Biol.* 9:505–12

Heggeness MH, Simon M, Singer SJ. 1978. Association of mitochondria with microtubules in cultured cells. *Proc. Natl. Acad. Sci. USA* 75:3863–66

Hermann GJ, King EJ, Shaw JM. 1997. The yeast gene, *MDM20*, is necessary for mitochondrial inheritance and organization of the actin cytoskeleton. *J. Cell Biol.* 137:141–53

Hinshaw JE, Schmid SL. 1995. Dynamin self-assembles into rings suggesting a mechanism for coated vesicle budding. *Nature* 374:190–92

Hirokawa N. 1982. Cross-linker systems between neurofilaments, microtubules, and membranous organelles in frog axons revealed by quick-freeze, deep-etching method. *J. Cell Biol.* 94:129–42

Hirokawa N. 1998. Kinesin and dynein superfamily proteins and the mechanism of organelle transport. *Science* 279:519–26

Hoch FL. 1992. Cardiolipins and biomembrane function. *Biochim. Biophys. Acta* 1113:71–133

Hoffman H, Avers CJ. 1973. Mitochondrion of yeast: ultrastructural evidence for one giant, branched organelle per cell. *Science* 181: 749–51

Hollenbeck PJ. 1996. The pattern and mechanism of mitochondrial transport in axons. *Front. Biosci.* 1:91–102

Huffaker TC, Hoyt MA, Botstein D. 1987. Genetic analysis of the yeast cytoskeleton. *Annu. Rev. Genet.* 21:259–84

Huffaker TC, Thomas JH, Botstein D. 1988. Diverse effects of β-tubulin mutations on microtubule formation and function. *J. Cell Biol.* 106:1997–2010

Jacobs CW, Adams AEM, Szaniszlo PJ, Pringle JR. 1988. Functions of microtubules in the *Saccharomyces cerevisiae* cell cycle. *J. Cell Biol.* 107:1409–26

Jamet-Vierny C, Contamine V, Boulay J, Zickler D, Picard M. 1997. Mutations in genes encoding the mitochondrial outer membrane proteins Tom70 and Mdm10 of *Podospora anserina* modify the spectrum of mitochondrial DNA rearrangements associated with cellular death. *Mol. Cell Biol.* 17:6359–66

Jiang B, Ram AFJ, Sheraton J, Klis FM, Bussey H. 1995. Regulation of cell wall β-glucan assembly: *PTC1* negatively affects *PBS2* action in a pathway that includes modulation of *EXG1* transcription. *Mol. Gen. Genet.* 248:260–69

Jiang F, Rizavi HS, Greenberg ML. 1997. Cardiolipin is not essential for the growth of *Saccharomyces cerevisiae* on fermentable or non-fermentable carbon sources. *Mol. Microbiol.* 26:481–91

Johnson LV, Walsh ML, Chen LB. 1980. Localization of mitochondria in living cells with rhodamine 123. *Proc. Natl. Acad. Sci. USA* 77:990–94

Jones BA, Fangman WL. 1992. Mitochondrial DNA maintenance in yeast requires a protein containing a region related to the GTP-binding domain of dynamin. *Genes Dev.* 6:380–89

Kent C. 1995. Eukaryotic phospholipid biosynthesis. *Annu. Rev. Biochem.* 64:315–43

Kilmartin JV, Adams AEM. 1984. Structural rearrangements of tubulin and actin during the cell cycle of the yeast *Saccharomyces. J. Cell Biol.* 98:922–33

Kleff S, Kemper B, Sternglanz R. 1992. Identification and characterization of yeast mutants and the gene for cruciform cutting endonuclease. *EMBO J.* 11:699–704

Kohlwein SD, Eder S, Oberhofer E, Jandrositz A. 1997. Organelle structure and dynamics in yeast. *Mol. Biol. Cell* 8:78a

Koning AJ, Lum PY, Williams JM, Wright R. 1993. DiOC$_6$ staining reveals organelle structure and dynamics in living yeast cells. *Cell Motil. Cytoskelet.* 25:111–28

Kovacova V, Irmlerova J, Kovac L. 1968. Oxidative phosphorylation in yeast. IV. Combination of a nuclear mutation affecting oxidative phosphorylation with a cytoplasmic mutation to respiratory deficiency. *Biochim. Biophys. Acta* 162:157–63

Kuznetsov SA, Langford GM, Weiss DG. 1992. Actin-dependent organelle movement in squid axoplasm. *Nature* 356:722–25

Landau EM, Kwanbunbumpen S. 1969. Morphology of motor nerve terminals subjected to polarizing currents. *Nature* 221:271–72

Lazzarino DA, Boldogh I, Smith MG, Rosand J, Pon LA. 1994. Yeast mitochondria contain ATP-sensitive, reversible actin-binding activity. *Mol. Biol. Cell* 5:807–18

Leonhard K, Herrmann JM, Stuart RA, Mannhaupt G, Neupert W, Langer T. 1996. AAA proteases with catalytic sites on opposite membrane surfaces comprise a proteolytic system for the ATP-dependent degradation of inner membrane proteins in mitochondria. *EMBO J.* 15:4218–29

Lill R, Neupert W. 1996. Mechanisms of protein import across the mitochondrial outer membrane. *Trends Cell Biol.* 6:56–61

Liu H, Bretscher A. 1989. Disruption of the single tropomyosin gene in yeast results in the disappearance of actin cables from the cytoskeleton. *Cell* 57:233–42

Liu H, Bretscher A. 1992. Characterization of *TPM1* disrupted yeast cells indicates an involvement of tropomyosin in directed vesicular transport. *J. Cell Biol.* 118:285–99

Lockshon D, Zweifel SG, Freeman-Cook LL, Lorimer HE, Brewer BJ, Fangman WL. 1995. A role for recombination junctions in the segregation of mitochondrial DNA in yeast. *Cell* 81:947–55

MacAlpine DM, Perlman PS, Butow RA. 1998. The high mobility group protein Abf2p influences the level of yeast mitochondrial DNA recombination intermediates in vivo. *Proc. Natl. Acad. Sci. USA* 95:6739–43

Maeda T, Tsai AYM, Sato H. 1993. Mutations in a protein tyrosine phosphatase gene (*PTP2*) and a protein serine/threonine phosphatase gene (*PTC1*) cause a synthetic growth defect in *Saccharomyces cerevisiae. Mol. Cell Biol.* 13:5408–17

Maeda T, Wurgler-Murphy SM, Saito H. 1994. A two-component system that regulates an osmosensing MAP kinase cascade in yeast. *Nature* 369:242–45

McConnell SJ, Stewart LC, Talin A, Yaffe MP. 1990. Temperature-sensitive yeast mutants defective in mitochondrial inheritance. *J. Cell Biol.* 111:967–76

McConnell SJ, Yaffe MP. 1992. Nuclear and mitochondrial inheritance in yeast depends on novel cytoplasmic structures defined by the MDM1 protein. *J. Cell Biol.* 118:385–95

McConnell SJ, Yaffe MP. 1993. Intermediate filament formation by a yeast protein essential for organelle inheritance. *Science* 260:687–89

Megraw TL, Chae CB. 1993. Functional complementarity between the HMG1-like yeast mitochondrial histone HM and the bacterial histone-like protein HU. *J. Biol. Chem.* 268:12758–63

Miyakawa I, Aoi H, Sando N, Kuroiwa T. 1984. Fluorescence microscopic studies of mitochondrial nucleoids during meiosis and sporulation in the yeast, *Saccharomyces cerevisiae. J. Cell Sci.* 66:21–38

Morgan BA, Bouquin N, Johnston LH. 1995. Two-component signal-transduction systems in budding yeast MAP a different pathway? *Trends Cell Biol.* 5:453–57

Morris RL, Hollenbeck PJ. 1995. Axonal transport of mitochondria along microtubules and

F-actin in living vertebrate neurons. *J. Cell Biol.* 131:1315–26

Mose-Larsen P, Bravo R, Fey SJ, Small JV, Celis JE. 1982. Putative association of mitochondria with a subpopulation of intermediate-sized filaments in cultured human skin fibroblasts. *Cell* 31:681–92

Nakai T, Yasuhara T, Fujiki Y, Ohashi A. 1995. Multiple genes, including a member of the AAA family, are essential for degradation of unassembled subunit 2 of cytochrome *c* oxidase in yeast mitochondria. *Mol. Cell Biol.* 15:4441–52

Nangaku M, Sato-Yoshitake R, Okada Y, Noda Y, Takemura R, et al. 1994. KIF1B, a novel microtubule plus end-directed monomeric motor protein for transport of mitochondria. *Cell* 79:1209–20

Neupert W. 1997. Protein import into mitochondria. *Annu. Rev. Biochem.* 66:863–917

Newman SM, Zelenaya-Troitskaya O, Perlman PS, Butow RA. 1996. Analysis of mitochondrial DNA nucleoids in wild-type and a mutant strain of *Saccharomyces cerevisiae* that lacks the mitochondrial HMG-box protein, Abf2p. *Nucleic Acids Res.* 24:386–93

Nickas ME, Yaffe MP. 1996. *BRO1*, a novel gene that interacts with components of the Pkc1p-mitogen-activated protein kinase pathway in *Saccharomyces cerevisiae*. *Mol. Cell Biol.* 16:2585–93

Novick P, Zerial M. 1997. The diversity of Rab proteins in vesicle transport. *Curr. Opin. Cell Biol.* 9:496–504

Nunnari J, Marshall WF, Straight A, Murray A, Sedat JW, Walter P. 1997. Mitochondrial transmission during mating in *Saccharomyces cerevisiae* is determined by mitochondrial fusion and fission and the intramitochondrial segregation of mitochondrial DNA. *Mol. Biol. Cell* 8:1233–42

Nunnari J, Walter P. 1996. Regulation of organelle biogenesis. *Cell* 84:389–94

Oakley BR, Reinhart JE. 1985. Mitochondria and nuclei move by different mechanisms in *Aspergillus nidulans*. *J. Cell Biol.* 101:2392–97

Okamoto K, Newman SM, Perlman PS, Butow RA. 1997. Sorting patterns of mitochondrial proteins in yeast zygotes. *Mol. Biol. Cell* 8:240a

Palade G. 1983. Membrane biogenesis: an overview. *Methods Enzymol.* 96:29–40

Pearce DA, Sherman F. 1995. Degradation of cytochrome oxidase subunits in mutants of yeast lacking cytochrome *c* and suppression of the degradation by mutation of *yme1*. *J. Biol. Chem.* 270:20879–82

Pereira AJ, Dalby B, Stewart RJ, Doxsey SJ, Goldstein LSB. 1997. Mitochondrial association of a plus end-directed microtubule motor expressed during mitosis in *Drosophila*. *J. Cell Biol.* 136:1081–90

Pfeffer SR. 1996. Transport vesicle docking: SNAREs and associates. *Annu. Rev. Cell Dev. Biol.* 12:441–61

Piskur J. 1994. Inheritance of the yeast mitochondrial genome. *Plasmid* 31:229–41

Pon L, Schatz G. 1991. Biogenesis of yeast mitochondria. In *The Molecular Biology of the Yeast Saccharomyces*, ed. JR Broach, JR Pringle, EW Jones, pp. 334–406. Cold Spring Harbor, NY: Cold Spring Harbor Lab. Press

Posas F, Wurgler-Murphy SM, Maeda T, Witten EA, Thai TC, Saito H. 1996. Yeast *HOG1* MAP kinase cascade is regulated by a multistep phosphorelay mechanism in the *SLN1-YPD1-SSK1* "two-component" osmosensor. *Cell* 86:865–75

Roeder AD, Hermann GJ, Keegan BR, Thatcher SA, Shaw JM. 1998. Mitochondrial inheritance is delayed in *Saccharomyces cerevisiae* cells lacking the serine/threonine phosphatase, *PTC1*. *Mol. Biol. Cell.* 9:917–30

Rothman JE. 1996. The protein machinery of vesicle budding and fusion. *Prot. Sci.* 5:185–94

Schatz G. 1996. The protein import system of mitochondria. *J. Biol. Chem.* 271:31763–66

Schmid SL. 1997. Clathrin-coated vesicle formation and protein sorting: an integrated process. *Annu. Rev. Biochem.* 66:511–48

Schmitt ME, Clayton DA. 1993. Conserved features of yeast and mammalian mitochondrial DNA replication. *Curr. Opin. Genet. Dev.* 3:769–74

Schneiter R, Kohlwein SD. 1997. Organelle structure, function, and inheritance in yeast: a role for fatty acid synthesis? *Cell* 88:431–34

Schultz J, Ferguson B, Sprague GF. 1995. Signal transduction and growth control in yeast. *Curr. Opin. Genet. Dev.* 5:31–37

Shadel GS, Clayton DA. 1997. Mitochondrial DNA maintenance in vertebrates. *Annu. Rev. Biochem.* 66:409–35

Shortle D, Haber JE, Botstein D. 1982. Lethal disruption of the yeast actin gene by integrative DNA transformation. *Science* 217:371–73

Simon VR, Karmon SL, Pon LA. 1997. Mitochondrial inheritance: cell cycle and actin cable dependence of polarized mitochondrial movements in *Saccharomyces cerevisiae*. *Cell Motil. Cytoskelet.* 37:199–210

Simon VR, Pon LA. 1996. Actin-based organelle movement. *Experientia* 52:1117–22

Simon VR, Swayne TC, Pon LA. 1995. Actin-dependent mitochondrial motility in mitotic yeast and cell-free systems: identification of a motor activity on the mitochondrial surface. *J. Cell Biol.* 130:345–54

Smith MG, Simon VR, O'Sullivan H, Pon LA. 1995. Organelle-cytoskeletal interactions: Actin mutations inhibit meiosis-dependent mitochondrial rearrangement in the budding yeast *Saccharomyces cerevisiae*. *Mol. Biol. Cell* 6:1381–96

Sogo LF, Yaffe MP. 1994. Regulation of mitochondrial morphology and inheritance by Mdm10p, a protein of the mitochondrial outer membrane. *J. Cell Biol.* 126:1361–73

Sprague GF, Thorner JW. 1994. Pheromone response and signal transduction during the mating process of *Saccharomyces cerevisiae*. In *The Molecular and Cellular Biology of the Yeast Saccharomyces*, ed. EW Jones, pp. 657–744. Cold Spring Harbor, NY: Cold Spring Harbor Lab. Press

Stevens B. 1981. Mitochondrial structure. In *The Molecular Biology of the Yeast Saccharomyces*, ed. JM Strathern, EW Jones, JR Broach, pp. 471–504. Cold Spring Harbor, NY: Cold Spring Harbor Lab. Press

Stevens BJ. 1977. Variation in number and volume of mitochondria in yeast according to growth conditions. A study based on serial sectioning and computer graphics reconstruction. *Biol. Cell.* 28:37–56

Stewart LC, Yaffe MP. 1991. A role for unsaturated fatty acids in mitochondrial movement and inheritance. *J. Cell Biol.* 115:1249–57

Strausberg RL, Perlman PS. 1978. The effect of zygotic bud position on the transmission of mitochondrial genes in *Saccharomyces cerevisiae*. *Mol. Gen. Genet.* 163:131–44

Stromer MH, Bendayan M. 1990. Immunocytochemical identification of cytoskeletal linkages to smooth muscle cell nuclei and mitochondria. *Cell Motil. Cytoskelet.* 17:11–18

Stukey JE, McDonough VM, Martin CE. 1989. Isolation and characterization of *OLE1*, a gene affecting fatty acid desaturation from *Saccharomyces cerevisiae*. *J. Biol. Chem.* 264:16537–44

Stukey JE, McDonough VM, Martin CE. 1990. The *OLE1* gene of *Saccharomyces cerevisiae* encodes the $\Delta 9$ fatty acid desaturase and can be functionally replaced by the rat stearoyl-CoA desaturase gene. *J. Biol. Chem.* 265:20144–49

Sturmer K, Baumann O, Walz B. 1995. Actin-dependent light-induced translocation of mitochondria and ER cisternae in the photoreceptor cells of the locust *Schistocerca gregaria*. *J. Cell Sci.* 108:2273–83

Summerhayes IC, Wong D, Chen LB. 1983. Effect of microtubules and intermediate filaments on mitochondrial distribution. *J. Cell Sci.* 61:87–105

Sweitzer SM, Hinshaw JE. 1998. Dynamin undergoes a GTP-dependent conformational change causing vesiculation. *Cell* 93:1021–29

Takei K, McPherson PS, Schmid SL, De Camilli P. 1995. Tubular membrane invaginations coated by dynamin rings are induced by GTP-gamma S in nerve terminal. *Nature* 374:186–90

Tandler B, Hoppel CL. 1972. *Mitochondria*. NY: Academic. 59 pp.

Teo SH, Grasser KD, Hardman CH, Broadhurst RW, Laue ED, Thomas JO. 1995. Two mutations in the HMG-box with very different structural consequences provide insights into the nature of binding to four-way junction DNA. *EMBO J.* 14:3844–53

Thomas DY, Wilkie D. 1968. Recombination of mitochondrial drug resistance factors in *Saccharomyces cerevisiae*. *Biochem. Biophys. Res. Commun.* 30:368–72

Thomas JH, Botstein D. 1986. A gene required for the separation of chromosomes on the spindle apparatus in yeast. *Cell* 44:65–76

Thorsness PE, Fox TD. 1993. Nuclear mutations in *Saccharomyces cerevisiae* that affect the escape of DNA from mitochondria to the nucleus. *Genetics* 134:21–28

Thorsness PE, Weber ER. 1996. Escape and migration of nucleic acids between chloroplasts, mitochondria, and the nucleus. *Int. Rev. Cytol.* 165:207–34

Thorsness PE, White KH, Fox TD. 1993. Inactivation of *YME1*, a member of the *ftsH-SEC18-PAS1-CDC48* family of putative ATPase-encoding genes, causes increased escape of DNA from mitochondria in *Saccharomyces cerevisiae*. *Mol. Cell Biol.* 13:5418–26

Tuller G, Hrastnik C, Achleitner G, Schiefthaler U, Klein F, Daum G. 1998. YDL142c encodes cardiolipin synthase (Cls1p) and is non-essential for aerobic growth of *Saccharomyces cerevisiae*. *FEBS Lett.* 421:15–18

Urrutia R, Henley JR, Cook T, McNiven MA. 1997. The dynamins: redundant or distinct functions for an expanding family of related GTPases? *Proc. Natl. Acad. Sci. USA* 94:377–84

van Zyl WH, Wills N, Broach JR. 1989. A general screen for mutants of *Saccharomyces cerevisiae* deficient in tRNA biosynthesis. *Genetics* 123:55–68

Warnock DE, Schmid SL. 1996. Dynamin GTPase, a force generating molecular switch. *BioEssays* 18:885–93

Warren G, Wickner W. 1996. Organelle inheritance. *Cell* 84:395–400

Weber ER, Hanekamp T, Thorsness PE. 1996. Biochemical and functional analysis of the *YME1* gene product, an ATP and zinc-dependent mitochondrial protease from *Saccharomyces cerevisiae*. *Mol. Biol. Cell* 7:307–17

Welch MD, Holtzman DA, Drubin DG. 1994. The yeast actin cytoskeleton. *Curr. Opin. Cell Biol.* 6:110–19

Williamson DH, Fennell DJ. 1979. Visualization of yeast mitochondrial DNA with the fluorescent stain "DAPI". *Methods Enzymol.* 56:728–33

Winsor B, Schiebel E. 1997. An overview of the *Saccharomyces cerevisiae* microtubule and microfilament cytoskeleton. *Yeast* 13:399–434

Wolstenholme DR, Fauron CM-R. 1995. Mitochondrial genome organization. In *The Molecular Biology of Plant Mitochondria*, ed. CS Levings, IK Vasil, 3:1–59. Dordrecht: Kluwer

Yaffe MP. 1991. Organelle inheritance in the yeast cell cycle. *Trends Cell Biol.* 1:160–63

Yaffe MP. 1996. The division and inheritance of mitochondria. *Adv. Mol. Cell Biol.* 17:341–50

Yaffe MP, Harata D, Verde F, Eddison M, Toda T, Nurse P. 1996. Microtubules mediate mitochondrial distribution in fission yeast. *Proc. Natl. Acad. Sci. USA* 93:11664–68

Yaffe MP, Schatz G. 1984. Two nuclear mutations that block mitochondrial protein import in yeast. *Proc. Natl. Acad. Sci. USA* 81:4819–23

Zelenaya-Troitskaya O, Newman SM, Okamoto K, Perlman PS, Butow RA. 1998. Functions of the high mobility group protein, Abf2p, in mitochondrial DNA segregation, recombination and copy number in *Saccharomyces cerevisiae*. *Genetics* 148:1763–76

Zhu Q, Hulen D, Liu T, Clarke M. 1997. The *cluA⁻* mutant of *Dictyostelium* identifies a novel class of proteins required for dispersion of mitochondria. *Proc. Natl. Acad. Sci. USA* 94:7308–13

Zinn AR, Pohlman JK, Perlman PP, Butow RA. 1987. Kinetic and segregational analysis of mitochondrial DNA recombination in yeast. *Plasmid* 17:248–56

Zweifel SG, Fangman WL. 1991. A nuclear mutation reversing a biased transmission of yeast mitochondrial DNA. *Genetics* 128:214–49

Annu. Rev. Cell Dev. Biol. 1998. 14:305–38

SIGNALING TO THE ACTIN CYTOSKELETON

Anja Schmidt and Michael N. Hall

Department of Biochemistry, Biozentrum, University of Basel, Basel, Switzerland;
e-mail: hall@ubaclu.unibas.ch

KEY WORDS: signal transduction, GTPase, Rho, actin, PI kinase

---

ABSTRACT

The actin cytoskeleton is a highly dynamic network composed of actin polymers and a large variety of associated proteins. The main functions of the actin cytoskeleton are to mediate cell motility and cell shape changes during the cell cycle and in response to extracellular stimuli, to organize the cytoplasm, and to generate mechanical forces within the cell. The reshaping and functions of the actin cytoskeleton are regulated by signaling pathways. Here we broadly review the actin cytoskeleton and the signaling pathways that regulate it. We place heavy emphasis on the yeast actin cytoskeleton.

CONTENTS

305

1081-0706/98/1115-0305$08.00

INTRODUCTION: THE ACTIN CYTOSKELETON

The cytoskeleton is composed of three major types of protein filaments: microtubules, microfilaments, and intermediate filaments. Microfilaments are polymers of actin that together with a large number of actin-binding and associated proteins constitute the actin cytoskeleton (Stössel 1993, Botstein et al 1997, Winsor & Schiebel 1997). Actin genes have been highly conserved during evolution, and actin molecules from various organisms are functionally interchangeable in vitro (Kron et al 1992, Nefsky & Bretscher 1992). Actin exists either in a monomeric (G-actin) or in a polymeric form (F-actin). Each actin molecule can bind ATP, which is hydrolyzed to ADP after incorporation of the actin molecule into the polymer. Polymers assemble spontaneously via noncovalent interactions between the monomeric subunits and are highly dynamic structures with subunit turnover at both ends. Energy is not required but contributes to polymerization, as shown by the observation that ATP-bound actin polymerizes faster than ADP-bound actin (Engel et al 1977). The rate-limiting step in actin polymerization is nucleation, the assembly of the first subunits to generate a new filament. Actin filaments are structurally polarized, and the kinetics of polymerization at each end are different. The plus (barbed) end grows more quickly than does the minus (pointed) end.

FUNCTIONS OF THE ACTIN CYTOSKELETON

In mammalian cells, the actin cytoskeleton is required for cell motility and surface remodeling. It mediates cell shape changes during mitosis; it is essential for several contractile activities, such as muscle contraction or the separation of daughter cells by the contractile ring during cytokinesis; it controls cell-cell and cell-substrate interactions together with adhesion molecules; and it participates in transmembrane signaling, endocytosis, and secretion (Salmon 1989, Luna & Hitt 1992, Stössel 1993, Gottlieb et al 1993, Bretscher 1993, Juliano & Haskill 1993, Nobes & Hall 1995).

The yeast *Saccharomyces cerevisiae* possesses a single essential gene, *ACT1*, that encodes actin (Gallwitz & Sures 1980, Ng & Abelson 1980). The phenotypes of *act1* mutants and the asymmetric cell cycle–dependent distribution of actin have implicated the yeast actin cytoskeleton in a variety of functions. The first actin mutants generated showed severe defects in bud formation, in the asymmetric distribution of actin during the cell cycle, in the movement of vesicles, in the secretion of invertase, and in the localization of chitin, suggesting that the main function of the actin cytoskeleton was to direct growth toward the budding daughter cell (Shortle et al 1984, Novick & Botstein 1985, Dunn & Shortle 1990). Other studies revealed roles for actin in nuclear division and cytokinesis (Palmer et al 1992), endocytosis (Holtzman et al 1993, Kübler & Riezman 1993, Benedetti et al 1994), bud site selection (Drubin et al 1993), and organelle movement and positioning (Drubin et al 1993, Lazzarino et al 1994). In addition, the actin cytoskeleton is also required for yeast cells to respond to extracellular cues. Changes in cell shape in response to changes in osmolarity or nutrient availability, as well as the formation of mating projections oriented along a pheromone gradient, depend on the assembly of an asymmetrically organized actin cytoskeleton (Chowdhury et al 1992, Read et al 1992, Kron & Gow 1995).

To perform all these biological functions, the organization of the actin cytoskeleton must be tightly regulated both temporally and spatially. Cytoskeletal rearrangements during the cell cycle must be triggered at the correct times, and intracellular signals must be able to recruit actin nucleation and polymerization to discrete sites in the cell. Many proteins associated with the actin cytoskeleton are thus likely targets of signaling pathways controlling actin assembly.

CONTROL OF ACTIN ASSEMBLY BY ACTIN BINDING PROTEINS

Actin cytoskeleton assembly is regulated at multiple levels, including the organization of actin monomers into actin polymers and the superorganization of actin polymers into a filamentous network. A large number of actin-binding proteins regulate actin assembly by controlling filament formation and cross-linking of the actin network (Pollard & Cooper 1986, Stössel 1993, Welch et al 1994, Schafer & Cooper 1995, Sun et al 1995). The activities of these proteins are often modulated by signaling molecules such as Ca^{2+} or phosphorylated phosphoinositides (Janmey 1994).

Actin Folding

Both yeast and higher eukaryotes possess a cytoplasmic chaperonin, the TCP-1/CCT complex, that is specific for the folding of actin and tubulin (Stoldt et al 1996). In yeast, CCT activity is essential, and *cct* mutants show defects in the organization of both the actin and the microtubule cytoskeleton (Ursic & Culbertson 1991, Vinh et al 1993, Chen et al 1994, Li et al 1994, Miklos et al 1994, Ursic et al 1994). The mammalian CCT complex was shown to associate with and facilitate the folding of newly synthesized actin and tubulin monomers in vitro (Yaffe et al 1992, Gao et al 1992, 1993, Sternlicht et al 1993). Because pure actin monomers can polymerize spontaneously in vitro, the function of the CCT complex is presumably to bring the monomers into an assembly-competent state rather than to mediate the polymerization event itself.

Actin Polymerization

In most cells, the pool of unpolymerized actin is usually held above the concentrations needed for spontaneous polymerization. Monomer availability and polymerization onto pre-existing filaments are regulated by actin monomer-binding, and by actin filament capping and severing proteins.

An important regulator of the intracellular concentration of monomeric actin is profilin (Carlsson et al 1976, Sohn & Goldschmidt-Clermont 1994). Profilin binds to free actin monomers and terminal actin subunits and thereby prevents further polymerization (Lassing & Lindberg 1985). Profilin contains an essential $PI(4,5)P_2$-binding site, and binding of $PI(4,5)P_2$ to this site triggers the dissociation of the profilin from the actin monomer or subunit. In addition, profilin can act as an exchange factor for actin and mediate the conversion of ADP-bound actin to ATP-bound actin (Goldschmidt-Clermont et al 1992). As an exchange factor, profilin may aid actin polymerization (Pantaloni & Carlier 1993). These properties make profilin an excellent target for the modulation of actin polymerization in response to phosphoinositide signaling. Yeast profilin, encoded by *PFY1*, is essential, and overexpression of *PFY1* suppresses the toxicity of *ACT1* overexpression, indicating that profilin can act as a monomer-sequestering protein in vivo (Magdolen et al 1998, 1993; Haarer et al 1990; Haarer et al 1993). Other known or putative monomer-sequestering proteins are thymosin β-4 and its homologs (Safer et al 1991, Nachmias 1993, Safer & Nachmias 1994), and the yeast OYE2, AIP2, and SRV2 proteins (Freeman et al 1995, Botstein et al 1997).

The capping of barbed filament ends to prevent addition or loss of actin subunits is mediated by the heterodimeric capping protein (Casella et al 1987, Caldwell et al 1989). Like profilin, this capping protein contains a $PI(4,5)P_2$-binding site, and binding of the phosphoinositide inhibits the association of the capping protein with actin (Heiss & Cooper 1991). Agonist-stimulated release of capping protein allows localized actin assembly. Yeast capping protein, encoded by *CAP1* and *CAP2*, is required for the stabilization of actin filaments (Amatruda et al 1990, 1992). *cap1* and *cap2* mutants show aberrant cell morphology and partial disappearance of actin cables.

Gelsolin, villin, fragmin, adseverin, and scinderin comprise a family of structurally related proteins that are able to sever actin filaments. These proteins bind to actin filaments, bend and cleave them in a Ca^{2+}-dependent manner, and afterwards cap the barbed filament ends (Matsudaira & Janmey 1988, Bearer 1991, Lamb et al 1993). The fragmented filaments may serve as new nuclei to allow rapid repolymerization in response to further signals. The activities of these severing proteins are inhibited by binding of $PI(4,5)P_2$ (Janmey et al 1987).

ADF (actin depolymerizing factor), or cofilin, is a less efficient severing protein than the gelsolins and promotes filament disassembly by extracting monomers from the filament interior and buffering released monomeric actin (Hawkins et al 1993, Hayden et al 1993, Moon & Drubin 1995). The protein is inhibited by PI(4)P and PI(4,5)P$_2$ (Yonezawa et al 1990). Mammalian ADF is also regulated by N-terminal phosphorylation, which inhibits the severing and monomer binding activity (Morgan et al 1993). Yeast ADF, encoded by *COF1*, is essential, and *cof1* mutants show a severe defect in actin filament disassembly (Iida et al 1993, Moon et al 1993).

Actin Cross-Linking

Superorganization of actin polymers into a filamentous network is mediated by actin side-binding or cross-linking proteins (Dubreuil 1991, Hartwig & Kwiatkowski 1991, Matsudaira 1991, 1994) that include α-actinin, filamin, fimbrin, and villin.

Several isoforms of α-actinin exist that form either high-angle branches between actin filaments or links between parallel filaments to generate actin bundles. The cross-linking activity of α-actinin is enhanced by PI(4)P or PI(4,5)P$_2$, and some isoforms are dependent on Ca^{2+} (Noegel et al 1987, Fukami et al 1992, Witke et al 1993). Filamin also cross-links actin filaments, but in contrast to α-actinin, its activity is diminished by phosphoinositide binding (Furuhashi et al 1992). Fimbrin binds to actin filament sides and causes bundle formation (de Arruda et al 1990). Yeast fimbrin, encoded by *SAC6*, is required for actin-based receptor-mediated endocytosis (Adams et al 1991, Küler & Riezman 1993). Villin is also able to bundle actin filaments in vitro at low Ca^{2+} concentrations, whereas it can act as a filament end-binding and severing protein at increased Ca^{2+} concentrations (Walsh et al 1984).

Actin Nucleation

The multiple functions of the actin cytoskeleton make it necessary that actin filaments are not generated randomly and uniformly throughout the whole cell, but rather at discrete sites at the plasma membrane. These nucleation sites are mostly multimolecular complexes that control actin nucleation.

Focal adhesions and adherens junctions are membrane-associated complexes that serve as nucleation sites for actin filaments and as cross-linkers between the cell exterior, the plasma membrane, and the actin cytoskeleton (Yamada & Geiger 1997). Focal adhesions mediate cell-substrate adhesion and consist of integrin-type receptors that are attached to the extracellular matrix and are intracellularly associated with protein complexes containing talin, vinculin, α-actinin, paxillin, tensin, zyxin, and focal adhesion kinase (FAK) (Burridge & Fath 1989, Burridge et al 1990, Turner & Burridge 1991). Talin has been demonstrated to nucleate actin polymerization in vitro (Kaufmann et al 1992). Adherens junctions mediate cell-cell interaction and consist of clusters of cadherins that are intracellularly complexed with vinculin, α-actinin, catenin, ERM (ezrin, radixin, moesin) proteins, and filamin (Geiger et al 1990). Many of these proteins contain phosphoinositide-binding sites and are likely targets of signaling pathways.

A role in mediating de novo nucleation of actin filaments has been proposed for a multi-protein complex containing the two actin-related proteins Arp2 and Arp3. The Arp2/3 complex has been identified in *Acanthamoeba castellanii* and human cells and colocalizes with regions of actin-based motility (Kelleher et al 1995, Machesky 1994, 1997). Yeast Arp proteins have recently been identified and shown to be required in vivo for the motility and integrity of cortical actin patches (McCollum et al 1996, Moreau et al 1996, Winter et al 1997). Because of their similarity to actin, Arps may mediate actin nucleation by serving as an actin template.

In yeast it has been shown by immunoelectron microscopy that cortical actin patches are almost always associated with invaginations of the plasma membrane (Mulholland et al 1994). Because actin cables are often seen extending from actin patches through the cell, it is possible that the membrane invaginations serve as anchorage or nucleation sites for actin cables.

Actin Movement

The movement of actin filaments within the cell is controlled by myosins. Myosins are motor proteins that interact with actin polymers and thereby transduce energy from the hydrolysis of ATP into mechanical force and movement. At least 13 classes of myosins can be distinguished. All myosin heavy chains share an N-terminal motor head domain of approximately 80 kDa. This is followed by the regulatory neck domain to which the light chain binds, and a C-terminal class-specific tail domain (Titus 1993, Cramer et al 1994, Hasson & Mooseker 1995, Ruppel & Spudich 1995, Bahler 1996, Goodson et al 1997).

Conventional myosins (class II myosins) were the first class of myosins to be described. They include muscle myosins, which drive contraction of the muscle sarcomere, and similar myosins from nonmuscle cells (Trybus 1994, Weiss & Leinwand 1996). Conventional myosins are hexamers consisting of two heavy chains and two pairs of light chains. They have long α-helical coiled-coil tails that enable the myosins to dimerize and form filaments with projecting motor domains. The motor domain is thought to undergo a conformational change while being bound to the actin filament. This results in force production and contraction. The release of the motor domain from the actin filament after binding to myosin allows the sliding of the actin filament past the myosin filament. Yeast possesses one conventional myosin, encoded by *MYO1*. *MYO1* has been implicated in cell separation and is thought to deliver components required for cell separation to the septum (Watts et al 1987, Rodriguez & Paterson 1990, Sweeney et al 1991).

Unconventional myosins are two-headed or single-headed. In contrast to conventional myosins, they do not appear to form filaments. Yeast possesses four unconventional myosins, *MYO2* and *MYO4* (class V), and *MYO3* and *MYO5* (class I). *MYO2* is thought to be required for polarized growth and the transport of certain secretory vesicles along actin cables from the mother to the bud (Johnston et al 1991, Govindan et al 1995, Kitayama et al 1997, Santos & Snyder 1997). *myo2-66* mutants are large and unbudded, presumably because they cannot direct secretion and thus growth into the daughter cell. *MYO4* controls the segregation of an mRNA encoding a cell-fate determinant and is involved in the establishment of developmental asymmetry (Haarer et al 1990, Bobola et al 1996, Jansen et al 1996, Long et al 1997, Takizawa et al 1997). *MYO3* and *MYO5* have been implicated in the control of receptor-mediated endocytosis (Goodson & Spudich 1995, VR Simon et al 1995, Geli & Riezman 1996, Goodson et al 1996). *myo5* single and *myo3 myo5* double mutants are defective in the uptake of α-factor and in the organization of the actin cytoskeleton.

ORGANIZATION OF THE ACTIN CYTOSKELETON DURING THE CELL CYCLE IN YEAST

In yeast, polymeric actin shows a characteristic cell cycle–dependent asymmetric distribution that reflects the role of the actin cytoskeleton in establishing polarized growth and in directing secretion to the growing bud (Adams & Pringle 1984, Kilmartin & Adams 1984) (Figure 1). In early G_1, cortical actin patches and cables are evenly distributed and randomly oriented in the cytoplasm of a cell. As a yeast cell initiates a new cell cycle, actin patches concentrate at the previously selected and marked bud site, actin cables orient to this area, and bud emergence begins. During the maturation of the bud, actin patches are found exclusively in the bud while cables run along the long axis from the mother to the daughter cell. In the early budded phase, localization of actin patches and thus growth predominates at the bud tip. As the bud enlarges, actin patches are distributed over the whole bud surface and the bud grows isotropically (isotropic switch) (Tkacz & Lampen 1972, Farkas et al 1974). Once the daughter cell reaches a critical size, the asymmetric distribution of actin structures is lost, and patches and cables show an even distribution in the mother and the daughter cell. Prior to cytokinesis, actin patches concentrate in a ring at the bud neck, and the cables radiate from this area.

How are the changes in the actin cytoskeleton triggered at the correct time during the cell cycle? The timing of bud emergence and polarization of growth depends on the activity of the cyclin-dependent kinase CDC28 (Lew & Reed 1993, 1995) (Figure 1). Bud emergence begins at START, coinciding with the

A

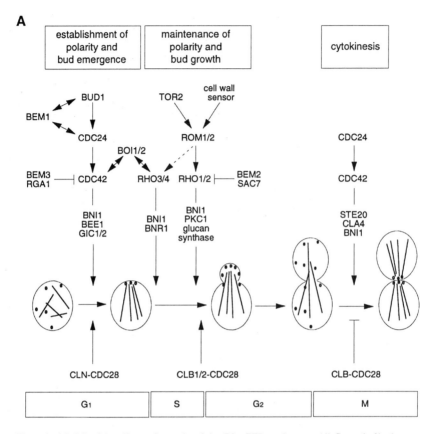

Figure 1 Models of signaling pathways involving Rho GTPases in yeast. (*A*) Control of bud emergence and cytokinesis by Rho GTPases. (*B*) Role of CDC42 in shmoo (mating projection) formation in response to mating pheromone. (*C*) Role of CDC42 in the induction of filamentous growth in response to starvation. *Dots* and *lines* in cells represent actin patches and cables, respectively.

onset of DNA synthesis and the duplication of the microtubule-organizing center, and requires the activity of CDC28 complexed with the CLN G_1 cyclins (Kim et al 1991). *cdc28*^{ts} mutants or cells lacking the CLN G_1 cyclins show a severe delay in bud formation, whereas overexpression of CLN1 or CLN2 results in premature bud formation (Lew et al 1992). The isotropic switch, which is required for uniform bud growth, occurs in early G_2 and is triggered by the activity of CLB-CDC28. Cells lacking the G_2 cyclin CLB2 show a delayed switch, and in cells lacking both CLB1 and CLB2 or CDC28, the isotropic switch is prevented and cells form elongated tubular buds. Overexpression of CLBs accelerates the switch so that spherical buds are formed. When CLB-CDC28

B

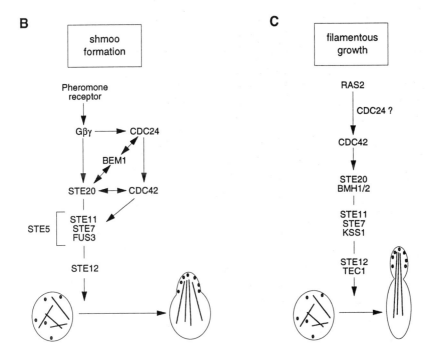

Figure 1   (Continued)

activity is maximal in late G_2, actin patches redistribute to the mother and the daughter cell. CDC28 inactivation following the destruction of CLBs mediates the repolarization of actin patches to the mother/bud neck. CLB overexpression delays the repolarization at the bud neck. Because changes in the timing of activation or inactivation of cyclin-CDC28 lead to changes in the timing of actin rearrangements or even prevent them, it appears likely that CDC28 directly controls the reorganization of actin during the cell cycle. The regulation of polarized growth by CDC28 does not require de novo protein synthesis, suggesting that CDC28 might directly phosphorylate proteins that regulate actin cytoskeleton assembly and thus bud growth.

SIGNALING TO THE ACTIN CYTOSKELETON BY RHO GTPASES

In recent years, evidence has accumulated indicating that in both mammalian cells and yeast cells, Rho-like GTPases are key regulators in signaling pathways that link extracellular growth signals or intracellular stimuli to the assembly and organization of the actin cytoskeleton (Hall 1994, Narumiya et al 1997, Tapon & Hall 1997, Van Aelst & D'Souza-Schorey 1997).

Rho (Ras homology) proteins belong to the Ras superfamily of small GTPases and share about 50–60% identity with each other and 30% identity with Ras. Based on sequence and functional differences, the Rho-GTPase family in mammalian cells can be further subdivided into five groups: (*a*) RhoA, RhoB, and RhoC; (*b*) Rac1, Rac2, and RhoG; (*c*) Cdc42 and TC10; (*d*) RhoD; and (*e*) RhoE and TTF (Foster et al 1996, Ridley 1996). In yeast, five Rho-GTPases have been identified: CDC42, RHO1, RHO2, RHO3, and RHO4 (Ridley 1995).

The Rho GTPase Switch and Its Regulators

Like other members of the Ras superfamily, Rho-like GTPases function as binary switches that cycle between an active GTP-bound form and an inactive GDP-bound form. The cycling between the active and inactive states is regulated by GDP/GTP exchange factors (GEFs), GTPase-activating proteins (GAPs), and guanine nucleotide dissociation inhibitors (GDIs) (Figure 2).

GEFs mediate the conversion of the inactive GDP-bound form of the GTP-ase to the active GTP-bound form (Quilliam et al 1995, Cerione & Zheng 1996, Whitehead et al 1997). GEFs trigger the release of GDP by binding and stabilizing the nucleotide-free form of the Rho protein. Because of the high intracellular ratio of GTP to GDP, the released GDP is immediately replaced with

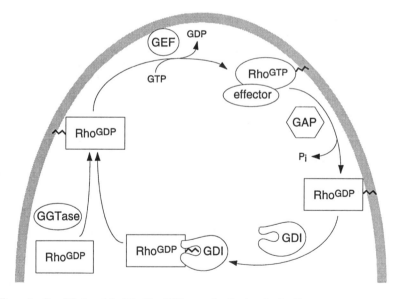

Figure 2   Simplified model of the Rho GTPase cycle. See text for details.

GTP. The Rho-GEF family currently contains more than 20 members. Most of the mammalian GEFs have been identified as oncogenes in transfections assays. In yeast, three GEFs, CDC24, ROM1, and ROM2, have been found (Ron et al 1991, Ozaki et al 1996). All Rho-GEFs share a domain (about 200 amino acids) termed a DH domain (for Dbl homology) that is necessary and sufficient for exchange activity toward Rho (Hart et al 1994, Yaku et al 1994, Cerione & Zheng 1996). [Dbl was the first mammalian GEF to be identified (Eva & Aaronson 1985).] In addition, all GEFs possess a pleckstrin homology (PH) domain C-terminally adjacent to the DH domain. PH domains have been shown to mediate both protein-protein and protein-phospholipid interactions (Musacchio et al 1993, Harlan et al 1994). For several mammalian GEFs, it was shown that mutating or deleting the PH domain results in the loss of their transforming capacity (Hori et al 1991, Ron et al 1991, Chan et al 1996, Whitehead et al 1995, 1996). The ability to transform could be restored by targeting the protein to the plasma membrane by addition of a CAAX-motif to the C terminus, suggesting that the PH domain is required for the proper cellular localization of the GEF (Whitehead et al 1995, Zheng et al 1996). The transforming activity of many mammalian GEFs is often associated with N-terminal truncations of the wild-type protein and always requires the presence of the DH and PH domains (Whitehead et al 1997). The GEF N terminus might thus be an auto-inhibitory domain. Outside the DH and PH domains, GEFs share little structural similarity. Most GEFs contain other types of functional domains, such as SH2 and SH3 (src homology), Ca^{2+}-binding EF hands, kinase domains, calmodulin-binding (IQ) domains, Ras-GEF domains, or Rho-GAP domains, which might be involved in mediating the stimulation of the GEF activity by upstream signaling molecules.

Recent findings indicate that Rho-GEFs are regulated. In mammalian cells, PDGF stimulates, via activation of PI 3-kinase, an increase in the level of GTP-bound Rac (Hawkins et al 1995). $PI(3,4,5)P_3$, the product of PI 3-kinase, stimulates the Rac-GEF Vav directly by binding to the Vav PH domain and stimulates indirectly by enhancing Lck-dependent phosphorylation of Vav (Han et al 1998). $PI(3,4,5)P_3$ also binds the Sos PH domain, which may account for the Ras-induced activation of Sos exchange activity toward Rac; Ras signals to Rac via PI 3-kinase (Rodriguez-Viciana et al 1997, Nimnual et al 1998). In yeast, the activity of the RHO1-GEF ROM2 is stimulated independently by cell wall defects and by the PI kinase homolog TOR2 (Schmidt et al 1997, Bickle et al 1998). TOR2 stimulates ROM2 activity, possibly via the ROM2 PH domain, in response to growth signals (Schmidt et al 1997). A cell wall defect activates ROM2 and ultimately RHO1, possibly because one of RHO1's many effectors, glucan synthase, is an enzyme involved in cell wall synthesis. The yeast CDC42-GEF CDC24 also appears to be activated by two independent

pathways. CDC24 is required for polarized cell growth and actin organization in response to mating pheromone and during vegetative growth (Leberer
et al 1997a). The response to mating pheromone requires a direct interaction
between the G$\beta\gamma$ subunit of the pheromone receptor-linked G protein and
CDC24, whereas during vegetative growth, CDC24 binds the GTP-bound form
of the Ras-like G protein BUD1 (Zhao et al 1995, Zheng et al 1995, Park
et al 1997, Nern & Arkowitz 1998). The precise mechanisms by which upstream
signals or regulators activate GEFs are poorly understood but may include recruitment to the plasma membrane or relief of auto-inhibition by a GEF's N
terminus.

GAPs bind to Rho^{GTP} and accelerate its low intrinsic GTPase activity, thereby
converting it into the GDP-bound inactive form (Lamarche & Hall 1994). Rho-
GAPs share a related catalytic domain of about 140 amino acids. More than 15
proteins containing such a GAP domain have been identified to date. These include the mammalian p50rhoGAP, Bcr, Abr, N- and β-chimaerin, p190, 3BP-1,
and the regulatory subunit of PI 3-kinase p85 (Lamarche & Hall 1994), as
well as the yeast BEM2, BEM3, RGA1, LRG1, SAC7, and BAG7 proteins
(Zheng et al 1993, 1994b; Müller et al 1994; Stevenson et al 1995; Chen
et al 1996a; Schmidt et al 1997). GAP proteins may also function as effectors of Rho proteins, whereas microinjection of the N-chimaerin GAP-domain
inhibits Rac- and Cdc42-induced actin reorganization (Diekmann et al 1991,
Leung et al 1993), and injection of full-length N-chimaerin induces cytoskeletal
rearrangement (Kozma et al 1996). It remains to be determined whether the
GAPs, like the GEFs, are themselves regulated.

Rho-like GTPases are targeted to membranes via a post-translational attachment of prenyl groups (Marshall 1993). This reaction is catalyzed by geranylgeranyl transferases (GGTases) and involves the covalent thioether linkage of
geranylgeranyl groups to the Cys residue in the C-terminal CAAX-box of the
GTPase, followed by the proteolytic removal of the -AAX and the subsequent
methylation of the exposed Cys residue (Katayama et al 1991, Adamson et al
1992). Prenylation is not only necessary for the proper localization of the GTP-
ase but also seems to be important for the interaction with the GEF. The Ras
exchange factor smg21 is active on processed but not on unprocessed RhoA
(Mizuno et al 1991). In yeast, the RHO1 exchange factor ROM2 exerts GEF
activity on RHO1 that contains a CAAX-box but not on RHO1 that lacks the
CAAX-box (Ozaki et al 1996).

Guanine nucleotide dissociation inhibitors (GDIs) were first identified as
proteins capable of inhibiting the dissociation of GDP from Rho, suggesting
a function of GDIs as GEF inhibitors (Ohga et al 1989, Fukumoto et al 1990,
Bollag & McCormick 1991). GDIs might also function as GAP inhibitors because binding of RhoGDI to RacGTP can protect the GTPase from the action

of the GAP (Segal & Abo 1993). GDIs interact with both Rho^{GDP} and Rho^{GTP} but prefer Rho^{GDP} (Ueda et al 1990, Sasaki et al 1993) and only with post-translationally modified Rho (Hori et al 1991). In vitro, GDIs are capable of solubilizing both GTP- and GDP-bound Rho from membranes (Isomura et al 1991, Leonard et al 1992, Quinn et al 1993). In resting cells, Rho proteins are associated with GDI in the cytoplasm, but upon cell activation they are released from GDI and translocated to the membrane (Takai et al 1995). These findings suggest that GDIs play an important role in regulating the proportion of Rho associated with membranes.

Rho, Rac, Cdc42, and the Actin Cytoskeleton in Mammalian Cells

RhoA (Rho), Cdc42, and Rac are activated by specific extracellular signals and direct the organization of a specific type of actin cytoskeleton to induce characteristic morphological changes. Furthermore, in Swiss 3T3 cells, the GTPases seem to act in a hierarchical cascade in which Cdc42 activates Rac and Rac activates Rho (Figure 3).

Rac controls the formation of lamellipodia and membrane ruffles (Ridley et al 1992). Lamellipodia are thin protrusive actin sheets that can lift up and fold backward at the leading edge of cells, giving rise to membrane ruffles.

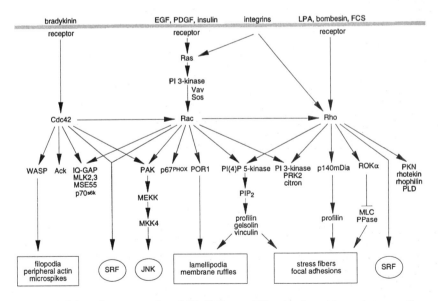

Figure 3 Schematic representation of Cdc42, Rac, and Rho signaling pathways in mammalian cells (modified and expanded from Giancotti 1997).

Treatment of Swiss 3T3 fibroblasts with growth factors such as PDGF, EGF, or insulin, as well as injection of activated Rac^{V12}, rapidly results in ruffling and lamellipodia formation, whereas injection of dominant-negative Rac prior to addition of growth factors inhibits these processes. Polymeric actin found in Rac-induced lamellipodia is associated with small focal complexes that are morphologically different from classical focal adhesions but are also composed of integrins, vinculin, paxillin, and FAK (Hotchin & Hall 1995, Nobes & Hall 1995). Injection of activated Ras (Ras^{V12}) also induces membrane ruffling in a Rac-dependent way, which suggests that Ras acts upstream of Rac (Ridley et al 1992).

Activation of Cdc42 by bradykinin results in the formation of peripheral-actin microspikes (PAM) including filopodia, which are finger-like protrusions consisting of bundles of actin filaments (Kozma et al 1995). The actin structures induced by Cdc42 are also associated with focal complexes (Nobes & Hall 1995). Filopodia formation in response to stimulation with bradykinin or microinjection of activated Cdc42 is followed by membrane ruffling. Both processes are inhibited by the injection of inhibitory $Cdc42^{N17}$, whereas only ruffling is inhibited by injection of inhibitory Rac^{N17}. This suggests that Cdc42 acts upstream of Rac.

Rho (RhoA) controls the generation of stress fibers and focal adhesions in fibroblasts in response to the mitogens, lysophosphatidic acid (LPA), bombesin, or fetal calf serum (FCS) (Ridley & Hall 1992). Stress fibers are bundles of actin filaments that traverse the cell and end in focal adhesions. Stress fiber assembly can be blocked by *Clostridium botulinum* C3 transferase, which ADP ribosylates Rho on its effector domain and thereby inactivates Rho signaling (Chardin et al 1989, Paterson et al 1990). Formation of stress fibers can also be observed as a late response following Rac activation and lamellipodia formation, suggesting that Rac is upstream of Rho (Ridley & Hall 1992). Rho-GTPases are also required to modulate additional actin-based cytoskeletal functions such as adherens junctions in polarized epithelial cells, axonal outgrowth, cleavage furrow contraction, antigen presentation in T cells, endocytosis, phagocytosis, and secretion (Van Aelst & D'Souza-Schorey 1997).

TARGETS OF RHO, RAC, AND CDC42   Several targets for Rho have been identified recently by their ability to interact with the activated form of Rho, using affinity chromatography or the yeast two-hybrid system (see Figure 3). These include the Ser/Thr kinases PKN and PRK2, which are related to protein kinase C (PKC) (Amano et al 1996, Quilliam et al 1996, Watanabe et al 1996, Vincent & Settleman 1997), and the rhophilin, rhotekin, and citron proteins, all of which contain a homologous Rho-binding motif (Madaule et al 1995, Reid et al 1996). The function and downstream targets of these proteins are largely unknown.

Other Rho targets about which more is known include ROKα and p140mDia. The myotonic dystrophy kinase-related ROKα (p164 Rho-associated kinase, Rho-K) and its close homolog ROKβ (ROCKII, p160^{ROCK}) were identified as interactors of Rho^{GTP} and act downstream of Rho in mediating stress fiber formation (Leung et al 1995, Matsui et al 1996, Ishizaki et al 1996, 1997). The binding of Rho to ROKα modestly increases its kinase activity and leads to the translocation of ROKα to the plasma membrane (Leung et al 1995). Transfection of full-length ROKα into serum-starved HeLa cells induces the formation of stress fibers and focal adhesions, whereas expression of a kinase-dead ROKα causes disassembly of stress fibers (Leung et al 1996). Interestingly, the myosin-binding subunit (MBS) of myosin-light chain (MLC) phosphatase has been identified as an in vitro target of ROKα (Kimura et al 1996, Matsui et al 1996). Phosphorylation of MBS decreases the activity of MLC and thus results in an increase in phosphorylated MLC. Phosphorylated MLC in turn can bind to actin filaments and trigger the formation of stress fibers (Chrzanowska-Wodnicka & Burridge 1996).

Another potentially interesting Rho-target is p140mDia, a member of the formin-related protein family (Watanabe et al 1997). These proteins have been implicated in the control of polarized growth and contain two formin homology domains through which they interact with profilin (Frazier & Field 1997). p140mDia, Rho, and profilin colocalize in fibroblasts, and overexpression of p140mDia stimulates actin polymerization in COS cells (Watanabe et al 1997).

Several proteins have been identified that interact with both Cdc42 and Rac (Figure 3). These include members of the Ser/Thr PAK kinase family (or the STE20 kinase family, as STE20 was the first member of this family), which are strongly activated upon binding to Cdc42/Rac. p65^{PAK} seems to mediate nuclear signaling events controlled by Cdc42/Rac (see below) but not formation of filopodia or lamellipodia. Cdc42/Rac mutants that are unable to bind PAK are defective in nuclear signaling but can still induce actin rearrangement (Joneson et al 1996, Lamarche et al 1996). However, PAK was also found to be associated with Cdc42/Rac-dependent focal complexes, and overexpression of PAK results in disassembly of focal adhesions, suggesting at least some involvement of the kinase in cytoskeletal rearrangement (Lim et al 1996). The closest homolog of PAK is the yeast STE20 kinase, which regulates both morphological changes such as shmoo (mating projection) formation and filamentous growth, as well as nuclear signaling leading to cell cycle arrest and transcription of mating-specific genes (Figure 1) (Leberer et al 1997a).

PAK contains an 18 amino acid domain, the CRIB (Cdc42/Rac interactive binding) domain, that mediates the interaction with Cdc42 and Rac. CRIB domains have so far been found in more than 25 proteins, including the tyrosine kinase p120^{Ack}, MLK2, MLK3, MSE55, and WASP (Burbelo et al 1995).

Alterations in the Wiskott-Aldrich syndrome protein WASP cause Wiskott-Aldrich disease (Aspenstrom et al 1996, Symons et al 1996). In rat kidney epithelial cells or in Jurkat cells, overexpression of WASP leads to the formation of large clusters of polymerized actin, an event that is inhibited by dominant-negative Cdc42. This suggests that Cdc42 signals to the actin cytoskeleton via WASP. In apparent contradiction to this, Lamarche et al (1996) showed that Cdc42 mutants not able to bind WASP are still able to induce filopodia and focal complexes.

Several proteins that bind Cdc42 and/or Rac but do not possess a CRIB domain have been found. IQ-GAP interacts with Cdc42 and Rac and colocalizes to membrane ruffles (Brill et al 1996, Hart et al 1996). The interacting protein $p67^{phox}$, a component of the NADPH oxidase complex, is found in phagocytotic cells and is involved in pathogen destruction (Diekmann et al 1994). Citron and $p160^{ROCK}$ also interact with Rac (Lamarche et al 1996). The physiological significance of these interactions is not known.

POR1 was identified as a two-hybrid interactor of Rac and seems to mediate Rac^{V12}-induced membrane ruffling (Joneson et al 1996, Van Aelst & D'Souza-Schorey 1997). Injection of POR1 deletion mutants inhibits ruffling, whereas co-expression of POR1 together with Ras^{V12} has synergistic effects on actin reorganization. Mutant Rac proteins that are defective in binding to POR1 are unable to induce actin reorganization.

RHO GTPASES AND PI KINASES   Phosphorylated phosphoinositides are important regulators of a variety of proteins linked to the actin cytoskeleton. Several lines of evidence suggest that PI kinases and Rho-like GTPases function together in the control of cytoskeletal rearrangements.

Both Rho and Rac physically interact with PI(4)P 5-kinase in a GTP-dependent manner (Chong et al 1994, Tolias et al 1995, Ren et al 1996) and thereby probably regulate the PI(4)P 5-kinase. In platelets, actin polymerization induced by thrombin or by activated Rac is brought about by an increase in the production of $PI(4,5)P_2$ and the subsequent binding of the phosphoinositide to capping protein (Hartwig et al 1995). Moreover, the LPA/Rho-induced formation of focal adhesions and stress fibers can be inhibited by injections of anti-PIP_2 antibodies (Gilmore & Burridge 1996).

PI 3-kinase is possibly downstream of Rho, since Rho is able to stimulate PI 3-kinase activity in platelets and fibroblasts (Kumagai et al 1993, Zhang et al 1993). PI 3-kinase likely functions upstream of Rac, as stimulation of cells with PDGF or insulin increases the exchange activity toward Rac in a PI 3-kinase–dependent manner (Hawkins et al 1995). Treatment of fibroblasts with the PI 3-kinase inhibitors wortmannin or LY294002 prevents the induction of membrane ruffling by PDGF or activated Ras but not by activated Rac (Kotani et al 1994, Wennstrom et al 1994, Nobes et al 1995, Rodriguez-Viciana et al 1997). Constitutively activated PI 3-kinase induces Rac-dependent membrane ruffling and Rho-dependent stress fiber formation (Reif et al 1996). Furthermore, in PDGF-stimulated fibroblasts, PI 3-kinase is bound to activated Cdc42 and Rac, which would place PI 3-kinase also downstream of Rac and Cdc42 (Zheng et al 1994a, Bokoch et al 1996).

RHO GTPASES AND CELL PROLIFERATION   In addition to functioning in the control of cell morphogenesis, Rho-like GTPases also play a role in the control of cell proliferation. A potential role of Rho-GTPases in growth control was already suggested by the finding that many GEFs for Rho, Rac, and Cdc42 are oncogenic (Michiels et al 1995, Cerione & Zheng 1996) and that, in some cell lines, Rho-GTPases themselves have transforming potential. Koshravi-Far et al (1995) reported that activated Rac and Rho enhanced cell growth and induced anchorage-independent growth and tumor formation. Rac, but not Rho, caused malignant transformation in rodent fibroblasts (Qiu et al 1995). Fibroblasts expressing activated Cdc42 showed anchorage independence, and activated Cdc42 induced tumor formation in nude mice (Qiu et al 1997). Finally, Rac, Rho, and Cdc42 were reported to be necessary for Ras-induced transformation (Qiu et al 1997).

In addition, Rho, Rac, and Cdc42 stimulate G_1 progression and DNA synthesis in fibroblasts (Olson et al 1995) and control intracellular signaling pathways leading to transcription. Rac and Cdc42 regulate activation of the Jun N-terminal kinase (JNK)/stress-activated protein kinase (SAPK) and p38/mpk1 mitogen-activated protein kinase (MAP) cascades (Coso et al 1995, Minden et al 1995). Rac, Cdc42, and Rho stimulate the activity of the serum response factor (SRF) and the translocation of NF-κB into the nucleus (Hill et al 1995, Perona et al 1997).

Although it is clear that Rho GTPases play an important role in mitogenesis, proliferation, actin rearrangement, and transformation, the relationship between these activities has yet to be clarified.

Rho GTPases and the Actin Cytoskeleton in Yeast

In yeast, five Rho-like GTPases, namely CDC42, RHO1, RHO2, RHO3, and RHO4, have been identified and implicated in organization of the actin cytoskeleton and control of bud formation (see Figure 1) (Adams et al 1990, Johnson & Pringle 1990, Madaule et al 1987, Matsui & Toh-e 1992b). In addition, at least CDC42 is required for the establishment of cell polarity and the organization of the actin cytoskeleton during shmoo formation in response to mating factor and during filamentous growth in response to nitrogen starvation (reviewed in Chant 1996, Leberer et al 1997a).

CDC42   Bud formation occurs in three major stages: First, a nonrandom bud site is selected; second, the selected bud site is organized, and the actin cytoskeleton is oriented toward this site; and third, cell surface growth is polarized to produce the daughter cell. Bud site selection in a cell-type-specific pattern is controlled by the Ras-like GTPase BUD1, its exchange factor BUD5, and its GAP BUD2 (Bender & Pringle 1989, Chant et al 1991, Chant & Herskowitz 1991, Chant & Pringle 1991, Powers et al 1991). Mutations in either of these genes disrupts the normal budding pattern of a yeast cell and causes random budding without disturbing the subsequent steps of bud formation. This suggests that the bud site selection pathway is restricted to the positioning of the bud and not to its assembly per se. Assembly of a selected bud site and the orientation of the actin cytoskeleton toward this site are controlled by the cell polarity establishment proteins that include the Rho-like GTPase CDC42, its exchange factor CDC24, the geranylgeranyl transferase for CDC42, CDC43, and the SH3 domain-containing protein BEM1 (Sloat et al 1981, Adams et al 1990, Chant et al 1991, Chenevert et al 1992). *CDC42*, *CDC43*, and *CDC24* were originally identified during screens for temperature-sensitive mutations that cause cells to arrest growth with a uniform terminal morphology (Sloat et al 1981, Adams et al 1990). Cells lacking CDC42, CDC24, CDC43, or BEM1 have a randomized actin cytoskeleton and, unable to form a bud, arrest as large unbudded multinucleate cells. Thus these mutants have a defect in cytoskeletal polarization, but not in cell surface growth (Sloat et al 1981, Bender & Pringle 1989, Johnson & Pringle 1990, Adams et al 1990, Chant et al 1991, Chenevert et al 1992). Consistent with their function in the establishment of cell polarity, CDC42 and BEM1 localize to the plasma membrane at the incipient bud site and at the bud tip (Ziman et al 1993, Chenevert 1994).

Overexpression of *CDC42* causes a randomized budding pattern, and overexpression of *BUD1* suppresses a *cdc24* mutation (Bender & Pringle 1989, Johnson & Pringle 1990). Furthermore, both CDC24 and BUD1 physically interact with each other and with BEM1 (Peterson et al 1994, Zheng et al 1995, Park et al 1997). This suggests that the BUD1 and the CDC42 GTPase switches act in a hierarchical cascade in which the *BUD* gene products select a bud site and then guide the positioning of the cell polarity establishment proteins to the selected site where these can organize the cytoskeleton and initiate bud growth (Chant & Herskowitz 1991, Zheng et al 1995).

Several regulators for CDC42 are known in addition to the exchange factor (CDC24) and the geranylgeranyl transferase (CDC43) mentioned above (Bender & Pringle 1989, Ohya et al 1993, Zheng et al 1994b). BEM3 and RGA1 are GTPase-activating proteins for CDC42 (Zheng et al 1994b, Stevenson et al 1995, Chen et al 1996a). BEM3 possesses GAP activity toward CDC42 in vitro, and BEM3 and RGA1 interact with activated CDC42 in the yeast two-hybrid system. ZDS1 and its homolog ZDS2 were identified in a screen for negative regulators of CDC42 (Bi & Pringle 1996). *zds1 zds2* double mutants display phenotypes suggesting that CDC42 is hyperactivated, and ZDS1 at least colocalizes with CDC42. However, it remains to be determined how direct the effects of ZDSs are on CDC42 function since both ZDS proteins have also been identified in a zillion different other seemingly unrelated screens (hence the name ZDS).

Although several putative CDC42 effectors have been identified by their ability to interact with GTP-bound CDC42, it is not clear how CDC42 signals to the actin cytoskeleton. CDC42 was shown to interact with BNI, a member of the formin family and a yeast homolog of mammalian p140mDia (Evangelista et al 1997). CDC42 might also control actin organization by interaction with BEE1/LAS17, the yeast homolog of WASP, which is required for the assembly of actin patches (Li 1997). *BEM4/ROM7* was identified as a multicopy suppressor of a *cdc42*[ts] mutation and independently as a multicopy suppressor of a dominant-negative *RHO1* allele (Hirano et al 1996, Mack et al 1996). Cells lacking *BEM4* arrest with phenotypes similar to *cdc42* mutants, and overexpression of CDC42 (in some strains requiring co-overexpression of *RHO1*) suppresses a *bem4* mutation. BEM4 interacts with both the active and inactive forms of CDC42, RHO1, RHO2, and RHO4, suggesting that BEM4 is a general modulator of Rho-like GTPases in yeast. Finally, two novel candidate effectors of CDC42—GIC1 and GIC2—have been identified in a database search for proteins that contain a CRIB domain (Burbelo et al 1995). GIC1 and GIC2 bind to the GTP-bound form of CDC42 and colocalize with the GTPase (Brown et al 1997, Chen et al 1997). Loss of GIC1 and GIC2 is lethal, with *gic* cells showing defects in actin and microtubule organization similar to those observed in *cdc42* mutants.

In vegetatively growing cells, CDC42 activity is also required for cytokinesis. Activated CDC42 interacts with CLA4 and STE20, two PAK-related Ser/Thr kinases (Cvrckova et al 1995, Benton et al 1997). CLA4 was originally identified genetically as a mutation that is lethal in the absence of the G_1 cyclins CLN1 and CLN2. *cla4* mutants, although viable, have a defect in cytokinesis, and *cla4 ste20* double mutants are inviable. The interaction with CDC42 activates CLA4 and presumably leads to the localization of the kinase to a particular part of the cell.

CDC42, CDC24, and BEM1 are also involved in mating (Figure 1*B*) (MN Simon et al 1995, Zhao et al 1995, Leberer et al 1997a, Nern & Arkowitz 1998). Binding of mating pheromone to the seven-transmembrane receptor STE2 results in the activation of a heterotrimeric G protein, and the activation of STE20. STE20 in turn activates a MAP kinase cascade consisting of the kinases STE11, STE7, and FUS3, and the scaffold protein STE5, which controls the many physiological responses required for mating (including transcriptional activation via STE12 and shmoo formation) (Leberer et al 1997a). Several lines of evidence suggest that the CDC42 GTPase switch lies directly downstream of the receptor-coupled G protein and is probably required for shmoo formation. The β-subunit of the receptor-coupled G protein binds directly to CDC24 (Zhao et al 1995). This interaction controls the localization of CDC24 and is required for the orientation of shmoo formation toward the source of pheromone (Nern & Arkowitz 1998). *cdc24, cdc42,* and *bem1* mutants are defective in pheromone signaling (MN Simon et al 1995, Zhao et al 1995), and in cells lacking the CDC42-GAP RGA1, pheromone-specific transcription is constitutively activated (Stevenson et al 1995). BEM1 binds directly to STE20, STE5, and CDC42 (Peterson et al 1994, Leeuw et al 1995, Lyons et al 1996). CDC42 colocalizes with STE20 to shmoo tips and binds STE20 in a GTP-dependent manner; this binding seems to be important for the localization, but not the activation, of STE20 (Ziman et al 1993, MN Simon et al 1995, Zhao et al 1995, Peter et al 1996, Leberer et al 1997b). Surprisingly, mutant STE20 that is unable to bind CDC42 is not defective in signaling transcriptional activation or shmoo formation, and overexpression of CDC42 suppresses the mating defect of cells lacking STE20, suggesting that CDC42 might have STE20-dependent and -independent functions in pheromone signaling (Leberer et al 1996, Peter et al 1996).

The induction of filamentous growth also requires CDC42, as well as STE20, STE11, STE7, KSS1, and the 14-3-3 proteins BMH1 and BMH2 (Figure 1*C*) (Leberer et al 1997a, Madhani et al 1997, Cook et al 1997, Roberts et al 1997). In response to nutritional stress, RAS2 appears to activate CDC42, which in turn activates STE20, the downstream MAP kinase pathway, and the transcription factors STE12 and TEC1 (Mösch et al 1996). This model is supported by the finding that STE20 lacking the CDC42-binding site cannot induce filamentous growth (Peter et al 1996, Leberer et al 1997b).

RHO1 AND RHO2   RHO1 and its nonessential homolog RHO2 have been implicated in the control of bud growth by controlling organization of the actin cytoskeleton and cell wall synthesis. Cells lacking RHO1 arrest as small-budded often-lysed cells but have a polarized actin cytoskeleton (Madaule et al 1987, Yamochi et al 1994). *rho2* cells have no obvious phenotype but overexpression of *RHO2* can suppress a dominant-negative *RHO1* mutation, suggesting that RHO1 and RHO2 have at least partly overlapping functions (Madaule et al 1987, Ozaki et al 1996).

Several regulators for RHO1 and RHO2 have been identified. BEM2, SAC7, and BAG7 function as GAPs for RHO1 in vitro (Peterson et al 1994, Schmidt et al 1997) (A Schmidt & MN Hall, unpublished data). ROM1 and ROM2 were originally isolated as multicopy suppressors of a dominant-negative *RHO1* allele and encode GEFs for RHO1 and RHO2 (Ozaki et al 1996). Deletion of both *ROM1* and *ROM2* is lethal and *rom1 rom2* mutants arrest as small-budded cells, as do *rho1* mutants. ROM2 activity can be regulated by two independent signaling pathways. The PI kinase homolog TOR2 controls actin organization by activating RHO1 and RHO2 via at least ROM2 (Schmidt et al 1997). *tor2* mutants are defective in organization of the actin cytoskeleton and show a severe decrease in exchange activity toward RHO1. In addition, ROM2 activity can be stimulated independently of TOR2 by alterations in the cell wall (Bickle et al 1998). Because RHO1 controls cell wall synthesis, such a mechanism would ensure that cell wall synthesis occurs where and when needed. RDI1 is a GDI for RHO1 (Masuda et al 1994). RDI1 associates with GDP-bound RHO1 in the cytosol, and RHO1 has to be released from RDI1 to be activated by ROM2 (Takai et al 1995, Ozaki et al 1996).

What is downstream of RHO1? RHO1 is a regulatory subunit of $\beta(1 \rightarrow 3)$ glucan synthase (Drgonova et al 1996, Qadota et al 1996). Glucan polymers are the major structural components of the yeast cell wall. Furthermore, RHO1 binds and activates PKC1 in a GTP-dependent manner (Nonaka et al 1995, Kamada et al 1996). PKC1 in turn, via a MAP kinase cascade consisting of BCK1, MKK1, MKK2, and MPK1, controls transcription of genes involved in cell wall synthesis (Levin et al 1994, Levin & Errede 1995, Errede et al 1995, Igual et al 1996). RHO1 also interacts with BNI1 (Kohno et al 1996, Evangelista et al 1997).

Several lines of evidence suggest that RHO1 and possibly also RHO2 controls organization of the actin cytoskeleton. RHO1 localizes to sites of growth and also colocalizes with cortical actin patches (Yamochi et al 1994). Human RhoA, which controls actin reorganization in mammalian cells, is highly homologous to RHO1 and can substitute for RHO1 in yeast (Qadota et al 1994). Overexpression of ROM2, RHO1, RHO2, or PKC1 restores growth in a *tor2* mutant that is defective in actin organization (Helliwell et al 1998, Schmidt et al 1997). Mutants lacking the PKC1-controlled MAP kinase MPK1 have a delocalized actin cytoskeleton (Mazzoni et al 1993). Finally, a normally nonlethal *bni1* mutation is lethal in a strain containing the human *RhoA* gene substituted for the endogenous *RHO1* gene; the *RhoA bni1* mutant arrests with a cytokinesis defect and has a randomized actin cytoskeleton (Kohno et al 1996). Overexpression of PKC1 suppresses the lethality of a *RhoA bni1* double mutant, suggesting that BNI1 and PKC1 have overlapping functions in controlling actin organization and cytokinesis.

RHO1 and RHO2 might also play a role in polarization of cell growth in response to mating pheromone. STE20 activates MPK1 in response to α-factor and cells lacking *MPK1* exhibit a slight mating defect (Errede et al 1995, Zarzov et al 1996). Finally, mutants lacking the exchange factor ROM2 are defective in shmoo formation (Manning et al 1997).

RHO3 AND RHO4   Bud growth is also controlled by RHO3 and RHO4 (Matsui & Toh-e 1992a,b). Disruption of *RHO4* alone does not confer any growth defect, whereas deletion of *RHO3* results in a severe slow growth phenotype, which is suppressed by overexpression of *RHO4*. Furthermore, loss of both RHO3 and RHO4 is lethal, suggesting that the GTPases have overlapping functions (Matsui & Toh-e 1992a,b). Cells lacking RHO3 and RHO4 arrest as small-budded cells that lyse. Osmotic stabilization partly rescues the lethality of a *rho3 rho4* double mutant. In the presence of an osmotic stabilizer, *rho3 rho4* cells become large and show a randomized actin distribution and delocalized chitin; about 20% of the cells are multinucleate. The phenotypes of osmotically stabilized *rho3 rho4* cells resemble those of a *cdc42* mutant, although in contrast to *cdc42* cells, *rho3 rho4* mutants are often budded. Deletion of *RHO3* is suppressed by overexpression of *SEC4*, encoding a rab-type GTPase that is essential for exocytosis and mediates the fusion of secretory vesicles with the plasma membrane (Imai et al 1996). Overexpression of *CDC42* or *BEM1*, but not overexpression of *RHO1* or *RHO2*, suppresses the growth defect of a *rho3* mutant, whereas overexpression of *RHO3* or *RHO4* exacerbates the growth defect of a *cdc42* mutant (Matsui & Toh-e 1992a). The above findings suggest a role for RHO3 and RHO4 in directing the actin cytoskeleton and the secretory apparatus to sites of growth. RHO3 and RHO4 probably act subsequently to CDC42 and are required for the maintenance of cell polarity. The lysis defect associated with a *rho3 rho4* double mutation is presumably the consequence of insufficient polarized transport of material for surface growth.

Thus far no GEFs and GAPs for the RHO3 and RHO4 GTPase switches have been identified. Overexpression of *RHO3* or *RHO4* partly suppresses a *rom2* deletion, suggesting that ROM2 might function as a GEF for RHO3 and RHO4 (Ozaki et al 1996).

BOI1 and BOI2 may be upstream regulators of RHO3 and RHO4. These proteins were originally identified as two-hybrid interactors of the SH3 domain of BEM1 (Hirano et al 1996, Mack et al 1996). BOI1 and BOI2 are homologous proteins, and both possess a PH domain, a SH3 domain, and a proline-rich domain through which they interact with BEM1. *boi1 boi2* double mutants are inviable at temperatures above 24°C and arrest growth as large or misshaped cells that lyse and have a randomized distribution of actin. Overexpression of *RHO3* or *RHO4* restores growth in a *boi1 boi2* mutant. BOI1 and BOI2, via their essential PH domain, interact directly with CDC42, and overexpression of BOI1 inhibits CDC42 function, as does overexpression of RHO3. This suggests that BOI promotes activation of RHO3 at sites of growth where CDC42 has previously acted, presumably by displacing CDC42.

The only downstream effectors of RHO3 and RHO4 identified so far are BNI1 and its homolog BNR1 (Evangelista et al 1997, Imamura et al 1997). In contrast to *bni1* or *bnr1* single mutants, which have no obvious growth defect, cells lacking both *BNI1* and *BNR1* are inviable and arrest growth as large, mostly unbudded multinucleate cells with delocalized actin and chitin. Whereas BNI1 appears to interact with all five Rho-like GTPases in yeast (see above), BNR1 seems to interact exclusively with RHO4.

CONCLUSIONS

Which areas of signaling to the actin cytoskeleton are in relatively good focus, and which areas are still conceptually fuzzy? The Rho GTPase switch is well established, as are actin and many actin-binding proteins, but in between still lies a black box. The link between a signaling pathway and a regulated event on the actin cytoskeleton remains to be defined. The near future should provide significant advances in the identification and characterization of the downstream effectors and upstream regulators of Rho GTPase switches. Likewise, there is a gap in our understanding of how cyclin-CDC28 controls the actin cytoskeleton in yeast. The regulation and in vivo role of phosphoinositides (PIP$_2$) in the control of the actin-binding proteins and ultimately the actin cytoskeleton remain to be firmly established. Finally, we must not forget that signaling to the actin cytoskeleton offers many opportunities for therapeutic intervention, such as in the treatment of cancer, hypertension, and fungal or bacterial infections (Chen et al 1996b, Cossart 1995, Janmey & Chaponnier 1995, Mösch et al 1996, Ireton et al 1996, Keely et al 1997, Leberer et al 1997a, Uehata et al 1997, Gale et al 1998).

ACKNOWLEDGMENTS

We thank the members of our laboratory for comments on the manuscript. Our laboratory was supported by grants from the Swiss National Science Foundation and the Canton of Basel to MNH.

> Visit the *Annual Reviews home page* at
> http://www.AnnualReviews.org

Literature Cited

Adams AE, Botstein D, Drubin DG. 1991. Requirement of yeast fimbrin for actin organization and morphogenesis in vivo. *Nature* 354:404–8

Adams AE, Johnson DI, Longnecker RM, Sloat BF, Pringle JR. 1990. CDC42 and CDC43, two additional genes involved in budding and the establishment of cell polarity in the yeast *Saccharomyces cerevisiae. J. Cell Biol.* 111:131–42

Adams AE, Pringle JR. 1984. Relationship of actin and tubulin distribution to bud growth in wild-type and morphogenetic-mutant *Saccharomyces cerevisiae. J. Cell Biol.* 98:934–45

Adamson P, Marshall CJ, Hall A, Tilbrook PA. 1992. Post-translational modifications of p21rho proteins. *J. Biol. Chem.* 267:20033–38

Amano M, Mukai H, Ono Y, Chihara K, Matsui T, et al. 1996. Identification of a putative target for Rho as the serine-threonine kinase protein kinase N. *Science* 271:648–50

Amatruda JF, Cannon JF, Tatchell K, Hug C, Cooper JA. 1990. Disruption of the actin cytoskeleton in yeast capping protein mutants. *Nature* 344:352–54

Amatruda JF, Gattermeir DJ, Karpova TS, Cooper JA. 1992. Effects of null mutations and overexpression of capping protein on morphogenesis, actin distribution and polarized secretion in yeast. *J. Cell Biol.* 119:1151–62

Aspenstrom P, Lindberg U, Hall A. 1996. Two GTPases, Cdc42 and Rac, bind directly to a protein implicated in the immunodeficiency disorder Wiskott-Aldrich syndrome. *Curr. Biol.* 6:70–75

Bahler M. 1996. Myosins on the move to signal transduction. *Curr. Opin. Cell Biol.* 8:18–22

Bearer EL. 1991. Direct observation of actin filament severing by gelsolin and binding by gCap39 and CapZ. *J. Cell Biol.* 115:1629–38

Bender A, Pringle JR. 1989. Multicopy suppression of the *cdc24* budding defect in yeast by *CDC42* and three newly identified genes including the ras-related gene *RSR1*. *Proc. Natl. Acad. Sci. USA* 86:9976–80

Benedetti H, Raths S, Crausaz F, Riezman H. 1994. The *END3* gene encodes a protein that is required for the internalization step of endocytosis and for actin cytoskeleton organization in yeast. *Mol. Biol. Cell* 5:1023–37

Benton BK, Tinkelenberg A, Gonzalez I, Cross FR. 1997. Cla4p, a *Saccharomyces cerevisiae* Cdc42p-activated kinase involved in cytokinesis, is activated at mitosis. *Mol. Cell Biol.* 17:5067–76

Bi E, Pringle JR. 1996. *ZDS1* and *ZDS2*, genes whose products may regulate Cdc42p in *Saccharomyces cerevisiae*. *Mol. Cell Biol.* 16:5264–75

Bickle M, Delley P-A, Schmidt A, Hall MN. 1998. Cell wall integrity modulates RHO1 activity via the exchange factor ROM2. *EMBO J.* 17:2235–45

Bobola N, Jansen RP, Shin TH, Nasmyth K. 1996. Asymmetric accumulation of Ash1p in postanaphase nuclei depends on a myosin and restricts yeast mating-type switching in mother cells. *Cell* 84:699–709

Bokoch GM, Vlahos CJ, Wang Y, Knaus UG, Traynor-Kaplan AE. 1996. Rac GTPase interacts specifically with phosphatidylinositol 3-kinase. *Biochem. J.* 315:775–79

Bollag G, McCormick F. 1991. Regulators and effectors of ras proteins. *Annu. Rev. Cell Biol.* 7:601–32

Botstein D, Amberg D, Mulholland J, Huffaker T, Adams A, et al. 1997. The yeast cytoskeleton. In *Yeast III*, pp. 1–80. Cold Spring Harbor, NY: Cold Spring Harbor Lab. Press

Bretscher A. 1993. Microfilaments and membranes. *Curr. Opin Cell Biol.* 5:653–60

Brill S, Li S, Lyman CW, Church DM, Wasmuth JJ, et al. 1996. The Ras GTPase-activating-protein-related human protein IQGAP2 harbors a potential actin binding domain and interacts with calmodulin and Rho family GTPases. *Mol. Cell Biol.* 16:4869–78

Brown JL, Jaquenoud M, Gulli MP, Chant J, Peter M. 1997. Novel Cdc42-binding proteins Gic1 and Gic2 control cell polarity in yeast. *Genes Dev.* 11:2972–82

Burbelo PD, Drechsel D, Hall A. 1995. A conserved binding motif defines numerous candidate target proteins for both Cdc42 and Rac GTPases. *J. Biol. Chem.* 270:29071–74

Burridge K, Fath K. 1989. Focal contacts: transmembrane links between the extracellular matrix and the cytoskeleton. *BioEssays* 10:104–8

Burridge K, Nuckolls G, Otey C, Pavalko F, Simon K, Turner C. 1990. Actin-membrane interaction in focal adhesions. *Cell Differ. Dev.* 32:337–42

Caldwell JE, Heiss SG, Mermall V, Cooper JA. 1989. Effects of CapZ, an actin capping protein of muscle, on the polymerization of actin. *Biochemistry* 28:8506–14

Carlsson L, Nystrom LE, Lindberg U, Kannan KK, Cid-Dresdner H, Lovgren S. 1976. Crystallization of a non-muscle actin. *J. Mol. Biol.* 105:353–66

Casella JF, Craig SW, Maack DJ, Brown AE. 1987. Cap Z(36/32), a barbed end actin-capping protein, is a component of the Z-line of skeletal muscle. *J. Cell Biol.* 105:371–79

Cerione RA, Zheng Y. 1996. The Dbl family of oncogenes. *Curr. Opin. Cell Biol.* 8:216–22

Chan AM, Takai S, Yamada K, Miki T. 1996. Isolation of a novel oncogene, *NET1*, from neuroepithelioma cells by expression cDNA cloning. *Oncogene* 12:1259–66

Chant J. 1996. Generation of cell polarity in yeast. *Curr. Opin. Cell Biol.* 8:557–65

Chant J, Corrado K, Pringle JR, Herskowitz I. 1991. Yeast *BUD5*, encoding a putative GDP-GTP exchange factor, is necessary for bud site selection and interacts with bud formation gene *BEM1*. *Cell* 65:1213–24

Chant J, Herskowitz I. 1991. Genetic control of bud site selection in yeast by a set of gene products that constitute a morphogenetic pathway. *Cell* 65:1203–12

Chant J, Pringle JR. 1991. Budding and cell polarity in *Saccharomyces cerevisiae*. *Curr. Opin. Genet. Dev.* 1:342–50

Chardin P, Boquet P, Madaule P, Popoff MR, Rubin EJ, Gill DM. 1989. The mammalian G protein rhoC is ADP-ribosylated by *Clostridium botulinum* exoenzyme C3 and affects actin microfilaments in Vero cells. *EMBO J.* 8:1087–92

Chen GC, Kim YJ, Chan CS. 1997. The Cdc42 GTPase-associated proteins Gic1 and Gic2 are required for polarized cell growth in *Saccharomyces cerevisiae*. *Genes Dev.* 11:2958–71

Chen GC, Zheng L, Chan CS. 1996a. The LIM domain-containing Dbm1 GTPase-activating protein is required for normal cellular morphogenesis in *Saccharomyces cerevisiae*. *Mol. Cell Biol.* 16:1376–90

Chen LM, Hobbie S, Galan JE. 1996b. Requirement of CDC42 for *Salmonella*-induced cytoskeletal and nuclear responses. *Science* 274:2115–18

Chen X, Sullivan DS, Huffaker TC. 1994. Two yeast genes with similarity to TCP-1 are required for microtubule and actin function in vivo. *Proc. Natl. Acad. Sci. USA* 91:9111–15

Chenevert J. 1994. Cell polarization directed by extracellular cues in yeast. *Mol. Biol. Cell* 5:1169–75

Chenevert J, Corrado K, Bender A, Pringle J, Herskowitz I. 1992. A yeast gene (*BEM1*) necessary for cell polarization whose product contains two SH3 domains. *Nature* 356:77–79

Chong LD, Traynor-Kaplan A, Bokoch GM, Schwartz MA. 1994. The small GTP-binding protein Rho regulates a phosphatidylinositol 4-phosphate 5-kinase in mammalian cells. *Cell* 79:507–13

Chowdhury S, Smith KW, Gustin MC. 1992. Osmotic stress and the yeast cytoskeleton: phenotype-specific suppression of an actin mutation. *J. Cell Biol.* 118:561–71

Chrzanowska-Wodnicka M, Burridge K. 1996. Rho-stimulated contractility drives the formation of stress fibers and focal adhesions. *J. Cell Biol.* 133:1403–15

Cook JG, Bardwell L, Thorner J. 1997. Inhibitory and activating functions for MAPK Kss1 in the *S. cerevisiae* filamentous-growth signalling pathway. *Nature* 390:85–88

Coso OA, Chiariello M, Yu JC, Teramoto H, Crespo P, et al. 1995. The small GTP-binding proteins Rac1 and Cdc42 regulate the activity of the JNK/SAPK signaling pathway. *Cell* 81:1137–46

Cossart P. 1995. Actin-based bacterial motility. *Curr. Opin. Cell Biol.* 7:94–101

Cramer LP, Mitchison TJ, Theriot JA. 1994. Actin-dependent motile forces and cell motility. *Curr. Opin. Cell Biol.* 6:82–86

Cvrckova F, De Virgilio C, Manser E, Pringle JR, Nasmyth K. 1995. Ste20-like protein kinases are required for normal localization of cell growth and for cytokinesis in budding yeast. *Genes Dev.* 9:1817–30

de Arruda MV, Watson S, Lin CS, Leavitt J, Matsudaira P. 1990. Fimbrin is a homologue of the cytoplasmic phosphoprotein plastin

and has domains homologous with calmodulin and actin gelation proteins. *J. Cell Biol.* 111:1069–79

Diekmann D, Abo A, Johnston C, Segal AW, Hall A. 1994. Interaction of Rac with p67phox and regulation of phagocytic NADPH oxidase activity. *Science* 265:531–33

Diekmann D, Brill S, Garrett MD, Totty N, Hsuan J, et al. 1991. Bcr encodes a GTPase-activating protein for p21rac. *Nature* 351:400–2

Drgonova J, Drgon T, Tanaka K, Kollar R, Chen GC, et al. 1996. Rho1p, a yeast protein at the interface between cell polarization and morphogenesis. *Science* 272:277–79

Drubin DG, Jones HD, Wertman KF. 1993. Actin structure and function: roles in mitochondrial organization and morphogenesis in budding yeast and identification of the phalloidin-binding site. *Mol. Biol. Cell* 4:1277–94

Dubreuil RR. 1991. Structure and evolution of the actin crosslinking proteins. *BioEssays* 13:219–26

Dunn TM, Shortle D. 1990. Null alleles of *SAC7* suppress temperature-sensitive actin mutations in *Saccharomyces cerevisiae*. *Mol. Cell Biol.* 10:2308–14

Engel J, Fasold H, Hulla FW, Waechter F, Wegner A. 1977. The polymerization reaction of muscle actin. *Mol. Cell Biochem.* 18:3–13

Errede B, Cade RM, Yashar BM, Kamada Y, Levin DE, et al. 1995. Dynamics and organization of MAP kinase signal pathways. *Mol. Reprod. Dev.* 42:477–85

Eva A, Aaronson SA. 1985. Isolation of a new human oncogene from a diffuse B-cell lymphoma. *Nature* 316:273–75

Evangelista M, Blundell K, Longtine MS, Chow CJ, Adames N, et al. 1997. Bni1p, a yeast formin linking cdc42p and the actin cytoskeleton during polarized morphogenesis. *Science* 276:118–22

Farkas V, Kovarik J, Kosinova A, Bauer S. 1974. Autoradiographic study of mannan incorporation into the growing cell walls of *Saccharomyces cerevisiae*. *J. Bacteriol.* 117:265–69

Foster R, Hu KQ, Lu Y, Nolan KM, Thissen J, Settleman J. 1996. Identification of a novel human Rho protein with unusual properties: GTPase deficiency and in vivo farnesylation. *Mol. Cell Biol.* 16:2689–99

Frazier JA, Field CM. 1997. Actin cytoskeleton: Are FH proteins local organizers? *Curr. Biol.* 7:R414–17

Freeman NL, Chen Z, Horenstein J, Weber A, Field J. 1995. An actin monomer binding activity localizes to the carboxyl-terminal half of the *Saccharomyces cerevisiae* cyclase-associated protein. *J. Biol. Chem.* 270:5680–85

Fukami K, Furuhashi K, Inagaki M, Endo T, Hatano S, Takenawa T. 1992. Requirement of phosphatidylinositol 4,5-bisphosphate for alpha-actinin function. *Nature* 359:150–52

Fukumoto Y, Kaibuchi K, Hori Y, Fujioka H, Araki S, et al. 1990. Molecular cloning and characterization of a novel type of regulatory protein (GDI) for the rho proteins, ras p21-like small GTP-binding proteins. *Oncogene* 5:1321–28

Furuhashi K, Inagaki M, Hatano S, Fukami K, Takenawa T. 1992. Inositol phospholipid-induced suppression of F-actin-gelating activity of smooth muscle filamin. *Biochem. Biophys. Res. Commun.* 184:1261–65

Gale CA, Bendel CM, McClellan M, Hauser M, Becker JM, Berman J, Hostetter MK. 1998. Linkage of adhesion, filamentous growth, and virulence in *Candida albicans* to a single gene, *INT1*. *Science* 279:1355–58

Gallwitz D, Sures I. 1980. Structure of a split yeast gene: complete nucleotide sequence of the actin gene in *Saccharomyces cerevisiae*. *Proc. Natl. Acad. Sci. USA* 77:2546–50

Gao Y, Thomas JO, Chow RL, Lee GH, Cowan NJ. 1992. A cytoplasmic chaperonin that catalyzes beta-actin folding. *Cell* 69:1043–50

Gao Y, Vainberg IE, Chow RL, Cowan NJ. 1993. Two cofactors and cytoplasmic chaperonin are required for the folding of alpha- and beta-tubulin. *Mol. Cell Biol.* 13:2478–85

Geiger B, Ginsberg D, Salomon D, Volberg T. 1990. The molecular basis for the assembly and modulation of adherens-type junctions. *Cell Differ. Dev.* 32:343–53

Geli MI, Riezman H. 1996. Role of type I myosins in receptor-mediated endocytosis in yeast. *Science* 272:533–35

Giancotti F. 1997. Integrin signaling: specificity and control of cell survival and cell cycle progression. *Curr. Opin. Cell Biol.* 9:691

Gilmore AP, Burridge K. 1996. Regulation of vinculin binding to talin and actin by phosphatidyl-inositol-4-5-bisphosphate. *Nature* 381:531–35

Goldschmidt-Clermont PJ, Furman MI, Wachsstock D, Safer D, Nachmias VT, Pollard TD. 1992. The control of actin nucleotide exchange by thymosin beta 4 and profilin. A potential regulatory mechanism for actin polymerization in cells. *Mol. Biol. Cell* 3:1015–24

Goodson HV, Anderson BL, Warrick HM, Pon LA, Spudich JA. 1996. Synthetic lethality screen identifies a novel yeast myosin I gene (*MYO5*): myosin I proteins are required for polarization of the actin cytoskeleton. *J. Cell Biol.* 133:1277–91

Goodson HV, Spudich JA. 1995. Identification and molecular characterization of a yeast myosin I. *Cell Motil. Cytoskelet.* 30:73–84

Goodson HV, Valetti C, Kreis TE. 1997. Motors and membrane traffic. *Curr. Opin. Cell Biol.* 9:18–28

Gottlieb TA, Ivanov IE, Adesnik M, Sabatini DD. 1993. Actin microfilaments play a critical role in endocytosis at the apical but not the basolateral surface of polarized epithelial cells. *J. Cell Biol.* 120:695–710

Govindan B, Bowser R, Novick P. 1995. The role of Myo2, a yeast class V myosin, in vesicular transport. *J. Cell Biol.* 128:1055–68

Haarer BK, Lillie SH, Adams AE, Magdolen V, Bandlow W, Brown SS. 1990. Purification of profilin from *Saccharomyces cerevisiae* and analysis of profilin-deficient cells. *J. Cell Biol.* 110:105–14

Haarer BK, Petzold AS, Brown SS. 1993. Mutational analysis of yeast profilin. *Mol. Cell Biol.* 13:7864–73

Hall A. 1994. Small GTP-binding proteins and the regulation of the actin cytoskeleton. *Annu. Rev. Cell Biol.* 1994;10:31–54

Han J, Luby-Phelps K, Das B, Shu X, Xia Y, et al. 1998. Role of substrates and products of PI 3-kinase in regulating activation of Rac-related guanosine triphosphatases by Vav. *Science* 279:558–60

Harlan JE, Hajduk PJ, Yoon HS, Fesik SW. 1994. Pleckstrin homology domains bind to phosphatidylinositol-4,5-bisphosphate. *Nature* 371:168–70

Hart MJ, Callow MG, Souza B, Polakis P. 1996. IQGAP1, a calmodulin-binding protein with a rasGAP-related domain, is a potential effector for cdc42Hs. *EMBO J.* 15:2997–3005

Hart MJ, Eva A, Zangrilli D, Aaronson SA, Evans T, et al. 1994. Cellular transformation and guanine nucleotide exchange activity are catalyzed by a common domain on the dbl oncogene product. *J. Biol. Chem.* 269:62–65

Hartwig JH, Bokoch GM, Carpenter CL, Janmey PA, Taylor LA, et al. 1995. Thrombin receptor ligation and activated Rac uncap actin filament barbed ends through phosphoinositide synthesis in permeabilized human platelets. *Cell* 82:643–53

Hartwig JH, Kwiatkowski DJ. 1991. Actin-binding proteins. *Curr. Opin. Cell Biol.* 3:87–97

Hasson T, Mooseker MS. 1995. Molecular motors, membrane movements and physiology: emerging roles for myosins. *Curr. Opin. Cell Biol.* 7:587–94

Hawkins M, Pope B, Maciver SK, Weeds AG. 1993. Human actin depolymerizing factor mediates a pH-sensitive destruction of actin filaments. *Biochemistry* 32:9985–93

Hawkins PT, Eguinoa A, Qiu RG, Stokoe D, Cooke FT, et al. 1995. PDGF stimulates an increase in GTP-Rac via activation of phosphoinositide 3-kinase. *Curr. Biol.* 5:393–403

Hayden SM, Miller PS, Brauweiler A, Bamburg JR. 1993. Analysis of the interactions of actin depolymerizing factor with G- and F-actin. *Biochemistry* 32:9994–10004

Heiss SG, Cooper JA. 1991. Regulation of CapZ, an actin capping protein of chicken muscle, by anionic phospholipids. *Biochemistry* 30:8753–58

Helliwell SB, Howald I, Barbet N, Hall MN. 1998. Evidence for two related TOR2 signaling pathways coordinating cell growth in *Saccharomyces cerevisiae. Genetics* 48:99–112

Hill CS, Wynne J, Treisman R. 1995. The Rho family GTPases RhoA, Rac1, and CDC42Hs regulate transcriptional activation by SRF. *Cell* 81:1159–70

Hirano H, Tanaka K, Ozaki K, Imamura H, Kohno H, et al. 1996. ROM7/BEM4 encodes a novel protein that interacts with the Rho1p small GTP-binding protein in *Saccharomyces cerevisiae. Mol. Cell Biol.* 16:4396–403

Holtzman DA, Yang S, Drubin DG. 1993. Synthetic-lethal interactions identify two novel genes, *SLA1* and *SLA2*, that control membrane cytoskeleton assembly in *Saccharomyces cerevisiae. J. Cell Biol.* 122:635–44

Hori Y, Kikuchi A, Isomura M, Katayama M, Miura Y, et al. 1991. Post-translational modifications of the C-terminal region of the rho protein are important for its interaction with membranes and the stimulatory and inhibitory GDP/GTP exchange proteins. *Oncogene* 6:515–22

Hotchin NA, Hall A. 1995. The assembly of integrin adhesion complexes requires both extracellular matrix and intracellular rho/rac GTPases. *J. Cell Biol.* 131:1857–65

Igual JC, Johnson AL, Johnston LH. 1996. Coordinated regulation of gene expression by the cell cycle transcription factor Swi4 and the protein kinase C MAP kinase pathway for yeast cell integrity. *EMBO J.* 15:5001–13

Iida K, Moriyama K, Matsumoto S, Kawasaki H, Nishida E, Yahara I. 1993. Isolation of a yeast essential gene, *COF1*, that encodes a homologue of mammalian cofilin, a low-M(r) actin-binding and depolymerizing protein. *Gene* 124:115–20

Imai J, Toh-e A, Matsui Y. 1996. Genetic analysis of the *Saccharomyces cerevisiae RHO3* gene, encoding a rho-type small GTPase, provides evidence for a role in bud formation. *Genetics* 142:359–69

Imamura H, Tanaka K, Hihara T, Umikawa M, Kamei T, et al. 1997. Bni1p and Bnr1p: downstream targets of the Rho family small G-proteins which interact with profilin and regulate actin cytoskeleton in *Saccharomyces cerevisiae. EMBO J.* 16:2745–55

Ireton K, Payrastre B, Chap H, Ogawa W, Sakaue H, et al. 1996. A role for phosphoinositide 3-kinase in bacterial invasion. *Science* 274:780–82

Ishizaki T, Maekawa M, Fujisawa K, Okawa K, Iwamatsu A, et al. 1996. The small GTP-binding protein Rho binds to and activates a 160 kDa Ser/Thr protein kinase homologous to myotonic dystrophy kinase. *EMBO J.* 15:1885–93

Ishizaki T, Naito M, Fujisawa K, Maekawa M, Watanabe N, et al. 1997. p160ROCK, a Rho-associated coiled-coil forming protein kinase, works downstream of Rho and induces focal adhesions. *FEBS Lett.* 404:118–24

Isomura M, Kikuchi A, Ohga N, Takai Y. 1991. Regulation of binding of rhoB p20 to membranes by its specific regulatory protein, GDP dissociation inhibitor. *Oncogene* 6:119–24

Janmey PA. 1994. Phosphoinositides and calcium as regulators of cellular actin assembly and disassembly. *Annu. Rev. Physiol.* 56:169–91

Janmey PA, Chaponnier C. 1995. Medical aspects of the actin cytoskeleton. *Curr. Opin. Cell Biol.* 7:111–17

Janmey PA, Iida K, Yin HL, Stossel TP. 1987. Polyphosphoinositide micelles and polyphosphoinositide-containing vesicles dissociate endogenous gelsolin-actin complexes and promote actin assembly from the fast-growing end of actin filaments blocked by gelsolin. *J. Biol. Chem.* 262:12228–36

Jansen RP, Dowzer C, Michaelis C, Galova M, Nasmyth K. 1996. Mother cell-specific HO expression in budding yeast depends on the unconventional myosin myo4p and other cytoplasmic proteins. *Cell* 84:687–97

Johnson DI, Pringle JR. 1990. Molecular characterization of *CDC42*, a *Saccharomyces cerevisiae* gene involved in the development of cell polarity. *J. Cell Biol.* 111:143–52

Johnston GC, Prendergast JA, Singer RA. 1991. The *Saccharomyces cerevisiae MYO2* gene encodes an essential myosin for vectorial transport of vesicles. *J. Cell Biol.* 113:539–51

Joneson T, McDonough M, Bar-Sagi D, Van Aelst L. 1996. RAC regulation of actin polymerization and proliferation by a pathway distinct from Jun kinase. *Science* 274:1374–76

Juliano RL, Haskill S. 1993. Signal transduction from the extracellular matrix. *J. Cell Biol.* 120:577–85

Kamada Y, Qadota H, Python CP, Anraku Y, Ohya Y, Levin DE. 1996. Activation of yeast protein kinase C by Rho1 GTPase. *J. Biol. Chem.* 271:9193–96

Katayama M, Kawata M, Yoshida Y, Horiuchi H, Yamamoto T, et al. 1991. The posttranslationally modified C-terminal structure of bovine aortic smooth muscle rhoA p21. *J. Biol. Chem.* 266:12639–45

Kaufmann S, Kas J, Goldmann WH, Sackmann E, Isenberg G. 1992. Talin anchors and nucleates actin filaments at lipid membranes. A direct demonstration. *FEBS Lett.* 314:203–5

Keely PJ, Westwick JK, Whitehead IP, Der CJ, Parise LV. 1997. Cdc42 and Rac1 induce integrin-mediated cell motility and invasiveness through PI(3)K. *Nature* 390:632–36

Kelleher JF, Atkinson SJ, Pollard TD. 1995. Sequences, structural models, and cellular localization of the actin-related proteins Arp2 and Arp3 from *Acanthamoeba. J. Cell Biol.* 131:385–97

Khosravi-Far R, Solski PA, Clark GJ, Kinch MS, Der CJ. 1995. Activation of Rac1, RhoA, and mitogen-activated protein kinases is required for Ras transformation. *Mol. Cell Biol.* 15:6443–53

Kilmartin JV, Adams AE. 1984. Structural rearrangements of tubulin and actin during the cell cycle of the yeast *Saccharomyces. J. Cell Biol.* 98:922–33

Kim HB, Haarer BK, Pringle JR. 1991. Cellular morphogenesis in the *Saccharomyces cerevisiae* cell cycle: localization of the *CDC3* gene product and the timing of events at the budding site. *J. Cell Biol.* 112:535–44

Kimura K, Ito M, Amano M, Chihara K, Fukata Y, et al. 1996. Regulation of myosin phosphatase by Rho and Rho-associated kinase (Rho-kinase). *Science* 273:245–48

Kitayama C, Sugimoto A, Yamamoto M. 1997. Type II myosin heavy chain encoded by the *myo2* gene composes the contractile ring during cytokinesis in *Schizosaccharomyces pombe. J. Cell Biol.* 137:1309–19

Kohno H, Tanaka K, Mino A, Umikawa M, Imamura H, et al. 1996. Bni1p implicated in cytoskeletal control is a putative target of Rho1p small GTP binding protein in *Saccharomyces cerevisiae. EMBO J.* 15:6060–68

Kotani K, Yonezawa K, Hara K, Ueda H, Kitamura Y, et al. 1994. Involvement of phosphoinositide 3-kinase in insulin- or IGF-1-induced membrane ruffling. *EMBO J.* 13:2313–21

Kozma R, Ahmed S, Best A, Lim L. 1995. The Ras-related protein Cdc42Hs and bradykinin promote formation of peripheral actin microspikes and filopodia in Swiss 3T3 fibroblasts. *Mol. Cell Biol.* 15:1942–52

Kozma R, Ahmed S, Best A, Lim L. 1996. The GTPase-activating protein n-chimaerin cooperates with Rac1 and Cdc42Hs to induce the formation of lamellipodia and filopodia. *Mol. Cell Biol.* 16:5069–80

Kron SJ, Drubin DG, Botstein D, Spudich JA. 1992. Yeast actin filaments display ATP-dependent sliding movement over surfaces

coated with rabbit muscle myosin. *Proc. Natl. Acad. Sci. USA* 89:4466–70

Kron SJ, Gow NA. 1995. Budding yeast morphogenesis: signalling, cytoskeleton and cell cycle. *Curr. Opin. Cell Biol.* 7:845–55

Kübler E, Riezman H. 1993. Actin and fimbrin are required for the internalization step of endocytosis in yeast. *EMBO J.* 12:2855–62

Kumagai N, Morii N, Fujisawa K, Nemoto Y, Narumiya S. 1993. ADP-ribosylation of rho p21 inhibits lysophosphatidic acid-induced protein tyrosine phosphorylation and phosphatidylinositol 3-kinase activation in cultured Swiss 3T3 cells. *J. Biol. Chem.* 268:24535–38

Lamarche N, Hall A. 1994. GAPs for rho-related GTPases. *Trends Genet.* 10:436–40

Lamarche N, Tapon N, Stowers L, Burbelo PD, Aspenstrom P, et al. 1996. Rac and Cdc42 induce actin polymerization and G1 cell cycle progression independently of p65PAK and the JNK/SAPK MAP kinase cascade. *Cell* 87:519–29

Lamb JA, Allen PG, Tuan BY, Janmey PA. 1993. Modulation of gelsolin function. Activation at low pH overrides Ca^{2+} requirement. *J. Biol. Chem.* 268:8999–9004

Lassing I, Lindberg U. 1985. Specific interaction between phosphatidylinositol 4,5-bisphosphate and profilactin. *Nature* 314:472–74

Lazzarino DA, Boldogh I, Smith MG, Rosand J, Pon LA. 1994. Yeast mitochondria contain ATP-sensitive, reversible actin-binding activity. *Mol. Biol. Cell* 5:807–18

Leberer E, Chenevert J, Leeuw T, Harcus D, Herskowitz I, Thomas DY. 1996. Genetic interactions indicate a role for Mdg1p and the SH3 domain protein Bem1p in linking the G-protein mediated yeast pheromone signalling pathway to regulators of cell polarity. *Mol. Gen. Genet.* 252:608–21

Leberer E, Thomas DY, Whiteway M. 1997a. Pheromone signalling and polarized morphogenesis in yeast. *Curr. Opin. Genet. Dev.* 7:59–66

Leberer E, Wu C, Leeuw T, Fourest-Lieuvin A, Segall JE, Thomas DY. 1997b. Functional characterization of the Cdc42p binding domain of yeast Ste20p protein kinase. *EMBO J.* 16:83–97

Leeuw T, Fourest-Lieuvin A, Wu C, Chenevert J, Clark K, et al. 1995. Pheromone response in yeast: association of Bem1p with proteins of the MAP kinase cascade and actin. *Science* 270:1210–13

Leonard D, Hart MJ, Platko JV, Eva A, Henzel W, et al. 1992. The identification and characterization of a GDP-dissociation inhibitor (GDI) for the CDC42Hs protein. *J. Biol. Chem.* 267:22860–68

Leung T, Chen XQ, Manser E, Lim L. 1996. The p160 RhoA-binding kinase ROK alpha is a member of a kinase family and is involved in the reorganization of the cytoskeleton. *Mol. Cell Biol.* 16:5313–27

Leung T, How BE, Manser E, Lim L. 1993. Germ cell beta-chimaerin, a new GTPase-activating protein for p21rac, is specifically expressed during the acrosomal assembly stage in rat testis. *J. Biol. Chem.* 268:3813–16

Leung T, Manser E, Tan L, Lim L. 1995. A novel serine/threonine kinase binding the Ras-related RhoA GTPase which translocates the kinase to peripheral membranes. *J. Biol. Chem.* 270:29051–54

Levin DE, Bowers B, Chen CY, Kamada Y, Watanabe M. 1994. Dissecting the protein kinase C/MAP kinase signalling pathway of *Saccharomyces cerevisiae*. *Cell Mol. Biol. Res.* 40:229–39

Levin DE, Errede B. 1995. The proliferation of MAP kinase signaling pathways in yeast. *Curr. Opin. Cell Biol.* 7:197–202

Lew DJ, Marini NJ, Reed SI. 1992. Different G1 cyclins control the timing of cell cycle commitment in mother and daughter cells of the budding yeast S. cerevisiae. *Cell* 69:317–27

Lew DJ, Reed SI. 1993. Morphogenesis in the yeast cell cycle: regulation by Cdc28 and cyclins. *J. Cell Biol.* 120:1305–20

Lew DJ, Reed SI. 1995. Cell cycle control of morphogenesis in budding yeast. *Curr. Opin. Genet. Dev.* 5:17–23

Li R. 1997. Bee1, a yeast protein with homology to Wiscott-Aldrich syndrome protein, is critical for the assembly of cortical actin cytoskeleton. *J. Cell Biol.* 136:649–58

Li WZ, Lin P, Frydman J, Boal TR, Cardillo TS, et al. 1994. Tcp20, a subunit of the eukaryotic TRiC chaperonin from humans and yeast. *J. Biol. Chem.* 269:18616–22

Lim L, Manser E, Leung T, Hall C. 1996. Regulation of phosphorylation pathways by p21 GTPases. The p21 Ras-related Rho subfamily and its role in phosphorylation signalling pathways. *Eur. J. Biochem.* 242:171–85

Long RM, Singer RH, Meng X, Gonzalez I, Nasmyth K, Jansen RP. 1997. Mating type switching in yeast controlled by asymmetric localization of ASH1 mRNA. *Science* 277:383–87

Luna EJ, Hitt AL. 1992. Cytoskeleton-plasma membrane interactions. *Science* 258:955–64

Lyons DM, Mahanty SK, Choi KY, Manandhar M, Elion EA. 1996. The SH3-domain protein Bem1 coordinates mitogen-activated protein kinase cascade activation with cell cycle control in *Saccharomyces cerevisiae*. *Mol. Cell Biol.* 16:4095–106

Machesky LM. 1997. Cell motility: complex dynamics at the leading edge. *Curr. Biol.* 7: R164–67

Machesky LM, Atkinson SJ, Ampe C, Vandekerckhove J, Pollard TD. 1994. Purification of a cortical complex containing two unconventional actins from *Acanthamoeba* by affinity chromatography on profilin-agarose. *J. Cell Biol.* 127:107–15

Mack D, Nishimura K, Dennehey BK, Arbogast T, Parkinson J, et al. 1996. Identification of the bud emergence gene *BEM4* and its interactions with rho-type GTPases in *Saccharomyces cerevisiae*. *Mol. Cell Biol.* 16:4387–95

Madaule P, Axel R, Myers AM. 1987. Characterization of two members of the rho gene family from the yeast *Saccharomyces cerevisiae*. *Proc. Natl. Acad. Sci. USA* 84:779–83

Madaule P, Furuyashiki T, Reid T, Ishizaki T, Watanabe G, et al. 1995. A novel partner for the GTP-bound forms of rho and rac. *FEBS Lett.* 377:243–48

Madhani HD, Styles CA, Fink GR. 1997. MAP kinases with distinct inhibitory functions impart signaling specificity during yeast differentiation. *Cell* 91:673–84

Magdolen V, Drubin DG, Mages G, Bandlow W. 1993. High levels of profilin suppress the lethality caused by overproduction of actin in yeast cells. *FEBS Lett.* 316:41–47

Magdolen V, Oechsner U, Müller G, Bandlow W. 1988. The intron-containing gene for yeast profilin (PFY) encodes a vital function. *Mol. Cell Biol.* 8:5108–15

Manning BD, Padmanabha R, Snyder M. 1997. The Rho-GEF Rom2p localizes to sites of polarized cell growth and participates in cytoskeletal functions in *Saccharomyces cerevisiae*. *Mol. Biol. Cell* 8:1829–44

Marshall CJ. 1993. Protein prenylation: a mediator of protein-protein interactions. *Science* 259:1865–66

Masuda T, Tanaka K, Nonaka H, Yamochi W, Maeda A, Takai Y. 1994. Molecular cloning and characterization of yeast rho GDP dissociation inhibitor. *J. Biol. Chem.* 269:19713–18

Matsudaira P. 1991. Modular organization of actin crosslinking proteins. *Trends Biochem. Sci.* 16:87–92

Matsudaira P. 1994. Actin crosslinking proteins at the leading edge. *Semin. Cell Biol.* 5:165–74

Matsudaira P, Janmey P. 1988. Pieces in the actin-severing protein puzzle. *Cell* 54:139–40

Matsui T, Amano M, Yamamoto T, Chihara K, Nakafuku M, et al. 1996. Rho-associated kinase, a novel serine/threonine kinase, as a putative target for small GTP binding protein Rho. *EMBO J.* 15:2208–16

Matsui Y, Toh-e A. 1992a. Yeast *RHO3* and *RHO4* ras superfamily genes are necessary for bud growth, and their defect is suppressed by a high dose of bud formation genes *CDC42* and *BEM1*. *Mol. Cell Biol.* 12:5690–99

Matsui Y, Toh-e A. 1992b. Isolation and characterization of two novel ras superfamily genes in *Saccharomyces cerevisiae*. *Gene* 114:43–49

Mazzoni C, Zarov P, Rambourg A, Mann C. 1993. The SLT2 (MPK1) MAP kinase homolog is involved in polarized cell growth in *Saccharomyces cerevisiae*. *J. Cell Biol.* 123:1821–33

McCollum D, Feoktistova A, Morphew M, Balasubramanian M, Gould KL. 1996. The *Schizosaccharomyces pombe* actin-related protein, Arp3, is a component of the cortical actin cytoskeleton and interacts with profilin. *EMBO J.* 15:6438–46

Michiels F, Habets GG, Stam JC, van der Kammen RA, Collard JG. 1995. A role for Rac in Tiam1-induced membrane ruffling and invasion. *Nature* 375:338–40

Miklos D, Caplan S, Mertens D, Hynes G, Pitluk Z, et al. 1994. Primary structure and function of a second essential member of the heterooligomeric TCP1 chaperonin complex of yeast, TCP1 beta. *Proc. Natl. Acad. Sci. USA* 91:2743–47

Minden A, Lin A, Claret FX, Abo A, Karin M. 1995. Selective activation of the JNK signaling cascade and c-Jun transcriptional activity by the small GTPases Rac and Cdc42Hs. *Cell* 81:1147–57

Mizuno T, Kaibuchi K, Yamamoto T, Kawamura M, Sakoda T, et al. 1991. A stimulatory GDP/GTP exchange protein for smg p21 is active on the post-translationally processed form of c-Ki-ras p21 and rhoA p21. *Proc. Natl. Acad. Sci. USA* 88:6442–46

Moon A, Drubin DG. 1995. The ADF/cofilin proteins: stimulus-responsive modulators of actin dynamics. *Mol. Biol. Cell* 6:1423–31

Moon AL, Janmey PA, Louie KA, Drubin DG. 1993. Cofilin is an essential component of the yeast cortical cytoskeleton. *J. Cell Biol.* 120:421–35

Moreau V, Madania A, Martin RP, Winson B. 1996. The *Saccharomyces cerevisiae* actin-related protein Arp2 is involved in the actin cytoskeleton. *J. Cell Biol.* 134:117–32

Morgan TE, Lockerbie RO, Minamide LS, Browning MD, Bamburg JR. 1993. Isolation and characterization of a regulated form of actin depolymerizing factor. *J. Cell Biol.* 122:623–33

Mösch HU, Roberts RL, Fink GR. 1996. Ras2 signals via the Cdc42/Ste20/mitogen-activated protein kinase module to induce filamentous growth in *Saccharomyces cere-*

visiae. *Proc. Natl. Acad. Sci. USA* 93:5352–56

Mulholland J, Preuss D, Moon A, Wong A, Drubin D, Botstein D. 1994. Ultrastructure of the yeast actin cytoskeleton and its association with the plasma membrane. *J. Cell Biol.* 125:381–91

Müller L, Xu G, Wells R, Hollenberg CP, Piepersberg W. 1994. LRG1 is expressed during sporulation in *Saccharomyces cerevisiae* and contains motifs similar to LIM and rho/racGAP domains. *Nucleic Acids Res.* 22:3151–54

Musacchio A, Gibson T, Rice P, Thompson J, Saraste M. 1993. The PH domain: a common piece in the structural patchwork of signalling proteins. *Trends Biochem. Sci.* 18:343–48

Nachmias VT. 1993. Small actin-binding proteins: the beta-thymosin family. *Curr. Opin. Cell Biol.* 5:56–62

Narumiya S, Ishizaki T, Watanabe N. 1997. Rho effectors and reorganization of actin cytoskeleton. *FEBS Lett.* 410:68–72

Nefsky B, Bretscher A. 1992. Yeast actin is relatively well behaved. *Eur. J. Biochem.* 206:949–55

Nern A, Arkowitz RA. 1998. A GTP-exchange factor required for cell orientation. *Nature* 391:195–98

Ng R, Abelson J. 1980. Isolation and sequence of the gene for actin in *Saccharomyces cerevisiae*. *Proc. Natl. Acad. Sci. USA* 77:3912–16

Nimnual AS, Yatsula BA, Bar-Sagi D. 1998. Coupling of Ras and Rac guanosine triphosphatases through the Ras exchanger Sos. *Science* 279:560–63

Nobes CD, Hall A. 1995. Rho, rac, and cdc42 GTPases regulate the assembly of multimolecular focal complexes associated with actin stress fibers, lamellipodia, and filopodia. *Cell* 81:53–62

Nobes CD, Hawkins P, Stephens L, Hall A. 1995. Activation of the small GTP-binding proteins rho and rac by growth factor receptors. *J. Cell Sci.* 108:225–33

Noegel A, Witke W, Schleicher M. 1987. Calcium-sensitive non-muscle alpha-actinin contains EF-hand structures and highly conserved regions. *FEBS Lett.* 221:391–96

Nonaka H, Tanaka K, Hirano H, Fujiwara T, Kohno H, et al. 1995. A downstream target of RHO1 small GTP-binding protein is PKC1, a homolog of protein kinase C, which leads to activation of the MAP kinase cascade in *Saccharomyces cerevisiae*. *EMBO J.* 14:5931–38

Novick P, Botstein D. 1985. Phenotypic analysis of temperature-sensitive yeast actin mutants. *Cell* 40:405–16

Ohga N, Kikuchi A, Ueda T, Yamamoto J, Takai Y. 1989. Rabbit intestine contains a protein that inhibits the dissociation of GDP from and the subsequent binding of GTP to rhoB p20, a ras p21-like GTP-binding protein. *Biochem. Biophys. Res. Commun.* 163:1523–33

Ohya Y, Qadota H, Anraku Y, Pringle JR, Botstein D. 1993. Suppression of yeast geranylgeranyl transferase I defect by alternative prenylation of two target GTPases, Rho1p and Cdc42p. *Mol. Biol. Cell* 4:1017–25

Olson MF, Ashworth A, Hall A. 1995. An essential role for Rho, Rac, and Cdc42 GTPases in cell cycle progression through G1. *Science* 269:1270–72

Ozaki K, Tanaka K, Imamura H, Hihara T, Kameyama T, et al. 1996. Rom1p and Rom2p are GDP/GTP exchange proteins (GEPs) for the Rho1p small GTP binding protein in *Saccharomyces cerevisiae. EMBO J.* 15:2196–207

Palmer RE, Sullivan DS, Huffaker T, Koshland D. 1992. Role of astral microtubules and actin in spindle orientation and migration in the budding yeast, *Saccharomyces cerevisiae. J. Cell Biol.* 119:583–93

Pantaloni D, Carlier MF. 1993. How profilin promotes actin filament assembly in the presence of thymosin beta 4. *Cell* 75:1007–14

Park HO, Bi E, Pringle JR, Herskowitz I. 1997. Two active states of the Ras-related Bud1/Rsr1 protein bind to different effectors to determine yeast cell polarity. *Proc. Natl. Acad. Sci. USA* 94:4463–68

Paterson HF, Self AJ, Garrett MD, Just I, Aktories K, Hall A. 1990. Microinjection of recombinant p21rho induces rapid changes in cell morphology. *J. Cell Biol.* 111:1001–7

Perona R, Montaner S, Saniger L, Sanchez-Perez I, Bravo R, Lacal JC. 1997. Activation of the nuclear factor-κB by Rho, CDC42, and Rac-1 proteins. *Genes Dev.* 11:463–75

Peter M, Neiman AM, Park HO, van Lohuizen M, Herskowitz I. 1996. Functional analysis of the interaction between the small GTP binding protein Cdc42 and the Ste20 protein kinase in yeast. *EMBO J.* 15:7046–59

Peterson J, Zheng Y, Bender L, Myers A, Cerione R, Bender A. 1994. Interactions between the bud emergence proteins Bem1p and Bem2p and Rho-type GTPases in yeast. *J. Cell Biol.* 127:1395–406

Pollard TD, Cooper JA. 1986. Actin and actin-binding proteins. A critical evaluation of mechanisms and functions. *Annu. Rev. Biochem.* 55:987–1035

Powers S, Gonzales E, Christensen T, Cubert J, Broek D. 1991. Functional cloning of BUD5, a CDC25-related gene from S. cerevisiae that can suppress a dominant-negative RAS2 mutant. *Cell* 65:1225–31

Qadota H, Anraku Y, Botstein D, Ohya Y. 1994. Conditional lethality of a yeast strain expressing human RHOA in place of RHO1. *Proc. Natl. Acad. Sci. USA* 91:9317–21

Qadota H, Python CP, Inoue SB, Arisawa M, Anraku Y, et al. 1996. Identification of yeast Rho1p GTPase as a regulatory subunit of 1,3-beta-glucan synthase. *Science* 272:279–81

Qiu RG, Abo A, McCormick F, Symons M. 1997. Cdc42 regulates anchorage-independent growth and is necessary for Ras transformation. *Mol. Cell Biol.* 17:3449–58

Qiu RG, Chen J, McCormick F, Symons M. 1995. A role for Rho in Ras transformation. *Proc. Natl. Acad. Sci. USA* 92:11781–85

Quilliam LA, Khosravi-Far R, Huff SY, Der CJ. 1995. Guanine nucleotide exchange factors: activators of the Ras superfamily of proteins. *BioEssays* 17:395–404

Quilliam LA, Lambert QT, Mickelson-Young LA, Westwick JK, Sparks AB, et al. 1996. Isolation of a NCK-associated kinase, PRK2, an SH3-binding protein and potential effector of Rho protein signaling. *J. Biol. Chem.* 271:28772–76

Quinn MT, Evans T, Loetterle LR, Jesaitis AJ, Bokoch GM. 1993. Translocation of Rac correlates with NADPH oxidase activation. Evidence for equimolar translocation of oxidase components. *J. Biol. Chem.* 268:20983–87

Read EB, Okamura HH, Drubin DG. 1992. Actin- and tubulin-dependent functions during *Saccharomyces cerevisiae* mating projection formation. *Mol. Biol. Cell* 3:429–44

Reid T, Furuyashiki T, Ishizaki T, Watanabe G, Watanabe N, et al. 1996. Rhotekin, a new putative target for Rho bearing homology to a serine/threonine kinase, PKN, and rhophilin in the rho-binding domain. *J. Biol. Chem.* 271:13556–60

Reif K, Nobes CD, Thomas G, Hall A, Cantrell DA. 1996. Phosphatidylinositol 3-kinase signals activate a selective subset of Rac/Rho-dependent effector pathways. *Curr. Biol.* 6:1445–55

Ren XD, Bokoch GM, Traynor-Kaplan A, Jenkins GH, Anderson RA, Schwartz MA. 1996. Physical association of the small GTPase Rho with a 68-kDa phosphatidylinositol 4-phosphate 5-kinase in Swiss 3T3 cells. *Mol. Biol. Cell* 7:435–42

Ridley AJ. 1995. Rho-related proteins: actin cytoskeleton and cell cycle. *Curr. Opin. Genet. Dev.* 5:24–30

Ridley AJ. 1996. Rho: theme and variations. *Curr. Biol.* 6:1256–64

Ridley AJ, Hall A. 1992. The small GTP-binding protein rho regulates the assembly of focal adhesions and actin stress fibers in response to growth factors. *Cell* 70:389–99

Ridley AJ, Paterson HF, Johnston CL, Diekmann D, Hall A. 1992. The small GTP-binding protein rac regulates growth factor-induced membrane ruffling. *Cell* 70:401–10

Roberts RL, Mösch H-U, Fink GR. 1997. 14-3-3 proteins are essential for RAS/MAPK cascade signaling during pseudohyphal development in S. cerevisiae. *Cell* 89:1055–65

Rodriguez JR, Paterson BM. 1990. Yeast myosin heavy chain mutant: maintenance of the cell type specific budding pattern and the normal deposition of chitin and cell wall components requires an intact myosin heavy chain gene. *Cell Motil. Cytoskelet.* 17:301–8

Rodriguez-Viciana P, Warne PH, Khwaja A, Marte BM, Pappin D, et al. 1997. Role of phosphoinositide 3-OH kinase in cell transformation and control of the actin cytoskeleton by Ras. *Cell* 89:457–67

Ron D, Zannini M, Lewis M, Wickner RB, Hunt LT, et al. 1991. A region of proto-dbl essential for its transforming activity shows sequence similarity to a yeast cell cycle gene, *CDC24*, and the human breakpoint cluster gene, *bcr*. *New Biol.* 3:372–79

Ruppel KM, Spudich JA. 1995. Myosin motor function: structural and mutagenic approaches. *Curr. Opin. Cell Biol.* 7:89–93

Safer D, Elzinga M, Nachmias VT. 1991. Thymosin beta 4 and Fx, an actin-sequestering peptide, are indistinguishable. *J. Biol. Chem.* 266:4029–32

Safer D, Nachmias VT. 1994. Beta thymosins as actin binding peptides. *BioEssays* 16:473–79

Salmon ED. 1989. Cytokinesis in animal cells. *Curr. Opin. Cell Biol.* 1:541–47

Santos B, Snyder M. 1997. Targeting of chitin synthase 3 to polarized growth sites in yeast requires Chs5p and Myo2p. *J. Cell Biol.* 136:95–110

Sasaki T, Kato M, Takai Y. 1993. Consequences of weak interaction of rho GDI with the GTP-bound forms of rho p21 and rac p21. *J. Biol. Chem.* 268:23959–63

Schafer DA, Cooper JA. 1995. Control of actin assembly at filament ends. *Annu. Rev. Cell Dev. Biol.* 11:497–518

Schmidt A, Bickle M, Beck T, Hall MN. 1997. The yeast phosphatidylinositol kinase homolog TOR2 activates RHO1 and RHO2 via the exchange factor ROM2. *Cell* 88:531–42

Segal AW, Abo A. 1993. The biochemical basis of the NADPH oxidase of phagocytes. *Trends Biochem. Sci.* 18:43–47

Shortle D, Novick P, Botstein D. 1984. Construction and genetic characterization of temperature-sensitive mutant alleles of the yeast actin gene. *Proc. Natl. Acad. Sci. USA* 81:4889–93

Simon MN, De Virgilio C, Souza B, Pringle JR, Abo A, Reed SI. 1995. Role for the Rho-family GTPase Cdc42 in yeast mating-pheromone signal pathway. *Nature* 376:702–5

Simon VR, Swayne TC, Pon LA. 1995. Actin-dependent mitochondrial motility in mitotic yeast and cell-free systems: identification of a motor activity on the mitochondrial surface. *J. Cell Biol.* 130:345–54

Sloat BF, Adams A, Pringle JR. 1981. Roles of the *CDC24* gene product in cellular morphogenesis during the *Saccharomyces cerevisiae* cell cycle. *J. Cell Biol.* 89:395–405

Sohn RH, Goldschmidt-Clermont PJ. 1994. Profilin: at the crossroads of signal transduction and the actin cytoskeleton. *BioEssays* 16:465–72

Sternlicht H, Farr GW, Sternlicht ML, Driscoll JK, Willison K, Yaffe MB. 1993. The t-complex polypeptide 1 complex is a chaperonin for tubulin and actin in vivo. *Proc. Natl. Acad. Sci. USA* 90:9422–26

Stevenson BJ, Ferguson B, De Virgilio C, Bi E, Pringle JR, et al. 1995. Mutation of *RGA1*, which encodes a putative GTPase-activating protein for the polarity-establishment protein Cdc42p, activates the pheromone- response pathway in the yeast *Saccharomyces cerevisiae*. *Genes Dev.* 9:2949–63

Stoldt V, Rademacher F, Kehren V, Ernst JF, Pearce DA, Sherman F. 1996. Review: the Cct eukaryotic chaperonin subunits of *Saccharomyces cerevisiae* and other yeasts. *Yeast* 12:523–29

Stössel TP. 1993. On the crawling of animal cells. *Science* 260:1086–94

Sun HQ, Kwiatkowska K, Yin HL. 1995. Actin monomer binding proteins. *Curr. Opin. Cell Biol.* 7:102–10

Sweeney FP, Pocklington MJ, Orr E. 1991. The yeast type II myosin heavy chain: analysis of its predicted polypeptide sequence. *J. Muscle Res. Cell Motil.* 12:61–68

Symons M, Derry JM, Karlak B, Jiang S, Lemahieu V, et al. 1996. Wiskott-Aldrich syndrome protein, a novel effector for the GT-Pase CDC42Hs, is implicated in actin polymerization. *Cell* 84:723–34

Takai Y, Sasaki T, Tanaka K, Nakanishi H. 1995. Rho as a regulator of the cytoskeleton. *Trends Biochem. Sci.* 20:227–31

Takizawa PA, Sil A, Swedlow JR, Herskowitz I, Vale RD. 1997. Actin-dependent localization of an RNA encoding a cell-fate determinant in yeast. *Nature* 389:90–93

Tapon N, Hall A. 1997. Rho, Rac and Cdc42 GT-Pases regulate the organization of the actin cytoskeleton. *Curr. Opin. Cell Biol.* 9:86–92

Titus MA. 1993. Myosins. *Curr. Opin. Cell Biol.* 5:77–81

Tkacz JS, Lampen JO. 1972. Wall replication in *Saccharomyces* species: use of fluorescein-conjugated concanavalin A to reveal the site of mannan insertion. *J. Gen. Microbiol.* 72:243–47

Tolias KF, Cantley LC, Carpenter CL. 1995.

Rho family GTPases bind to phosphoinositide kinases. *J. Biol. Chem.* 270:17656–59

Trybus KM. 1994. Role of myosin light chains. *J. Muscle Res. Cell Motil.* 15:587–94

Turner CE, Burridge K. 1991. Transmembrane molecular assemblies in cell-extracellular matrix interactions. *Curr. Opin. Cell Biol.* 3: 849–53

Ueda T, Kikuchi A, Ohga N, Yamamoto J, Takai Y. 1990. Purification and characterization from bovine brain cytosol of a novel regulatory protein inhibiting the dissociation of GDP from and the subsequent binding of GTP to rhoB p20, a ras p21-like GTP-binding protein. *J. Biol. Chem.* 265:9373–80

Uehata M, Ishizaki T, Satoh H, Ono T, Kawahara T, et al. 1997. Calcium sensitization of smooth muscle mediated by a Rho-associated protein kinase in hypertension. *Nature* 389:990–94

Ursic D, Culbertson MR. 1991. The yeast homolog to mouse Tcp-1 affects microtubule-mediated processes. *Mol. Cell Biol.* 11:2629–40

Ursic D, Sedbrook JC, Himmel KL, Culbertson MR. 1994. The essential yeast Tcp1 protein affects actin and microtubules. *Mol. Biol. Cell* 5:1065–80

Van Aelst L, D'Souza-Schorey C. 1997. Rho GTPases and signaling networks. *Genes Dev.* 11:2295–322

Vincent S, Settleman J. 1997. The PRK2 kinase is a potential effector target of both Rho and Rac GTPases and regulates actin cytoskeletal organization. *Mol. Cell Biol.* 17:2247–56

Vinh DB, Welch MD, Corsi AK, Wertman KF, Drubin DG. 1993. Genetic evidence for functional interactions between actin noncomplementing (Anc) gene products and actin cytoskeletal proteins in *Saccharomyces cerevisiae*. *Genetics* 135:275–86

Walsh TP, Weber A, Davis K, Bonder E, Mooseker M. 1984. Calcium dependence of villin-induced actin depolymerization. *Biochemistry* 23:6099–102

Watanabe G, Saito Y, Madaule P, Ishizaki T, Fujisawa K, et al. 1996. Protein kinase N (PKN) and PKN-related protein rhophilin as targets of small GTPase Rho. *Science* 271:645–48

Watanabe N, Madaule P, Reid T, Ishizaki T, Watanabe G, et al. 1997. p140mDia, a mammalian homolog of *Drosophila diaphanous*, is a target protein for Rho small GTPase and is a ligand for profilin. *EMBO J.* 16:3044–56

Watts FZ, Shiels G, Orr E. 1987. The yeast *MYO1* gene encoding a myosin-like protein required for cell division. *EMBO J.* 6:3499–505

Weiss A, Leinwand LA. 1996. The mammalian myosin heavy chain gene family. *Annu. Rev. Cell Dev. Biol.* 1996;12:417–39

Welch MD, Holtzman DA, Drubin DG. 1994. The yeast actin cytoskeleton. *Curr. Opin. Cell Biol.* 6:110–19

Wennstrom S, Hawkins P, Cooke F, Hara K, Yonezawa K, et al. 1994. Activation of phosphoinositide 3-kinase is required for PDGF-stimulated membrane ruffling. *Curr. Biol.* 4: 385–93

Whitehead IP, Campbell S, Rossman KL, Der CJ. 1997. Dbl family proteins. *Biochim. Biophys. Acta* 1332:F1–23

Whitehead IP, Khosravi-Far R, Kirk H, Trigo-Gonzalez G, Der CJ, Kay R. 1996. Expression cloning of lsc, a novel oncogene with structural similarities to the Dbl family of guanine nucleotide exchange factors. *J. Biol. Chem.* 271:18643–50

Whitehead IP, Kirk H, Tognon C, Trigo-Gonzalez G, Kay R. 1995. Expression cloning of lfc, a novel oncogene with structural similarities to guanine nucleotide exchange factors and to the regulatory region of protein kinase C. *J. Biol. Chem.* 270:18388–95

Winsor B, Schiebel E. 1997. Review: an overview of the *Saccharomyces cerevisiae* microtubule and microfilament cytoskeleton. *Yeast* 13:399–434

Winter D, Podtelejnikov AV, Mann M, Li R. 1997. The complex containing actin-related proteins Arp2 and Arp3 is required for the motility and integrity of yeast actin patches. *Curr. Biol.* 7:519–29

Witke W, Hofmann A, Koppel B, Schleicher M, Noegel AA. 1993. The Ca(2+)-binding domains in non-muscle type alpha-actinin: biochemical and genetic analysis. *J. Cell Biol.* 121:599–606

Yaffe MB, Farr GW, Miklos D, Horwich AL, Sternlicht ML, Sternlicht H. 1992. TCP1 complex is a molecular chaperone in tubulin biogenesis. *Nature* 358:245–48

Yaku H, Sasaki T, Takai Y. 1994. The Dbl oncogene product as a GDP/GTP exchange protein for the Rho family: its properties in comparison with those of Smg GDS. *Biochem. Biophys. Res. Commun.* 198:811–17

Yamada KM, Geiger B. 1997. Molecular interactions in cell adhesion complexes. *Curr. Opin. Cell Biol.* 9:76–85

Yamochi W, Tanaka K, Nonaka H, Maeda A, Musha T, Takai Y. 1994. Growth site localization of Rho1 small GTP-binding protein and its involvement in bud formation in *Saccharomyces cerevisiae*. *J. Cell Biol.* 125:1077–93

Yonezawa N, Nishida E, Iida K, Yahara I, Sakai H. 1990. Inhibition of the interactions of cofilin, destrin, and deoxyribonuclease I with actin by phosphoinositides. *J. Biol. Chem.* 265:8382–86

Zarzov P, Mazzoni C, Mann C. 1996. The SLT2(MPK1) MAP kinase is activated during periods of polarized cell growth in yeast. *EMBO J.* 15:83–91

Zhang J, King WG, Dillon S, Hall A, Feig L, Rittenhouse SE. 1993. Activation of platelet phosphatidylinositide 3-kinase requires the small GTP-binding protein Rho. *J. Biol. Chem.* 268:22251–54

Zhao ZS, Leung T, Manser E, Lim L. 1995. Pheromone signalling in *Saccharomyces cerevisiae* requires the small GTP-binding protein Cdc42p and its activator CDC24. *Mol. Cell Biol.* 15:5246–57

Zheng Y, Bagrodia S, Cerione RA. 1994a. Activation of phosphoinositide 3-kinase activity by Cdc42Hs binding to p85. *J. Biol. Chem.* 269:18727–30

Zheng Y, Bender A, Cerione RA. 1995. Interactions among proteins involved in bud-site selection and bud-site assembly in *Saccharomyces cerevisiae*. *J. Biol. Chem.* 270:626–30

Zheng Y, Cerione R, Bender A. 1994b. Control of the yeast bud-site assembly GTPase Cdc42. Catalysis of guanine nucleotide exchange by Cdc24 and stimulation of GTPase activity by Bem3. *J. Biol. Chem.* 269:2369–72

Zheng Y, Hart MJ, Shinjo K, Evans T, Bender A, Cerione RA. 1993. Biochemical comparisons of the *Saccharomyces cerevisiae* Bem2 and Bem3 proteins. Delineation of a limit Cdc42 GTPase-activating protein domain. *J. Biol. Chem.* 268:24629–34

Zheng Y, Zangrilli D, Cerione RA, Eva A. 1996. The pleckstrin homology domain mediates transformation by oncogenic *dbl* through specific intracellular targeting. *J. Biol. Chem.* 271:19017–20

Ziman M, Preuss D, Mulholland J, O'Brien JM, Botstein D, Johnson DI. 1993. Subcellular localization of Cdc42p, a *Saccharomyces cerevisiae* GTP-binding protein involved in the control of cell polarity. *Mol. Biol. Cell* 4:1307–16

Annu. Rev. Cell Dev. Biol. 1998. 14:339–72

ISOFORM SORTING AND THE CREATION OF INTRACELLULAR COMPARTMENTS

Peter Gunning and Ron Weinberger

The Oncology Research Unit, The New Children's Hospital, PO Box 3515, Parramatta, NSW 2124, and Department of Pediatrics and Child Health, University of Sydney, NSW 2006, Australia; e-mail: Peterg3@nch.edu.au

Peter Jeffrey and Edna Hardeman*

Developmental Neurobiology and *Muscle Development Units, Children's Medical Research Institute, Locked Bag 23, Wentworthville, NSW 2145, Australia

KEY WORDS: protein targeting, mRNA targeting, cytoskeleton, microfilaments

---

ABSTRACT

The generation of isoforms via gene duplication and alternative splicing has been a valuable evolutionary tool for the creation of biological diversity. In addition to the formation of molecules with related but different functional characteristics, it is now apparent that isoforms can be segregated into different intracellular sites within the same cell. Sorting has been observed in a wide range of genes, including those encoding structural molecules, receptors, channels, enzymes, and signaling molecules. This results in the creation of intracellular compartments that (*a*) can be independently controlled and (*b*) have different functional properties. The sorting mechanisms are likely to operate at the level of both proteins and mRNAs. Isoform sorting may be an important consequence of the evolution of isoforms and is likely to have contributed to the diversity of functional properties within groups of isoforms.

CONTENTS

339

1081-0706/98/1115-0339$08.00

ISOFORMS AND THE GENERATION OF BIOLOGICAL DIVERSITY

Gene duplication and alternative splicing have been extensively used to generate genetic complexity. Increasing genetic complexity seems to be associated with progressive expansion of multigene families and the generation of alternative exons. For example, some of the earliest genes cloned—actin, myosin, histones, and globin—show a clear trend to increased gene number with increasing genetic complexity. The point at which expansion occurs and plateaus differs for each of these products. Yeast has 1 actin gene (Gallwitz & Sures 1980), whereas *Dictyostelium* has 17 (Romans & Firtel 1985), and *Drosophila* (Fyrberg et al 1981) and mammals (Vandekerckhove & Weber 1978) have 6. In contrast, yeast and *Dictyostelium* have 1 conventional myosin II, *Drosophila* has 1 myosin II gene that uses alternative splicing to generate 4 isoforms, and mammals have at least 9 (Warrick & Spudich 1987).

It is becoming clear that gene duplication has created both closely related gene families and more distantly related superfamilies of which one of the best characterized is the myosin superfamily (Bement et al 1994). The distinction between isoforms and distantly related proteins can become blurred. For the purpose of clarity in this review, we consider isoforms to be highly similar at the level of primary sequence and to perform highly related functions. Thus we consider isoforms to exist within one family and not between members of different families within a superfamily. In general, isoforms arise by gene duplication or alternative splicing whereas the superfamilies may come from ancient duplications, exon/domain duplication, or convergent evolution.

Isoforms exist as mRNAs and proteins. In many cases the 5' and/or 3' untranslated regions of isoform mRNAs differ in addition to the protein coding region. The evolutionary conservation of some of these isoform-specific untranslated regions suggests that they are likely to be of functional significance (Gunning et al 1984, Yaffe et al 1985). Indeed, there are several cases where multiple genes in an organism encode the identical protein, the only difference is the nucleotide sequence of the mRNA (Romans & Firtel 1985, Beach & Jeffery 1992). This serves to emphasize the importance of considering the biological significance of the mRNA as well as the protein.

FUNCTIONAL DIVERSITY VERSUS FUNCTIONAL REDUNDANCY

The discovery of extensive numbers of families of isoforms suggests that gene duplication has made a major contribution to functional diversity in higher organisms. There are three levels at which this may be manifested: First, multiple genes may use different promoter elements to generate the complex gene regulatory programs required in development or in different tissues. In the case of the transcription factor engrailed (*en*), knock-in of the *en2*-coding region into the *en1* gene revealed apparent functional redundancy of the protein-coding region but not the gene regulatory sequences (Hanks et al 1995). Second, isoform mRNAs with different untranslated regions may have different functional properties at the level of the mRNA. Finally, the protein isoforms may have distinct functional properties.

The use of gene knockouts in mice has raised the surprising possibility that members of multigene families may be functionally redundant. This concept has been the subject of considerable debate because it seems at first incompatible with our expectation of the evolutionary process (for example, see Wilkins 1997 and references therein). The dilemma posed by these studies is that they will not necessarily detect small but biologically significant differences. More importantly, they highlight the ability of multigene families to compensate for the elimination of one member. This suggests that in many families, isoforms retain sufficient similarity to rescue deletion of a family member.

Recent work has provided compelling evidence that isoforms can be sorted at the level of protein and/or mRNA (Herman 1993, Gunning et al 1997). This has provided a novel twist on the biological function of isoforms. At least for some isoforms, it appears that the cell can sort them into different intracellular compartments, which provides a potential opportunity to independently control similar biological processes in different cellular sites. The emerging concept is of a highly ordered cytoplasm containing discrete compartments with specialized functions composed of molecules of related evolutionary origin.

ISOFORMS AND CELLULAR COMPARTMENTS—HISTORICAL PERSPECTIVE

The idea that isoforms may contribute to the creation of intracellular compartments is not new; indeed, it is almost as old as the discovery of the isoforms themselves. The first direct experimental evidence came from the study of actin and myosin isoforms in skeletal muscle. In mammals, actin is encoded by six genes, two nonmuscle (β and γ), two striated muscle (α-skeletal, α_{sk}, and α-cardiac, α_{ca}), and two smooth muscle (α_{sm} and γ_{sm}) isoforms (Vandekerckhove & Weber 1978). The majority of actin and myosin II in striated muscle is localized to the thin and thick filaments, respectively, of the contractile apparatus (Figure 1). Antibodies that recognize all actin and myosin II isoforms or just the muscle-specific isoforms show intense staining of the cross-striated contractile apparatus and virtually no other structures (Fallon & Nachmias 1980, Craig & Pardo 1983). However, antibodies that specifically recognize the nonmuscle isoforms fail to react with the contractile apparatus but reveal the presence of additional cytoskeletal structures within skeletal muscle cells (Figure 1). Nonmuscle β-actin is associated with the plasma membrane, possibly with the sarcoplasmic reticulum, and is highly enriched in the post-synaptic folds of the neuromuscular junction (Lubit & Schwartz 1980, Hall et al 1981, Lubit 1984). The other nonmuscle actin, γ-actin, is found associated with the plasma membrane, costameres, and surrounding mitochondria (Craig & Pardo 1983, Pardo et al 1983). Similarly, the nonmuscle conventional myosin II is found in fine stress fibers and the submembranous rim of skeletal muscle myotubes, whereas the muscle isoforms are located in the central region in the contractile apparatus (Fallon & Nachmias 1980) (Figure 1).

The early excitement generated by these studies did not immediately lead to extension of the work and investigation of the underlying mechanisms. This reflected both the lack of suitable reagents to dissect the problem and the increasing complexity of structural protein gene families that were subsequently discovered. This was coupled with concern that the observations did not reflect fundamental functional differences between isoforms. For example, β- and γ-actin account for only a vanishingly small fraction of total skeletal muscle actin. It is now clear, however, that these original observations reflect a fundamental role for isoforms.

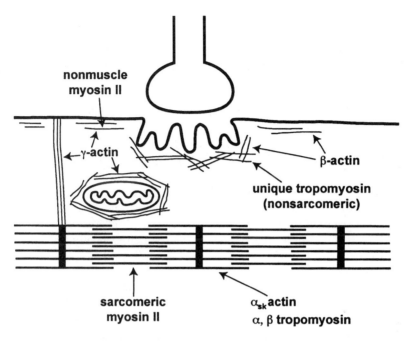

Figure 1   Isoform sorting of actin, myosin, and tropomyosin isoforms in striated muscle. The muscle isoforms of actin (α_{sk}), tropomyosin (α, β), and myosin II (sarcomeric) are located in the cross-striated contractile apparatus, which fills the center of the muscle cell. Nonmuscle isoforms are located in a membrane-linked cytoskeleton with β-actin and a novel tropomyosin enriched at the neuromuscular junction. γ-Actin is found in costameres (linking the Z-disk with the plasma membrane) and in filaments surrounding mitochondria and associated with the plasma membrane. Nonmuscle myosin II is also located near the plasma membrane (Fallon & Nachmias 1980, Lubit & Schwartz 1980, Hall et al 1981, Craig & Pardo 1983, Pardo et al 1983, Lubit 1984, Anthony et al 1988).

STRUCTURAL PROTEINS—CYTOSKELETON

Actin and Myosin Sorting in Muscle Cells

ACTIN   The sorting of muscle and nonmuscle isoforms of actin in skeletal muscle (Figure 1) has not been easily detected in skeletal myotubes in cell culture. Otey et al (1988) observed a small preference for α_{sk} actin in myofibrils and cytoplasmic γ-actin in the cortical region, but sorting in myotubes was clearly less stringent than that observed in adult muscle (Figure 1). A similar study of initial skeletal muscle differentiation found no significant sorting of α_{sk} and γ-actin (Handel et al 1989). This suggests that during initial assembly of the skeletal muscle contractile apparatus considerable mixing of the actin isoforms may be tolerated. Alternatively, this may reflect less rigid control of myofibril assembly in an in vitro environment.

Cardiomyocytes cultured in vitro have proven to be a better system than skeletal myotubes for examining the sorting of actin isoforms. Eppenberger-Eberhardt et al (1990) found that striated muscle α_{sk}/α_{ca}-actin was primarily located in myofibrillar structures, whereas α-smooth actin was enriched in non-myofibrillar stress fiber-like structures in regenerating adult cardiomyocytes. In contrast, fetal tissue sections revealed that α-smooth actin can accumulate in myofibrillar structures in the myocardium. It is unclear if this represents a difference in the stage of myofibrillar assembly (remodeling verses initial assembly) or the induction of structures in vitro not generated in vivo. von Arx et al (1995) have used gene transfections of tagged actins into cardiomyocytes to demonstrate that all four muscle actins localize to myofibrillar structures, in comparison with the two nonmuscle isoforms. Similarly, Mournier et al (1997) found that these tagged actin isoforms are differentially targeted upon transfection into both smooth muscle and nonmuscle cells.

Sorting of actin isoforms has also been observed in smooth muscle cells. DeNofrio et al (1989) observed that α_{sm} was restricted in its localization to stress fibers, whereas the nonmuscle actins were also located in motile areas of the cytoplasm. This was confirmed biochemically by characterization of the actins selectively extracted from motile cytoplasm (DeNofrio et al 1989). North et al (1994) have shown clear sorting of β-actin and smooth muscle actins (primarily γ_{sm}). Furthermore, in chicken gizzard, β-actin was restricted in location to dense bodies and longitudinal channels linking consecutive dense bodies. Smooth muscle actin was also observed throughout the cell but was conspicuously absent from the β-actin-containing cores of the dense bodies. This finding suggests that β-actin is segregated away from the smooth muscle contractile apparatus and preferentially localizes into a cytoskeletal compartment, a conclusion with a striking parallel in striated muscle (Figure 1).

ACTIN-BINDING PROTEINS   Anthony et al (1988) have generated an antibody that recognizes a muscle-specific tropomyosin (Tm) localized to the non-myofibrillar regions of skeletal muscle fibers. This isoform shows a preferential association with the neuromuscular junction, a remarkable similarity to the report of β-actin enrichment in these same structures (Hall et al 1981). Unfortunately, neither the specific Tm isoform nor the gene involved in its generation has been identified. Nevertheless, this work suggests that the actin filaments associated with the neuromuscular junction are composed of an actin and a Tm isoform specifically sorted into this compartment.

The actin filaments of striated muscle cells are also discriminated by the $\beta1$ and $\beta2$ isoforms of the β subunit of the actin-capping protein. The nonmuscle

β2 isoform is enriched at intercalated discs, whereas the β1 muscle isoform is located at myofibrillar Z-disks in cardiac muscle (Schafer et al 1994).

MYOSIN   Myosin motor proteins are encoded by a super gene family of at least 13 classes (Mooseker & Cheney 1995, Cope et al 1996). Most classes are composed of multiple isoforms of which type II myosins consist of both muscle and nonmuscle isoforms. Type II myosins are exemplified by the contractile myosins found in muscle cells. These myosins exist as dimers of myosin heavy chains in which their long tails form a coiled coil and the globular head region contains the motor domain. Embryonic cardiomyocytes express both muscle and nonmuscle type II isoforms and undergo cytokinesis in cell culture. Conrad et al (1991) found that the nonmuscle myosin preferentially localizes to premyofibril structures at the cell periphery, yet is excluded from mature myofibrils at the center of the cell (Rhee et al 1994). This indicates a clear distinction in cardiomyocytes between contractile and cytoskeletal function at the level of isoform sorting.

Cardiomyocytes also sort the muscle myosin light chains (MLC) between contractile and cytoskeletal structures. Epitope tagged muscle MLC-1f and 3f localize almost exclusively to the myofibrillar structures and parallel endogenous type II muscle myosin staining (Soldati & Perriard 1991). In contrast, the tagged nonmuscle MLC-3nm is equally well localized to myofibrillar and cytoskeletal structures. Competition experiments suggest that the different MLC isoforms compete for inclusion into myofibrillar structures and that MLC-3f can exclude MLC-3nm from these structures (Komiyama et al 1996).

Sorting has also been observed between the different muscle type II myosins contained within the same skeletal muscle cell. The A and B type II isoforms in the body wall muscle cells of *Caenorhabditis elegans* are differentially localized to the central and polar regions, respectively, of the thick myosin filaments (Miller et al 1983). Segregation of embryonic and neonatal type II isoforms has been detected in immature chicken muscle cells (Gauthier 1990), and Rosser et al (1995) have found the neonatal isoform to be restricted to the tapered end of adult muscle cells. Because skeletal muscle cells are multinucleated, it is not clear whether the sorting of embryonic and neonatal myosins reflects different transcriptional activity of nuclei in the same cell or active sorting along the length of the whole cell.

Actin Cytoskeleton in Nonmuscle Cells

ACTIN   Several studies have suggested that the actin isoforms β and γ are colocalized in nonmuscle cells. Otey et al (1986) compared the staining of various nonmuscle cells using a total actin and their γ-actin antibodies. γ-Actin was found in all actin-containing structures. Similarly, using the same antibody combination, no difference was observed in myoblasts (Hill & Gunning 1993). The staining for β-actin versus γ-actin in 3T3 fibroblasts also revealed no consistent differences (Hill et al 1994). Therefore it was concluded that these nonmuscle cells, under normal growth conditions in culture, do not segregate β from γ.

In contrast, there is strong evidence for enrichment of β-actin at the site of rapid membrane remodeling. Hoock et al (1991) have shown a clear segregation of nonmuscle actins associated with wound healing of endothelial and 3T3 fibroblast cells. Analysis of anti-β versus phalloidin (to visualize all polymeric actin) staining revealed an enrichment of β-actin in motile cytoplasm associated with wound closure. This enrichment disappeared after monolayer restoration, therefore implying that polarized membrane remodeling involves a segregation of β and γ. This is further supported by observations of differentiating neuroblastoma cells. Prior to differentiation, β-actin is enriched in the cell cortex relative to γ-actin and is strongly enriched in the terminal tips of neurites in differentiating cells (Ulloa & Avila 1996) (Figure 2).

The segregation of β- and γ-actin has also been convincingly demonstrated in gastric parietal cells and neurons in vivo. β-Actin is enriched in the apical membrane and secretory canaliculus of parietal cells whereas γ-actin is enriched near the basolateral membrane (Yao et al 1995, 1996). β-Actin is also enriched in growing axons relative to the neuronal cell body in vivo (Weinberger et al 1996). However, this sorting is subject to developmental regulation. β-Actin is lost from mature axons over a short period and redistributed to dendritic synapse-enriched sites (Figure 2). In contrast, γ-actin is uniformly distributed at all times (Weinberger et al 1996). Thus there is general agreement that γ-actin tends to be present in most, if not all, nonmuscle microfilaments whereas β-actin is enriched in cytoplasmic and membrane structures undergoing or

--→

Figure 2   Isoform sorting in embryonic and adult neurons. β-Actin and tropomyosin isoforms Tm5a/b, TmNM1/2, TmNM3/4, and Tm4 show sorting in embryonic neurons. β-Actin[+] shows very low levels in axons and very high levels[*] in the growth cone. TmNM3/4 is also enriched in growth cones but its presence in axons is unclear[Δ] due to cross reactivity of the antibody with other isoforms. Each compartment (cell body, axon, and growth cone) has a unique combination of actin and tropomyosin isoforms (Had et al 1994, Hannan et al 1995, 1998, Ulloa & Avila 1996, Weinberger et al 1996, Schevzov et al 1997, Bassell et al 1998). Adult neurons display increased segregation with β-actin highly enriched in dendrites, present at low levels in the cell body[#] and not detected in axons. Tm4 and TmNM1/2 isoforms are relocated to the cell body and dendrites, and a neuron-specific tropomyosin TmBr3 now appears in axons and the presynaptic bouton. Spectrin and ankyrin isoforms also segregate into somatodendritic and axonal compartments, as do acid phosphatase isoforms (Malchiodi-Albedi et al 1993, Clark et al 1994, Had et al 1994, Weinberger et al 1996, Krizbai et al 1997, Hannan et al 1998).

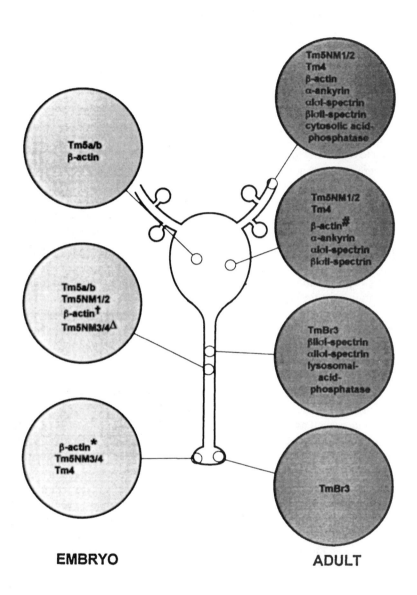

EMBRYO   **ADULT**

capable of undergoing rapid remodeling or polarized movement (reviewed in Herman 1993, Gunning et al 1997, 1998).

TROPOMYOSIN   Tropomyosin isoforms display a remarkable diversity of sorting to different actin filament populations and have been the subject of recent reviews (Pittenger et al 1994; Gunning et al 1997, 1998; Lin et al 1997). Tropomyosins are coiled-coil dimers that form polymers inserted into the α-helical groove of the actin filament. There are four genes of which three give rise to additional diversity by alternative splicing, resulting in a current estimate of a total of 22 isoforms (Pittenger et al 1994). Lin et al (1988) were the first to report that the low molecular weight tropomyosins from the Tm5NM gene were enriched at the cell periphery of bladder carcinoma cells in culture relative to the high molecular weight Tm3. A similar conclusion was reached in studies of chicken embryo fibroblasts (Lin et al 1988).

Neuronal development in vivo is accompanied by profound changes in Tm isoform organization. Antibody staining for the isoforms Tm5NM1/2 is highly enriched in growing axons but not the cell body (Weinberger et al 1996). Had et al (1994) also found that the Tm4 isoform was enriched in growth cones. Staining for both Tm5NM1/2 and Tm4 is lost from mature axons and replaced by the brain-specific TmBr3 isoform (Had et al 1994, Weinberger et al 1996). The replacement of Tm5NM1/2 is found to occur over a very rapid period, 2–4 days, both in the rat and chicken (Weinberger et al 1996). Tm5NM1/2 and Tm4 are not eliminated entirely, however, but rather are relocated to the cell body and dendrites. This is summarized in Figure 2.

Cell culture of embryonic neurons has provided increased resolution of tropomyosin isoform sorting. The Tm5NM1/2 isoform is excluded from most of the cell body and the growth cone and is found highly enriched at the axon pole of the soma, as well as along the length of the axon (Hannan et al 1995). Other isoforms from this gene, Tm5NM3/4, are strongly detected in the growth cone using an antibody that detects all products from the *TM5NM* gene (Schevzov et al 1997). Low-molecular-weight tropomyosin isoforms from another gene, Tm5a/b, are found uniformly distributed throughout freshly plated neurons but are excluded from the growth cone over time in culture, which correlates with reduced motility and size of the growth cone (Schevzov et al 1997) (Figure 2). It therefore appears that the spatial and temporal segregation of tropomyosin isoforms is very finely tuned in the developing and mature nervous system.

MEMBRANE SKELETON   The spectrin-based membrane skeleton has been implicated in the establishment of specialized membrane domains (see general review by Bennett & Gilligan 1993). In the neuron, isoforms of spectrin and ankyrin are sorted to different domains (reviewed in Lazarides & Nelson 1985).

Mitotic neuronal precursors initially express $\alpha\gamma$-spectrin, which is uniformly located on all plasma membranes of differentiating neurons together with the β isoform of ankyrin (Lazarides & Nelson 1983, Nelson & Lazarides 1984). Neuronal maturation is accompanied by decreased synthesis of β-ankyrin and the γ subunit of spectrin, as well as the induction of α-ankyrin and the β' subunit of spectrin. This mechanism is associated with an altered distribution; α-ankyrin and $\alpha\beta'\beta$-spectrin are restricted to the plasma membrane of the cell body and dendrite, whereas β-ankyrin and $\alpha\gamma$-spectrin remain in all plasma membranes (Lazarides & Nelson 1983, Lazarides et al 1984, Nelson & Lazarides 1984). Spectrin isoforms are also sorted in other polarized cells. Dubreuil et al (1997) observed that $\alpha\beta$-spectrin is located at the lateral domain of *Drosophila* salivary gland cells, whereas $\alpha\beta_H$-spectrin is sorted to the apical domain.

The generation of additional spectrin antibodies has revealed further segregation of spectrin isoforms in adult neurons. Clark et al (1994) reported that the $\beta I\sigma II$ and $\alpha I\sigma I$ isoforms colocalize to cell bodies and dendrites whereas the $\beta II\sigma I$ and $\alpha II\sigma I$ isoforms colocalize to axons. An additional β isoform generated by alternative splicing, $\beta I\sigma II$-A, is concentrated at postsynaptic densities in dendritic spines (Malchiodi-Albedi et al 1993) (Figure 2). The sorting of spectrin isoforms parallels that of actin and tropomyosin isoforms (Figure 2) and may reflect coassembly of specific isoform combinations because actin and tropomyosin are integral components of the spectrin-based membrane skeleton (Bennett & Gilligan 1993).

Myosins in Nonmuscle Cells

The myosin superfamily consists of at least 13 classes that have in common a globular myosin motor domain (Mooseker & Cheney 1995, Cope et al 1996). The so-called conventional myosins (myosin II) are those that provide contractile motive force in muscle and contain a long coiled coil attached to the motor domain. The unconventional myosins (myosin I, myosins III-XIII) differ from myosin II and each other in terms of the regions that are attached to the motor. In addition to the two myosin II isoforms, A and B, many nonmuscle cells also express multiple isoforms from the other different classes of myosin (Bement et al 1994). With increasing numbers of isoform-specific antibodies, it is becoming clear that in addition to sorting between members of different myosin classes, there is also sorting between isoforms from the same class.

CONVENTIONAL TYPE II MYOSIN   Kelley et al (1996) have demonstrated distinct localizations for the two *Xenopus* myosin II isoforms, IIA and IIB. In interphase cells, IIB was present in the cell cortex and highly enriched in the lamellipodia of rapidly migrating cells. In contrast, IIA was only observed in fibrillar staining in the cytoplasm. During prophase, IIB localized to the nuclear membrane but thereafter returned to its interphase location, whereas some IIA staining localized to the mitotic spindle. However, both isoforms were enriched in the contractile ring, indicating functionally distinct roles for each isoform during the cell cycle. It is notable that the IIB isoform was also enriched relative to IIA at the marginal zone of the growth cone of neurons in culture (Rochlin et al 1995), further indicating a role for the IIA isoform in membrane motility.

UNCONVENTIONAL MYOSINS   The class I unconventional myosins are composed of multiple isoforms in most, if not all, eukaryotic organisms (Mooseker & Cheney 1995). The localization of two isoforms of this class, IA and IB, has been extensively studied in *Drosophila*. In the larval brush border, IA is enriched in the subapical terminal web and IB is conversely enriched in the apical microvillar domain. During development, the distribution of IA spreads such that it is more apical in the adult gut (Morgan et al 1995). Sorting of type I myosin isoforms has also been detected in *Dictyostelium*. Morita et al (1996) found IB to be concentrated at the leading edge of lamellipodia and at sites of cell-cell contact, whereas ID was also present in filipodia. In aggregation stage cells, ID, but not IB, relocates from the periphery to the cytoplasm.

Isoform sorting has not yet been demonstrated within any of the other unconventional myosin classes. However, Hasson et al (1997) have compared the localization of Class I, V, VI, and VII myosins in sensory epithelia of the inner ear. The diversity of distributions is extensive and raises the possibility of even greater specialization once isoform-specific antibodies are generated within each class. Indeed, antibodies to adrenal myosin I has recently demonstrated that this myosin type represents a unique isoform with a nuclear location (Nowak et al 1997).

Microtubules and Intermediate Filaments

MICROTUBULES   Despite the existence of multiple α- and β-tubulins and extensive coexpression of isoforms, there is remarkably little evidence for the sorting of isoforms. Lewis et al (1987) and Gu et al (1988) found no evidence for isoform sorting in cultured cells. Bond et al (1986) demonstrated that a chicken-yeast chimeric β-tubulin was incorporated into all microtubule structures in mouse 3T3 cells. The only suggestion of isoform sorting has been reported for the partial exclusion of the $\beta(v)$-tubulin isoform from the growing neurites of PC12 cells (Joshi & Cleveland 1989).

The discovery that the microtubules of axons and dendrites differ in terms of the composition of microtubule-associated proteins (MAPs) raised the possibility of isoform sorting in neurons (Matus et al 1981). However, the only isoforms of MAPs known to be sorted result from phosphorylation. MAP1b is phosphorylated in axons but not in dendrites (Sato-Yoshitake et al 1989) and the highly phosphorylated isoform of tau is also restricted to axons (Mandell & Banker 1996). It therefore appears that neuronal microtubule populations are discriminated primarily by class of associated MAP and not by the use of isoforms.

INTERMEDIATE FILAMENTS   Intermediate filaments are encoded by a super gene family consisting of six classes. Unlike actin, tropomyosin, myosin, and tubulin, there is not extensive coexpression of isoforms within the same cell. The neurofilament subunits of the neuronal intermediate filament system are subject to phosphorylation, and only the highly phosphorylated isoform is found in axons (Sternberger & Sternberger 1983). Desmin and vimentin are members of the same class of filament proteins and are coexpressed during early muscle differentiation. Cary & Klymkowsky (1994) found that transfected vimentin and desmin gene constructs in *Xenopus* myotomal cells revealed a difference in localization. Vimentin forms longitudinal filament systems, whereas desmin forms both a reticular meshwork and non-filamentous aggregates. Sorting has also been detected for keratin isoforms in post-mitotic keratinocytes located at the edge of a wound. The K6/K16 keratin isoform pair is induced following injury and forms short filaments that accumulate near the nucleus in contrast to the constitutively expressed K5/K14 isoform pair that is distributed throughout the cytoplasm (Paladini et al 1996). In general, however, it is unlikely that isoform sorting will play a major role in intermediate filament biology because isoforms are not usually coexpressed in the same cell.

STRUCTURAL PROTEINS—ORGANELLES

Golgi

There is increasing evidence that the Golgi contains a spectrin-based membrane skeleton composed in part of unique isoforms of some of these structural proteins (reviewed in Mays et al 1994, Beck & Nelson 1996, Stow et al 1998). Beck et al (1994) were the first to discover a unique spectrin isoform ($\beta I\sigma^*$) localized to the Golgi. Subsequently, two novel ankyrin isoforms, AnkG119 (Devarajan et al 1996) and 195-kDa ankyrin (Beck et al 1997), have also been localized to the Golgi. Both ankyrins bind β-spectrin and are colinear with microtubules in Golgi ghost tubules (Devarajan et al 1996, Beck et al 1997). This is consistent with a role for both the Golgi membrane skeleton and microtubules in the spatial localization of the Golgi (Beck et al 1997).

Myosin IIA (but not IIB) has also been specifically detected in the Golgi (Ikonen et al 1997). The IIA isoform copurifies with an intracellular membrane vesicle fraction enriched in a single type of chloride channel (Ecay et al 1997). Finally, the recruitment of myosin IIA to Golgi membranes is dependent on actin and is involved in the assembly of basolateral transport vesicle from the *trans*-Golgi network (Musch et al 1997). This has led to the suggestion that the Myosin IIA is involved in vesicle budding and trafficking (see Stow et al 1998). The Golgi may therefore contain a cytoskeleton that utilizes specifically sorted isoforms of structural proteins.

Vesicles

ADP-ribosylation factors (ARFs) are small GTP-binding proteins implicated in the formation of coated transport vesicles. Mammals express at least six isoforms. The diversity of vesicle destinations within the cell provides an opportunity to use isoforms to regulate targeting of vesicles. Transfection studies with epitope-tagged ARFs suggest that ARFs 1–3 have a perinuclear Golgi localization, whereas the remaining ARFs, 4–6, are generally dispersed through the cytoplasm (Hosaka et al 1996). Cavenagh et al (1996) demonstrated that the ARF 6 isoform is uniquely localized to the plasma membrane of CHO cells, whereas ARFs 1, 3, 4, and 5 are cytosolic but can be recruited to a number of intracellular membranes. It is unclear if the differences between these two studies are due to the cell types.

Syntaxins are part of a complex thought to act as a target membrane receptor during vesicle docking and fusion. Subcellular localization of syntaxin isoforms in macrophages indicates that plasma membranes and intracellular vesicles contain syntaxins 3 and 4, whereas phagosomes contain syntaxins 2, 3, and 4 (Hackam et al 1996). In polarized epithelial cells, each syntaxin isoform was found to have a unique localization pattern (Low et al 1996). Syntaxins 1A and 1B were only present on intracellular structures, syntaxin 2 was found on both apical and basolateral surfaces, and syntaxins 3 and 4 were segregated to the apical and basolateral domains, respectively. This provides a potential mechanisms to control the specificity of vesicle docking and fusion.

Nucleus

The nuclear mitotic apparatus protein (NuMA) is composed of at least three isoforms that display some differences in localization (Tang et al 1994). In interphase cells, NuMA-1 is located in the nucleus, whereas NuMA-m and -s are cytosolic and enriched at the centrosomal region. However, all three are located at the spindle pole in mitotic cells. The significance of the sorting in interphase cells remains unclear.

RECEPTORS, TRANSPORTERS, AND CHANNELS

Cell asymmetry and the resulting specialized function of membrane domains provides an opportunity for isoforms to contribute to this specificity. Isoform sorting has now been observed for a number of membrane components, including receptors, transporters, and ion channels, which indicates that at least some specialized membrane domains result from different distributions of isoforms.

Receptors

Sorting has been observed for isoforms within two families of receptors. The GABA A receptor is the principal inhibitory receptor in the central nervous system and can be formed by different subunit isoforms. The ability of the different isoforms to influence location has been tested by transfection into epithelial cells. The $\alpha 1$ subunit is targeted to the basolateral surface, whereas $\beta 1$ is sorted to the apical membrane (Perez-Velazquez & Angelides 1993). Coexpression of both isoforms causes $\alpha 1$ to accumulate with $\beta 1$ at the apical surface. The second receptor, inositol 1,4,5-triphosphate receptor (InsP$_3$), exists as two isoforms in platelets. Subfractionation has revealed that internal cell membranes contain both type 1 and type 2 isoforms of InsP$_3$ receptor, while the plasma membrane contains only the type 2 isoform (Quinton & Dean 1996).

Transporters

The glucose transporters GLUT-1–4 are subject to isoform-specific sorting. When expressed in NIH 3T3 cells, GLUT-1 is primarily located on the plasma membrane, whereas GLUT-4 is associated with vesicles in a perinuclear distribution and throughout the cytoplasm (Hudson et al 1992). Thomas et al (1993) used *Xenopus* oocytes to show that GLUT-2 and -3 accumulate on the plasma membrane, while GLUT-1 is enriched in an intracellular membrane pool. In myoblasts and myotubes, GLUT-1 is located on the plasma membrane, GLUT-3 shifts from being solely located to intracellular membranes in myoblasts to include plasma membrane localization in myotubes, and GLUT-4 is induced only in contracting myotubes where it localizes to small intracellular vesicles (Guillet-Deniau et al 1994). There is, therefore, general agreement that GLUT-4 is associated with a vesicle population and that the other transporters can be located on the plasma membrane.

The Na$^+$/H$^+$ exchangers (NHEs) exist as three isoforms that are also subject to sorting. In epithelial cells, the NHE3 isoform is exclusively apical, whereas the NHE1 isoform accumulates in both apical and basolateral membranes (Noel et al 1996). Similarly in the rat submandibular gland, NHE1 is found on the basolateral membranes, whereas NHE2 and 3 are found on the apical membrane (He et al 1997). NHE3 is also found on the apical membrane of the developing nephron (Biemesderfer et al 1997).

The three isoforms of the catalytic (α) subunit of the plasma membrane Na$^+$ pump are also distributed between different compartments. In astrocytes, neurons and arterial myocytes, $\alpha 1$ is ubiquitously distributed over the cell surface whereas $\alpha2$ and $\alpha3$ are confined to a reticular distribution within the plasma membrane that parallels underlying the endoplasmic or sarcoplasmic reticulum (Juhaszova & Blaustein 1997).

Channels

The B1 and rbA isoforms of the αIA subunits of the brain calcium channels are differentially located in adult neurons. Both isoforms are located in nerve terminals; however, B1 is also located in dendrites whereas rbA is prominently located in cell bodies (Sakurai et al 1996).

Isoform sorting can therefore be used to create a variety of types of membrane domains. This covers domains within the plasma membrane, particularly in polarized cells, and between internal membranes and the plasma membrane.

SIGNALING MOLECULES

Protein Kinase C

There are at least 11 different protein kinase C (PKC) isoforms implicated in a wide variety of cellular responses to specific signals. Although these isoforms have very similar enzymatic properties, differences in their tissue- and cell-type-specific expression patterns suggest isoform-specific functions for at least some. Evidence for isoform-specific functions has been strongly supported by the observation that activation of PKC is associated with translocation of these enzyme isoforms to specific intracellular sites. This finding has led to the proposal that specificity of PKC signaling involves, in part, targeting of different isoforms to specific substrates (Goodnight et al 1995).

Disatnik et al (1994) observed that stimulation of cardiomyocytes with norepinephrine or PMA induces isoform-specific translocation of activated PKC isoforms. This process involved localization inside the nucleus and for some isoforms to the cardiac myofibrils. The presence or absence of serum in the medium influenced the pattern of relocalization, suggesting that the destination for activated PKC isoforms is regulated depending upon the range of stimulatory signals supplied to the cell. This ability to regulate target destination of isoforms was confirmed using acidic FGF and TGF-β1 (Disatnik et al 1995). Differential translocation has also been observed in rat aorta. In normal cells, α- and ζ-PKC were located in the cytoplasm and δ was perinuclear, whereas in hypertrophied cells, α was translocated to the plasma membrane, ζ was intranuclear, and δ was diffuse in the cytoplasm (Liou & Morgan 1994). Lehrich & Forrest (1994) observed PKC-ζ to specifically colocalize with microtubules associated with the mitotic apparatus.

The most comprehensive analysis of PKC isoform translocation comes from studies in which NIH 3T3 cells overexpress each of eight different isoforms

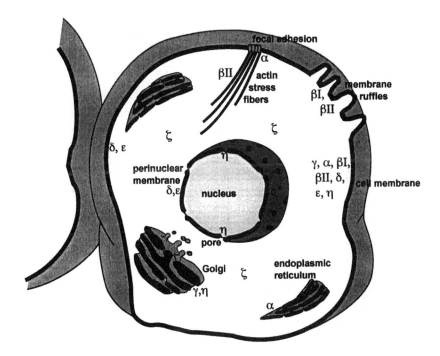

Figure 3 Localization of activated PKC isoforms in NIH 3T3 cells. Following activation, most isoforms are observed associated with the plasma membrane. In addition, a number also translocate to specific locations: endoplasmic reticulum (α), membrane ruffles (βI, βII), focal adhesions (α), actin stress fibers (βII), points of cell-cell contact (δ, ϵ), perinuclear membrane (δ, ϵ), nuclear pores (η), and the Golgi (γ, η). This is based on the work of Goodnight et al (1995). Different cell types may locate these isoforms to different intracellular sites.

(Goodnight et al 1995) (Figure 3). Prior to activation, the majority of isoforms are diffusely distributed through the cytoplasm and not membrane bound except for a fraction of δ and η, which are concentrated in the Golgi. Activation with phorbol ester results in isoform-specific relocation of PKCs (Figure 3). α Accumulates at cell margins and the endoplasmic reticulum, ϵ at cell margins and nuclear membranes, γ in the Golgi, and βII with actin microfilaments. The association of βII with the actin cytoskeleton parallels other findings in T lymphocytes (Gregorio et al 1994) and cardiomyocytes (Disatnik et al 1994). This suggests that PKC substrate specificity may in part be mediated by the isoform-specific location of activated PKCs.

More recent data have confirmed the isoform-specific destinations of translo-cated activated PKCs and have begun delineation of specific protein-protein interactions that may account for such unique localization patterns. Isoform-specific translocation has now been reported in a wide variety of cell types, including adipocytes (Frevert & Kahn 1996), placental epithelial cells (Ruzycky et al 1996), spermatozoa (Zini et al 1997), T lymphocytes (Keenan et al 1997), neurons (Cardell et al 1998), and neutrophils (Sergeant & McPhail 1997). The specificity of translocation of several isoforms may relate to specific protein-protein interactions. PKC-ζ shows isoform-specific binding to heterogeneous nuclear ribonucleoprotein A1 (Municio et al 1995), whereas PKC-ϵ is specifically bound by actin filaments (Prekeris et al 1996), and PKC-θ may have an isoform specific interaction with 14-3-3 tau protein (Meller et al 1996). Some differences observed in the location of PKC isoforms between cell types may reflect the ability to regulate the location of these isoforms.

Other Kinases and Phosphatases

A variety of kinases have been observed to show isoform specific localization. The S6 kinase isoform p85^{s6k} has a predominantly nuclear location, whereas the p70^{s6k} isoform is primarily cytoplasmic (Reinhard et al 1994). Similar nucleus/cytoplasm sorting is seen for α-, β-, and δ-CaM kinase isoforms (Srinivasan et al 1994, Brocke et al 1995); p58^{GTA} protein kinase isoforms (Xiang et al 1994); and pp90^{rsk} Ser/Thr kinase isoforms (Zhao et al 1995). In the latter case, one isoform, RSK3, undergoes serum-stimulated nuclear translocation analogous to the specific translocation observed with PKC isoforms (see above). The protein phosphatase type IC α and δ isoforms also differ in their sorting between nucleus and cytoplasm and within the cytoplasm (Murata et al 1997). The α isoform localized to actin stress fibers and the nucleus, whereas the δ isoform was predominantly nuclear and also located in focal adhesions. The MAP/ERK kinase MEK5 isoforms are also differentially sorted in the cytoplasm (English et al 1995). MEK5 β is primarily cytosolic, whereas the α isoform is associated with the actin cytoskeleton.

Enzymes associated with phosphatidylinositol metabolism also display isoform-specific sorting. A number of phosphoinositidase C (PIC) isoforms are responsible for phosphoinositide breakdown in the nucleus. The PIC $\beta 1$ isoform is associated with the inner nuclear matrix but not the nuclear pore-lamina complex, whereas the PIC $\gamma 1$ isoform is associated with actin filaments (Maraldi et al 1994). Isoforms of the phosphatidylinositol transfer protein are sorted between a preferential perinuclear membrane location (β) and a more general nuclear and cytoplasmic location (α) (De Vries et al 1996).

The extensive sorting of isoforms involved in signaling indicates that this process may be used to regulate the specificity of signaling in some systems. Variations in both the isoforms present and their location allow a common external signal to generate cell-type-specific targeting of the signal to unique combinations of targets.

OTHER ENZYMES

The classic example of isoform sorting is the existence of mitochondrial and cytosolic isozymes. Enzymes with such isoforms include glutamine synthetase (Caggese et al 1994) and glycogen synthetase kinase-3 (Hoshi et al 1995). Deoxyuridine triphosphate nucleotidohydrolase is found as a nuclear and a second mitochondrial isoform (Ladner et al 1996). Sorting between the nucleus and the cytosol occurs for the two isoforms of calcineurin, the catalytic subunit of a calmodulin-dependent protein phosphatase (Usuda et al 1996).

Subdomains of the cytoplasm are also revealed by sorting of enzymes. The neuronal acid phosphatases are sorted in neurons. The lysosomal isoform is enriched in axons, whereas the cytosolic isoform is predominantly located in dendrites (Krizbai et al 1997). Creatine kinase isoforms are sorted both in heart cells and neurons. The MM isoform is specifically associated with the contractile apparatus (at the M line); the BB isoform is diffusely localized in the cytoplasm and nucleus (Schafer & Perriard 1988). In neurons, the mitochondrial uMtCK isoform is restricted to the cell body, and the BB isoform is primarily nuclear in embryonic neurons (Chen et al 1995). In adults, however, the BB isoform is found through the entire cytoplasm and nucleus but is most prominent in the dendrites (Friedman & Roberts 1994).

The sarco/endoplasmic reticulum Ca^{2+}-ATPase displays enzyme sorting between membranes. In platelets, the SERCA 2b isoform is found in membranes associated with the plasma membrane and the open canalicular system, the SERCA 3 isoform localizes to plasma and intracellular membranes, and a third novel isoform is restricted to the cytoplasmic face of plasma membranes (Kovacs et al 1997). This reflects a subcompartmental organization of these isoforms with some overlap between the membrane domains.

MECHANISMS OF ISOFORM SORTING

Microinjection experiments have provided indirect evidence that sorting of protein isoforms may be related to their site of synthesis. McKenna et al (1985) co-injected rhodamine-labeled nonmuscle β- and γ-actin and fluorescein-labeled muscle α_{sk} actin into cardiomyocytes and fibroblasts. In both cell types, no preferential segregation of either actin type into any subcellular compartment was observed. In addition, all polymeric actin structures visualized by phalloidin staining incorporated both actin types. This observation suggests that the internal site of synthesis plays a role in sorting because gene transfections of actin isoforms into cardiomyocytes does show isoform sorting (Mounier et al 1997). Pittenger & Helfman (1992) performed a similar experiment in which different tropomyosin isoforms were labeled and injected into fibroblasts. Tropomyosin

2 and 3 showed no restriction in their localization in contrast to the stress fiber-restricted location of the cellularly synthesized isoforms (Lin et al 1988).

The cellular synthesis of isoforms could contribute to sorting in at least two ways. If mRNAs encoding isoforms are themselves sorted, it is obvious that synthesis could directly establish the sorting of the protein isoforms. Alternatively, local synthesis may be directly involved in the production of multimeric structures and/or polymers, possibly via cotranslational assembly (Fulton 1993, Fulton & L'Ecuyer 1993), that serve as units subject to sorting. In other words, multimeric structures rather than single molecules may be the unit that is sorted, and injection of individual molecules may bypass this mechanism.

Sorting of mRNAs Encoding Isoforms

β-ACTIN   Evidence for sorting based on intracellular sites of synthesis has come from mRNA localization studies. The concept that mRNA can be localized to discrete sites was pioneered by the work of Singer and co-workers, who originally demonstrated the existence of a pool of peripheral actin mRNA associated with motile regions in fibroblasts (Lawrence & Singer 1986). Hoock et al (1991) demonstrated that during wound closure, β-actin mRNA was relocated to the motile region of cytoplasm in which the β-actin protein isoform was preferentially accumulated. This is consistent with the proposal that mRNA redistribution can produce segregated protein distribution and is by far the most convincing evidence for a direct relationship between the sorting of mRNA and the corresponding protein.

The existence of a peripheral pool of β-actin mRNA has been detected in myoblasts (Hill & Gunning 1993, Kislauskis et al 1993), myotubes (Kislauskis et al 1993), fibroblasts (Lawrence & Singer 1986, Hill et al 1994), and neurons (Olink-Coux & Hollenbeck 1996, Bassell et al 1998, Hannan et al 1998). In addition, β-actin mRNA is restricted in location to the cortical mat of corneal epithelial cells in vivo (Yeh & Svoboda 1994). It is tempting to speculate that this will prove to be a general property of β-actin mRNA both in vitro and in vivo.

The location of β-actin mRNA to the cell periphery may be unique to that isoform. Colocalization studies of β- and γ-actin mRNAs have revealed differential localization in myoblasts (Hill & Gunning 1993) and fibroblasts (Hill et al 1994). In both cell types γ-actin mRNA is restricted to a perinuclear location. β-actin mRNA exists in two compartments, one coincident with γ mRNA and the second located at the cell periphery associated with regions of cell motility. Similarly, Kislauskis et al (1993) have shown that β- but not α_{ca}-actin mRNA is located in a peripheral pool in myoblasts and newly formed myotubes. The segregation of mRNAs in myotubes is consistent with the reported segregation of nonmuscle actin (Lubit & Schwartz 1980) and sarcomeric actin (Otey et al 1988) in myotubes in culture (Figure 1). In contrast, no sorting of β- and γ-actin proteins has been observed in myoblasts and fibroblasts where the mRNAs are clearly sorted. However, subtle differences between the distribution of these two proteins may be masked by their large steady state levels. It is certainly clear that γ-actin protein location is not restricted by the perinuclear location of its mRNA (Hill & Gunning 1993, Hill et al 1994).

A similar conclusion regarding the relationship of mRNA and protein sorting can be derived from studies of neuronal development. β-Actin protein is very highly enriched in cultured neuronal growth cones relative to γ-actin (Ulloa & Avila 1996). Although β-actin but not γ-actin mRNA is detected in axons and growth cones, the great majority of β-actin mRNA resides in the cell body (Olink-Coux & Hollenbeck 1996, Bassell et al 1998, Hannan et al 1998) (Figure 4). It is therefore unlikely that all growth cone β-actin derives from local synthesis.

The sorting of β-actin mRNA to the cell periphery may be related to a specific β-actin subpopulation. Treatment of fibroblasts with antisense oligonucleotides that inhibit peripheral localization of β-actin mRNA results in a dramatic change in lamellipodial structure (Kislauskis et al 1994) and reduces cell motility (Kislauskis et al 1997). It has also been demonstrated that this

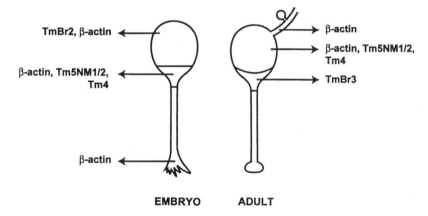

EMBRYO   ADULT

Figure 4 Sorting of mRNAs encoding actin and tropomyosin isoforms in neurons. Three mRNA compartments can be detected in embryonic neurons: cell body (to which TmBr2 is restricted), axon hillock (highly enriched for Tm5NM1/2 and Tm4), and axon plus growth cone. β-Actin is found in all three compartments but the vast majority of this mRNA is found in the cell body (Hannan et al 1995, 1998, Olink-Coux & Hollenbeck 1996, Bassell et al 1998). In the adult, β-actin mRNA is uniformly present in the cell body and dendrite, whereas Tm5NM1/2 and Tm4 mRNAs are now present in the cell body and excluded from the axon hillock. The mRNA encoding the adult axonal tropomyosin TmBr3 is restricted to the axon hillock in adult neurons (Hannan et al 1995, 1998). Neuronal development therefore is accompanied not only by altered isoform sorting (see Figure 2) but also by a change in the location of the corresponding mRNAs.

peripheral pool of β-actin mRNA is under growth factor regulation, which argues for a functional role related to membrane signaling in response to sensing of the external environment (Hill et al 1994, Latham et al 1994). This suggests that local synthesis of β-actin at the cell periphery is involved in some aspect of actin function that cannot be completely provided by the local pools of monomeric β- and γ-actin.

TROPOMYOSINS   Sorting of mRNAs encoding tropomyosin isoforms has also been observed in neurons both in vivo and in vitro (Hannan et al 1995, 1998). The mRNA encoding Tm5NM1/2 is localized to the axonal pole of differentiating embryonic rat neurons, whereas an mRNA encoding the isoform TmBr2 is distributed throughout the cell body but excluded from the axonal pole (Figure 4). The restricted location of Tm5NM1/2 mRNA correlates with the corresponding protein isoform, which is found only in the axon and axon hillock of developing neurons (Hannan et al 1995, Weinberger et al 1996). Mature neurons relocate Tm5NM1/2 mRNA and protein in a manner suggestive of a potential mechanistic relationship. The Tm5NM1/2 mRNA is distributed throughout the cell body of mature neurons (Hannan et al 1995, 1998) (Figure 4), and the corresponding protein isoform is found in the cell body and proximal dendrites but specifically excluded from the mature axon (Weinberger et al 1996). Although the mRNA and protein location for Tm5NM1/2 appears related, it is important to note that there is no one-to-one correspondence between them; the protein always extends into zones that lack the mRNA (Hannan et al 1998).

CREATINE KINASE   There is a striking parallel between the sorting of mRNAs encoding creatine kinase isoforms and the location of the proteins in myoblasts. Wilson et al (1995) observed that mRNA for the M form is localized at the cell periphery, whereas the B form mRNA is primarily perinuclear. This shows a striking similarity to the corresponding location of the protein isoforms.

The existence of potential relationships between mRNA and protein sorting of isoforms suggests that mRNA sorting may at least play a partial role in creating domains of sorted isoforms. However, it is apparent in a number of cases that mRNA location does not absolutely correlate with that of the protein. Other mechanisms, such as preferred protein-protein interactions, must therefore contribute to the observed segregation of protein isoforms.

Isoform-Specific Interactions in Multimeric Structures

PROTEIN SEQUENCES CAN ACCOUNT FOR SORTING   A number of studies have demonstrated that protein sequence differences between isoforms are sufficient to account for sorting of isoforms in at least some isoform families. The Perriard laboratory has pioneered this approach and successfully dissected the isoform-specific sorting sequences in creatine kinase and myosin light chains. In cardiomyocytes, the M form of creatine kinase locates to the M-band of myofibrils plus the cytosol, whereas the B form never associates with myofibrils. Microinjection of chimeric M/B form mRNAs reveals that the head portion of the M isoform is sufficient to confer myofibril association (Schafer & Perriard 1988). Soldati & Perriard (1991) used cultured adult rat cardiomyocytes to demonstrate that muscle isoforms of myosin light chain are restricted to contractile structures containing muscle isoforms of myosin heavy chain, whereas a nonmuscle myosin light chain is found both in contractile- and stress fiber-like structures. The specific sorting of the muscle myosin light chain could be accounted for by the existence of isoform-specific sequences in the middle of the molecule that promote preferential interactions with the muscle myosin heavy chain.

Gene transfections have convincingly demonstrated that specific protein sequences contribute to isoform sorting for a variety of proteins. Sequences responsible for sorting of glucose transporter isoforms have been dissected in some detail (Verhey et al 1995, Inukai et al 1997). Both the regulatory and catalytic domains of PKC isoforms may contribute to isoform sorting (Acs et al 1997). In the case of the intermediate filament isoforms vimentin and desmin, it is the head region that accounts for sorting in muscle cells (Cary & Klymkowsky 1994).

ISOFORM COMPETITION AND DIFFERENCES IN AFFINITY FOR BINDING PARTNERS   Sorting of myosin light chain isoforms suggest that competition between isoforms can determine intracellular localization. Komiyama et al (1996) used cotransfection experiments to test the effect of competition on isoform segregation in cardiomyocytes. They found a sorting specificity to the myofibrillar sites that followed the normal sequence of developmental expression of the isoforms. Differential competition of isoforms could therefore provide a mechanism for the ordered displacement of isoforms during development based on progressive increases in the affinity of isoforms for muscle myosin heavy chain. This is a particularly attractive model for creating cellular compartments/structures based on the preferred affinities of groups of isoforms that are involved in multimeric structures. It is easy to see how such structures can then serve as templates to sort isoforms of additional families. Indeed, Fanning et al (1994) have shown preferred interactions between tropomyosin isoforms and myosin I versus myosin II, which suggests a means by which tropomyosin isoform sorting could create myosin compartments.

Gene transfection experiments have provided evidence for preferred association of actin and Tm isoforms. Schevzov et al (1993) found that elevation of γ- but not β-actin protein levels in myoblasts resulted in a reduced ability of the Tm2 isoforms, but not the Tm5NM isoforms, to segregate into stress fibers. In addition, levels of Tm2 protein and mRNA, but not of Tm5NM, were down-regulated. This suggests that different isoforms are competing for inclusion in specific structures and that failure to stably associate may result in turnover of the protein and/or down-regulation of its mRNA. Isoform sorting may therefore potentially result from preferential turnover of an isoform at a specific intracellular site where it cannot stably associate with other structural components.

Actin isoforms can differ in the affinity of their association with myofibrils. Peng & Fischman (1991) have used cell-free synthesis of actin isoforms to test their incorporation into intact myofibrils. They observed a preferential incorporation of the muscle isoforms relative to that of β-actin into these structures. This suggests that the segregation of muscle- and β-actin isoforms in striated muscle is promoted by preferred isoform interactions in addition to the sorting of mRNAs (Kislauskis et al 1993).

Preferential isoform associations may also contribute to segregation of syntrophin isoforms. Syntrophins are dystrophin-associated proteins. Peters et al (1997) observed a preferential association of utrophin with β-1 and β-2 syntrophins, whereas dystrophin complexes contained mostly α-1 and β-1 syntrophins. The neuromuscular junction enriched location of utrophin and β-2 syntrophin could therefore be related to their preferential association. It is notable that this preferred association does not reflect intrinsic binding specificity, suggesting that preferential pairing observed by immunoprecipitation must depend on extrinsic regulatory mechanisms.

The preferential localization of β-actin to the site of wound healing and to the apical cortex in parietal cells may be related to specific but indirect interaction with ezrin. In both cases, there is striking colocalization between β-actin and ezrin (Shuster & Herman 1995, Yao et al 1995). The Herman laboratory has demonstrated isoform specific binding of β-actin to ezrin (Shuster & Herman 1995), which may be mediated by a novel β-actin–specific binding protein, CAP73. The finding that βCAP73 colocalizes with β-actin in cortical cytoplasm is certainly consistent with the creation of isoform-specific structures using this multimeric complex.

Spectrin isoform sorting may also depend on isoform-specific interactions with spatially segregated structures and molecules. Dubreuil et al (1997) observed isoform specific recruitment of $\alpha\beta$- but not $\alpha\beta_H$-spectrin to sites of cell-cell contact in cells expressing the homophilic adhesion molecule neuroglian. Their data suggests that $\alpha\beta$-spectrin is sorted by association with a locally activated cell-cell adhesion molecule, whereas $\alpha\beta_H$-spectrin responds to an apically sorted receptor in the salivary gland epithelium.

HIGHER-ORDER STRUCTURES   Disruption of actin filaments and microtubules impacts on the sorting of tropomyosin isoforms. Segregation of tropomyosin isoforms between axon and growth cone in neurons is eliminated by cytochalasin B, which fragments the actin filaments (Schevzov et al 1997). Removal of cytochalasin B allows re-establishment of isoform sorting, suggesting that the sorting is a dynamic process dependent on an intact actin filament system. Schevzov et al (1997) also found that disruption of microtubules with nocodazole resulted in the segregation of tropomyosin isoforms that had been colocalized in the axon. This also argues for the role of higher-order polymeric structures in the establishment and maintenance of isoform location.

Regulation of isoform sorting at the level of protein-protein interactions may therefore require a variety of levels of control. Sorting may not depend simply on which partner molecules exist in the cell but also on the presence of potential competitor isoforms and their assembly into stable higher-order multimeric structures. What is not clear is whether isoform-specific transport mechanisms exist at the level of protein isoforms.

FUNCTION OF ISOFORM SORTING—CREATING INTRACELLULAR COMPARTMENTS

Multiple Roles for Sorting

There is evidence for at least three functional roles for isoform sorting. First, sorting provides a mechanism for the cell to independently control the amount of a particular type of protein at different intracellular sites. In other words, they would be functionally indistinguishable if they were in the same compartment. For example, the existence of cytosolic and mitochondrial isoforms of enzymes allows the cell to independently regulate the size of both pools. Similarly, the existence of different tropomyosins in different neuronal compartments allows the neuron to control the amount of tropomyosin-associated actin filament in these areas independent of one another (see Figure 2). The finding that PKC isoforms have quite distinct effects on cell morphology may reflect the differing sites of action of these isoforms following activation rather than any intrinsic catalytic differences between these isoforms (Goodnight et al 1995). It is important to note that this may provide the primary selective pressure to maintain some isoforms independent of any intrinsic functional differences between each isoform.

The sorting may confer unique physical/enzymatic/regulatory properties to different intracellular compartments. This is strongly supported in the case of the actin cytoskeleton. Actin isoforms show isoform-specific functions in cell morphology, motility, and contractility (Schevzov et al 1992, Hewett et al 1994, Kislauskis et al 1994, von Arx et al 1995, Ronnov-Jessen & Petersen 1996, Kislauskis et al 1997, Kumar et al 1997). Similar conclusions can be drawn for tropomyosin (Prasad et al 1993, Boyd et al 1995, Gimona et al 1996) and myosin (Jung et al 1996, Tullio et al 1997). In all cases, the results are compatible with disruption of specific intracellular compartments or structures (Had et al 1994, Pittenger et al 1994, Janmey & Chaponnier 1995, Gunning et al 1997). This is most obvious in striated muscle where there is a cytoskeleton involved in organizing membranes and a contractile apparatus composed of a completely different set of isoforms involved in generating contractile force along the length of the muscle (Figure 1).

Finally, the sorting of some isoforms may be used as templates for sorting other molecules which may, or may not, consist of other families of isoforms. For example, the sorting of spectrin and ankyrin isoforms may play a major role in sorting membrane-bound molecules to different intracellular domains (Beck & Nelson 1996, Devarajan et al 1997). Similarly, the preferential interaction between tropomyosin isoforms and myosin subtypes suggests that tropomyosin sorting may contribute to the sorting of myosins, as discussed earlier (Fanning et al 1994).

Evolution of Sorting

The three different potential roles for isoform sorting are not mutually exclusive and may indeed all operate for the same family of isoforms. For example, the initial generation of some isoforms may have allowed for spatial sorting to create independently regulated intracellular compartments. This sorting would then have generated the opportunity to further modify the physical/enzymatic/regulatory properties of individual isoforms to suit their spatially specialized role. The ability to sort isoforms can therefore be seen as a potentially important step in generating the diversity of function of intracellular compartments. One of the most obvious systems in which this is likely to play a fundamental role in cell function is the neuron. The different compartments of the neuron that are apparent at a morphological and functional level are also characterized by different isoform composition (Figure 2). Isoform sorting may therefore have provided an important mechanism in the establishment of these compartments and/or the generation of their specialized function.

FUTURE: DISSECTING INTRACELLULAR ANATOMY

The demonstration of cellular compartments composed of different isoforms of structural proteins, receptors, enzymes, and signaling molecules provides a new way to view intracellular space. It is increasingly clear that the assembly of cellular domains will be approachable at a molecular level using current genetic techniques. The work on *Dictyostelium* myosin I is a clear example of how systematic deletion of individual and combinations of isoforms can provide an insight into shared versus specialized functions (Jung et al 1996). In some cases it is likely that deletion of one isoform may allow another isoform to take its place via shared binding motifs such as that observed with the myosin light chains (Komiyama et al 1996). Gene knockouts are therefore likely to be very powerful in revealing the role of isoforms in assembling specialized domains. This will provide an approach toward understanding some important principles governing intracellular anatomy.

The mechanisms responsible for sorting are likely to be revealed by mutagenesis of sites in isoforms that are responsible for sorting. However, it is not clear the extent to which localized synthesis, directed transport, and preferential protein interactions at destination sites contribute to isoform sorting. This may differ from family to family. Indeed, for the specialized sorting of the β isoform of actin, it appears that the bulk of β-actin enriched in neuronal growth cones is provided by protein movement away from the site of synthesis (Ulloa & Avila 1996, Bassell et al 1998, Hannan et al 1998). The small amount of β-actin mRNA in the growth cone may provide an additional small pool of β-actin involved in specialized function related to organization or motility (Kislauskis et al 1994, Kislauskis et al 1997). Thus sorting may occur at different levels for different reasons.

Understanding the mechanisms underpinning isoform sorting will be crucial in providing strategies for relocating isoforms in order to evaluate the function of compartments. In the case of structural molecules, the major challenge is to integrate the biophysical properties of isoforms with their compartmentalized function. For example, what is it about the physical properties of isoforms found in areas of cell remodeling that provides a selective advantage for their use in this process?

Finally, the multimeric nature of the many units of sorting suggest that alterations in the function of one isoform may impact not only on the function of other isoforms from that family but also on partner molecules from other families. This may predict extensive pleiotrophic effects within and between gene families. Such observations have been made for the ability of one keratin to induce expression of a partner isoform (Giudice & Fuchs 1987). Similar observations have been reported for the ability of actin isoforms to regulate isoform-specific tropomyosin organization and gene expression (Schevzov et al 1993). The mechanisms that allow changes in isoforms to direct changes in gene expression are currently unknown and represent another important issue intrinsic to our understanding of the role of isoform sorting.

In conclusion, the concept of isoform sorting as a core component contributing to the creation of cellular compartments has been popular since the early 1980s. It is the advent of molecular genetic techniques, however, that have now allowed for a systematic experimental approach to the mechanisms of sorting and their functional consequences. The next decade will see a revolution in the way we understand the organization of intracellular space and its integration with cell and tissue function.

ACKNOWLEDGMENTS

We thank all the members of the Oncology Research Unit for their helpful comments. We especially thank Janett Clarkson for preparation of the manuscript and Greg Seeto for all the Figures. The authors have been supported by grants from the NHMRC (PG, RW, PJ, EH), the NSW Cancer Council (PG, EH), and the Ramaciotti Foundation (PG, RW). PG is a Senior Research Fellow of the NHMRC.

Visit the *Annual Reviews home page* at
http://www.AnnualReviews.org

Literature Cited

Acs P, Bogi K, Lorenzo PS, Marquez AM, Biro T, et al. 1997. The catalytic domain of protein kinase C chimeras modulates the affinity and targeting of phorbol ester-induced translocation. *J. Biol. Chem.* 272:22148–53

Anthony DT, Jacobs-Cohen RJ, Marazzi G, Rubin LL. 1988. A molecular defect in virally transformed muscle cells that cannot cluster acetylcholine receptors. *J. Cell Biol.* 106:1713–21

Bassell GJ, Zhang H, Byrd AL, Femino AM, Singer RH, et al. 1998. Sorting of β-actin mRNA and protein to neurites and growth cones in culture. *J. Neurosci.* 18:251–65

Beach RL, Jeffery WR. 1992. Multiple actin genes encoding the same α-muscle isoform are expressed during ascidian development. *Dev. Biol.* 151:55–66

Beck KA, Buchanan JA, Malhotra V, Nelson WJ. 1994. Golgi spectrin: identification of an erythroid β-spectrin homolog associated with the Golgi complex. *J. Cell Biol.* 127:707–23

Beck KA, Buchanan JA, Nelson WJ. 1997. Golgi membrane skeleton: identification, localization and oligomerization of a 195 kDa ankyrin isoform associated with the Golgi complex. *J. Cell Sci.* 110:1239–49

Beck KA, Nelson WJ. 1996. The spectrin-based membrane skeleton as a membrane protein-sorting machine. *Am. J. Physiol.* 270:C1263–70

Bement WM, Hasson T, Wirth JA, Cheney RE, Mooseker MS. 1994. Identification and overlapping expression of multiple unconventional myosin genes in vertebrate cell types. *Proc. Natl. Acad. Sci. USA* 91:6549–53

Bennett V, Gilligan DM. 1993. The spectrin-based membrane skeleton and micron-scale organization of the plasma membrane. *Annu. Rev. Cell Biol.* 9:27–66

Biemesderfer D, Rutherford PA, Nagy T, Pizzonia JH, Abu-Alfa AK, Aronson PS. 1997. Monoclonal antibodies for high-resolution localization of NHE3 in adult and neonatal rat kidney. *Am. J Physiol.* 273:F289–99

Boyd J, Risinger JI, Wiseman RW, Merrick BA, Selkirk JK, Barrett JC. 1995. Regulation of microfilament organization and anchorage-independent growth by tropomyosin 1. *Proc. Natl. Acad. Sci. USA* 92:11534–38

Brocke L, Srinivasan M, Schulman H. 1995. Developmental and regional expression of multifunctional Ca^{2+}/calmodulin-dependent protein kinase isoforms in rat brain. *J. Neurosci.* 15:6797–808

Caggese C, Barsanti P, Viggiano L, Bozzetti MP, Caizzi R. 1994. Genetic, molecular and developmental analysis of the glutamine synthetase isozymes of *Drosophila melanogaster. Genetica* 94:275–81

Cardell M, Landsend AS, Eidet J, Wieloch T, Blackstad TW, Ottersen OP. 1998. High resolution immunogold analysis reveals distinct subcellular compartmentation of protein kinase C γ and δ in rat Purkinje cells. *Neuroscience* 82:709–25

Cary RB, Klymkowsky MW. 1994. Differential organization of desmin and vimentin in muscle is due to differences in their head domains. *J. Cell Biol.* 126:445–56

Cavenagh MM, Whitney JA, Carroll K, Zhang CJ, Boman AL, et al. 1996. Intracellular distribution of Arf proteins in mammalian cells. Arf6 is uniquely localized to the plasma membrane. *J. Biol. Chem.* 271:21767–74

Chen L, Roberts R, Friedman DL. 1995. Expression of brain-type creatine kinase and ubiquitous mitochondrial creatine kinase in the fetal rat brain: evidence for a nuclear energy shuttle. *J. Comp. Neurol.* 363:389–401

Clark MB, Ma Y, Bloom ML, Barker JE, Zagon IS, et al. 1994. Brain α erythroid spectrin: identification, compartmentalization, and β spectrin associations. *Brain Res.* 663:223–36

Conrad AH, Clark WA, Conrad GW. 1991. Subcellular compartmentalization of myosin isoforms in embryonic chick heart ventricle myocytes during cytokinesis. *Cell Motil. Cytoskelet.* 19:189–206

Cope MJT, Whisstock J, Rayment I, Kendrick-Jones J. 1996. Conservation within the myosin motor domain: implications for structure and function. *Structure* 4:969–87

Craig SW, Pardo JV. 1983. Gamma actin, spectrin, and intermediate filament proteins colocalize with vinculin at costameres, myofibril-to-sarcolemma attachment sites. *Cell Motil.* 3:449–62

DeNofrio D, Hoock TC, Herman IM. 1989. Functional sorting of actin isoforms in microvascular pericytes. *J. Cell Biol.* 109:191–202

Devarajan P, Stabach PR, De Matteis MA, Morrow JS. 1997. Na,K-ATPase transport from endoplasmic reticulum to Golgi requires the Golgi spectrin-ankyrin G119 skeleton in Madin Darby canine kidney cells. *Proc. Natl. Acad. Sci. USA* 94:10711–16

Devarajan P, Stabach PR, Mann AS, Ardito T, Kashgarian M, Morrow JS. 1996. Identification of a small cytoplasmic ankyrin (Ank$_{G119}$) in the kidney and muscle that binds $\beta 1\sigma$ spectrin and associates with the Golgi apparatus. *J. Cell Biol.* 133:819–30

De Vries KJ, Westerman J, Bastiaens PI, Jovin TM, Wirtz KW, Snoek GT. 1996. Fluorescently labeled phosphatidylinositol transfer protein isoforms (α and β), microinjected into fetal bovine heart endothelial cells, are targeted to distinct intracellular sites. *Exp. Cell Res.* 227:33–39

Disatnik MH, Buraggi G, Mochly-Rosen D. 1994. Localization of protein kinase C isozymes in cardiac myocytes. *Exp. Cell Res.* 210:287–97

Disatnik MH, Jones SN, Mochly-Rosen D. 1995. Stimulus-dependent subcellular localization of activated protein kinase C; a study with acidic fibroblast growth factor and transforming growth factor-beta 1 in cardiac myocytes. *J. Mol. Cell Cardiol.* 27:2473–81

Dubreuil RR, Maddux PB, Grushko TA, MacVicar GR. 1997. Segregation of two spectrin isoforms: polarized membrane-binding sites direct polarized membrane skeleton assembly. *Mol. Biol. Cell* 8:1933–42

Ecay TW, Conner TD, Decker ER. 1997. Nonmuscle myosin IIA copurifies with chloride channel-enriched membranes from epithelia. *Biochem. Biophys. Res. Commun.* 231:369–72

English JM, Vanderbilt CA, Xu S, Marcus S, Cobb MH. 1995. Isolation of MEK5 and differential expression of alternatively spliced forms. *J. Biol. Chem.* 270:28897–902

Eppenberger-Eberhardt M, Flamme I, Kurer V, Eppenberger HM. 1990. Reexpression of α-smooth muscle actin isoform in cultured adult rat cardiomyocytes. *Dev. Biol.* 139:269–78

Fallon JR, Nachmias VT. 1980. Localization of cytoplasmic and skeletal myosins in developing muscle cells by double-label immunofluorescence. *J. Cell Biol.* 87:237–47

Fanning AS, Wolenski JS, Mooseker MS, Izant JG. 1994. Differential regulation of skeletal muscle myosin-II and brush border myosin-I enzymology and mechanochemistry by bacterially produced tropomyosin isoforms. *Cell Motil. Cytoskelet.* 29:29–45

Frevert EU, Kahn BB. 1996. Protein kinase C isoforms ϵ, η, δ and ζ in murine adipocytes: expression, subcellular localization and tissue-specific regulation in insulin-resistant states. *Biochem. J.* 316:865–71

Friedman DL, Roberts R. 1994. Compartmentation of brain-type creatine kinase and ubiquitous mitochondrial creatine kinase in neurons: evidence for a creatine phosphate energy shuttle in adult rat brain. *J. Comp. Neurol.* 343:500–11

Fulton AB. 1993. Spatial organization of the synthesis of cytoskeletal proteins. *J. Cell Biochem.* 52:148–52

Fulton AB, L'Ecuyer T. 1993. Cotranslational assembly of some cytoskeletal proteins: implications and prospects. *J. Cell Sci.* 105:867–71

Fyrberg EA, Bond BJ, Hershey ND, Mixter KS, Davidson N. 1981. The actin genes of Drosophila: protein coding regions are highly conserved but intron positions are not. *Cell* 24:107–16

Gallwitz D, Sures I. 1980. Structure of a split yeast gene: complete nucleotide sequence of the actin gene in *Saccharomyces cerevisiae*. *Proc. Natl. Acad. Sci. USA* 77:2546–50

Gauthier GF. 1990. Differential distribution of myosin isoforms among the myofibrils of individual developing muscle fibers. *J. Cell Biol.* 110:693–701

Gimona M, Kazzaz JA, Helfman DM. 1996. Forced expression of tropomyosin 2 or 3 in v-Ki-ras-transformed fibroblasts results in distinct phenotypic effects. *Proc. Natl. Acad. Sci. USA* 93:9618–23

Giudice GJ, Fuchs E. 1987. The transfection of epidermal keratin genes into fibroblasts and simple epithelial cells: evidence for inducing a type I keratin by a type II gene. *Cell* 48:453–63

Goodnight JA, Mischak H, Kolch W, Mushinski JF. 1995. Immunocytochemical localization of eight protein kinase C isozymes overexpressed in NIH 3T3 fibroblasts. Isoform-specific association with microfilaments, Golgi, endoplasmic reticulum, and nuclear and cell membranes. *J. Biol. Chem.* 270: 9991–10001

Gregorio CC, Repasky EA, Fowler VM, Black JD. 1994. Dynamic properties of ankyrin in T lymphocytes: colocalization with spectrin and protein kinase C β. *J. Cell Biol.* 125:345–58

Gu W, Lewis SA, Cowan NJ. 1988. Generation of antisera that discriminate among mammalian α-tubulins: introduction of specialized isotypes into cultured cells results in their coassembly without disruption of normal microtubule function. *J. Cell Biol.* 106: 2011–22

Guillet-Deniau I, Leturque A, Girard J. 1994. Expression and cellular localization of glucose transporters (GLUT1, GLUT3, GLUT4) during differentiation of myogenic cells isolated from rat foetuses. *J. Cell Sci.* 107:487–96

Gunning P, Hardeman E, Jeffrey P, Weinberger R. 1998. Creating intracellular structural domains: spatial segregation of actin and tropomyosin isoforms in neurons. *BioEssays.* In press

Gunning P, Mohun T, Ng SY, Ponte P, Kedes L. 1984. Evolution of the human sarcomeric-actin genes: evidence for units of selection within the 3′ untranslated regions of the mRNAs. *J. Mol. Evol.* 20:202–14

Gunning P, Weinberger R, Jeffrey P. 1997. Actin and tropomyosin isoforms in morphogenesis. *Anat. Embryol.* 195:311–15

Hackam DJ, Rotstein OD, Bennett MK, Klip A, Grinstein S, Manolson MF. 1996. Characterization and subcellular localization of target membrane soluble NSF attachment protein receptors (t-SNAREs) in macrophages. Syntaxins 2, 3, and 4 are present on phagosomal membranes. *J. Immunol.* 156:4377–83

Had L, Faivre-Sarrailh C, Legrand C, Mery J, Brugidou J, Rabie A. 1994. Tropomyosin isoforms in rat neurons: the different developmental profiles and distributions of TM-4 and TMBr-3 are consistent with different functions. *J. Cell Sci.* 107:2961–73

Hall ZW, Lubit BW, Schwartz JH. 1981. Cytoplasmic actin in postsynaptic structures at the neuromuscular junction. *J. Cell Biol.* 90:789–92

Handel SE, Wang SM, Greaser ML, Schultz E, Bulinski JC, Lessard JL. 1989. Skeletal muscle myofibrillogenesis as revealed with a monoclonal antibody to titin in combination with detection of the α- and γ-isoforms of actin. *Dev. Biol.* 132:35–44

Hanks M, Wurst W, Anson-Cartwright L, Auerbach AB, Joyner AL. 1995. Rescue of the En-1 mutant phenotype by replacement of En-1 with En-2. *Science* 269:679–82

Hannan AJ, Gunning P, Jeffrey PL, Weinberger RP. 1998. Structural compartments within neurons: developmentally regulated organization of microfilament isoform mRNA and protein. *Mol. Cell. Neurosci.* In press

Hannan AJ, Schevzov G, Gunning P, Jeffrey PL, Weinberger RP. 1995. Intracellular localization of tropomyosin mRNA and protein is associated with development of neuronal polarity. *Mol. Cell. Neurosci.* 6:397–412

Hasson T, Gillespie PG, Garcia JA, MacDonald RB, Zhao Y, et al. 1997. Unconventional myosins in inner-ear sensory epithelia. *J. Cell Biol.* 137:1287–307

He X, Tse CM, Donowitz M, Alper SL, Gabriel SE, Baum BJ. 1997. Polarized distribution of key membrane transport proteins in the rat submandibular gland. *Pflügers Arch.* 433:260–68

Herman IM. 1993. Actin isoforms. *Curr. Opin. Cell Biol.* 5:48–55

Hewett TE, Grupp IL, Grupp G, Robbins J. 1994. α-Skeletal actin is associated with increased contractility in the mouse heart. *Circ. Res.* 74:740–46

Hill MA, Gunning P. 1993. Beta and gamma actin mRNAs are differentially located within myoblasts. *J. Cell Biol.* 122:825–32

Hill MA, Schedlich L, Gunning P. 1994. Serum-induced signal transduction determines the peripheral location of β-actin mRNA within the cell. *J. Cell Biol.* 126:1221–29

Hoock TC, Newcomb PM, Herman IM. 1991. β actin and its mRNA are localized at the plasma membrane and the regions of moving cytoplasm during the cellular response to injury. *J. Cell Biol.* 112:653–64

Hosaka M, Toda K, Takatsu H, Torii S, Murakami K, Nakayama K. 1996. Structure and intracellular localization of mouse ADP-ribosylation factors type 1 to type 6 (ARF1-ARF6). *J. Biochem. (Tokyo)* 120:813–19

Hoshi M, Sato M, Kondo S, Takashima A, Noguchi K, et al. 1995. Different localization of tau protein kinase I/glycogen synthase kinase-3 β from glycogen synthase kinase-3 α in cerebellum mitochondria. *J. Biochem. (Tokyo)* 118:683–85

Hudson AW, Ruiz M, Birnbaum MJ. 1992. Isoform-specific subcellular targeting of glucose transporters in mouse fibroblasts. *J. Cell Biol.* 116:785–97

Ikonen E, de Almeid JB, Fath KF, Burgess DR,

Ashman K, et al. 1997. Myosin II is associated with Golgi membranes: identification of p200 as nonmuscle myosin II on Golgi-derived vesicles. *J. Cell Sci.* 110:2155–64

Inukai K, Takata K, Asano T, Katagiri H, Ishihara H, et al. 1997. Targeting of GLUT1-GLUT5 chimeric proteins in the polarized cell line Caco-2. *Mol. Endocrinol.* 11:442–49

Janmey PA, Chaponnier C. 1995. Medical aspects of the actin cytoskeleton. *Curr. Opin. Cell Biol.* 7:111–17

Joshi HC, Cleveland DW. 1989. Differential utilization of β-tubulin isotypes in differentiating neurites. *J. Cell Biol.* 109:663–73

Juhaszova M, Blaustein MP. 1997. Na+ pump low and high ouabain affinity α subunit isoforms are differently distributed in cells. *Proc. Natl. Acad. Sci. USA* 94:1800–5

Jung G, Wu X, Hammer JA III. 1996. *Dictyostelium* mutants lacking multiple classic myosin I isoforms reveal combinations of shared and distinct functions. *J. Cell Biol.* 133:305–23

Keenan C, Long A, Volkov Y, Kelleher D. 1997. Protein kinase C isotypes theta, delta and eta in human lymphocytes: differential responses to signalling through the T-cell receptor and phorbol esters. *Immunology* 90:557–63

Kelley CA, Sellers JR, Gard DL, Bui D, Adelstein RS, Baines IC. 1996. *Xenopus* nonmuscle myosin heavy chain isoforms have different subcellular localizations and enzymatic activities. *J. Cell Biol.* 134:675–87

Kislauskis EH, Li Z, Singer RH, Taneja KL. 1993. Isoform-specific 3′-untranslated sequences sort α-cardiac and β-cytoplasmic actin messenger RNAs to different cytoplasmic compartments. *J. Cell Biol.* 123:165–72

Kislauskis EH, Zhu X, Singer RH. 1994. Sequences responsible for intracellular localization of β-actin messenger RNA also affect cell phenotype. *J. Cell Biol.* 127:441–51

Kislauskis EH, Zhu X, Singer RH. 1997. β-Actin messenger RNA localization and protein synthesis augment cell motility. *J. Cell Biol.* 136:1263–70

Komiyama M, Soldati T, von Arx P, Perriard JC. 1996. The intracompartmental sorting of myosin alkali light chain isoproteins reflects the sequence of developmental expression as determined by double epitope-tagging competition. *J. Cell Sci.* 109:2089–99

Kovacs T, Berger G, Corvazier E, Paszty K, Brown A, et al. 1997. Immunolocalization of the multi-sarco/endoplasmic reticulum Ca^{2+} ATPase system in human platelets. *Br. J. Haematol.* 97:192–203

Krizbai I, Joo F, Pestean A, Preil J, Botcher H,

Wolff JR. 1997. Localization and biochemical characterization of acid phosphatase isoforms in the olfactory system of adult rats. *Neuroscience* 76:799–807

Kumar A, Crawford K, Close L, Madison M, Lorenz J, et al. 1997. Rescue of cardiac α-actin-deficient mice by enteric smooth muscle γ-actin. *Proc. Natl. Acad. Sci. USA* 94:4406–11

Ladner RD, Carr SA, Huddleston MJ, McNulty DE, Caradonna SJ. 1996. Identification of a consensus cyclin-dependent kinase phosphorylation site unique to the nuclear form of human deoxyuridine triphosphate nucleotidohydrolase. *J. Biol. Chem.* 271:7752–57

Latham VM, Kislauskis EH, Singer RH, Ross AF. 1994. β-Actin mRNA localization is regulated by signal transduction mechanisms. *J. Cell Biol.* 126:1211–19

Lawrence JB, Singer RH. 1986. Intracellular localization of messenger RNAs for cytoskeletal proteins. *Cell* 45:407–15

Lazarides E, Nelson WJ. 1983. Erythrocyte and brain forms of spectrin in cerebellum: distinct membrane-cytoskeletal domains in neurons. *Science* 220:1295–96

Lazarides E, Nelson WJ. 1985. Expression and assembly of the erythroid membrane-skeletal proteins ankyrin (goblin) and spectrin in the morphogenesis of chicken neurons. *J. Cell Biochem.* 27:423–41

Lazarides E, Nelson WJ, Kasamatsu T. 1984. Segregation of two spectrin forms in the chicken optic system: a mechanism for establishing restricted membrane-cytoskeletal domains in neurons. *Cell* 36:269–78

Lehrich RW, Forrest JN Jr. 1994. Protein kinase C ζ is associated with the mitotic apparatus in primary cell cultures of the shark rectal gland. *J. Biol. Chem.* 269:32446–50

Lewis SA, Gu W, Cowan NJ. 1987. Free intermingling of mammalian β-tubulin isotypes among functionally distinct microtubules. *Cell* 49:539–48

Lin JJ, Hegmann TE, Lin JL. 1988. Differential localization of tropomyosin isoforms in cultured nonmuscle cells. *J. Cell Biol.* 107:563–72

Lin JJ, Warren KS, Wamboldt DD, Wang T, Lin JL. 1997. Tropomyosin isoforms in nonmuscle cells. *Int. Rev. Cytol.* 170:1–38

Liou YM, Morgan KG. 1994. Redistribution of protein kinase C isoforms in association with vascular hypertrophy of rat aorta. *Am. J Physiol.* 267:C980–89

Low SH, Chapin SJ, Weimbs T, Komuves LG, Bennett MK, Mostov KE. 1996. Differential localization of syntaxin isoforms in polarized Madin-Darby canine kidney cells. *Mol. Biol. Cell* 7:2007–18

Lubit BW. 1984. Association of β-cytoplasmic

actin with high concentrations of acetylcholine receptor (AChR) in normal and anti-AChR-treated primary rat muscle cultures. *J. Histochem. Cytochem.* 32:973–81

Lubit BW, Schwartz JH. 1980. An antiactin antibody that distinguishes between cytoplasmic and skeletal muscle actins. *J. Cell Biol.* 86: 891–97

Malchiodi-Albedi F, Ceccarini M, Winkelmann JC, Morrow JS, Petrucci, TC. 1993. The 270 kDa splice variant of erythrocyte beta-spectrin ($\beta 1 \sigma 2$) segregates in vivo and in vitro to specific domains of cerebellar neurons. *J. Cell Sci.* 106:67–78

Mandell JW, Banker GA. 1996. A spatial gradient of tau protein phosphorylation in nascent axons. *J. Neurosci.* 16:5727–40

Maraldi NM, Cocco L, Capitani S, Mazzotti G, Barnabei O, Manzoli FA. 1994. Lipid-dependent nuclear signalling: morphological and functional features. *Adv. Enzyme Regul.* 34:129–43

Matus A, Bernhardt R, Hugh-Jones T. 1981. High molecular weight microtubule-associated proteins are preferentially associated with dendritic microtubules in brain. *Proc. Natl. Acad. Sci. USA* 78:3010–14

Mays RW, Beck KA, Nelson WJ. 1994. Organization and function of the cytoskeleton in polarized epithelial cells: a component of the protein sorting machinery. *Curr. Opin. Cell Biol.* 6:16–24

McKenna N, Meigs JB, Wang YL. 1985. Identical distribution of fluorescently labeled brain and muscle actins in living cardiac fibroblasts and myocytes. *J. Cell Biol.* 100:292–96

Meller N, Liu YC, Collins TL, Bonnefoy-Berard N, Baier G, et al. 1996. Direct interaction between protein kinase C θ (PKC θ) and 14–3–3 τ in T cells: 14–3–3 overexpression results in inhibition of PKC θ translocation and function. *Mol. Cell Biol.* 16:5782–91

Miller DM III, Ortiz I, Berliner GC, Epstein HF. 1983. Differential localization of two myosins within nematode thick filaments. *Cell* 34:477–90

Mooseker MS, Cheney RE. 1995. Unconventional myosins. *Annu. Rev. Cell Dev. Biol.* 11: 633–75

Morgan NS, Heintzelman MB, Mooseker MS. 1995. Characterization of myosin-IA and myosin-IB, two unconventional myosins associated with the *Drosophila* brush border cytoskeleton. *Dev. Biol.* 172:51–71

Morita YS, Jung G, Hammer JA III, Fukui Y. 1996. Localization of *Dictyostelium* myoB and myoD to filopodia and cell-cell contact sites using isoform-specific antibodies. *Eur. J Cell Biol.* 71:371–79

Mounier N, Perriard JC, Gabbiani G, Chaponnier C. 1997. Transfected muscle and non-muscle actins are differentially sorted by cultured smooth muscle and non-muscle cells. *J. Cell Sci.* 110:839–46

Municio MM, Lozano J, Sanchez P, Moscat J, Diaz-Meco MT. 1995. Identification of heterogeneous ribonucleoprotein A1 as a novel substrate for protein kinase C ζ. *J. Biol. Chem.* 270:15884–91

Murata K, Hirano K, Villa-Moruzzi E, Hartshorne DJ, Brautigan DL. 1997. Differential localization of myosin and myosin phosphatase subunits in smooth muscle cells and migrating fibroblasts. *Mol. Biol. Cell* 8:663–73

Musch A, Cohen D, Rodriguez-Boulan E. 1997. Myosin II is involved in the production of constitutive transport vesicles from the TGN. *J. Cell Biol.* 138:291–306

Nelson WJ, Lazarides E. 1984. The patterns of expression of two ankyrin isoforms demonstrate distinct steps in the assembly of the membrane skeleton in neuronal morphogenesis. *Cell* 39:309–20

Noel J, Roux D, Pouysségur J. 1996. Differential localization of Na$^+$/H$^+$ exchanger isoforms (NHE1 and NHE3) in polarized epithelial cell lines. *J. Cell Sci.* 109:929–39

North AJ, Gimona M, Lando Z, Small JV. 1994. Actin isoform compartments in chicken gizzard smooth muscle cells. *J. Cell Sci.* 107: 445–55

Nowak G, Pestic-Dragovich L, Hozak P, Philimonenko A, Simerly C, et al. 1997. Evidence for the presence of myosin I in the nucleus. *J. Biol. Chem.* 272:17176–81

Olink-Coux M, Hollenbeck PJ. 1996. Localization and active transport of mRNA in axons of sympathetic neurons in culture. *J. Neurosci.* 16:1346–58

Otey CA, Kalnoski MH, Bulinski JC. 1988. Immunolocalization of muscle and nonmuscle isoforms of actin in myogenic cells and adult skeletal muscle. *Cell Motil. Cytoskelet.* 9:337–48

Otey CA, Kalnoski MH, Lessard JL, Bulinski JC. 1986. Immunolocalization of the gamma isoform of nonmuscle actin in cultured cells. *J. Cell Biol.* 102:1726–37

Paladini RD, Takahashi K, Bravo NS, Coulombe PA. 1996. Onset of re-epithelialization after skin injury correlates with a reorganization of keratin filaments in wound edge keratinocytes: defining a potential role for keratin 16. *J. Cell Biol.* 132:381–97

Pardo JV, Pittenger MF, Craig SW. 1983. Subcellular sorting of isoactins: selective association of γ actin with skeletal muscle mitochondria. *Cell* 32:1093–103

Peng I, Fischman DA. 1991. Post-translational incorporation of actin into myofibrils in vitro:

evidence for isoform specificity. *Cell Motil. Cytoskelet.* 20:158–68

Perez-Velazquez JL, Angelides KJ. 1993. Assembly of GABA$_A$ receptor subunits determines sorting and localization in polarized cells. *Nature* 361:457–60

Peters MF, Adams ME, Froehner SC. 1997. Differential association of syntrophin pairs with the dystrophin complex. *J. Cell Biol.* 138:81–93

Pittenger MF, Helfman DM. 1992. In vitro and in vivo characterization of four fibroblast tropomyosins produced in bacteria: TM-2, TM-3, TM-5a, and TM-5b are co-localized in interphase fibroblasts. *J. Cell Biol.* 118:841–58

Pittenger MF, Kazzaz JA, Helfman DM. 1994. Functional properties of non-muscle tropomyosin isoforms. *Curr. Opin. Cell Biol.* 6:96–104

Prasad GL, Fuldner RA, Cooper HL. 1993. Expression of transduced tropomyosin 1 cDNA suppresses neoplastic growth of cells transformed by the *ras* oncogene. *Proc. Natl. Acad. Sci. USA* 90:7039–43

Prekeris R, Mayhew MW, Cooper JB, Terrian DM. 1996. Identification and localization of an actin-binding motif that is unique to the epsilon isoform of protein kinase C and participates in the regulation of synaptic function. *J. Cell Biol.* 132:77–90

Quinton TM, Dean WL. 1996. Multiple inositol 1,4,5-trisphosphate receptor isoforms are present in platelets. *Biochem. Biophys. Res. Commun.* 224:740–46

Reinhard C, Fernandez A, Lamb NJ, Thomas G. 1994. Nuclear localization of p85^{s6k}: functional requirement for entry into S phase. *EMBO J.* 13:1557–65

Rhee D, Sanger JM, Sanger JW. 1994. The premyofibril: evidence for its role in myofibrillogenesis. *Cell Motil. Cytoskelet.* 28:1–24

Rochlin MW, Itoh K, Adelstein RS, Bridgman PC. 1995. Localization of myosin II A and B isoforms in cultured neurons. *J. Cell Sci.* 108:3661–70

Romans P, Firtel RA. 1985. Organization of the actin multigene family of *Dictyostelium discoideum* and analysis of variability in the protein coding regions. *J. Mol. Biol.* 186:321–35

Ronnov-Jessen L, Petersen OW. 1996. A function for filamentous α-smooth muscle actin: retardation of motility in fibroblasts. *J. Cell Biol.* 134:67–80

Rosser BW, Waldbillig DM, Lovo SD, Armstrong JD, Bandman E. 1995. Myosin heavy chain expression within the tapered ends of skeletal muscle fibers. *Anat. Rec.* 242:462–70

Ruzycky AL, Jansson T, Illsley NP. 1996. Differential expression of protein kinase C isoforms in the human placenta. *Placenta* 17:461–69

Sakurai T, Westenbroek RE, Rettig J, Hell J, Catterall WA. 1996. Biochemical properties and subcellular distribution of the BI and rbA isoforms of α 1A subunits of brain calcium channels. *J. Cell Biol.* 134:511–28

Sato-Yoshitake R, Shiomura Y, Miyasaka H, Hirokawa N. 1989. Microtubule-associated protein 1B: molecular structure, localization, and phosphorylation-dependent expression in developing neurons. *Neuron* 3:229–38

Schafer BW, Perriard JC. 1988. Intracellular targeting of isoproteins in muscle cytoarchitecture. *J. Cell Biol.* 106:1161–70

Schafer DA, Korshunova YO, Schroer TA, Cooper JA. 1994. Differential localization and sequence analysis of capping protein β-subunit isoforms of vertebrates. *J. Cell Biol.* 127:453–65

Schevzov G, Gunning P, Jeffrey PL, Temm-Grove CJ, Helfman DM, et al. 1997. Tropomyosin localization reveals distinct populations of microfilaments in neurites and growth cones. *Mol. Cell Neurosci.* 8:439–54

Schevzov G, Lloyd C, Gunning P. 1992. High level expression of transfected β- and γ-actin genes differentially impacts on myoblast cytoarchitecture. *J. Cell Biol.* 117:775–85

Schevzov G, Lloyd C, Hailstones D, Gunning P. 1993. Differential regulation of tropomyosin isoform organization and gene expression in response to altered actin gene expression. *J. Cell Biol.* 121:811–21

Sergeant S, McPhail LC. 1997. Opsonized zymosan stimulates the redistribution of protein kinase C isoforms in human neutrophils. *J. Immunol.* 159:2877–85

Shuster CB, Herman IM. 1995. Indirect association of ezrin with F-actin: isoform specificity and calcium sensitivity. *J. Cell Biol.* 128:837–48

Soldati T, Perriard JC. 1991. Intracompartmental sorting of essential myosin light chains: molecular dissection and in vivo monitoring by epitope tagging. *Cell* 66:277–89

Srinivasan M, Edman CF, Schulman H. 1994. Alternative splicing introduces a nuclear localization signal that targets multifunctional CaM kinase to the nucleus. *J. Cell Biol.* 126:839–52

Sternberger LA, Sternberger NH. 1983. Monoclonal antibodies distinguish phosphorylated and nonphosphorylated forms of neurofilaments in situ. *Proc. Natl. Acad. Sci. USA* 80:6126–30

Stow JL, Fath KR, Burgess DR. 1998. Myosin II traffics its way into new roles on the Golgi complex. *Trends Cell Biol.* In press

Tang TK, Tang CJ, Chao YJ, Wu CW. 1994. Nuclear mitotic apparatus protein (NuMA):

spindle association, nuclear targeting and differential subcellular localization of various NuMA isoforms. *J. Cell Sci.* 107:1389–402

Thomas HM, Takeda J, Gould GW. 1993. Differential targeting of glucose transporter isoforms heterologously expressed in *Xenopus* oocytes. *Biochem. J.* 290:707–15

Tullio AN, Accili D, Ferrans VJ, Yu ZX, Takeda K, et al. 1997. Nonmuscle myosin II-B is required for normal development of the mouse heart. *Proc. Natl. Acad. Sci. USA* 94:12407–12

Ulloa L, Avila J. 1996. Involvement of γ and β actin isoforms in mouse neuroblastoma differentiation. *Eur. J. Neurosci.* 8:1441–51

Usuda N, Arai H, Sasaki H, Hanai T, Nagata T, et al. 1996. Differential subcellular localization of neural isoforms of the catalytic subunit of calmodulin-dependent protein phosphatase (calcineurin) in central nervous system neurons: immunohistochemistry on formalin-fixed paraffin sections employing antigen retrieval by microwave irradiation. *J. Histochem. Cytochem.* 44:13–18

Vandekerckhove J, Weber K. 1978. At least six different actins are expressed in a higher mammal: an analysis based on the amino acid sequence of the amino-terminal tryptic peptide. *J. Mol. Biol.* 126:783–802

Verhey KJ, Yeh JI, Birnbaum MJ. 1995. Distinct signals in the GLUT4 glucose transporter for internalization and for targeting to an insulin-responsive compartment. *J. Cell Biol.* 130:1071–79

von Arx P, Bantle S, Soldati T, Perriard JC. 1995. Dominant negative effect of cytoplasmic actin isoproteins on cardiomyocyte cytoarchitecture and function. *J. Cell Biol.* 131:1759–73

Warrick HM, Spudich JA. 1987. Myosin structure and function in cell motility. *Annu. Rev. Cell Biol.* 3:379–421

Weinberger R, Schevzov G, Jeffrey P, Gordon K, Hill M, Gunning P. 1996. The molecular composition of neuronal microfilaments is spatially and temporally regulated. *J. Neurosci.* 16:238–52

Wilkins AS. 1997. Canalization: a molecular genetic perspective. *BioEssays* 19:257–62

Wilson IA, Brindle KM, Fulton AM. 1995. Differential localization of the mRNA of the M and B isoforms of creatine kinase in myoblasts. *Biochem. J.* 308:599–605

Xiang J, Lahti JM, Grenet J, Easton J, Kidd VJ. 1994. Molecular cloning and expression of alternatively spliced PITSLRE protein kinase isoforms. *J. Biol. Chem.* 269:15786–94

Yaffe D, Nudel U, Mayer Y, Neuman S. 1985. Highly conserved sequences in the 3′ untranslated region of mRNAs coding for homologous proteins in distantly related species. *Nucleic Acids Res.* 13:3723–37

Yao X, Chaponnier C, Gabbiani G, Forte JG. 1995. Polarized distribution of actin isoforms in gastric parietal cells. *Mol. Biol. Cell* 6:541–57

Yao X, Cheng L, Forte JG. 1996. Biochemical characterization of ezrin-actin interaction. *J. Biol. Chem.* 271:7224–29

Yeh B, Svoboda KK. 1994. Intracellular distribution of β-actin mRNA is polarized in embryonic corneal epithelia. *J. Cell Sci.* 107:105–15

Zhao Y, Bjorbaek C, Weremowicz S, Morton CC, Moller DE. 1995. RSK3 encodes a novel pp90[rsk] isoform with a unique N-terminal sequence: growth factor-stimulated kinase function and nuclear translocation. *Mol. Cell Biol.* 15:4353–63

Zini N, Matteucci A, Sabatelli P, Valmori A, Caramelli E, Maraldi NM. 1997. Protein kinase C isoforms undergo quantitative variations during rat spermatogenesis and are selectively retained at specific spermatozoon sites. *Eur. J Cell Biol.* 72:142–50

Annu. Rev. Cell Dev. Biol. 1998. 14:373–98

THE SPECIFICATION OF LEAF IDENTITY DURING SHOOT DEVELOPMENT

R. A. Kerstetter and R. S. Poethig

Plant Science Institute, Department of Biology, University of Pennsylvania, Philadelphia, Pennsylvania 19104-6018; e-mail: randallk@sas.upenn.edu; spoethig@sas.upenn.edu

KEY WORDS: leaf development, organ identity, cotyledon, phase change, heteroblasty

ABSTRACT

A single plant produces several different types of leaves or leaf-like organs during its life span. This phenomenon, which is termed heteroblasty, is an invariant feature of shoot development but is also regulated by environmental factors that affect the physiology of the plant. Invariant patterns of heteroblastic development reflect global changes in the developmental status of the shoot, such as the progression from embryogenesis through juvenile and adult phases of vegetative development, culminating in the production of reproductive structures. Genes that regulate these phase-specific aspects of leaf identity have been identified by mutational analysis in both maize and *Arabidopsis*. These mutations have revealed that leaf production is regulated independently of leaf identity, implying that the identity of a leaf at a particular position on the shoot may depend on when the leaf was initiated in relation to a temporal program of shoot development.

CONTENTS

373

INTRODUCTION

The term leaf commonly evokes an image of the prominent photosynthetic foliage of most plants; however, a tremendous diversity of leaf form and function is found in nature (Gifford & Foster 1989). For example, leaves form elaborate insect traps in carnivorous plants; brightly colored floral bracts; the hollow trunks of banana trees; thorns and spines; inconspicuous protective scales on buds and rhizomes; vestigial fragments of tissue on tubers and cactus stems; nonphotosynthetic storage organs in bulbs; and many other unique shapes and structures. Although much of the variation in leaf shape observed in nature involves species-specific patterns of leaf development, the leaves formed by a single plant can also display remarkable diversity of form. In most, if not all, plant species, leaves formed early in shoot development (juvenile leaves) are morphologically and physiologically different from leaves formed late (adult leaves). These differences may be fairly subtle or quite dramatic. *Eucalyptus albida* provides a dramatic example of the remarkable dimorphism between juvenile and adult leaves. In this species, the juvenile foliage is opposite, elliptical in shape, and glaucous (covered in a white wax), which gives the leaf a dull whitish or blue-gray appearance in sharp contrast to the deep green, glossy, lanceolate, and sub-decussate adult leaves. In addition to developmentally determined variation in leaf identity, most plants have the capacity to produce different types of leaves in response to environmental conditions such as light quantity or intensity, nutrient availability, or, in the case of aquatic plants, terrestrial or aquatic environments. This phenomenon is termed heterophylly to distinguish it from developmental variation in leaf morphology, which is called heteroblasty.

Here we review research related to the various modifications of leaves that occur during the plant life cycle, with particular emphasis on the changes in vegetative leaf identity that take place during shoot ontogeny. In addition, we discuss spatial and temporal models for the specification of leaf identity. An excellent review of classical research on the regulation of heteroblasty is provided by Allsopp (1967), and recent reviews of leaf morphogenesis (Poethig 1997), cellular differentiation of leaf tissues (Hall & Langdale 1996), and the mechanisms that control the acquisition of regional identity within a leaf (Sylvester et al 1996) are also relevant to this discussion.

VARIATION IN LEAF IDENTITY

Developmental Variation in Leaf Identity

Higher plants develop in a modular and iterative fashion. Over the course of the life cycle of a plant, the shoot apex initiates coordinated and repeating sets of structures (phytomers) that ultimately constitute the mature shoot. As a consequence of this growth strategy, structures formed late in shoot development occur in apical portions of the shoot whereas parts of the plant produced early in shoot development are retained basally. Thus, variation in the character of the leaves, buds, and internodes produced at different times in shoot development is recorded as spatial variation in these structures along the axis of the plant. Although many aspects of shoot anatomy and morphology change continuously throughout shoot development, other traits are expressed in a more discontinuous fashion (Borchert 1976, Hackett 1985, Poethig 1990, Haffner et al 1991, Greenwood 1995). The appearance of both continuous and discontinuous changes in traits suggests that at least two different developmental or physiological processes contribute to heteroblasty (Wareing 1959, Allsopp 1967). One of these is a gradual change in the physiological vigor of the plant, a process that Wareing (1959) termed aging, and the second is the progression from one discrete developmental phase to another, a process known as maturation or phase change.

Coordinated changes in particular sets of morphological, physiological, and biochemical traits make it possible to define four more-or-less distinct phases of shoot development (Greenwood 1987, Poethig 1990): (a) an embryonic phase where shoot and root meristems are first established, (b) a post-embryonic juvenile phase where the plant is incapable of sexual reproduction, (c) an adult (or mature) phase where reproductive potential is established, and (d) an adult reproductive phase. During the transition between phases, the traits that characterize one phase are gradually replaced by those that characterize the next, often resulting in the production of transition organs that combine traits from successive phases. This model of shoot development is likely to be an oversimplification, however, because intermediate stages within a particular phase of development might be distinguished by a unique trait or pattern of gene expression.

The developmental phases listed above are recorded most dramatically in the type of leaves produced by the shoot. During embryogenesis, the embryo produces one (in the case of monocotyledons) or two (in the case of dicotyledons) leaf-like structures known as cotyledons. Cotyledons form during embryo morphogenesis as the basic architecture of the seedling is established (for review, see West & Harada 1993, Goldberg et al 1994). Some debate has arisen as to whether cotyledons are products of an embryonic shoot apical meristem or form independently during embryogenesis. Kaplan & Cooke (1997) argue that cotyledons are indeed derived from an embryonic shoot apical meristem, that they are homologous to leaves, and that their formation reflects the initiation of the same iterative process of meristematic activity and leaf initiation that continues throughout plant development. Other investigators have argued that cotyledons and foliage leaves arise from fundamentally different developmental processes (Wardlaw 1955, Barton & Poethig 1993). Whatever the case, cotyledons can be distinguished from so-called true leaves by their distinctive anatomy and morphology and by specific patterns of gene expression (Goldberg et al 1989, Thomas 1993). Although the structure and function of cotyledons vary greatly among species (for review, see Bewley & Black 1978), cotyledons are usually morphologically and anatomically simpler than true leaves. The cotyledons of *Arabidopsis*, for example, are round, glabrous, and have a simpler venation pattern than the elliptical, serrate, and pubescent leaves initiated after germination (Meinke 1992, Conway & Poethig 1997). In addition, cotyledons exhibit a variety of physiological and molecular traits that are not often found in foliage leaves. During later stages of embryogenesis, cotyledon development is often marked by the accumulation of nutrient reserves, the acquisition of desiccation tolerance, loss of photosynthetic pigments, and dormancy. Exceptions to this developmental strategy, however, are common among higher plants and include vivipary, found in mangroves and some other species, and the limited development characteristic of many orchid embryos. The structural genes responsible for some of the traits expressed late in embryogenesis have been identified, and their expression patterns have been characterized (Crouch 1988, Goldberg et al 1989, Thomas 1993).

It should be noted that while cotyledons possess a number of molecular and physiological traits that distinguish them from true leaves, some of these features are actually characteristic of tissues produced during seed development rather than specific to cotyledons. Seed storage protein mRNAs from many species are rigorously tissue specific during embryo maturation and normally do not appear during post-germinative growth or in vegetative tissues (Goldberg et al 1989, Perez-Grau & Goldberg 1989, Guerche et al 1990, Thomas 1993). Upon germination, cotyledons resume their metabolic activity and in some epigeal species expand and become photosynthetic. During this post-embryonic stage, seedlings also specifically express genes involved in the breakdown and mobilization of storage products located within the cotyledon or in adjacent endosperm tissue. In situ localization studies have shown, however, that while these embryo-specific and germination-specific programs of gene expression occur within cotyledons, the same genes may be expressed in other embryonic tissues, including the stem, root, and endosperm (Harada et al 1988, Dietrich et al 1989, Thomas 1993, Wobus et al 1995). As far as we know, no cotyledon-specific marker has been identified.

The first true leaves produced by the shoot often resemble cotyledons in some aspects of their anatomy or morphology, but they are generally larger and morphologically and anatomically more complex than cotyledons, and they do not possess storage products (Gifford & Foster 1989). As the shoot develops,

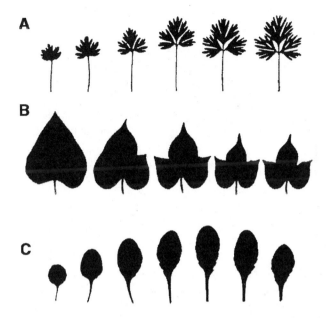

Figure 1   Patterns of heteroblastic development. (*A*) The first six leaves of *Delphinium ajacis*. (*B*) The first five leaves of *Ipomea caerulea*. (*C*) Leaves two through eight in the Columbia ecotype of *Arabidopsis thaliana*. *A* and *B* redrawn from Ashby (1948b). Drawings are not to scale.

it usually produces increasingly larger and more complex leaves until a final climax leaf type is achieved (Figure 1). Many woody plants produce this climax leaf type throughout most of their lives. In plants with shorter life spans, leaf size and shape often vary continuously along the shoot axis. In most cases it is possible to identify three more-or-less discrete classes of leaves: juvenile leaves, transition leaves, and adult leaves. However, some strongly heteroblastic species produce a much wider range of leaf forms. For example, *Pseudopanax crassifolius*, a strongly heteroblastic tree from New Zealand, produces eight different types of leaves: five types of seedling leaves and juvenile, transition, and adult leaf forms (Gould 1993). In addition to these leaf types, plants may produce rudimentary scale leaves surrounding dormant buds and distinctive cauline leaves or bracts on inflorescence shoots.

Although leaf size and shape are the most obvious heteroblastic traits, leaves in different morphological categories usually exhibit a variety of other distinctive traits. These include differences in types of epicuticular wax (Franich et al 1977, Blaker & Greyson 1988), types of trichomes or patterns of trichome distribution (Brand & Lineberger 1992, Evans et al 1994, Moose & Sisco 1994, Telfer et al 1997), cuticle thickness/structure (Franich et al 1977,

Bongard-Pierce et al 1996), anthocyanin (Murray et al 1994), chlorophyll (Bauer & Bauer 1980, Hutchinson et al 1990, James & Mantell 1994) and terpene (Bryant et al 1991) production, photosynthetic rates (Bauer & Bauer 1980, Thiagarajah et al 1981, Hutchinson et al 1990), and a variety of histological features (Allsopp 1967, Bauer & Bauer 1980, Gould 1993, James & Mantell 1994, Lawson & Poethig 1995, Bongard-Pierce et al 1996). Although many chemical and metabolic differences between juvenile and adult shoots have been described (Haffner et al 1991), little is known about the molecular differences between organs produced during these phases or the factors that control the process of vegetative phase change (Poethig 1990, Greenwood 1995, Lawson & Poethig 1995). Differences in the protein composition of juvenile and adult leaves have been observed in several tree species by immunological approaches or by PAGE (Bon 1988, Snowball et al 1991, Huang et al 1992, Besford et al 1996), but none of these genes has been cloned. In *Hedera helix*, the absence of anthocyanin in adult leaves is correlated with the lack of transcription of dihydroflavonal reductase, an enzyme in the anthocyanin biosynthetic pathway (Murray et al 1994). Phase-specific differences in the induction or accumulation of mRNA for a chlorophyll a/b binding protein and a cell wall proline-rich protein have also been reported in this species (Woo et al 1994). In larch, immature juvenile and adult leaves have different amounts of mRNA for chlorophyll a/b binding proteins (Hutchinson et al 1990), but this difference does not persist in fully mature leaves (Hutchinson et al 1991). The only phase-specific gene cloned from a herbaceous plant is the *Glossy15* (*Gl15*) gene of maize (Moose & Sisco 1996), which is specifically expressed in late juvenile leaves (leaves 3–6).

Goebel (1900) originally proposed that cotyledons and juvenile leaves are simply arrested forms of a foliage leaf. He assumed that there is a single morphogenetic pathway for leaf production and that heteroblastic variation in leaf morphology arises because different parts of a leaf primordium are arrested at different points along this pathway. In contradiction to this hypothesis, histological and morphological analyses of leaf development in a wide variety of heteroblastic species have shown that heteroblastic leaf forms become distinct very early in development (Foster 1935, Kaplan 1973, Bruck & Kaplan 1980, Kaplan 1980, Müller 1982, Richards 1983, Merrill 1986, Jones 1993, Clearwater & Gould 1994). This observation, and the qualitative differences in the patterns of cellular differentiation in heteroblastic leaf types described above, support the modern view that juvenile and adult leaves are specified by different developmental programs. As discussed below, this interpretation is also supported by the existence of mutations that affect the expression of some or all of the traits that distinguish juvenile and adult leaves without affecting the overall size of the leaf or its morphology.

Variation in Leaf Identity in Response to Environmental Conditions

Although the basic form of a leaf is largely dependent on the stage of shoot development in which the leaf is initiated, environmental conditions can have significant effects on leaf development. Temperature, photoperiod, light quality, light intensity, mineral and carbohydrate nutrition, and water availability have all been shown to affect the growth and morphology of leaves in a variety of species. Leaf development in aquatic plants is particularly susceptible to modification, making these species popular experimental systems. Many of the classic studies on the effects of environment on leaf shape have been reviewed in detail (Allsopp 1967, Vince-Prue & Tucker 1983) and therefore are not discussed here. In general, treatments that limit the supply of carbohydrate or mineral nutrients, e.g. defoliation (Ashby 1948a, Njoku 1956a), growth at low light intensity (Njoku 1956b, Cameron 1970), in vitro culture of shoots or leaf primordia in nutrient-poor media (Sussex & Clutter 1960, Feldman & Cutter 1970), or reduction in the activity of ribulose bisphosphate carboxylase by antisense RNA (Tsai et al 1997), cause the shoot to produce small, morphologically simple leaves. In species with lobed or pinnate leaves, these experimental conditions often reduce or eliminate leaf lobing or pinnae production (Allsopp 1967). Light quality also has significant effects on leaf anatomy and morphology. Leaves exposed to far-red enriched light are usually smaller, more elongated, less lobed, and thinner than leaves grown in white light (Vince-Prue & Tucker 1983). In the aquatic plant *Hippuris vulgaris*, submerged shoots can be induced to produce aerial leaves by exposure to a low ratio of red to far-red light either throughout their growth or for a brief period at the end of each photoperiod (Bodkin et al 1980). In these experiments, the effects of far-red light treatment have been shown to be reversible by exposure to red light, demonstrating that the effect is mediated by phytochrome.

The observation that leaf forms similar to those encountered in a normal heteroblastic series can be produced by varying nutritional conditions or light quality and intensity has led many investigators to conclude that developmental changes in leaf morphology are a consequence of quantitative or qualitative changes in the nutritional status of the shoot (Allsopp 1967). The validity of this hypothesis is difficult to evaluate, however, because most experimental analyses of leaf development have focused on leaf shape, and this trait is not necessarily a good marker of developmental identity. Recent studies have shown that similar types of leaves can arise by very different mechanisms (McLellan 1993; Jones 1993, 1995; Poethig 1997). A striking example of this is offered by *Cucurbita argyrosperma*. In this species, the overt similarity between shade leaves and juvenile leaves and between sun leaves and adult leaves is not reflected in the developmental morphology of these leaf types. Sun and shade leaf primordia are initially indistinguishable and become morphologically divergent late in leaf development, whereas juvenile and adult leaves are morphologically distinct shortly after initiation (Jones 1995). Another difficulty with the concept that the morphology of juvenile and adult leaves is nutritionally regulated is the observation that adult phase shoots can be induced to produce juvenile leaf forms by a variety of conditions, but juvenile shoots cannot be readily induced to produce adult leaves (Cook 1969, Telfer et al 1997). To our knowledge, no one has identified experimental conditions (other than mutations) that completely block juvenile leaf production (Hackett 1985). Whether phase-specific features of leaf identity are regulated by the same mechanism that regulates environmentally induced changes in leaf identity remains an open question.

THE REGULATION OF LEAF IDENTITY

When Is Fate Specified?

Experimental studies of leaf development in both angiosperms and non-flowering plants have demonstrated that leaves are determined gradually, with different aspects of anatomy and morphology determined at different times in development. Major morphological features, such as the dorsiventral polarity of the leaf primordium and the subdivision of the lamina into lobes or pinnae, are usually specified very early in leaf development (reviewed in Sylvester et al 1996, Poethig 1997), whereas many histological aspects of leaf identity are determined only after a leaf primordium is already well established. Results from a variety of systems suggest that this temporal difference probably reflects the activity of several independently regulated genetic programs that are differentially responsive to developmental and environmental factors.

A dramatic demonstration of the developmental plasticity of leaf primordia is provided by heterophyllous aquatic plants that produce different types of leaves in aquatic and aerial environments. In *H. vulgaris*, leaves produced while the shoot is submerged have a relatively long, narrow lamina, a single layer of mesophyll cells, a single central vein, and elongated epidermal cells, and they produce a hydathode but not stomata. By contrast, leaves produced in an aerial environment are broad and have several layers of mesophyll cells, both central and lateral veins, relatively isodiametric epidermal cells, and they lack a hydathode but have stomata (McCully & Dale 1961, Goliber & Feldman 1990). In this species, submerged shoots can be induced to produce aerial leaves by growing them in a medium containing 5 μM abscisic acid (ABA). Using this technique, Goliber & Feldman (1990) found that submerged leaf primordia can be completely converted into aerial leaves if they are exposed to ABA before they reach a length of 300 μm and can be partially transformed into aerial leaves up until they are about one half their final length. Similar results were obtained for aerial shoots induced to form submerged leaf types. An interesting feature of the intermediate leaves produced in this study is that they possessed discrete sectors of submerged- and aerial-type tissue along the proximal-distal axis of the leaf in a pattern that corresponds to the basipetal pattern of leaf maturation. Leaves that were relatively large at the time the shoot was exposed to ABA had only a small basal region of aerial tissue. In successively younger leaves, the basal region of the leaf that was capable of responding to this treatment was progressively larger. This result implies that the particular traits examined in this study (stomatal density, lateral vein formation, and epidermal cell shape) are determined late in leaf development in a local region of the leaf, rather than at the level of the entire organ. In a similar study of the aquatic plant *Ranunculus flabellaris*, Bruni and coworkers (1996) found that different aspects of leaf anatomy and morphology were specified at different stages of leaf development. Lobe number was specified earliest, followed by lobe length and leaf area, and finally stomatal density, leaf thickness, palisade differentiation, and the volume of intercellular air space.

Gradual, local determination of different aspects of leaf identity has also been observed for phase-specific traits in the case of *Impatiens balsamina* (Battey & Lyndon 1988, Pouteau et al 1997). This species is somewhat unusual in that flower primordia can be readily induced to revert to leaf production or vice versa by photoperiodic treatments. As in the case of *H. vulgaris*, the susceptibility of organ primordia to this treatment depends on their size at the time of treatment and the maturity stage of the tissue within the primordium. Intermediate organs consist of a combination of petal and leaf-like tissue, with reverted tissue always being located at the base of the organ. Interestingly, cells and tissues in reverted regions exhibit a combination of traits not normally found in leaves or petals. For example, anthocyanin (a petal trait) is produced by cells that otherwise resemble leaf cells. This remarkable result demonstrates that different programs of cellular differentiation operate independently even in individual cells.

When phase-specific vegetative traits become determined has not been carefully examined. It is significant, however, that the character of the transition leaves produced during the shift from juvenile-to-adult or from vegetative-to-reproductive development is often strikingly similar to the types of organs produced by the reversion experiments described above. Within this series of transition leaves, the change from one phase-specific form to the next may occur gradually for one particular group of traits and abruptly for another, resulting in combinations of phase-specific traits that do not normally occur in either juvenile or adult leaves (Hackett & Murray 1992). Furthermore, in many cases, the expression of phase-specific cellular markers of leaf identity in transition leaves occurs in discrete apical and basal domains of the leaf, as occurs in transition leaves in *H. vulgaris* and *I. balsamina*. The anatomy and morphology of leaves produced during the juvenile-to-adult transition has been well documented in maize (Bongard-Pierce et al 1996). In maize, cuticle thickness and cross-sectional cell shape change gradually from one transition leaf to the next, and there is no evidence for cell-to-cell variation in these traits within a transition leaf. In contrast, epicuticular wax production, the shape of lateral cell walls, and the staining pattern of epidermal cells change abruptly within single cells in predictable domains of the leaf (Moose & Sisco 1994, Lawson & Poethig 1995). In the basal-most transition leaves, adult tissue occupies a relatively small region at the base of the leaf, and this region expands acropetally in successively higher leaves. Frequently, individual cells express different phase-specific traits in the same region of the leaf. Thus transition leaves in maize may produce trichomes (an adult trait) in regions of the leaf that otherwise exhibit a juvenile pattern of cellular differentiation. The best evidence that different phase-specific aspects of leaf development are regulated independently in maize is provided by the phenotype of *gl15* mutants (Evans et al 1994, Moose & Sisco 1994). Mutations in the *Gl15* gene replace juvenile epidermal traits with adult traits. Only certain phase-specific epidermal traits are affected with no effect on either the character of the mesophyll or the overall morphology of the leaf. Spontaneous wild-type sectors resulting from the excision of the *Spm* element in the *gl15-m1* allele demonstrate that *Gl15* gene product functions cell autonomously and is required late in leaf development (Moose & Sisco 1994). In summary, these observations suggest that developmentally regulated components of leaf identity are regulated in the same way as environmentally determined ones, namely, by parallel developmental programs that either operate early in development and affect the entire leaf or act later in local regions of the leaf. It must be reiterated, however, that the similarity in the temporal progression of leaf determination in these two instances does not necessarily mean that environmental cues operate by the same mechanism as developmental programs of leaf specification.

Genetic Analysis of Leaf Identity

THE REGULATION OF COTYLEDON IDENTITY   In *Arabidopsis*, genes required for cotyledon identity have been defined by mutations that transform cotyledons into leaves. Recessive mutations in these so-called leafy cotyledon genes result in the partial or complete replacement of cotyledon-specific traits, such as storage product accumulation, desiccation tolerance, a simple vascular pattern, etc, with features normally restricted to vegetative leaves, i.e. trichomes, desiccation sensitivity, a complex vascular pattern (Meinke 1992, 1994; Bäumlein et al 1994; Keith et al 1994; West et al 1994). Three such genes have been discovered and can be grouped into two classes based on the severity of their mutant phenotype. The *LEAFY COTYLEDON2* (*LEC2*) locus appears to specifically regulate cotyledon/leaf identity because the single existing mutant allele of this gene has no other obvious effects on embryonic or post-embryonic development. *lec2* mutant embryos are not viviparous, are desiccation tolerant, and produce storage products in approximately normal amounts and in the correct distribution in the embryo (except in the cotyledons). *LEAFY COTYLEDON1* (*LEC1*) and *FUSCA3* (*FUS3*) appear to have a more general role in embryogenesis (Meinke et al 1994, West et al 1994, Parcy et al 1997). Homozygous *lec1* and *fus3* mutant embryos are viviparous and completely desiccation intolerant. Lipid and protein storage bodies are reduced throughout the entire embryonic axis in these mutants, indicating their effect is not limited to cotyledons. This conclusion is also supported by the observation that leaf primordia are initiated precociously in these mutants. As is the case with *LEC2*, *LEC1* and *FUS3* are not essential for post-embryonic development, since viable and essentially normal plants can be grown to maturity from mutant embryos rescued in culture.

Two interpretations have been offered to explain the phenotypes of these mutations. Keith and coworkers (1994) have suggested that the leafy cotyledon phenotype is heterochronic and is a consequence of the precocious activation of a vegetative developmental program. Their hypothesis is that the premature exposure of cotyledons to vegetative signals causes them to differentiate as vegetative organs. An alternative interpretation is that *LEC1* and *FUS3* are required for cotyledon differentiation and thus the mutant phenotypes result from the loss of cotyledon identity functions rather than a change in developmental timing (Meinke et al 1994, Parcy et al 1997). West and coworkers (1994) emphasize that both interpretations may be correct because the leafy cotyledons in *lec1* mutants express a combination of cotyledon and leaf traits. They note that if *LEC* genes function independently to promote the expression of cotyledon traits and to repress the expression of a post-embryonic pattern of development, then some aspects of their mutant phenotype may result from the failure of the cotyledon identity pathway, whereas others may result from the inappropriate expression of a post-germination pathway.

Whichever hypothesis is correct, the fact that the phenotype of *lec2* is limited to cotyledons suggests that the programs for seed desiccation and dormancy are separable from the specification of cotyledon cell specialization and that cotyledon identity may be regulated by a hierarchical pathway in which genes that regulate the expression of general seed-specific traits activate downstream organ identity determinants such as *LEC2*. A major problem with this hypothesis is that only a single mutant allele of *lec2* exists. If this mutation is leaky, then the relatively weak phenotype of *lec2* may reflect the residual activity of the *LEC2* gene product rather than the true function of this gene.

It is interesting that leaves initiated by the shoot meristem during embryogenesis may be morphologically and anatomically intermediate between cotyledons and true leaves formed after germination. In *Arabidopsis*, for example, the first two rosette leaves are morphologically similar to cotyledons and share with cotyledons a reduced potential for trichome production (Poethig 1997, Telfer et al 1997). Although maize does not produce a leaf-like cotyledon, the first two leaves produced during seed development have a pattern of epidermal differentiation similar to that of later-formed leaves but are molecularly (Moose & Sisco 1996), morphologically, and anatomically (Bongard-Pierce et al 1996) different from these leaves. This phenomenon raises the interesting question of whether factors that regulate the development of the embryo also have some influence on the developmental potential of leaves produced by the shoot apical meristem during embryogenesis.

Evidence that leaf identity may be regulated by factors that also operate to regulate cotyledon identity is provided by the production of "extra cotyledons" in precociously germinating *Brassica napus* embryos and in several mutants of *Arabidopsis*. When immature *B. napus* embryos are transferred to minimal medium (without added hormones), they germinate precociously, and the shoot meristem begins to initiate lateral organs (Finkelstein & Crouch 1984). In older immature embryos, these organs develop into vegetative leaves, but in embryos cultured at an early stage of development, they develop as either cotyledons or chimeric organs with sectors of cotyledon and leaf character (Finkelstein & Crouch 1984, Bisgrove et al 1995, Fernandez 1997). These extra cotyledons are recognizable as cotyledons because they have the anatomy and morphology of cotyledons and accumulate storage protein mRNAs in the same spatial and temporal pattern as true cotyledons. However, like leaves, they arise sequentially from the shoot meristem in a spiral phyllotaxy. Thus these unusual embryos simultaneously express an embryonic program of cotyledon identity and a post-embryonic program of shoot growth.

In situ hybridization analysis indicates that embryo-specific genes and germination-specific genes are expressed simultaneously in mosaic organs but in spatially separate domains (Fernandez 1997). This feature implies that these identities are regulated by one or more local cell-autonomous factors that act on the entire suite of genes involved in cotyledon differentiation. One of the striking features of this phenomenon is the spatial relationship between sectors in different organs. When sectors occur on more than one organ, they are always located in adjacent regions of these organs rather than in discontinuous domains. This feature was originally interpreted to mean that embryonic tissue is capable of influencing the fate of nearby cells. An alternative possibility is suggested by the fact that these sectors more closely reflect the cell lineage of a leaf than its temporal pattern of determination. These sectors may be derived from one or more adjacent cells that simultaneously underwent a stable change in fate very early in leaf development. The observation that this transformation takes place in leaves that are already present at the time the embryo is placed in culture implies that the cells in these primordia are not determined at this stage and that there is stochastic, local variation in the conditions that predispose cells to undergo this fate change.

Three mutations in *Arabidopsis*—*extra cotyledon 1 (xtc1)*, *extra cotyledon 2 (xtc2)*, and *altered meristem program 1 (amp1)*—display a phenotype similar to that of precociously germinated *B. napus* embryos, namely the formation of leaves that have been partially transformed into cotyledons (Conway & Poethig 1997). The extra cotyledons produced in these mutants can be distinguished from true cotyledons by their position on the shoot (formed at 90° from the cotyledons, the normal position of the first leaf), by their time of emergence (after cotyledons emerge, but before the first leaves of a wild-type plant), and by their small size and often irregular shape. They resemble true cotyledons in that they have few or no trichomes, a simple venation pattern, and they possess storage products normally present in cotyledons but not in leaves. This phenotype is different from mutations or natural variants of *Arabidopsis* that produce more than two cotyledons. In the case of *fass* mutants, which produce extra cotyledons and partially uncouple cell division and morphogenesis (Torres-Ruiz & Jürgens 1994), the production of additional cotyledons is presumed to be a result of an increase in the size of the shoot meristem, with the cotyledons all arising at the same nodal position and at the same time.

As in the case of *B. napus*, the extra cotyledons produced by *xtc1*, *xtc2*, and *amp1* mutants are a consequence of a change in the relative timing of embryo and shoot development (Conway & Poethig 1997). In both *xtc1* and *xtc2*, the morphogenesis of the embryo is delayed between the globular and heart stages of embryogenesis, and the shoot apical meristem enlarges precociously, producing one or two prominent leaf primordia. *amp1* has a different effect on embryogenesis in that it causes the upper half of the embryo to proliferate abnormally. It is similar to *xtc1* and *xtc2* because it also causes the precocious production of leaf primordia in the developing seed. The transformation of leaf primordia into cotyledons in these mutants is believed to be a consequence of this change in the timing of leaf initiation because only leaf primordia that are initiated precociously undergo this transformation. Furthermore, in the case of *amp1*, this developmental transformation is prevented by another mutation, *paused*, that delays leaf production.

Although the transformation of leaves into cotyledons can result from a variety of different abnormal conditions in *Arabidopsis* and *Brassica* embryos, a common feature of these conditions is the precocious activation of the shoot meristem that leads to the premature initiation of leaf primordia. Whether these leaf primordia then take on cotyledon identity owing to proximity to differentiating cotyledons or from some other source of phase information is unknown. It should be emphasized that the specification of an organ primordium as a cotyledon undoubtedly involves more than simply being initiated during embryogenesis, especially when one considers that mature seeds of many species contain numerous leaf primordia in addition to the cotyledons. In maize, for example, five to seven leaf primordia can be found in a mature dry seed. These vegetative leaves form in close proximity to the cotyledon and undergo the same processes of seed maturation and desiccation, yet display morphological and physiological features distinct from the cotyledon.

THE REGULATION OF FOLIAGE LEAF IDENTITY   Mutations that affect the production of juvenile or adult leaves have been identified in both maize and *Arabidopsis*. These mutations can be divided into two broad categories. One group of mutations affects a large number of phase-specific traits (including flowering) and may therefore represent genes involved in regulating the transition between juvenile and adult phases of shoot development. The other category includes mutations that affect a more limited set of phase-specific traits. This group is predicted to represent genes that play roles in establishing juvenile or adult leaf identity in response to phase change signals.

In maize, genes in the latter category include *Teopod1* (*Tp1*), *Teopod2* (*Tp2*), *Teopod3* (*Tp3*)/*Corngrass* (*Cg*), and *Gl15*. The first three genes (*Tp1*, *Tp2*, *Tp3*/*Cg*) are defined by dominant gain-of-function mutations that result in prolonged expression of a large number of juvenile traits. These mutations affect all known juvenile vegetative traits (including leaf shape, epicuticular wax production, and hair or trichome initiation) and have profound effects on the overall vegetative morphology of the plant (Lindstrom 1925, Galinat 1954a,b, Poethig 1988a, Bongard-Pierce et al 1996). They have relatively little effect, however, on the timing of the expression of adult traits or on the reproductive competence of the shoot. The leaves of *Tp2* mutants, for example, are morphologically and anatomically intermediate structures, combining features that are normally specific to either juvenile or adult leaves (Bongard-Pierce et al 1996). In addition, although *Tp2* increases the number of leaves produced by the shoot, it does not affect the time at which the shoot becomes reproductively competent or the time at which the primary shoot meristem finally ceases growth (Bassiri et al 1992). This aspect of their phenotype implies that the *Tp* genes regulate a juvenile program of leaf identity that operates in parallel to, and to some extent independently of, the programs that specify adult and reproductive traits. Mosaic analysis demonstrates that *Tp1* and *Tp2* function non–cell-autonomously and may therefore regulate a diffusible factor (Poethig 1988b, Dudley & Poethig 1993).

By contrast, recessive mutations in the *Gl15* locus result in a premature switch in the expression of a subset of vegetative phase-specific traits (Evans et al 1994, Moose & Sisco 1994). Mutant plants cease displaying juvenile epidermal traits (e.g. epicuticular wax) and begin to display adult epidermal traits (e.g. macrohairs and bulliform cells) much earlier than their normal siblings, with no other effects on overall vegetative morphology. Double mutants between *gl15* and *Tp1* and between *Tp2* and *Cg* indicate that *Gl15* is required for the effects of these dominant mutations on epidermal traits but not for other aspects of the *Tp* phenotype (Evans et al 1994, Moose & Sisco 1994). *gl15* mutations, therefore, uncouple epidermal differentiation aspects of leaf identity from the overall process of phase change in the vegetative shoot. This result implies that *Gl15* acts downstream of the *Tp* genes and is required specifically to promote the expression of a subset of juvenile epidermal traits and to repress the expression of an alternative set of adult traits. *Gl15* has been cloned and is predicted to encode a product that shows significant similarity to the putative DNA binding domain of the *APETALA2* gene of *Arabidopsis* (Moose & Sisco 1996).

Genes that may be involved in regulating the transition from juvenile-to-adult growth in maize include *viviparous8* (*vp8*) and genes involved in gibberellin (GA) biosynthesis, such as *dwarf1* (*d1*), *dwarf3* (*d3*), *dwarf5* (*d5*), and *anther ear1* (*an1*). Mutations that block GA production prolong the production of juvenile leaf traits, delay the expression of adult leaf traits including flowering, and dramatically enhance the phenotype of the *Tp* mutations (Olson 1954, Evans & Poethig 1995). Exogenous applications of GA_3 suppress the effect of *d3* on *Tp1* and *Tp2*, demonstrating that the effect of *d3* on these dominant mutations is mediated by a reduction in GA (Evans & Poethig 1995). These results suggest that GA acts to promote the adult phase of vegetative development and reproductive development in maize. However, the observation that the effect of GA-deficient mutations on phase-specific traits is relatively minor, even in double mutants of *d1* and *d3*, indicates that GA is not the only factor involved in this process (Evans & Poethig 1995). At present, the *Vp8* gene is a candidate for encoding such an additional factor (Evans & Poethig 1997). Like GA-deficient mutations, the *vp8* mutation prolongs the expression of juvenile traits and delays the expression of adult traits, although its effect on these traits is more pronounced than that of the *dwarf* mutations. *vp8* interacts synergistically with both the *Tp* mutations and the *dwarf* mutations, implying that it is not in the same pathway as these genes. Furthermore, *vp8* differs from the *dwarf* mutations in that it does not have a significant effect on flowering time. Thus *Vp8* appears to act in a pathway that promotes vegetative phase change but that does not directly regulate reproductive maturation. Another gene that is believed to be involved in regulating phase transitions in maize is defined by the dominant mutation *Hairy sheath frayed1-O* (Bertrand-Garcia & Freeling

1991). This mutation has a complex phenotype that includes the prolonged expression of many juvenile traits and the accelerated expression of some adult traits. It is expressed non–cell-autonomously in genetic mosaics, although to a more limited extent than *Tp1* and *Tp2* (Saberman & Bertrand-Garcia 1997).

The morphological changes that accompany vegetative phase change in *Arabidopsis* have only recently been investigated (Telfer et al 1997). As a result, only a few traits that differ between early and late stages of shoot development have been identified. In *Arabidopsis*, the first leaves produced are small and round, whereas later rosette leaves are larger, more elliptical, and more serrated (Röbbelen 1957, Poethig 1997) (Figure 1). Although these changes in leaf shape are predictable and easily observed, they occur in a continuous fashion, making them of limited utility as an unambiguous marker of leaf identity. Currently, the most readily quantifiable difference detected between leaves produced at different times in shoot development is the distribution of trichomes on the leaf blade (Chien & Sussex 1996, Telfer et al 1997). Trichomes are normally formed on the adaxial surface of all rosette leaves. Abaxial trichomes, however, are absent from the early rosette leaves and only appear later in vegetative development. While the first appearance of abaxial trichomes differs from one ecotype to the next, the presence or absence of abaxial trichomes serves as a useful trait to distinguish juvenile and adult phases of vegetative growth in *Arabidopsis*.

One of the reasons that abaxial trichome production in *Arabidopsis* is considered a good marker for the developmental phase of the shoot is that this trait responds to factors known to affect phase change in other species. In *Arabidopsis*, as in maize (Evans & Poethig 1995), GA acts to promote the adult form of this trait. Leaves with abaxial trichomes appear precociously in plants treated with regular applications of GA, as well as in *spindly-4* mutant plants that display a constitutive GA response. Conversely, GA-insensitive and GA-deficient mutants delay the production of leaves possessing abaxial trichomes (Chien & Sussex 1996, Telfer et al 1997). Abaxial trichome production is also affected by environmental conditions (e.g. day length) and by some mutations that affect flowering time (Chien & Sussex 1996, Telfer et al 1997). However, changes in the size of the shoot or the rate of leaf initiation do not affect the time at which the first abaxial trichomes appear (Telfer et al 1997).

A number of mutations that alter the appearance of abaxial trichomes have been described. Seedlings homozygous for the recessive mutation *paused* (*psd*) produce a normal embryo but fail to produce true leaves for several days after germination (Telfer et al 1997). The first leaves eventually formed are morphologically distinct from the first leaves made by wild-type seedlings. Instead, they resemble normal leaves initiated at the same time by wild-type siblings, although in a different position on the shoot. The *psd* mutation therefore generates a specific deletion of the first two to three juvenile leaves of the *Arabidopsis* shoot (Telfer et al 1997). The *amp1* mutation has an opposite phenotype; it increases the rate of leaf production, thereby increasing the number of juvenile leaves produced by the shoot. As in the case of *psd*, *amp1* has relatively little effect on the time at which the shoot begins to produce adult leaves. Thus both mutations alter leaf production without affecting the timing of the juvenile-to-adult transition.

In contrast to *psd* and *amp1* mutations, *hasty* (*hst*) mutations accelerate the first appearance of abaxial trichomes without significantly affecting the rate of leaf production (Telfer & Poethig 1998). *hst* mutations also accelerate the loss of adaxial trichomes (a trait typical of bracts), reduce the total number of leaves produced by the shoot, and have a number of other effects on shoot morphology. The interactions between *hst* and genes that regulate floral induction or floral morphogenesis (such as *LEAFY, APETALA1*, the GA-deficient mutation *ga1-3*, and the GA-insensitive mutation *gai*) indicate that *hasty* increases the reproductive competence of the shoot and does not require GA or a GA response for its effect on vegetative or reproductive maturation.

Another class of genes that may function to regulate vegetative phase change in *Arabidopsis* has been identified based on effects on flowering time. Several of the late flowering mutations affect vegetative morphology as well as the timing of flower initiation (Martínez-Zapater et al 1995, Telfer et al 1997). Although most of these mutations have a relatively small effect on abaxial trichomes, most of the extra leaves in the *fpa1* mutant lack abaxial trichomes, indicating that this mutation delays the transition to the adult vegetative phase (Telfer et al 1997). Most of these genes are defined by only a single allele, so it is possible that more severe alleles of the other late flowering loci will also reveal a role for these genes in vegetative phase change.

A Temporal Model for Vegetative Leaf Identity

In recent years, rapid progress has been made in understanding the factors that regulate some of the changes in meristem and organ identity that accompany the transition to reproductive growth. The ABC model for the regulation of floral organ identity postulates that the floral meristem is divided into four concentric domains by interactions between genes with three types of functions (A, B, and C), and that the fate of floral organs is specified by the domain in which they originate (Coen & Meyerowitz 1991, Weigel & Meyerowitz 1994). The model assumes that the demarcation of the meristem into these four domains occurs prior to the initiation of floral organs and that this process is independent of the process of organ initiation because mutations that change organ identity generally have no effect on the number, growth rate, size, and cell lineage of the organs located in the affected whorl of the floral primordium. The major exception to this rule is *AGAMOUS*, which specifies stamen and carpel identity and is also responsible for suppressing organ initiation in the central-most region of floral primordium. Thus floral morphogenesis is generally viewed as involving two processes: one that establishes a precise pattern of expression of organ identity genes within the floral primordium (meristem patterning) and a subsequent process that regulates the production of organs within these domains (Coen & Meyerowitz 1991, Weigel & Meyerowitz 1994).

Our current understanding of the regulation of vegetative organ identity is consistent with this view insofar as it predicts that organ identity and organ initiation are separable processes that can be altered independently of one another. However, it is difficult to apply all aspects of this model to vegetative development because there is no evidence that the vegetative meristem is divided into domains that are fated to produce juvenile, adult, and reproductive organs (Figure 2A). This is particularly obvious in the case of reproductive organs. Clonal analyses of the seedling meristems of maize (Johri & Coe 1983, McDaniel & Poethig 1988), sunflower (Jegla & Sussex 1989), and *Arabidopsis* (Johri & Coe 1983, Furner & Pumfrey 1992, Irish & Sussex 1992) have shown that at this stage in development there is no lineage restriction between adult vegetative organs and organs in the inflorescence. Unfortunately, the cell lineage relationship between juvenile and adult parts of the shoot has never been explicitly examined. Nevertheless, a reevaluation of data from a clonal analysis of embryogenesis in maize (Poethig et al 1986) suggests that there is no cell lineage restriction between these regions prior to the initiation of leaf one. The observation that adult phase maize shoots can be readily induced to revert to the juvenile phase in culture (Irish & Karlen 1998) further supports the conclusion that the shoot meristem does not possess developmentally determined juvenile and adult domains.

Perhaps the strongest argument against a meristem patterning model for the specification of vegetative leaf identity comes from a consideration of the type of intermediate organs produced during the transition from one developmental phase to the next. In those cases in which juvenile and adult leaves are distinguished by obvious cell-autonomous traits, transition organs are often divided into a distal region that expresses juvenile traits and a basal region that expresses adult traits (Goebel 1900, Bongard-Pierce et al 1996, Telfer et al 1997). In successively higher leaves, the juvenile domain is confined to a progressively smaller region at the distal end of the leaf blade. This proximal-distal pattern of cell identity is not predicted by a meristem patterning model; instead, transition organs are predicted to straddle the boundary between different domains in the meristem. Clonal analysis demonstrates that the adaxial and abaxial surfaces of a leaf are derived from different cells in the radial dimension of the shoot (Poethig & Sussex 1985, Poethig & Szymkowiak 1995). Thus a meristem patterning model would predict that in a transition leaf, cells with different

A

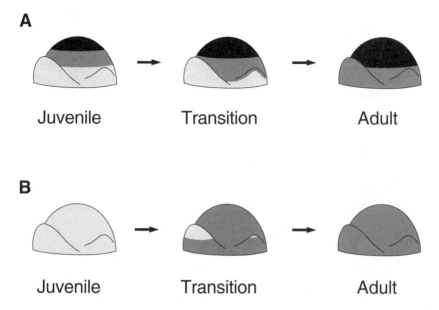

Juvenile   Transition   Adult

B

Juvenile   Transition   Adult

Figure 2 (*A*) Meristem patterning model for the regulation of organ identity. This model assumes that organ identity is specified by the spatial pattern of expression of organ identity genes in the apical meristem and that organ initiation is independent of this pattern. Organs that arise at the boundary between two domains are predicted to display different patterns of cellular differentiation on their adaxial and abaxial surfaces. (*B*) An alternative model for the regulation of organ identity. This model assumes that cells in the meristem only express a single fate at any given time in development. When the shoot apex switches to a new developmental phase, all of the cells in the shoot meristem and all of the undetermined cells in pre-existing leaf primordia adopt this new identity. This model predicts that the distribution of cell types in transition organs reflects the determination state of the organ at the time of the transition. Thus organs that mature in a basipetal fashion will possess proximal and distal domains with different developmental identities.

developmental identities will be located on the adaxial and abaxial sides of the leaf, not in distal and proximal regions as is generally observed.

An alternative model for the regulation of vegetative organ identity that is consistent with the character of the transition leaves is illustrated schematically in Figure 2*B*. This model is similar to the one proposed by Hempel & Feldman (1995, Hempel 1996) to explain the morphology of the inflorescence in *Arabidopsis* and is based on the observation that the character of a leaf can be modified even after the leaf has been initiated. As noted previously, there is considerable evidence that this is true both in aquatic plants (Goliber & Feldman 1990, Bruni et al 1996) and in *Impatiens balsimina* (Battey & Lyndon 1988), and preliminary results indicate that it is also true for juvenile and adult traits

in maize (H Passas & RS Poethig, unpublished observations). The most important assumption of this model is that all the undetermined organs on the shoot
meristem are in a single identity state (juvenile, adult, reproductive) at any
given time. A second assumption of the model is that the factors responsible
for the transition to a different developmental state (e.g. the juvenile-to-adult
transition or the vegetative-to-reproductive transition) act both on the meristem
and on all undetermined organs (leaves, buds, internodes) at the shoot apex.
All of the cells in the meristem switch to the next developmental state immediately upon induction, as do all of the undetermined cells in preexisting organs.
Because leaves mature basipetally, regions at the tip of preexisting leaves are
likely to have already become determined for the previous developmental state,
whereas basal regions of the leaf will still have the capacity to switch to the new
state. Thus, variation in the amount of juvenile and adult tissue in successive
transition leaves is assumed to result from the relative age of these leaves at the
time the phase transition occurs.

A prediction of this model is that the progression of heteroblastic leaf forms
during shoot development depends on the way in which the timing of leaf
initiation is coordinated with temporal expression patterns of genes that regulate
organ identity (Figure 3). As described above, the effect of *xtc1*, *xtc2*, and
amp1 on leaf identity appears to be a result of the inappropriate production
of leaves during embryogenesis (Conway & Poethig 1997). Similarly, the *psd*
mutation of *Arabidopsis* reduces the number of juvenile leaves by blocking leaf
production, not by affecting the timing of the transition from juvenile-to-adult
development (Telfer et al 1997). Mutations that affect the expression of phase-
specific traits without affecting the onset or rate of leaf production include
the *dwarf* (Evans & Poethig 1995), *gl15* (Evans et al 1994), and *Tp2* (Bassiri
et al 1992) mutations in maize, and the *hst* mutation in *Arabidopsis* (Telfer &
Poethig 1998). These mutations define genes that function independently of
leaf initiation and are involved either in regulating the switch between different
developmental phases or in regulating the expression of a set of phase-specific
leaf traits.

Given that floral organs evolved from leaves (Gifford & Foster 1989) and, at
least in *Arabidopsis*, can be transformed into leaves by loss-of-function mutations in floral organ identity genes (Bowman et al 1991), it is not unreasonable to
expect that the mechanism of vegetative organ specification and the mechanism
of floral organ specification may be similar in some respects. Whereas highly
evolved flowers are characterized by the rapid production of four different types
of organs in discrete whorls, more primitive flowers initiate floral organs in a
spiral and produce a graded series of organ types. A striking example of this
is provided by *Astrobaileyea scandens*, in which each floral organ is unique
(Endress 1980). This pattern is similar to that observed during vegetative phase

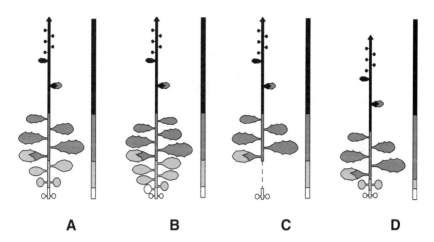

Figure 3   A model for heteroblastic leaf development. This model assumes that leaf initiation is regulated independently of organ identity. Organ identity is regulated by a mechanism that specifies different morphogenetic patterns at different times in shoot development. In this figure, the timing of leaf initiation is represented by the distance between leaves on the schematic illustration of an *Arabidopsis* plant, and the timing of organ identity programs is represented by the line to the *right* of each plant. The identity of a leaf at any particular position on the shoot depends on the way in which these processes are coordinated. (*A*) Wild-type plant. (*B*) Acceleration of leaf initiation relative to the organ identity program leads to the transformation of leaves into cotyledons and the production of extra juvenile leaves; this is the phenotype of the *amp1* mutant (Telfer et al 1997). (*C*) A delay in leaf initiation causes the shoot to produce adult leaves at basal nodes, as in the *psd* mutant (Telfer et al 1997). (*D*) Truncation of the juvenile phase of shoot development leads to the precocious production of adult leaves, as in the *hasty* mutant (Telfer & Poethig 1998).

transitions and suggests that floral morphogenesis in primitive flowers may involve the same sort of temporal progression of identity states that we propose for vegetative development. Whether this model is correct, it is worth noting that the ABC model does not readily explain the morphogenesis of flowers in which organ identity changes gradually. The mechanism of vegetative organ specification is therefore of interest both in its own right and because of what it may tell us about the evolutionary origin of the mechanism of floral morphogenesis.

CONCLUSIONS

Heteroblasty is an ancient and universal feature of plant development. Even primitive plants, such as green algae and bryophytes, exhibit heteroblastic patterns of organ development similar to those observed in more highly evolved species (Goebel 1900, Mishler 1986, Nishimura & Mandoli 1992). In 1790, von Goethe proposed that all of the organs on the shoot arise from a single foliar structure, leaving it to succeeding generations of biologists to define the nature of this structure and the mechanism of its metamorphosis into cotyledons, juvenile leaves, adult leaves, bracts, and foliar organs. Although considerable progress has been made in elucidating the molecular-genetic mechanism of floral morphogenesis, the way in which vegetative organ identity is regulated is still largely unknown. Two of the major problems in trying to define the factors that regulate leaf identity have been the paucity of cellular or molecular markers for vegetative organ identity in some species and the difficulty of distinguishing phase-specific traits from those that are regulated by reversible changes in the physiological status of the shoot. Techniques that allow investigators to visualize patterns of gene expression make it possible to observe the extent of the differences between organs and tissues and should resolve some of these problems. In combination with genetic analysis of model plant systems, which provides a means for identifying the factors that regulate organ identity, these tools offer new opportunities for studying this fundamental aspect of plant development.

Visit the *Annual Reviews home page* at
http://www.AnnualReviews.org

Literature Cited

Allsopp A. 1967. Heteroblastic development in vascular plants. In *Advances in Morphogenesis*, ed. M Abercrombie, J Brachet, 6:127–71. New York: Academic

Ashby E. 1948a. Studies in the morphogenesis of leaves. II. The area, cell size and cell number of leaves of *Ipomoea* in relation to their position on the shoot. *New Phytol.* 47:177–95

Ashby E. 1948b. Studies on the morphogenesis of leaves. I. An essay on leaf shape. *New Phytol.* 47:153–76

Barton MK, Poethig RS. 1993. Formation of the shoot apical meristem in *Arabidopsis thaliana*—an analysis of development in the wild type and in the *shoot meristemless* mutant. *Development* 119:823–31

Bassiri A, Irish EE, Poethig RS. 1992. Heterochronic effects of *Teopod2* on the growth and photosensitivity of the maize shoot. *Plant Cell* 4:497–504

Battey NH, Lyndon RF. 1988. Determination and differentiation of leaf and petal primordia in *Impatiens balsamina*. *Ann. Bot.* 61:9–16

Bauer H, Bauer U. 1980. Photosynthesis of the juvenile and adult phase of ivy (*Hedera helix*). *Physiol. Plant.* 49:366–72

Bäumlein H, Miséra S, Luerssen H, Kölle K,

Horstmann C, et al. 1994. The *FUS3* gene of *Arabidopsis thaliana* is a regulator of gene expression during late embryogenesis. *Plant J.* 6:379–87

Bertrand-Garcia R, Freeling M. 1991. *Hairy sheath frayed1-O*: a systemic, heterochronic mutant of maize that specifies slow developmental stage transitions. *Am. J. Bot.* 78:747–65

Besford RT, Hand P, Peppitt SD, Richardson CM, Thomas B. 1996. Phase change in *Prunus avium*: differences between juvenile and mature shoots identified by 2-dimensional protein separation and in vivo translation of mRNA. *J. Plant Physiol.* 147:534–38

Bewley JD, Black M. 1978. *Physiology and Biochemistry of Seeds in Relation to Germination*. Vol. 1. Berlin: Springer-Verlag. 306 pp.

Bisgrove SR, Crouch ML, Fernandez DE. 1995. Chimeric nature of precociously-germinating *Brassica napus* embryos: mRNA accumulation patterns. *J. Exp. Bot.* 46:27–33

Blaker TW, Greyson RI. 1988. Developmental variation of leaf surface wax of maize, *Zea mays*. *Can. J. Bot.* 66:839–46

Bodkin PC, Spence DHN, Weeks DC. 1980.

Photoreversible control of heterophylly in *Hippuris vulgaris* L. *New Phytol.* 84:533–42

Bon M-C. 1988. J16: an apex protein associated with juvenility of *Sequoiadendron giganteum*. *Tree Physiol.* 4:381–87

Bongard-Pierce DK, Evans MMS, Poethig RS. 1996. Heteroblastic features of leaf anatomy in maize and their genetic regulation. *Int. J. Plant Sci.* 157:331–40

Borchert R. 1976. The concept of juvenility in woody plants. *Acta Hortic.* 56:21–33

Bowman JL, Smyth DR, Meyerowitz EM. 1991. Genetic interactions among floral homeotic genes of *Arabidopsis*. *Development* 112:1–20

Brand MH, Lineberger RD. 1992. In vitro rejuvenation of Betulaceae: morphological evaluation. *Am. J. Bot.* 79:618–25

Bruck DK, Kaplan DR. 1980. Heterophyllic development in *Muehlenbeckia* (Polygonaceae). *Am. J. Bot.* 67:337–46

Bruni NC, Young JP, Dengler NG. 1996. Leaf developmental plasticity of *Ranunculus flabellaris* in response to terrestrial and submerged environments. *Can. J. Bot.* 74:823–37

Bryant JP, Provenza FD, Pastor J, Reichart PB, Clausen TP, du Toit JT. 1991. Interactions between woody plants and browsing mammals mediated by secondary metabolites. *Annu. Rev. Ecol. Syst.* 22:431–46

Cameron RJ. 1970. Light intensity and the growth of *Eucalyptus* seedlings I. Ontogenetic variation in *E. fastigata*. *Aust. J. Bot.* 18:29–43

Chien JC, Sussex IM. 1996. Differential regulation of trichome formation on the adaxial and abaxial leaf surfaces by gibberellins and photoperiod in *Arabidopsis thaliana* (L.) Heynh. *Plant Physiol.* 111:1321–28

Clearwater MJ, Gould KS. 1994. Comparative leaf development of juvenile and adult *Pseudopanax crassifolius*. *Can. J. Bot.* 72:658–70

Coen ES, Meyerowitz EM. 1991. The war of the whorls: genetic interactions controlling flower development. *Nature* 353:31–37

Conway LJ, Poethig R. 1997. Mutations of *Arabidopsis thaliana* that transform leaves into cotyledons. *Proc. Natl. Acad. Sci. USA* 94:10209–14

Cook CDK. 1969. On the determination of leaf form in *Ranunculus aquatilis*. *New Phytol.* 68:469–80

Crouch ML. 1988. Regulation of gene expression during seed development in flowering plants. In *The Molecular Biology of Cell Determination and Cell Differentiation, Developmental Biology: A Comprehensive Synthesis*, ed. LW Browder, 5:367–404. New York: Plenum

Dietrich RA, Maslyar DJ, Heupel RC, Harada JJ. 1989. Spatial patterns of gene expression in *Brassica napus* seedlings: identification of a cortex-specific gene and localization of m-RNAs encoding isocitrate lyase and a polypeptide homologous to proteinases. *Plant Cell* 1:73–80

Dudley M, Poethig RS. 1993. The heterochronic *Teopod1* and *Teopod2* mutations of maize are expressed non-cell-autonomously. *Genetics* 133:389–99

Endress PK. 1980. The reproductive structures and systematic position of the Austrobaileyaceae. *Bot. Jahrb. Syst.* 101:393–433

Evans MMS, Passas H, Poethig RS. 1994. Heterochronic effects of *glossy15* mutations on epidermal cell identity in maize. *Development* 120:1971–81

Evans MMS, Poethig RS. 1995. Gibberellins promote vegetative phase change and reproductive maturity in maize. *Plant Physiol.* 108:475–87

Evans MMS, Poethig RS. 1997. The *viviparous8* mutation delays vegetative phase change and accelerates the rate of seedling growth in maize. *Plant J.* 12:769–79

Feldman LJ, Cutter EG. 1970. Regulation of leaf form in *Centaurea solstitialis* L. I. Leaf development on whole plants in sterile culture. *Bot. Gaz.* 131:31–39

Fernandez DE. 1997. Developmental basis of homeosis in precociously germinating *Brassica napus* embryos: phase change at the shoot apex. *Development* 124:1149–57

Finkelstein RR, Crouch ML. 1984. Precociously germinating rapeseed embryos retain characteristics of embryogeny. *Planta* 162:125–31

Foster AS. 1935. A histogenic study of foliar determination in *Carya buckleyi* var. arkansana. *Am. J. Bot.* 22:88–147

Franich RA, Wells LG, Barnett JR. 1977. Variation with tree age of needle cuticle topography and stomatal structure in *Pinus radiata* D. Don. *Ann. Bot.* 41:621–26

Furner IJ, Pumfrey JE. 1992. Cell fate in the shoot apical meristem of *Arabidopsis thaliana*. *Development* 115:755–64

Galinat WC. 1954a. Corn grass: I. Corn grass as a prototype or a false progenitor of maize. *Am. Nat.* 88:101–4

Galinat WC. 1954b. Corn grass: II. Effect of the corn grass gene on the development of the maize inflorescence. *Am. J. Bot.* 41:803–6

Gifford EM Jr, Foster AS. 1989. *Morphology and Evolution of Vascular Plants*. New York: Freeman. 3rd ed.

Goebel K. 1900. *Organography of Plants. Part 1. General Organography*. Transl. IB Balfour. Oxford: Clarendon (from German)

Goldberg RB, Barker SJ, Perez-Grau L. 1989.

Regulation of gene expression during plant embryogenesis. *Cell* 56:149–60

Goldberg RB, de Paiva G, Yadegari R. 1994. Plant embryogenesis: zygote to seed. *Science* 266:605–14

Goliber TE, Feldman LJ. 1990. Developmental analysis of leaf plasticity in the heterophyllous aquatic plant *Hippuris vulgaris*. *Am. J. Bot.* 77:399–412

Gould KS. 1993. Leaf heteroblasty in *Pseudopanax crassifolius*: functional significance of leaf morphology and anatomy. *Ann. Bot.* 71:61–70

Greenwood MS. 1987. Rejuvenation of forest trees. *Plant Growth Regul.* 6:1–12

Greenwood MS. 1995. Juvenility and maturation in conifers: current concepts. *Tree Physiol.* 15:433–38

Guerche P, Tire C, Grossi de Sa F, De Clercq A, Van Montagu M, Krebbers E. 1990. Differential expression of the *Arabidopsis* 2S albumin genes and the effect of increasing gene family size. *Plant Cell* 2:469–78

Hackett WP. 1985. Juvenility, maturation and rejuvenation in woody plants. *Hortic. Rev.* 7: 109–55

Hackett WP, Murray JR. 1992. Maturation and rejuvenation in woody plants. *Acta Hortic.* 314: 195–203

Haffner V, Enjalric F, Lardet L, Carron MP. 1991. Maturation in woody plants: a review of metabolic and genomic aspects. *Ann. Sci. For.* 48:615–30

Hall LN, Langdale JA. 1996. Molecular genetics of cellular differentiation in leaves. *New Phytol.* 132:533–53

Harada JJ, Baden CS, Comai L. 1988. Spatially regulated genes expressed during seed germination and post-germinative development are activated during embryogeny. *Mol. Gen. Genet.* 212:466–73

Hempel FD. 1996. Morphology of the transition to flowering in mustards. *Semin. Cell Dev. Biol.* 7:391–400

Hempel FD, Feldman LJ. 1995. Specification of chimeric flowering shoots in wild-type *Arabidopsis*. *Plant J.* 8:725–31

Huang L-C, Lius S, Huang B-L, Murashige T, Mahdi EFM, van Gundy R. 1992. Rejuvenation of *Sequoia sempervirens* by repeated grafting of shoot tips onto juvenile rootstocks in vitro. *Plant Physiol.* 98:166–73

Hutchinson KW, Sherman CD, Weber J, Smith SS, Singer PB, Greenwood MS. 1990. Maturation in larch II. Effects of age on photosynthesis and gene expression in developing foliage. *Plant Physiol.* 94:1308–15

Hutchinson KW, Singer PB, Greenwood MS. 1991. Gene expression during growth and maturation. In *Woody Plant Biotechnology*, ed. MR Ahuja, pp. 69–75. New York: Plenum

Irish E, Karlen K. 1998. Restoration of juvenility in maize shoots by meristem culture. *Int. J. Plant Sci.* 158:In press

Irish V, Sussex IM. 1992. A fate map of the *Arabidopsis* shoot apical meristem. *Development* 115:745–53

James AC, Mantell SH. 1994. Characterization of developmental phases of the woody perennial shrub, *Solanum aviculare* Forst. *New Phytol.* 127:591–600

Jegla DE, Sussex IM. 1989. Cell lineage patterns in the shoot meristem of the sunflower embryo in the dry seed. *Dev. Biol.* 131:215–25

Johri MM, Coe EH. 1983. Clonal analysis of corn plant development I. The development of the tassel and ear shoot. *Dev. Biol.* 97:154–72

Jones CS. 1993. Heterochrony and heteroblastic leaf development in two subspecies of *Cucurbita argyrosperma* (Cucurbitaceae). *Am. J. Bot.* 80:778–95

Jones CS. 1995. Does shade prolong juvenile development? A morphological analysis of leaf shape changes in *Cucurbita argyrosperma* ssp. *sororia* (Cucurbitaceae). *Am. J. Bot.* 82:346–59

Kaplan DR. 1973. Comparative developmental analysis of the heteroblastic leaf series of axillary shoots of *Acorus calamus* L. (Araceae). *La Cell.* 69:253–90

Kaplan DR. 1980. Heteroblastic leaf development in *Acacia*. Morphological and morphogenetic implications. *La Cell.* 73:137–203

Kaplan DR, Cooke TL. 1997. Fundamental concepts in the embryogenesis of dicotyledons: a morphological interpretation of embryo mutants. *Plant Cell* 9:1903–19

Keith K, Kraml M, Dengler NG, McCourt P. 1994. *fusca3*: a heterochronic mutation affecting late embryo development in *Arabidopsis*. *Plant Cell* 6:589–600

Lawson EJR, Poethig RS. 1995. Shoot development in plants: time for a change. *Trends Genet. Sci.* 11:263–68

Lindstrom EW. 1925. Heritable characters of maize XVI. A new dominant hereditary character—Teopod*. *J. Hered.* 16:135–40

Martínez-Zapater JM, Jarillo JA, Cruz-Alvarez M, Roldán M, Salinas J. 1995. *Arabidopsis* late-flowering *fve* mutants are affected in both vegetative and reproductive development. *Plant J.* 7:543–51

McCully ME, Dale HM. 1961. Heterophylly in *Hippuris*: a problem in identification. *Can. J. Bot.* 39:1099–116

McDaniel CN, Poethig RS. 1988. Cell-lineage patterns in the apical meristem of the germinating maize embryo. *Planta* 175:13–22

McLellan T. 1993. The roles of heterochrony and heteroblasty in the diversification of leaf shapes in *Begonia dregei* (Begoniaceae). *Am. J. Bot.* 80:796–804

Meinke DW. 1992. A homoeotic mutant of *Arabidopsis thaliana* with leafy cotyledons. *Science* 258:1647–50

Meinke DW, Franzmann LH, Nickle TC, Yeung EC. 1994. Leafy cotyledon mutants of *Arabidopsis*. *Plant Cell* 6:1049–64

Merrill EK. 1986. Heteroblastic seedlings of green ash II. Early development of simple and compound leaves. *Can. J. Bot.* 64:2650–61

Mishler BD. 1986. Ontogeny and phylogeny in *Tortula* (Musci: Pottiacea). *Syst. Bot.* 11: 189–208

Moose SP, Sisco PH. 1994. *Glossy15* controls the epidermal juvenile-to-adult phase transition in maize. *Plant Cell* 6:1343–55

Moose SP, Sisco PH. 1996. *Glossy15*, an *APETALA2*-like gene from maize that regulates leaf epidermal cell identity. *Genes Dev.* 10:3018–27

Müller RJ. 1982. Shoot ontogeny and the comparative development of the heteroblastic leaf series in *Lygodium japonicum* (Thunb.). *Bot. Gaz.* 143:424–38

Murray JR, Smith AG, Hackett WP. 1994. Differential dihydroflavonol reductase transcription and anthocyanin pigmentation in the juvenile and mature phases of ivy (*Hedera helix* L). *Planta* 194:102–9

Nishimura NJ, Mandoli DF. 1992. Vegetative growth of *Acetabularia acetubulum chlorophyta*. Structural evidence for juvenile and adult phases of development. *J. Phycol.* 28: 669–77

Njoku E. 1956a. The effect of defoliation on leaf shape in *Ipomoea caerulea*. *New Phytol.* 55:213–28

Njoku E. 1956b. Studies on the morphogenesis of leaves XI. The effect of light intensity on leaf shape in *Ipomoea caerulea*. *New Phytol.* 55:91–110

Olson JW. 1954. A comparison of leaf number, internode and mesocotyl lengths in *dwarf1* and normal *Zea mays* L. *Proc. Minn. Acad. Sci.* 22:99–104

Parcy F, Valon C, Kohara A, Misera S, Giraudat J. 1997. The *ABSCISIC ACID-INSENSITIVE3, FUSCA3*, and *LEAFY COTYLEDON1* loci act in concert to control multiple aspects of Arabidopsis seed development. *Plant Cell* 9:1265–77

Perez-Grau L, Goldberg RB. 1989. Soybean seed protein genes are regulated spatially during embryogenesis. *Plant Cell* 1:1095–109

Poethig RS. 1988a. Heterochronic mutations affecting shoot development in maize. *Genetics* 119:959–73

Poethig RS. 1988b. A non-cell-autonomous mutation regulating juvenility in maize. *Nature* 336:82–83

Poethig RS. 1990. Phase change and the regulation of shoot morphogenesis in plants. *Science* 250:923–30

Poethig RS. 1997. Leaf morphogenesis in flowering plants. *Plant Cell* 9:1077–87

Poethig RS, Coe EH, Johri MM. 1986. Cell lineage patterns in maize embryogenesis: a clonal analysis. *Dev. Biol.* 117:392–404

Poethig RS, Sussex IM. 1985. The cellular parameters of leaf development in tobacco: a clonal analysis. *Planta* 165:170–84

Poethig RS, Szymkowiak EJ. 1995. Clonal analysis of leaf development in maize. *Maydica* 40:67–76

Pouteau S, Nicholls D, Tooke F, Coen E, Battey N. 1997. The induction and maintenance of flowering in *Impatiens*. *Development* 124: 3343–51

Richards J. 1983. Heteroblastic development in the water hyacinth *Eichhornia crassipes* Solms. *Bot. Gaz.* 144:247–59

Röbbelen G. 1957. Über Heterophyllie bei *Arabidopsis thaliana* (L) Hehn. *Ber. Dtsch. Bot. Ges.* 70:39–44

Saberman J, Bertrand-Garcia R. 1997. *Hairysheath-frayed1-O* is a non-cell-autonomous mutation that regulates developmental stage transitions in maize. *J. Hered.* 88:549–53

Snowball AM, Zeman AM, Tichan YT, Mullins MG, Goodwin PB. 1991. Phase change in *Citrus*: immunologically detetectable differences between juvenile and mature plants. *Aust. J. Plant Physiol.* 18:385–96

Sussex IM, Clutter ME. 1960. A study of the effect of externally supplied sucrose on the morphology of excised fern leaves in vitro. *Phytomorphology* 10:87–99

Sylvester AW, Smith L, Freeling M. 1996. Acquisition of identity in the developing leaf. *Annu. Rev. Cell Dev. Biol.* 12:257–304

Telfer A, Bollman KM, Poethig RS. 1997. Phase change and the regulation of trichome distribution in *Arabidopsis thaliana*. *Development* 124:645–54

Telfer A, Poethig RS. 1998. *HASTY*: a gene that regulates the timing of shoot maturation in *Arabidopsis thaliana*. *Development* 125: 1889–98

Thiagarajah MR, Hunt LA, Mahon JD. 1981. Effect of leaf position and age on leaf photosynthesis in corn (*Zea mays*). *Can. J. Bot.* 59: 28–33

Thomas TL. 1993. Gene expression during plant embryogenesis and germination: an overview. *Plant Cell* 5:1401–10

Torres-Ruiz RA, Jürgens G. 1994. Mutations in the *FASS* gene uncouple pattern formation and morphogenesis in *Arabidopsis* development. *Development* 120:2967–78

Tsai C-H, Miller A, Spalding M, Rodermel S. 1997. Source strength regulates an early phase transition of tobacco shoot morphogenesis. *Plant Physiol.* 115:907–14

Vince-Prue D, Tucker DJ. 1983. Photomorphogenesis in leaves. In *The Growth and Functioning of Leaves*, ed. JE Dale, FL Milthorpe, pp. 233–69. Cambridge, UK: Cambridge Univ. Press

von Goethe JW. 1790. *Versuch die Metamorphose der Pflanzen zu erklären.* Gotha, Ger.: Ettinger

Wardlaw CW. 1955. *Embryogenesis in Plants.* New York: Wiley & Sons. 381 pp.

Wareing PF. 1959. Problems of juvenility and flowering in trees. *J. Linn. Soc. London Bot.* 56:282–89

Weigel D, Meyerowitz EM. 1994. The ABCs of floral homeotic genes. *Cell* 78:203–9

West MAL, Harada JJ. 1993. Embryogenesis in higher plants: an overview. *Plant Cell* 5:1361–69

West MAL, Yee KM, Danao J, Zimmerman JL, Fischer RL, et al. 1994. *LEAFY COTYLEDON1* is an essential regulator of late embryogenesis and cotyledon identity in *Arabidopsis. Plant Cell* 6:1731–45

Wobus U, Borisjuk L, Panitz R, Manteuffel R, Bäumlein H, et al. 1995. Control of seed storage protein gene expression: new aspects on an old problem. *J. Plant Physiol.* 145:592–99

Woo H-H, Hackett WP, Das A. 1994. Differential expression of a chlorophyll a/b binding protein gene and a proline rich gene in juvenile and mature phase English ivy (*Hedera helix*). *Physiol. Plant.* 92:69–78

Annu. Rev. Cell Dev. Biol. 1998. 14:399–458

CONTROL OF TRANSLATION INITIATION IN ANIMALS

Nicola K. Gray and Marvin Wickens

Department of Biochemistry, 433 Babcock Dr., University of Wisconsin, Madison, Wisconsin 53706; e-mail: wickens@biochem.wisc.edu

KEY WORDS: translation, initiation factors, maternal mRNAs, polyadenylation, RNA-protein interactions, untranslated regions (UTRs)

ABSTRACT

Regulation of translation initiation is a central control point in animal cells. We review our current understanding of the mechanisms of regulation, drawing particularly on examples in which the biological consequences of the regulation are clear. Specific mRNAs can be controlled via sequences in their 5′ and 3′ untranslated regions (UTRs) and by alterations in the translation machinery. The 5′UTR sequence can determine which initiation pathway is used to bring the ribosome to the initiation codon, how efficiently initiation occurs, and which initiation site is selected. 5′UTR-mediated control can also be accomplished via sequence-specific mRNA-binding proteins. Sequences in the 3′ untranslated region and the poly(A) tail can have dramatic effects on initiation frequency, with particularly profound effects in oogenesis and early development. The mechanism by which 3′UTRs and poly(A) regulate initiation may involve contacts between proteins bound to these regions and the basal translation apparatus. mRNA localization signals in the 3′UTR can also dramatically influence translational activation and repression. Modulations of the initiation machinery, including phosphorylation of initiation factors and their regulated association with other proteins, can regulate both specific mRNAs and overall translation rates and thereby affect cell growth and phenotype.

CONTENTS

1081-0706/98/1115-0399$08.00

INTRODUCTION

The importance of the translation machinery and its fidelity have been apparent since the discovery of the genetic code. However, the broad impact of translational regulation in eukaryotic cells has emerged explosively only in the last few years. This new appreciation of translational regulation has been propelled by work in systems as diverse as budding yeast and human tumors, and approaches that range from genetics to biochemistry and cell biology. It is the diversity of these controls, their biological implications, and increasing access to key regulators that prompts this review.

There are two general forms of translational control: In one, a specific mRNA or subset of mRNAs is regulated. Such regulation can be quantitative, determining the amount of protein produced; this may be all-or-none, or graded. Specific regulation can also be qualitative, enabling a single mRNA to produce several different proteins. In the second form, regulation is global and modulates rates and patterns of protein synthesis, thereby contributing to the overall regulation of cell growth and metabolism. These two forms of regulation are not mutually exclusive.

Translational control is important throughout development but nowhere more so than in the oocyte and early embryo. This is not entirely surprising: Early embryos are commonly transcriptionally inactive, or nearly so, yet require rapid changes in the proteins they contain in order to regulate key developmental decisions. Consequently, translation during early development has been the subject of intense genetic and biochemical scrutiny. The earliest steps in pattern formation in *Drosophila* emphasize the importance and intricacy of translational control (St Johnston & Nüsslein-Volhard 1992, Wharton 1992, Curtis et al 1995, Macdonald & Smibert 1996). The circuitry is sophisticated enough to rival any in molecular biology (Figure 1). Formation of the anterior-posterior axis requires a cascade of translational regulation in which, for example, the translational activation of one mRNA generates a protein product that in turn represses or activates the translation of another. Similarly, in *Caenorhabditis elegans*, translational controls contribute to the determination of cell fates, pattern formation, and the timing of development events (Schnabel & Priess 1997, Wickens et al 1996). We discuss these processes and many of the interactions depicted in Figure 1 in detail below. Here, we emphasize two perspectives. First, genetic analysis has revealed that these controls are indispensable and often require regulatory elements in the 3'UTR. Yet in virtually none of these genetically defined instances of 3'UTR-based control has the molecular mechanism been elucidated. This stands as a primary and immediate goal.

Second, our understanding of the basic mechanisms of translation initiation, as well as 5'UTR-mediated and global forms of control, has obtained a greater degree of molecular detail. Much of this knowledge has been obtained biochemically and completing this picture is an immediate objective. Determining the precise biological role of such events in the intact organism is an equally pressing and formidable challenge.

We discuss the regulation of translation initiation in eukaryotes, considering both mRNA-specific and global controls. In general, we focus on examples from multicellular animals, emphasizing cases with particular relevance to developmental biology. We refer to the translation of yeast, plant, and viral mRNAs only as needed. Several reviews of related topics that we do not consider here include the regulation of elongation (Proud 1994) and termination (Tuite & Stansfield

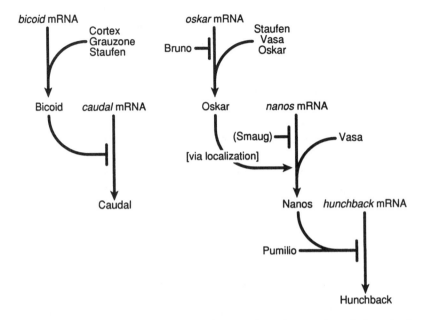

Figure 1 Specific RNA-protein interactions that control anterior-posterior axis formation in *Drosophila*. A series of opposing protein gradients help determine the anterior-posterior axis of *Drosophila* and are established by a regulated cascade involving mRNA localization and translation (see text for references; St Johnston et al 1992). *Arrowheads* depict positive events, and *blunt ends* indicate repressive events. All of these events occur either in the growing oocyte or in syncitial early embryo. mRNAs produced in nurse cells enter the growing oocyte from the presumptive anterior end; some mRNAs must move across the oocyte to the presumptive posterior. Activation of *bicoid* mRNA, which is localized to the anterior end and repressed during oogenesis, requires Cortex, Grauzone, and Staufen proteins. Bicoid protein then represses the translation in the anterior of uniformly distributed *caudal* mRNA, establishing a gradient of Caudal protein. In the posterior end, the initial event is localized expression of Oskar. Translation of *oskar* mRNA during its transit from the anterior end of the oocyte is repressed by Bruno, and its localization and full activation require Staufen, Vasa, and Oskar proteins. *nanos* mRNA is also localized to the posterior pole, a process that requires the presence of Oskar. Its mis-localized expression is prevented by sequences in its 3'UTR that appear to interact with Smaug, although the role of that protein has not been shown directly. Activation of *nanos* mRNA translation requires Vasa. Posteriorly localized Nanos, in concert with Pumilio, represses the translation of uniformly distributed *hunchback* mRNA in the posterior. Repression occurs in the posterior because there Nanos is present at its highest concentration. In this figure we include genes and proteins that are discussed in the text; many other genes such as *cappuccino*, *spire*, and *egalitarian* contribute to these processes but have not been included. In particular, proteins that participate in localization but not explicitly in translational regulation are not depicted. A similar figure appears in Macdonald & Smibert 1996.

1994) and translational regulation in plants (Browning 1996) and prokaryotes (McCarthy & Brimaconbe 1994, Voorma et al 1994, Jackson 1996).

We begin with a brief summary of the roles of the core components in translation initiation in eukaryotes. Our intent is to provide an outline of the pathway sufficient for discussion of its regulation. More detailed information is available elsewhere (Jackson 1996, Merrick & Hershey 1996, Pain 1996, Sachs et al 1997).

MECHANISMS OF INITIATION: OVERVIEW

Initiation is a complex multi-step process involving a large number of protein factors and multi-protein complexes, in addition to ribosomes. At least 25 proteins are involved in the initiation process per se, excluding ribosomal proteins and tRNA synthetases (Merrick & Hershey 1996). Additional proteins modulate the activities of the core translational components. Given this complexity, it is not surprising that cells and viruses regulate initiation through a diverse array of mechanisms.

A single, cap-dependent mechanism accounts for the translation of the vast majority of cellular mRNAs. A collection of alternative initiation mechanisms, one of which is cap-independent, is responsible for translation of a small number of mRNAs.

Cap-Dependent

A working model for cap-dependent initiation, consistent with most of the current data, is depicted in Figure 2. Although this model represents a general consensus, it is not unambiguously established (discussed in Jackson 1996, Merrick & Hershey 1996, Pain 1996), and we refer only to those factors that are relevant to later discussions. Following ribosomal subunit dissociation, which is assisted by a number of initiation factors (eIFs), including eIF-3, the small (40S) ribosomal subunit (carrying eIF-3) associates with a ternary complex to generate a 43S pre-initiation complex. The ternary complex contains the methionine-charged initiator tRNA, initiation factor eIF-2, and GTP. This 43S complex is then recruited, with the aid of the eIF-4 group of initiation factors, to the 5' end of the mRNA. Mammalian eIF-4F is normally considered to be composed of three subunits: eIF-4E (which binds to the m7GpppG cap, an interaction crucial to recruiting eIF-4F), eIF-4A (which has ATPase-dependent RNA helicase activity), and eIF-4G (which through its interaction with eIF-3 aids the binding of the 43S pre-initiation complex). In plants and yeast only, eIF-4E and eIF-4G [and eIF-iso4E and eIF-iso4G in plants (Browning 1996)] can be isolated as a complex. It is generally accepted that the helicase activity of eIF-4F unwinds secondary structures from the 5' untranslated region (UTR),

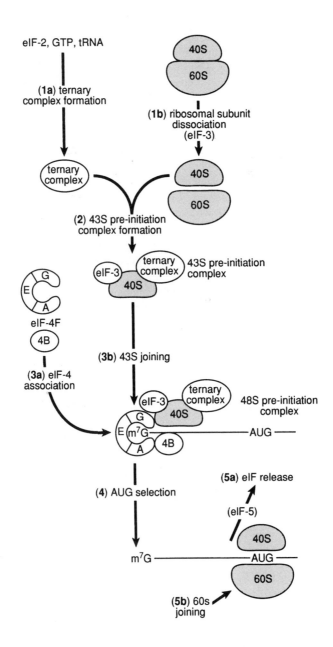

which would otherwise impede the initiation apparatus. This helicase activity is stimulated by eIF-4B, which binds simultaneously with, or very closely after, eIF-4F. The interaction of eIF-4B with eIF-3 may also aid in the binding of the 43S complex. Once bound, the 43S complex migrates along the 5′UTR in an ATP-dependent process known as scanning, until it encounters an initiator AUG codon, normally the first AUG. The exact nature of the scanning process remains unclear. For example, it is unclear whether ATP hydrolysis is required purely for helicase activity or whether movement of the 43S complex also requires ATP (discussed in Jackson 1996). Following AUG recognition, eIF-5 triggers hydrolysis of the GTP in the ternary complex, initiation factor release occurs, and the large (60S) ribosomal subunit enters. Elongation now begins.

The minimal features of an mRNA essential for cap-dependent initiation are deceptively simple: a m7GpppG cap structure and an AUG in a favorable context (see LEAKY SCANNING). Non-AUG codons, such as a GUG or CUG, occasionally serve as initiators but are inherently inefficient (Kozak 1989b). However, an AUG in an optimal context does not ensure efficient initiation. Rather, the frequency of subunit loading is set by the accessibility of the 5′ end of the mRNA to initiation factors and small ribosomal subunits. Subunit migration to the initiator is limited by features of the 5′UTR, which can impede or perhaps even derail the scanning complex. Thus in simplest form, although the context surrounding the initiation codon influences which initiation site is used, it may not be the primary determinant of the total number of initiation events per mRNA. The translational efficiency of an mRNA can also be influenced by sequences at or near the 3′ end of the mRNA. Thus although its essential features may be simple, initiation can be regulated through a wide diversity of mechanisms (see Figure 3).

Variations of the Cap-Dependent Scanning Model

LEAKY SCANNING   This variation of the scanning model relates to the choice of initiation codon. In general, the first AUG encountered by a scanning ribosome

---

Figure 2   Cap-dependent translation initiation pathway. Step (1a): A ternary complex is formed between eIF-2, GTP, and the initiator tRNA. Step (1b): Dissociation of ribosomal subunits is aided by initiation factors including eIF-3. Step (2): The ternary complex is recruited by the small ribosomal subunit to form a 43S pre-initiation complex. Step (3a): The eIF-4 group of the initiation factors interacts with the 5′ end of the mRNA and aids in Step (3b), the binding of the 43S pre-initiation complex to form a 48S pre-initiation complex. Step (4): The 43S pre-initiation complex, aided by associated factors, migrates to the initiator AUG. This process is termed scanning. Step (5a): eIF-5 hydrolyzes the GTP in the ternary complex, initiation factor release occurs, and in Step (5b), the 60S ribosomal subunit joins. The role of a number of initiation factors is not depicted. See Merrick & Hershey (1996) for a more detailed description of initiation factors. The figure is schematic and is not meant to indicate the spatial arrangement of proteins within the various complexes nor the full extent of RNA-protein interactions.

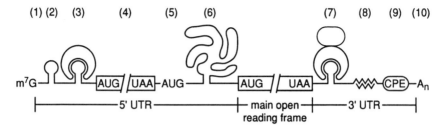

Figure 3 Forms of translational regulation by the 5′ and 3′ ends of the mRNA. Regulation via the 5′ UTR can be mediated by (1) modification of the cap structure, (2) secondary structure, (3) RNA-protein interactions, (4) upstream open reading frames, (5) upstream AUGs, and (6) IRES elements. 3′UTR-mediated regulation can occur through (7) RNA-protein interactions, which may involve multi-protein complexes, (8) RNA-RNA interactions, (9) cytoplasmic polyadenylation elements, and (10) changes in poly(A) tail length. The figure is diagrammatic and does not infer any organization of these elements within the 5′ and 3′ UTRs.

is selected as the site of initiation (Kozak 1983, 1987a). However, an AUG or non-AUG initiator codon may be inefficiently recognized or ignored if it is located very close to the cap (Sedman et al 1990, Kozak 1991c), or if it lies in a poor context (Kozak 1984a,b, 1986b, 1989b). A consensus sequence GCCGCC$^{A/G}$CCAUGG for initiator codons has been defined by a survey of vertebrate mRNAs (Kozak 1987a). The most important positions for efficient translation are a purine at position −3 and a G at position +4, where A of the AUG codon is position +1 (reviewed in Kozak 1991a, 1997). The effects of other positions become apparent when either of the main features is unfavorable. Positions +5 and +6 can also influence start site efficiency, with a A or C being preferred at position 5 and a U at position 6 (Boeck & Kolakofsky 1994, Grünert & Jackson 1994). Inefficient recognition of an initiator codon results in a portion of 43S pre-initiation complexes continuing to scan and initiating at a downstream site, in a process known as leaky scanning.

RE-INITIATION   Re-initiation is a relatively rare and inefficient initiation mechanism in which a second initiation event occurs following the translation of an upstream open reading frame (uORF) (Liu et al 1984, Kozak 1984b, 1987b). By definition re-initiation can occur only on mRNAs that are bi- or polycistronic. A genuinely bi-cistronic mRNA, containing two extensive ORFs, has recently been reported in *Drosophila* (Brogna & Ashburner 1997). However, it is not clear whether translation of the downstream ORF in this mRNA involves re-initiation or internal initiation (Brogna & Ashburner 1997). Regardless, this rare, functionally bi-cistronic eukaryotic mRNA is exceptional: uORFs are mostly short, a property that is generally thought to enhance re-initiation. After translation of a short uORF is complete, it is postulated that the 60S ribosome dissociates from the mRNA while the 40S ribosomal subunit resumes scanning. However, it remains to be directly determined which, if any, of the components of the translation initiation machinery remain associated with the mRNA after translation of short uORFs; at a minimum, a new ternary complex (Figure 2) must be acquired to allow re-initiation at downstream sites.

DISCONTINUOUS SCANNING OR HOPPING   A small number of viral mRNAs have been described containing structures within their 5'UTRs that are unfavorable to progression of scanning complexes but yet do not promote internal initiation (Fütterer et al 1993, Yeuh & Schneider 1996, Dominguez et al 1998). These mRNAs, exemplified by the cauliflower mosaic virus (CMV) 35S mRNA, are translated by a discontinuous scanning mechanism (Fütterer et al 1993). The pre-initiation complex begins scanning at the 5' end of the mRNA but by-passes this structure by hopping (also known as shunting and jumping). The mechanism of the hop is unclear, but requires specialized sequence elements (Fütterer et al 1993, Yeuh & Schneider 1996, Dominguez et al 1998, Hemmings-Mieszczak et al 1998).

Alternative Modes of Initiation

INTERNAL INITIATION   Internal initiation, sometimes referred to as cap-independent initiation, is mediated by a secondary structure within the 5'UTR known as an internal ribosome entry site (IRES) and was first discovered in picornaviruses (Jackson & Kaminski 1995). IRES-mediated translation does not require a free 5' end, as demonstrated by the translation of circular IRES-containing RNAs (Chen & Sarnow 1995). Viral IRESes can be divided into several functional groups based on their primary sequence and structure (Jackson & Kaminski 1995). IRESes can be functionally discriminated from other 5' UTR secondary structures by their ability to mediate translation of the downstream ORF of a bi-cistronic reporter mRNA, independent of the translational status of the first ORF (Jang et al 1988, Pelletier & Sonenberg 1988).

The majority of general initiation factors, including eIF-4F, appear to be required for IRES-mediated translation (reviewed in Jackson 1995). Exceptionally, the IRESes from hepatitis C and classical swine fever viruses appear to bind the small ribosomal subunit and position it properly at the AUG, without the need for initiation factors (Pestova et al 1998). This mechanism of initiation may be most analogous to prokaryotic translation, in that the IRES may be functionally equivalent to Shine-Dalgarno sequences (Pestova et al 1998). Translation from other IRESes requires additional *trans*-acting factors, such as polypyrimidine tract-binding protein (PTB) (Hellen et al 1993, Kaminski et al 1995) and the La autoantigen (Meerovitch et al 1993, Svitkin et al 1994a).

The function of some of these proteins may be to maintain the structure of the IRES in a favorable conformation (Svitkin et al 1994b, Kaminski et al 1995). Different cellular factors appear to be required to mediate internal initiation from the different viral classes (discussed in Jackson & Kaminski 1995).

Internal initiation allows picornaviruses, which do not possess a cap structure, to escape the shut down of host translation machinery that occurs during picornaviral infection. Translation of host mRNA is shut off, in part, by the cleavage of eIF-4G. The cleavage separates the eIF-4E binding domain of eIF-4G (in the N-terminal portion of the protein) from those that interact with eIF-4A and eIF-3, located nearer the C terminus (Lamphear et al 1995). This separates the cap-binding function of eIF-4G from its RNA-helicase and ribosome-binding activities and thus inactivates translation of most cellular mRNAs. However, the C-terminal fragment of eIF-4G can substitute for intact eIF-4G in IRES-mediated translation and in fact may be more efficient (Buckley & Ehrenfeld 1987, Liebig et al 1993, Ziegler et al 1995, Ohlmann et al 1996, Pestova et al 1996).

REGULATION VIA 5'UTRs

The majority of eukaryotic mRNAs have 5'UTRs of 20–100 nucleotides (Kozak 1987a). Shortening the 5'UTR of reporter mRNAs to less than 12 nucleotides impairs the efficiency of translation from the first AUG (Sedman et al 1990, Kozak 1991c). Increasing the length of a 5'UTR can increase the efficiency of translation, as additional 43S pre-initiation complexes can be loaded. This is sometimes described as pre-loading (Kozak 1991b). However, many cellular mRNAs with unusually long 5'UTRs are poorly translated owing to the presence of upstream AUGs, uORFs, and/or secondary structure (Kozak 1987a, 1991a; summarized in Figure 3). This appears to be especially common in mRNAs encoding proto-oncogenes, transcription factors, growth factors, and their receptors (Kozak 1987a, 1991a), which suggests that their translation is tightly controlled.

Short uORFs

MECHANISMS THAT ARE INDEPENDENT OF uORF PEPTIDE SEQUENCE   uORFs in the 5'UTR can modulate translation of the main ORF. Much of the current information about the function of uORFs has been obtained through elegant studies of the yeast *GCN4* mRNA, whose 5'UTR contains four short uORFs. These uORFs function together to regulate the translation of *GCN4* mRNA in response to amino acid starvation. This has been thoroughly reviewed elsewhere (Hinnebusch 1996).

In general, the first AUG encountered by a scanning ribosome is selected as the site of initiation (Kozak 1983, 1987a). uORFs and upstream AUGs can modulate initiation from the main ORF simply by exploiting this polarity. uORFs also provide a termination site before the main ORF, allowing a degree of re-initiation and thus are less inhibitory than uAUGs (Kozak 1984b, Liu et al 1984). The sequences of the uORF are typically unimportant.

Translation of the main ORF of uORF-containing mRNAs can occur by two mechanisms: leaky scanning and re-initiation. Factors that influence the efficiency of these processes determine the magnitude of inhibition. For example, uORFs with less efficient start sites are less inhibitory (e.g. Cao & Geballe 1994). Surprisingly, the frequency with which scanning is resumed can be modulated by the uORF stop codon and downstream sequences, at least in yeast (Miller & Hinnebusch 1989). The resumption of scanning may also be affected by the length of the uORF, although this has never been systematically tested. In addition, uORFs in close proximity to the main ORF are more inhibitory, possibly because insufficient time is available for a complete initiation complex to re-assemble (Kozak 1987b).

uORF PEPTIDES   In an expanding number of cases, the peptide encoded by a uORF contributes to translational inhibition of the downstream ORF. Translational control of S-adenosylmethionine decarboxylase (AdoMet) mRNA in response to polyamine levels is regulated in this manner. Translation of the AdoMet uORF is predicted to produce a hexapeptide, MAGDIS (Hill & Morris 1993). A number of mutations that alter the sequence of the peptide enhance translation of the main ORF, whereas those that preserve the peptide do not. Surprisingly, the uORF peptide does not inhibit translation in *trans*, leading to a model in which the nascent peptide stalls the ribosome, preventing or delaying termination (Hill & Morris 1993, Geballe & Morris 1994). A decrease in intracellular polyamine concentration may disrupt interactions between the peptide and translational machinery, allowing translation of the main ORF to proceed (Ruan et al 1996). However, the mechanisms of repression and de-repression have not been elucidated. Other examples of this regulatory strategy include yeast *CPA1* (Werner et al 1987, Delbecq et al 1994) and *Neurospora* arg-2 (Wang & Sachs 1997), mammalian β2 adrenergic receptor (Parola & Kobilka 1994), mouse retinoic acid receptor β2 mRNA (Reynolds et al 1996), and the human cytomegalovirus gp48 transcript (Schleiss et al 1991, Degnin et al 1993).

It is unclear how frequently the peptide sequences of uORFs are important because detailed mutational studies are required to differentiate between uORFs that produce inhibitory peptides and uORFs that function simply by providing upstream initiation and termination sites. Nor does the presence of uORFs in a 5′UTR necessarily indicate that they account for the inefficient translation of an mRNA. Human PDGF2 mRNA contains three uORFs (Rao et al 1988), but it is the presence of extensive secondary structure within its 5′UTR that causes its poor translation, at least under the conditions tested.

uORFs can occasionally have a stimulatory effect on translation, as in the case of the first of four uORFs in yeast GCN4 mRNA. uORF1 stimulates translation from the main ORF by decreasing the frequency of re-initiation from downstream uORFs (reviewed in Hinnebusch 1996). uORFs may also play a role in overcoming secondary structure by facilitating formation of 80S ribosomes upstream of the structured area and appear to enhance shunting on CMV 35S mRNA (Dominguez et al 1998).

Regulation via Selective Use of Alternative Initiation Sites

Many mRNAs contain AUGs within their 5′UTR that are not followed by in-frame stop codons prior to the start of the main ORF. Initiation at the downstream AUGs is the result of leaky scanning. Interestingly, several mRNAs produce full-length proteins from both upstream and downstream AUGs.

LIP (liver-enriched transcriptional inhibitor protein) and LAP (liver-enriched transcriptional activator protein) provide an elegant example of this type of translational control (Descombes & Schibler 1991). LAP is a transcriptional activator most abundant in liver. The mRNA that encodes LAP also gives rise to a shorter protein product, LIP, owing to leaky scanning at the LAP initiation codon. LIP does not contain the transcriptional activation domain and is therefore thought to impede the activity of LAP by occlusion of the promoter (Descombes & Schibler 1991). Interestingly, during postnatal development, a shift in the LAP/LIP ratio coincides with the function of LAP in terminal liver differentiation.

The use of leaky scanning to produce more than one protein from a single mRNA is not restricted to the use of alternative AUGs. For example, the mRNA encoding Int-2, an FGF related protein that functions in mouse embryonic development, uses both an initiator AUG and an upstream initiator CUG to synthesize an N-terminal extended protein (Acland et al 1990). The protein produced from the CUG is targeted to the nucleus while the AUG-initiated protein is shuttled through the endoplasmic reticulum and Golgi (Acland et al 1990). Other examples of this type of bifunctional mRNA exist including human bFGF (Florkiewicz & Sommer 1989, Prats et al 1989), murine *pim-1* (Saris et al 1991), *Drosophila oskar* (Markussen et al 1995), and human c-*myc* (Hann et al 1988, 1992).

The effects of uORFs and upstream AUGs can vary with cell type and during differentiation (e.g. Descombes & Schibler 1991, Lin et al 1993, Imataka et al 1994, Zimmer et al 1994). Regulation of initiation factor activity may play a role by influencing the recognition of AUGs and/or the rate of re-initiation. Indeed, preferential selection of cap-proximal, rather than subsequent AUGs, can be influenced by the phosphorylation state of initiation factor eIF-2 (Dasso et al 1990), as can the rate of reinitiation.

Secondary Structure

The inhibitory effect of introducing secondary structures into the 5'UTR depends on their stability and position and can be elicited by at least two mechanisms (Pelletier & Sonenberg 1985a, Kozak 1986a, 1998, 1989a). First, cap-proximal, moderately stable structures block the access of 43S pre-initiation complexes (Kozak 1989a) and initiation factors eIF-4A and eIF-4B to reporter mRNAs (Pelletier & Sonenberg 1985b, Lawson et al 1986). However, when the distance between the cap and the structure is sufficient to allow 43S entry, a moderately stable stem-loop is insufficient to inhibit translation (Kozak 1989a). The translational machinery appears to progress linearly through the stem-loop, rather than by hopping, since an AUG introduced into the distal side of the stem can be utilized as an initiation site (Kozak 1986a).

Second, insertion of a more stable stem-loop structure ($-50/61$ kcal/mol) blocks translation even when located downstream of the cap (Kozak 1986a, 1989b). RNAse protection experiments identified a stalled 43S pre-initiation complex 5' to the inhibitory structure, suggesting that the stem-loop was an impenetrable barrier to the migration of this complex (Kozak 1989a).

As implied by these examples using artificial mRNAs, secondary structure in the 5'UTR can also regulate cellular mRNAs. Ornithine decarboxylase (ODC) is involved in the synthesis of polyamines required for cell proliferation. Translation of its mRNA is normally inefficient but can be stimulated by growth factors and mitogens such as insulin. An approximately 140 nucleotide region close to the cap of rat and hamster ODC mRNAs is responsible for its inefficient translation (Grens & Scheffler 1990, Manzella & Blackshear 1990). This G-C–rich region forms an inhibitory secondary structure and does not appear to be a protein-binding site because inverting the region does not diminish repression (Grens & Scheffler 1990). Interestingly, the translation of ODC mRNA in renal tissues of two murine species, *Mus domesticus* and *Mus pahari*, differs significantly (Johannes & Berger 1992) and may be caused by small differences in their 5'UTRs that alter their predicted structures. Because the translation of reporter mRNAs with 5' secondary structure is increased in response to eIF-4E overexpression (Koromilas et al 1992a), it is possible that the stimulation of ODC mRNA translation by mitogens is achieved through elevated eIF-4E activity. Consistent with this, eIF-4E (and eIF-4B) are phosphorylated in response to insulin (Manzella et al 1991), and overexpression of eIF-4E increases ODC translation (Shantz & Pegg 1994). Other well-characterized examples of mRNAs that are regulated through secondary structure include human PDGF2 mRNA (Rao et al 1988).

In experimentally manipulated mRNAs, secondary structure can also increase the use of a particular initiation site when located downstream of that site. This effect requires the presence of an inefficient initiation site, due to either a poor context, a non-AUG initiator, or a very short 5'UTR (Kozak 1989b, 1990, 1991c). The optimal placement for the structure is 14 nucleotides downstream from the initiation codon, which corresponds well with the distance between the leading edge of the ribosome and the initiation codon, as measured by RNAse protection (Kozak 1990). Thus it seems that the structure pauses the 43S pre-initiation complex at or near the initiation codon, presumably allowing more time for its recognition (Kozak 1990). The resulting 80S ribosome is not impeded by the secondary structure and initiates elongation.

RNA-Protein Interactions

Proteins can regulate translation by interacting with target sequences within the 5' UTR. The best characterized of these is iron regulatory protein (IRP)-mediated regulation, first identified in mammalian cells. IRP-1 and IRP-2 regulate the translation of a number of mRNAs, including ferritin (reviewed in Hentze & Kuhn 1996), erythroid 5-aminolevulinate synthase (eALAS) (Cox et al 1991, Dandekar et al 1991, Bhasker et al 1993, Melefors et al 1993), mitochondrial aconitase (Gray et al 1996, Schalinske et al 1998), and succinate dehydrogenase-iron protein (Kohler et al 1995, Gray et al 1996, Melefors 1996), in response to a number of physiological stimuli. The binding site for IRP, the iron responsive element (IRE) (Aziz & Munro 1987, Hentze et al 1987), is generally located close to the 5' cap in these messages. In transfection studies, when the IRE is moved to a more cap-distal position, IRP-mediated regulation is diminished; this is described as the position effect (Goossen et al 1990, Goossen & Hentze 1992). This suggests that IRP may prevent a relatively early mRNA-dependent step in translational initiation. Indeed, binding of the 43S pre-initiation complex is prevented by the presence of IRP-1 (Figure 2, step 3b; Gray & Hentze 1994a). Moving the IRE to a more cap-distal position allows free access to this complex: Residual regulation by cap-distal IRE/IRP complexes results from their ability to pause scanning (Figure 2, step 4; E Paraskeva, NK Gray, B Schlaeger, K Wehr, MW Hentze, submitted). These stalled scanning complexes appear to overcome cap-distal IRE/IRP complexes by active displacement of IRP-1, rather than by hopping or waiting for passive dissociation of IRP (E Paraskeva, NK Gray, B Schlaeger, K Wehr, MW Hentze, submitted). It remains to be determined whether displacement of cap-distal regulatory proteins is achieved by a novel protein-removal activity or via disruption of protein binding sites, which tend to be structured, by RNA helicases. Interestingly, reporter mRNAs in yeast and plants, which do not contain endogenous IRP, are equally repressed by cap-distal and cap-proximal IREs (Koloteva et al 1997; E Paraskeva, NK Gray, B Schlaeger, K Wehr, MW Hentze, submitted).

Although IRP-1 prevents the association of the 43S complex with the mRNA, previous mRNA-dependent steps in initiation (Figure 2, step 3a) can occur

(Muckenthaler et al 1998). Thus the cap-binding complex is present on IRP-1–repressed mRNAs. The function of this complex may be to stabilize the mRNA by preventing decapping or to allow rapid translation once cellular conditions change.

Interestingly, IREs can be replaced by binding sites for proteins such as U1A or MS2 coat protein that have no function in eukaryotic translation (Stripecke & Hentze 1992, Stripecke et al 1994). Translational repression by at least one of these proteins occurs by the same mechanism as IRP-1 and displays a position effect (Stripecke & Hentze 1992, Gray & Hentze 1994a). These findings establish that the presence of an RNA-protein complex in the 5′ untranslated region of mRNAs can modulate both ribosomal subunit entry and migration, depending on the position of the complex (Gray & Hentze 1994a; E Paraskeva, NK Gray, B Schlaeger, K Wehr, MW Hentze, submitted). Species vary in whether they are more strongly inhibited by cap-proximal or cap-distal RNA/protein complexes. Thus some species (e.g. yeast and wheat germ) can strongly repress translation via RNA/protein complexes located at various positions in the 5′ UTR; others (e.g. mammalian cells) can modulate the degree of repression by altering the position of the complex.

The number of mRNAs for which good evidence for the involvement of 5′UTR-bound repressor proteins exists is surprisingly small (reviewed by Gray & Hentze 1994b). It includes Mst87F and related genes in *Drosophila* spermatogenesis (Schäfer et al 1990, Kempe et al 1993), mouse superoxide dismutase mRNA (Gu & Hecht 1996), and the autoregulation of poly(A) binding protein mRNA (de Melo Neto et al 1995). Proteins also have been implicated in the 5′UTR-mediated control of TOP mRNAs (see *Ribosomal Protein S6*).

Internal Initiation of Cellular mRNAs

Certain cellular mRNAs possess IRES elements, as defined by bi-cistronic assays (Jang et al 1988, Pelletier & Sonenberg 1988). IRESes in cellular mRNAs appear similar but less complex than those of viruses, consisting of as little as 55 nucleotides (OH & Sarnow 1993). The specialized *trans*-acting factors involved in cellular IRES-mediated translation may differ from those utilized by their viral counterparts (Vagner et al 1996, Yang & Sarnow 1997).

From the biological standpoint, IRES-mediated translation of cellular mRNAs provides a simple way to allow translation of a specific mRNA in circumstances in which the cap-dependent mechanism is impaired. The rich potential of such a regulatory device has been realized in several biological contexts with mRNAs that include human immunoglobulin heavy-chain-binding protein (BiP) (Macejak & Sarnow 1991), human IGF-II (Teerink et al 1995), human FGF-2 (Vagner et al 1995), human PDGF2 (Bernstein et al 1997), *Drosophila antennapedia* (OH et al 1992, OH & Sarnow 1993), and the proto-oncogene c-*myc* (Stoneley et al 1998).

Platelet-derived growth factor-2 (PDGF2/c-*sis*) mRNA is exemplary. It encodes one of two proteins that form PDGF, a powerful mitogen, important in wound healing, embryogenesis, and development. Its role in wound healing involves its expression in bone marrow. Prior to megakaryocytic differentiation, PDGF2 translation is thought to be repressed by extensive secondary structure. Differentiation appears to activate IRES-mediated translation of PDGF2 mRNA, circumventing the impediment to cap-dependent initiation (Bernstein et al 1995, 1997). Thus several features of the mRNA act in concert to achieve its correct expression.

5' UTRs: Problems and Perspectives

In light of the diversity of mechanisms through which 5'UTRs can modulate translation, it is difficult to predict the biological effects of a 5'UTR if one is armed with only its sequence. The presence of a long 5'UTR seems to be good a priori evidence that some form of control lies within it.

Yet many mRNAs, particularly those that encode growth regulators and transcription factors, seem to have adopted 5'UTR regulation in excess and appear not very different from the absurdly crowded mRNA depicted in Figure 3. They have long 5'UTRs, laden with potential structure and upstream AUGs. The speculation that these multiple control elements allow complex responses to different cellular requirements, permit regulation among cell types, or modulate translation during differentiation is appealing. This complex responsiveness appears to be true for PDGF2 mRNA. Multiple transcription start sites and alternative splicing patterns offer yet more versatility: They can enhance, reduce, or eliminate the effect of a regulatory element by altering its position with respect to the cap or the initiation codon, or by eliminating it altogether.

From one perspective, the pressing questions of 5'UTR-mediated and 3'UTR-mediated control are at present mirror images. In the 5'UTR, our understanding of the mechanisms of regulation and their diversity is relatively advanced, although key mechanistic questions remain. Another priority is to uncover how the mechanisms revealed by studying reporter mRNAs are exploited to control specific cellular mRNAs, with interpretable physiological consequences. To date, this has been achieved with only a modest number of mRNAs, some of which we have chosen as examples. It may ultimately be necessary to analyze the expression of genes bearing manipulated 5'UTRs in a variety of physiological circumstances, and perhaps ideally, in transgenic animals. If the correlation between long 5'UTRs and growth regulators is any indication, it seems inescapable that a wealth of biological information embedded in the 5'UTR will emerge from such analyses. For 3'UTRs, biological significance often is demonstrable; it is molecular mechanisms that are elusive.

REGULATION BY 3'UTRS

Surprisingly, many mRNAs are translationally controlled via sequences in their 3'UTR (Figure 3; reviewed in Sonenberg 1994, Curtis et al 1995, Macdonald & Smibert 1996, Wickens et al 1996). The challenges of understanding how such elements work are intimately linked to understanding the role of poly(A) in translation. In part, this is because both reside far from the cap and initiation codon: Action at an apparent distance raises questions of how both 3'UTR- or poly(A)-bound factors communicate with the initiation apparatus, and with the 5' end of the mRNA.

Yet the link between 3'UTRs and poly(A) is more intimate than this apparent spatial problem. During early development, specific mRNAs undergo changes in poly(A) tail length that are often accompanied by changes in translational activity: increases in poly(A) length generally correlate with increases in translation, and decreases correlate with repression (Richter 1996, Wickens et al 1997). Moreover, sequences in the 3'UTR identified genetically by their effects on translation often also govern poly(A) length, e.g. elimination of a negative regulatory element may cause both translational activation and a longer poly(A) tail. Similarly, elements identified through their effects on poly(A) length can also regulate translation. Although most of the relevant studies have been performed in oocytes and embryos, the same phenomena exist in somatic cells.

For simplicity, we have divided our consideration of 3'UTRs and poly(A) into two separate sections, followed by a single speculative discussion of how they may exert their effects.

Regulatory Elements and Cascades

Developmental genetics in *Drosophila* (Figure 1) and *C. elegans* has revealed cascades of 3' UTR-based translational control. In *C. elegans*, the first concerns the determination of cell fate and patterning in its germ line (reviewed in Puoti et al 1997). *C. elegans* hermaphrodites produce sperm first and then switch to producing oocytes. The *tra-2* gene is required for the female phase of development, including oogenesis, whereas the *fem-3* gene is required to promote male development, including spermatogenesis. Early in gametogenesis, *tra-2* must be repressed to make sperm, and later *fem-3* must be repressed to make oocytes. Regulation of both of these mRNAs is achieved through their 3'UTRs; however, although *fem-3* is post-transcriptionally regulated, it has not been conclusively shown to be at the level of translation.

A second cascade of 3'UTR-mediated translational controls in *C. elegans* contributes to cell fate determination in the early embryo (Schnabel & Priess 1997). *glp-1* mRNA encodes a transmembrane receptor required to specify anterior cell fates. Although its mRNA is uniformly distributed in the early embryo, it is translated in only presumptive anterior blastomeres beginning at the 2-cell stage (Evans et al 1994). Reciprocally, *pal-1* mRNA is translated only in posterior blastomeres (Hunter & Kenyon 1997); its repression in anterior cells may require *mex-3*, a putative RNA-binding protein (Draper et al 1996). The cascade of spatial and temporal control likely encompasses several other mRNAs that play key roles in cell fate decisions, including *skn-1*, *pie-1*, and *apx-1*, each of which produces maternal mRNAs that are distributed throughout the early embryo but translated only in specific blastomeres (Schnabel & Priess 1997).

Positive Elements that Enhance Translation of Uncapped mRNA

The role of positive elements in translational control is emphasized by work with certain plant viruses in which the 3'UTR enhances translation. Several of these elements can also function in animal cells (Gallie & Walbot 1990, Hann et al 1997). Often, an interaction between the 3' and 5'UTR is required (Gallie & Walbot 1990, Danthinne et al 1993, Timmer et al 1993, Wang & Miller 1995). For example, an element in the 3'UTR of the barley yellow dwarf virus (BYDV-PAV) genome can act when separated from the stimulated AUG by several ORFs and kilobases of sequence; in this situation, stimulation requires the presence of the natural 5'UTR (Wang & Miller 1995, Wang et al 1997). When placed at the 5' end of the mRNA, the element can function on its own (Wang et al 1997). This suggests that the natural 5' UTR is required to mediate long-range interactions (Wang et al 1997). Such interactions may be mediated by base-pairing or, potentially, by protein-protein interactions.

These positive elements are often suggested to be the functional equivalents of the cap or poly(A) tail in cognito and may bind basal initiation factors. A poly(A) tail can functionally replace a positive element in the 3'UTR of tobacco mosaic virus (Gallie & Walbot 1990), whereas a cap can substitute for the elements in BYDV-PAV and satellite tobacco necrosis virus (STNV) (Timmer et al 1993, Wang & Miller 1995). Moreover, addition of eIF-4F can overcome translational inhibition by excess BYDV-PAV element in *trans* (Wang et al 1997) and is also implicated in the enhancement by the STNV element (Timmer et al 1993). However they act, these positive elements emphasize the diversity of modes through which 3'UTRs can modulate translation.

Regulatory Proteins: Negative and Positive Factors

Relatively few of the cognate repressors that bind to repressive elements in the 3'UTR have been identified. In part, this may be due to the involvement of multiprotein complexes and to the fact that the proteins providing the RNA-binding activity do not necessarily directly affect repression.

The control of *Drosophila hunchback*, which encodes a transcription factor, exemplifies this situation (reviewed by St Johnston & Nüsslein-Volhard 1992,

Wharton 1992, Curtis et al 1995, Macdonald & Smibert 1996). *hunchback* mRNA, which is present throughout the early syncitial embryo (Tautz & Pfeifle 1989), is initially repressed by Nanos protein in the posterior, where it is later degraded. Nanos-dependent repression is mediated via nanos response elements (NREs) in the 3′UTR (Wharton & Struhl 1991). Yet Nanos does not specifically bind to the NREs (Curtis et al 1997). Rather, another protein, Pumilio, does so: Pumilio is not localized nor does its mere presence lead to repression (Murata & Wharton 1995). In one simple model, Pumilio binds to NREs throughout the embryo and Nanos, which is restricted to the posterior, either binds to or modifies the Pumilio/*hunchback* mRNA complex. Additional proteins may also be needed, as no direct interaction between Nanos and Pumilio has been demonstrated. Interestingly, FBF, recently identified as a factor required for repression of *C. elegans fem-3* mRNA, shares sequence similarity with *Drosophila* Pumilio (Zhang et al 1997). Moreover, like Pumilio, FBF represses by binding to a site within the 3′UTR and causes a switch in cells fates.

Regulation of 15-lipoxygenase (LOX) mRNA via its 3′UTR involves more than one protein but differs conspicuously from regulation of *hunchback* mRNA. The LOX enzyme participates in internal membrane breakdown during the later stages of reticulocyte maturation (Rapoport & Schewe 1986). Its mRNA is controlled via CU-rich sequences known as DICE within its 3′UTR (Ostareck-Lederer et al 1994). Although rabbit LOX mRNA contains ten tandem repeats, two are sufficient for repression (Ostareck et al 1997). A complex of two proteins, hnRNP K and hnRNP E1 (αCP-1), interact with each DICE to mediate repression (Ostareck et al 1997). In contrast to Nanos, both proteins have specific DICE-binding activity and can repress translation in vitro to a lesser degree alone (Ostareck et al 1997). Additional components of this complex, if any, must be neither tissue nor species specific (Ostareck et al 1997).

Translational repression of *tra-2* in *C. elegans* requires GLD-1 protein, which binds specifically to the regulatory elements in the mRNA's 3′ UTR (E Jan et al, submitted). GLD-1 is necessary for repression in vivo and sufficient for repression in a cell-free yeast extract. GLD-1 is a member of the STAR subfamily of KH-domain RNA-binding proteins (Jones & Schedl 1995, Vernet & Artzt 1997). Other members of this subfamily may also be translational repressors (E Jan et al, submitted).

Regulation via 3′UTRs involves not only repressors but activators. In *Drosophila*, many of the proteins required to activate mRNA expression act indirectly through their role in mRNA localization. These include gene products that affect cytoskeletal organization and function (e.g. *cappuccino* and *spire*) (Ephrussi et al 1991, Kim-Ha et al 1991, Theurkauf 1994), as well as proteins that interact with specific mRNAs (e.g. Staufen) (St Johnston et al 1991). Staufen appears to contribute to the expression of *oskar* mRNA by establishing and maintaining its localization and is a double-stranded RNA-binding protein (St Johnston et al

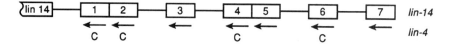

Figure 4   Regulation of *lin-14* mRNA by *lin-4*. The 3′UTR of *lin-14* mRNA is depicted. Seven sequence elements within the 3′UTR have the capacity to form anti-sense duplexes with *lin-4* RNA. The elements predicted to form duplexes with a bulged C residue are indicted by the letter C.

1992). Vasa protein (Hay et al 1988, Lasko & Ashburner 1988) is also required for complete activation of *oskar* mRNA translation (Rongo et al 1995) through an unknown mechanism. However, since it is an ATP-dependent RNA helicase, unwinding of an RNA structure may be important (Liang et al 1994).

Proteins that promote cytoplasmic polyadenylation of specific mRNAs constitute another group of positive-acting factors in translational control. These are discussed in the context of changes in poly(A) length.

RNAs as Regulators

3′UTR repressors can be RNA, as well as protein (see Figures 3 and 4). *lin-14* is required for the proper timing of a range of developmental events in *C. elegans* (Ambros & Horvitz 1987). Temporal repression of *lin-14* requires sequences in its 3′UTR, and the *lin-4* gene product (Wightman et al 1991, 1993; Lee et al 1993). Repression likely involves regulation of translation, although effects on mRNA transport have not been eliminated. Surprisingly, *lin-4* encodes two short mRNAs of 22 and 61 nucleotides, not a protein (Lee et al 1993). *lin-4* RNA can potentially base-pair with seven sequence elements of 14–19 nucleotides within the *lin-14* 3′UTR, prompting the proposal that *lin-4/lin-14* RNA duplexes cause translational repression (Lee et al 1993, Wightman et al 1993) (Figure 4). Four of the predicted duplexes contain a bulged C residue, whereas the other three do not. The bulged C appears to be critical for repression: Only those reporter mRNAs containing multiple copies of the elements that form putative bulged C duplexes were subject to *lin-4* regulation, and the bulged C could not be substituted by another nucleotide (Ha et al 1996). It appears likely that the bulged duplexes may bind an as yet unidentified repressor protein (Ha et al 1996). *lin-28*, another gene that regulates timing of developmental decisions, is also controlled by *lin-4* and contains only a single sequence complementary to *lin-4* in its 3′UTR that does not form the bulged duplex (Moss et al 1997).

POLY(A)

The effects of poly(A) on translation have two distinct facets. First, the mere presence of a poly(A) tail can stimulate translation, as demonstrated by comparing the translation of reporter mRNAs with and without a poly(A) tail. The magnitude of the effects varies between assay systems but is very substantial in yeast extracts (Iizuka et al 1994), electroporated cells (Gallie 1991), and oocytes and embryos (e.g. Sheets et al 1994).

A second facet of poly(A)'s effects on translation concerns regulated changes in the length of poly(A) on specific mRNAs (Richter 1996, Wickens et al 1997). For example, c-*mos* mRNA receives poly(A) in the cytoplasm as its translation increases (Sheets et al 1994). However, such mRNAs typically have respectably long poly(A) tails when they are repressed, longer than would be required to enhance translation when appended to a reporter mRNA (Richter 1996, Wickens et al 1997). This apparent contradiction emphasizes the importance of dissecting the mechanism by which regulated changes in poly(A) length regulate translation and raises the possibility that the mechanism may differ from that observed by comparing mRNAs with and without poly(A).

Cytoplasmic Poly(A) Addition and Removal

mRNAs initially receive poly(A) tails of approximately 250 nucleotides in the nucleus of vertebrate cells. Upon entering the cytoplasm, poly(A) is slowly removed in most cells. Abrupt changes in poly(A) length can occur at specific times and have been extensively characterized during oocyte maturation and early development in frogs and mice (Richter 1996, Wickens et al 1996). During oocyte maturation, frog and mouse oocytes advance from first to second meiosis and can then be fertilized. During maturation, specific mRNAs gain poly(A) in the cytoplasm and become active or lose poly(A) and become inactive. Other mRNAs undergo these reactions after fertilization. The apparatus that adds poly(A) appears to be quiescent during oogenesis, and becomes active in *Xenopus* at the onset of maturation. The mechanism of its activation is unclear.

Signals that control poly(A) length during oocyte maturation and after fertilization have been identified in frogs and mice (Richter 1996, Wickens et al 1996). These signals are bipartite and lie within the 3'UTR: They are AAUAAA, a highly conserved sequence that is required for nuclear polyadenylation and present in every mRNA, and a separate sequence that is typically U-rich. Because the U-rich sequence distinguishes those mRNAs that receive poly(A) from those that do not, it has been termed a cytoplasmic polyadenylation element (CPE) or an adenylation control element (ACE). The precise sequence of the CPE can control both the timing and extent of polyadenylation, determining, for example, whether the mRNA will receive poly(A) early or late in maturation or 50 versus 300 adenosine monophosphates (e.g. Simon et al 1992, Sheets et al 1994). Insertion of a CPE into the 3'UTR of a reporter mRNA is sufficient to cause both polyadenylation and translational stimulation during oocyte maturation or early development (Fox et al 1989, McGrew et al 1989, Huarte et al 1992).

Changes in Poly(A) Tail Length and Translation

CHANGES IN POLY(A) TAIL LENGTH AS A CAUSE OF TRANSLATIONAL CONTROL Cytoplasmic polyadenylation has been shown to be required for the translational activation of a number of mRNAs. In *Drosophila*, translational activation of *bicoid* mRNA is required for the determination of anterior structures in the embryo and is accompanied by polyadenylation. Injection of wild-type *bicoid* mRNA but not a mutant mRNA, which lacks polyadenylation signals, can rescue the lethal phenotype of a *bicoid* mutant embryo (Salles et al 1994). A mutant mRNA that lacks the polyadenylation signals but has an artificial poly(A) tail also rescued (Salles et al 1994), strongly suggesting that *bicoid* polyadenylation is critical to its translational activation and hence pattern formation. Similarly, the over-expression phenotype of injected *Xenopus* activin receptor mRNA requires its polyadenylation (Simon et al 1996).

The role of polyadenylation in translation activation has also been examined in *Xenopus* by manipulating an endogenous mRNA, c-*mos*. It encodes a serine-threonine kinase and is required for the resumption of meiosis and initiation of oocyte maturation (Gebauer & Richter 1997, Sagata 1997). Removal of the polyadenylation signals from endogenous c-*mos* mRNA by targeted RNAse H cleavage blocks its translational activation and oocyte maturation (Sheets et al 1995). c-*mos* translation and maturation can be rescued by the use of prosthetic mRNAs, which bind to sequences in the truncated 3′ UTR and contain polyadenylation signals (Sheets et al 1995) or a long synthetic poly(A) tail (Barkoff et al 1998). Thus polyadenylation is critical for the translation of c-*mos* and maturation of *Xenopus* oocytes. Similarly, polyadenylation of c-*mos* mRNA in the mouse is required for its translational activation (Gebauer et al 1994).

While cytoplasmic polyadenylation can activate translation, so can regulated decreases in poly(A) length cause repression. For example, in *Drosophila*, translational repression of *hunchback* mRNA by Nanos and Pumilio involves rapid deadenylation mediated by regulatory elements in the *hunchback* 3′UTR (Wreden et al 1997). In mice, mutations in the CPE (or ACE) of mouse tPA mRNA cause a failure to remove the poly(A) tail when the mRNA emerges from the nucleus and prevent silencing of the mRNA prior to meiotic maturation (Huarte et al 1992). In *Xenopus*, overexpression of poly(A) binding-protein, the main protein bound to cytoplasmic poly(A) tails, prevents deadenylation and silencing of mRNAs that normally would undergo such regulation during maturation, strongly suggesting that removal of the tail is required for repression (Wormington et al 1996).

Changes in polyadenylation may also play a role in the regulation of some mRNAs controlled via their 5'UTRs. For example, the mRNAs encoded by Mst87F and related genes in *Drosophila* undergo polyadenylation when they are activated during spermatogenesis (Kuhn et al 1991). It remains to be determined whether these poly(A) tail length changes are casual in the translational activation of these mRNAs.

CHANGES IN POLY(A) TAIL LENGTH AS AN EFFECT OF TRANSLATIONAL CONTROL Studies of 5'UTR-mediated repression in somatic cells have revealed that deadenylation can also be a consequence of translational control, rather than a cause. IRP-mediated repression can cause partial deadenylation in mammalian somatic cells (Muckenthaler et al 1997), as can repression by proteins targeted to the 5'UTR that do not normally function in eukaryotic translational control. Deadenylation can also be caused by translational inhibitors that promote ribosomal release but not by those that maintain the mRNA on polyribosomes. Since IRP-mediated repression prevents ribosomal association (Gray & Hentze 1994a), and because changes in polyadenylation are not essential to this repression either in vitro (Walden et al 1988, Brown et al 1989, Gray et al 1993) or for one of the two forms of ferritin mRNA in cells (Muckenthaler et al 1997), deadenylation appears to be a consequence, rather than a cause, of the release of repressed mRNAs from ribosomes (Muckenthaler et al 1997). However, the absence of measurable poly(A) shortening of one form of ferritin mRNA raises the possibility that deadenylation is not an inevitable consequence of repression.

CHANGES IN POLY(A) TAIL LENGTH UNCOUPLED FROM TRANSLATIONAL CONTROL   Translational activation of clam ribonucleotide reductase in vitro is not accompanied by changes in polyadenylation (Standart et al 1990). This suggests that the polyadenylation of this mRNA observed during its activation following fertilization in *Spisula solidissima* may not be causal to its activation. Similarly, in *Xenopus*, translation of FGF receptor mRNA can be activated even in circumstances in which its normal extensive polyadenylation does not occur (Culp & Musci 1998).

CONTROLS THAT ARE INDEPENDENT OF CHANGES IN POLY(A) TAIL LENGTH Changes in poly(A) tail length are not an inevitable corollary of 3'UTR-mediated translational control. For example, in the *Drosophila* embryo, poly(A) tail changes accompany the regulation of *toll*, *torso*, *hunchback*, and *bicoid* mRNAs, but not the activation of *nanos* and *oskar* mRNAs (Salles et al 1994, Webster et al 1997, Wreden et al 1997). Furthermore, *nanos* mRNA activation is unimpaired in *cortex* and *grauzone* mutant embryos, which are defective in polyadenylation and activation of *bicoid* mRNA (Lieberfarb et al 1996). Repression of LOX mRNA in somatic cells can be reconstituted in cell-free systems using non-adenylated mRNAs (Ostareck-Lederer et al 1994). However the poly(A) status of LOX mRNA has not been examined in cells.

In summary, while changes in poly(A) tail length can cause changes in translational activity, as in the case of *bicoid* and c-*mos*, it is also clear that changes in poly(A) tail length can be secondary effects of repression. In some cases, changes in poly(A) tail length may sustain the change in translational activity achieved by independent mechanisms, including relief of sequence-specific repression (reviewed by Standart & Jackson 1994, Wickens et al 1996). For example, de-repression may be perpetuated or enhanced by elongation of the poly(A) tail.

Variations in the Magnitude of Poly(A) Stimulation

The magnitude of translational stimulation of mRNAs that are activated in a poly(A)-dependent manner varies. This may relate in part to their basal translational efficiency, such that mRNAs which are inefficiently translated may be stimulated the most. The relief of repression of regulated mRNAs may be accompanied by polyadenylation, both effects stimulating translation independently or coordinately.

The effects of poly(A) during development may be especially profound owing to strong competition between mRNAs for the translational machinery, as exists in *Xenopus* oocytes (Laskey et al 1977). This is supported by studies showing that the effects of poly(A) are greatest under competitive conditions (Proweller & Butler 1994, 1997; Preiss & Hentze 1998). Competition, and hence the effects of poly(A), may also be modulated by modification of the translational apparatus.

Poly(A) Length Changes in Somatic Cells

As alluded to above, changes in poly(A) length also occur in somatic cells, although in most cases it is unclear whether these are a consequence of the modifications that occur in the cytoplasm. Examples include human and rat growth hormone mRNA (Paek & Axel 1987, Jones et al 1990, Murphy et al 1992) and rat insulin mRNA (Muschel et al 1986). Poly(A) tail length changes have also be observed when the translation of *Chlamydomonas* α-tubulin is perturbed (Baker et al 1989), or when β-interferon-expressing cells are infected with Sendai virus (Dehlin et al 1996). Heat shock causes a dramatic increase in the proportion of poly(A)-deficient mRNAs in *Drosophila* (Spradling et al 1975, Storti et al 1980). Although these examples are consistent with direct effects of poly(A) on translation in somatic cells, they should interpreted with caution. For example, the change in the length of an mRNA's poly(A) tail can be an effect rather than a cause of translational control (Muckenthaler et al 1997). Future work examining the polyadenylation of specific somatic mRNAs in detail, including the identification of their repressors and activators, will be needed to clarify the issue.

End-to-End Interactions and the Role of Poly(A) Binding Protein

The finding that poly(A) and 3'UTRs can affect initiation suggests that the two ends of the mRNA may interact or be in close proximity (Jacobson 1996). Consistent with this view, electron micrographs show polysomes with nearby 5' and 3' ends (e.g. Christensen et al 1987), and the translational effects of the cap structure and poly(A) tails are synergistic rather than additive (e.g. Gallie 1991). The finding that loss of poly(A) triggers enzymatic cleavage of the cap in vivo also provides strong circumstantial evidence for an end-to-end interaction (Muhlrad et al 1994).

In spite of apparent 5'-3' interactions, the poly(A) tail can also stimulate translation of uncapped reporter mRNAs (e.g. Munroe & Jacobson 1990, Gallie 1991, Iizuka et al 1994). It is unclear how to interpret these effects in terms of cellular capped mRNAs. Recent studies underline the importance of a cap in poly(A)-mediated stimulation: The cap tethers the stimulatory effect of the poly(A) tail to the 5' end of the mRNA and prevents spurious initiation at downstream initiator codons (Preiss & Hentze 1998).

One likely participant in poly(A)'s effects is poly(A)-binding protein (PAB), the most abundant protein associated with cytoplasmic poly(A) tails. A single molecule of PAB requires 10–12 nucleotides to bind tightly (Sachs et al 1987) and occupies roughly 25 adenosine monophosphates, such that multiple PAB molecules can reside on a single poly(A) tail (Baer & Kornberg 1983). The gene encoding PAB, *pab-1*, is essential for viability in yeast (Sachs et al 1987).

Two different models have been proposed for the mechanism by which PAB enhances translation. The first proposes that poly(A)/PAB complexes increase the efficiency of 60S subunit joining (step 5b in Figure 2). Consistent with this hypothesis, a number of mutations in yeast that increase the 40S/60S ribosomal subunit ratio (Sachs & Davis 1989, 1990) suppress the lethality of PAB deletions. Additionally, poly(A) mildly stimulates the formation of 80S ribosomes on mRNAs bound by 40S ribosomal subunits in a rabbit reticulocyte lysate (Munroe & Jacobson 1990). The second model has been derived from experiments conducted in a poly(A)-dependent yeast cell-free translation system. In this model, 40S ribosomal subunit joining is stimulated by the PAB/poly(A) tail complex (step 3b in Figure 2; Tarun & Sachs 1995). However, the inhibitory effect of PAB immunodepletion in this system on translation and ribosomal association of capped-and-polyadenylated mRNAs varies and can be modest. The two models are not mutually exclusive, and poly(A)/PAB may stimulate both events.

THE EIF-4G CONNECTION   Recently, it was proposed that the stimulation of small subunit joining in *S. cerevisiae* is facilitated by an interaction between PAB and yeast eIF-4G (Tarun & Sachs 1996, Tarun et al 1997). Since eIF-4G is associated with eIF-4E, this could bring the two ends of the mRNA together (Figure 5*A*). An interaction between eIF-iso4G and PAB has also been detected in wheat germ extracts (Le et al 1997, Wei et al 1998). The yeast eIF-4G/PAB interaction in vitro is RNA dependent, a finding that could reflect a need for a PAB/poly(A) complex for eIF-4G interactions. (Tarun & Sachs 1996, Tarun et al 1997). However, point mutations in the site in eIF-4G required for this RNA-dependent interaction do not significantly affect the translation of capped, or capped-and-polyadenylated, mRNAs, nor lead to a loss of synergistic translation in vitro, nor

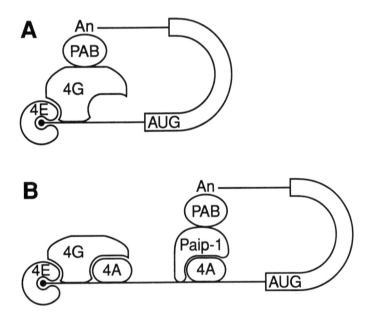

Figure 5   Models for 5′-3′ interactions mediated by PAB. *A*. The direct interaction between the PAB and eIF-4G mediates an indirect interaction between the cap-binding complex and the poly(A) tail. Although this model depicts PAB interacting through the 4E component of the cap-associated eIF-4F, point mutations that disrupt PAB-eIF-4G interactions in vitro do not strongly affect translation of capped mRNAs (see text). A similar interaction has been proposed based on experiments in wheat germ extract. In both yeast and plants, eIF-4F contains only eIF-4E and eIF-4G when isolated. The positions of eIF-4A and eIF-4B are not indicated. Figure adapted from Sachs & Buratowski (1997). *B*. The interaction of Paip-1 with eIF-4A and PAB forms a bridging interaction between the 5′ and 3′ ends of the mRNA. This interaction does not include the cap-binding complex. The position of eIF-4B is not indicated. Figure adapted from Craig et al (1998). Both models predict that the interactions depicted lead to a stimulation of small ribosomal recruitment; the small ribosomal subunit is not depicted.

to inviability in vivo (Tarun & Sachs 1996, Tarun et al 1997). Thus although interactions mediated by this site in eIF-4G contribute to the translation of uncapped-polyadenylated mRNAs, they are not required for protein synthesis in the cell under standard laboratory conditions (Tarun et al 1997).

AN ALTERNATIVE ROUTE: PAIP-1   In mammalian cells, a PAB-interacting protein (Paip-1), with some homology to eIF-4G, has been identified (Craig et al 1998). It mildly stimulates both cap-dependent and IRES-mediated translation in transfected COS cells. Unlike eIF-4G, Paip-1 does not contain a eIF-4E-binding site, but has homology through the region that contains eIF-3 and eIF-4A binding sites. However, no interaction with eIF-3 has been detected, suggesting that Paip-1 may not directly link PAB with the 40S ribosomal subunit, as suggested in the model depicted for yeast in Figure 5A. Paip-1 does interact with eIF-4A, and this could link the two ends of the mRNA (Figure 5B). Several lines of evidence suggest that eIF-4A cycles in and out of eIF-4F complexes. This is proposed to facilitate the delivery of multiple molecules of eIF-4A to the mRNA, which migrate through the 5'UTR to achieve unwinding (Pause et al 1994b). Paip-1 may interact with free eIF-4A rather than with eIF-4A as part of the eIF-4F complex (Craig et al 1998). Despite the lack of a direct interaction with the small ribosomal subunit, Paip-1/eIF-4A interactions are proposed to cause more efficient recruitment or reinitiation of small ribosomal subunits (Craig et al 1998).

POSSIBLE MEDIATORS OF POLY(A)-STIMULATED TRANSLATION IN EARLY DEVELOPMENT   In oocytes and embryos, where the effect of poly(A) tails can be profound, it is unclear whether eIF-4G, Paip-1, or even PAB is involved. *Xenopus* oocytes apparently contain very little PAB protein (Zelus et al 1989), and no role for PAB in translation stimulation in *Xenopus* or other oocytes or embryos has been reported. Furthermore, mRNAs that are repressed often contain poly(A) tails of respectable, though short lengths; it is unclear why doubling the length of the tail should make a dramatic difference in translational activity if it is solely mediated through PAB (Wickens et al 1996). Finally, in *Xenopus* oocytes and embryos, translational activation of some mRNAs requires the presence of a long poly(A) tail, whereas for others the act of poly(A) addition appears to be critical (McGrew et al 1989, Simon et al 1992). For such mRNAs, ribose methylation of the cap structure has been linked to polyadenylation (Kuge & Richter 1995). The recent discovery of Paip-1 raises the possibility of variations of the recruitment theme, including the possibility that multiple protein factors may function in ribosomal recruitment in oocytes and embryos.

CPEB: Activator, Repressor, or Both?

mRNAs that undergo cytoplasmic polyadenylation contain specific sequences (CPEs) that promote the reaction. CPEs are thereby implicated in translational activation. However, earlier in oogenesis, the CPE (or ACE) of mouse tPA mRNA, which receives poly(A) during maturation, is required for poly(A) tail shortening and translational repression (Huarte et al 1992). Thus CPE-mediated activation could include loss of a repressor, accumulation of an activator that might attract the polyadenylation machinery, or both.

Cytoplasmic polyadenylation element-binding protein (CPEB) binds the CPEs of a variety of mRNAs (Paris et al 1991, Stebbins-Boaz et al 1996) and has been isolated and cloned from *Xenopus* and mouse (Hake & Richter 1994, Gebauer & Richter 1996). It is a positive-acting factor in that CPEB-immunodepletion prevents polyadenylation in frog egg extracts (Hake & Richter 1994), and injection of anti-CPEB into intact oocytes prevents oocyte maturation and polyadenylation of c-*mos* mRNA (Stebbins-Boaz et al 1996). The protein complex that binds to the AAUAAA element, called the cleavage and polyadenylation specificity factor (CPSF), is likely a second positive-acting factor. Subunits of CPSF are detected in the oocyte cytoplasm, and their immunodepletion reduces polyadenylation efficiency in egg extracts (A Bilger, K Dickson, S Ballantyne, A Jenny, M Wickens, in preparation). Interactions between CPEB and CPSF could underlie the problematic reconstitution of polyadenylation activity by recombinant CPEB in depleted extracts (Stebbins-Boaz et al 1996).

Two provocative CPEB orthologues have been identified. The first, Orb, is a *Drosophila* protein involved in mRNA localization. *orb* mutants are defective in several aspects of oogenesis and in the establishment of polarity in the oocyte and embryo (Lantz et al 1992, Christerson & Mckearin 1994, Lantz et al 1994). The second orthologue, p82, is a protein isolated from the surf clam *S. solidissima* that is 41% identical to CPEB overall (N Standart, personal communication). Interestingly, p82 was first identified via its role in maintaining the repression of ribonucleotide reductase mRNA in oocytes (Walker et al 1996). After fertilization the same protein appears to be required for polyadenylation, suggesting that it may be a functional homologue of CPEB (N Standart, unpublished observation). The conservation between p82 and CPEB is most striking in the region that confers RNA binding, containing two RRM motifs and a zinc finger (Hake et al 1998; N Standart, unpublished observation). During maturation, *Xenopus* CPEB decreases dramatically in abundance, consistent with a function as a repressor. Both CPEB and p82 are phosphorylated during translational de-repression, but remain mRNA associated (Paris et al 1991, Standart 1992). Thus phosphorylation may modulate translation through effects on interactions with other proteins, rather than by affecting mRNA binding.

If CPEB and p82 are indeed functional homologues, then this protein is likely to be both a translational activator and repressor. Although the mechanism of repression is unclear, activation might be the result of recruitment of the polyadenylation apparatus, including CPSF and poly(A) polymerase.

PLAUSIBLE MODELS OF 3' END–MEDIATED REGULATION

Mechanisms of Repression

The mechanism by which repressors inhibit translation through the 3'UTR is not understood and is likely more complex than repression mediated by the 5'UTR. In the 5'UTR, a single protein is often sufficient for repression; in the 3'UTR, multi-protein complexes may be the norm. Moreover, repression in the 5'UTR can be achieved by simple steric inhibition of the translational machinery (Stripecke & Hentze 1992, Gray & Hentze 1994a); this is not possible, at least in a simple fashion, in the 3'UTR.

Models have been proposed for the mechanism by which negative elements in the 3'UTR repress translation (reviewed by Sonenberg 1994, Standart & Jackson 1994, Wickens et al 1996). We briefly present several such speculations below, recognizing that a diversity of mechanisms may be employed and that those we list are not mutually exclusive. We draw particularly on those examples discussed in the preceding sections.

NUCLEATION SITES   Negative elements may form a nucleation site for large protein complexes that make the mRNA inaccessible to the translational machinery. For example, a sequence-specific RNA-binding protein could recruit other factors that sequester the mRNA, much as higher order chromatin structure can sequester DNA from the transcriptional machinery. Such repressed structures could include the FRGY proteins since FRGY2 is found associated with many repressed mRNAs in the oocyte cytoplasm and can inhibit their translation in vitro (reviewed by Sommerville & Ladomery 1996, Wolffe & Meric 1996). The role of FRGY proteins is unclear because of their ubiquitous association with mRNAs, including both translationally competent and repressed mRNAs (Tafuri & Wolffe 1993). Their role may be to prevent spurious initiation at internal sites within the mRNA rather than to mediate mRNA-specific regulation. A requirement for non-specific RNA-binding proteins to ensure faithful initiation has been described in vitro (Svitkin et al 1996).

DISRUPTION OF END-TO-END CONTACTS   The growing body of evidence that the two ends of the mRNA interact has led to many models in which 3'UTR-binding proteins either directly interrupt that interaction or prevent its activity in initiation. 3'UTR-binding proteins might hide the cap from initiation factors or interfere with any of the protein-protein contacts necessary for initiation. The ability of a repressor to mediate repression of uncapped mRNAs or of IRES-mediated translation would strongly argue against cap-occlusion models because neither the cap nor eIF-4E are required: Repression of LOX mRNA satisfies these criteria (Ostareck-Lederer et al 1994, Ostareck et al 1997).

A specific form of this model posits that repressor proteins sequester PAB, prevent its binding to poly(A), or sterically occlude its interactions with initiation factors. In those cases, mRNAs lacking a poly(A) tail should not be subject to regulation. For that reason, this model is unlikely to apply to LOX mRNA because its repression can be reconstituted in cell-free systems using unadenylated mRNAs (Ostareck-Lederer et al 1994).

One provocative model suggests that ribosomes or ribosomal subunits enter the 3'UTR and commonly reinitiate translation on the same mRNA. Circumstantial evidence that ribosomes or subunits may continue past a termination codon exist (Peabody & Berg 1986, Kaufman et al 1987, Hinnebusch 1996), as do indications that ribosomes may preferentially reinitiate (Nelson & Winkler 1987, Galili et al 1988). In this view, factors bound to the 3'UTR might repress or enhance reinitiation.

MICROLOCALIZATION   Repressors bound to the 3'UTR might place an mRNA in a micro-environment in which translation is inefficient. Upon their activation, an mRNA might, for example, associate with the cytoskeleton where translation is more efficient, without any gross movement within the cell (Decker & Parker 1995, Bassell & Singer 1997). The identification of specific mutant alleles of cytoskeletal components, such as actin and tubulin, that are specifically defective in translation, would strongly support this model. It is unlikely that mRNAs whose repression can be reconstituted in cell-free translation systems, including LOX (Ostareck-Lederer et al 1994) and clam ribonucleotide reductase (Standart et al 1990), are regulated in this manner.

Regulation linked to the large scale movement of mRNAs within a cell (e.g. *oskar* mRNA) may differ from that of micro-localization. Regulation of *oskar* and *nanos* translation is intimately linked to their being positioned in the correct place within the oocyte (see LOCALIZATION AND TRANSLATION). One might expect that this form of control requires localized activators or repressors; microlocalization does not, as it modulates interactions with the cytoskeleton that are not necessarily involved in trafficking. The growing collection of putative localization proteins may provide an entree into this important problem. It will be of considerable interest to determine whether the same proteins that mediate an mRNA's association with microtubules or microfilaments are also required for that mRNA's proper translation, as with Staufen and *oskar* mRNA.

CHANGES IN POLY(A) LENGTH   For those mRNAs whose translational control requires changes in poly(A) length, repressor proteins bound to the 3'UTR may directly modulate accessibility of the mRNA to the cytoplasmic polyadenylation or deadenylation apparatus (Standart & Jackson 1994, Wickens et al 1996). It remains unclear why poly(A) tail lengths sufficient to mediate translational stimulation of reporter mRNAs are shorter than the tails of many repressed messages. Perhaps repression of these mRNAs involves both components that modulate poly(A) tail length and repressors that act independently, modulating end-to-end contacts for example. The specific contribution of polyadenylation or deadenylation might be assessed using mutants in the enzymes or sequence-specific factors involved. To date, no such studies have been reported.

Regardless, these models leave open the question of how changes in poly(A) length facilitate translation. In brief, current models are divided into two categories: those that posit an effect of poly(A) and PAB on the translation apparatus, and those that suggest that the mRNA is covalently modified by N-7 or ribose methylation of the cap to facilitate initiation. Tests of the involvement of specific initiation factors in poly(A)-mediated enhancement in vivo are needed, especially in oocytes and embryos. In simple form, the ribose methylation model predicts an enhanced affinity of an initiation component for a ribose-methylated cap and raises the issue of whether removal of the modification is required for the repression owing to deadenylation.

Mechanisms of De-Repression

Whatever the mechanism by which a 3'UTR-bound protein represses translation, that effect must be relieved at a specific time or place. Potential mechanisms of de-repression include loss or modification of the repressor and recruitment of an activator. In several cases, phosphorylation of 3'UTR-bound factors correlates with activation, e.g. clam p82 and CPEB (Paris et al 1991, Standart 1992). The functional significance of the modifications is not clear however.

ROLE OF 5' END MODIFICATIONS DURING DEVELOPMENT

The majority of nuclear encoded mRNAs receive a $5'm^7GpppG$ co-transcriptionally. This cap promotes translation initiation via interaction with eIF-4F (Banerjee 1980, Sonenberg 1996). Changes in its structure may regulate translation. Developmentally regulated changes in cap structures were first reported over two decades ago. N-7 methylation of the cap structure occurs following fertilization in the hornworm *Manduca sexta* (Kastern & Berry 1976, Kastern et al 1982) and the sea urchin, *Stronglyocentrotus purpuratus* (Caldwell & Emerson 1985). Cytoplasmic N-7 methyltransferase activity is present in frog oocytes and increases during oocyte maturation and could contribute to such control (Gillian-Daniel et al 1998). However, to date, the only specific mRNA thought to be selectively N-7-methylated is histone mRNA in *S. purpuratus* (Caldwell & Emerson 1985). Clearly, the absence of the N-7 methyl group would require that it was either removed or never put on in the nucleus.

Methylation of the 2′ position of the second and third ribose moieties of the mRNA (i.e. 7mGpppGmGm) may be linked to polyadenylation and hence to translational control of certain mRNAs. Polyadenylation-dependent ribose methylation has been reported using synthetic B4 RNA injected into *Xenopus* oocytes (Kuge & Richter 1995). Methylation inhibitors prevent both the modification and translational stimulation (Kuge & Richter 1995). A precedent for a functional link between polyadenylation and cap ribose methylation comes from vaccinia virus, in which the poly(A) polymerase has ribose methylation activity (Schnierle et al 1992). Early studies of the effects of ribose methylation indicated only small differences in translational efficiency (Muthukrishnan et al 1978). Moreover, ribose methylation cannot be the universal cause of the effects of poly(A) on translation because translation of injected reporter RNAs that do not undergo efficient ribose methylation nonetheless can be dramatically enhanced by polyadenylation (Gillian-Daniel et al 1998). Similarly, yeast mRNAs lack ribose methylation, yet poly(A) enhances their translation (Banerjee 1980). Nevertheless, a model in which polyadenylation in situ causes activation of N-7 or ribose methylation can accommodate repression of mRNAs with respectable tail lengths simply by inferring that they lack the methyl or ribose group prior to polyadenylation. However, this applies equally to any event that may occur in response to polyadenylation in situ, and not to pre-existing poly(A) tails.

Deadenylation leads to enzymatic cleavage of the cap structure and hence to mRNA decay in yeast (reviewed by Beelman & Parker 1995). A comparable deadenylation-dependent decapping reaction could, in principle, provide a simple mechanism by which poly(A) removal results in translational repression. However, this does not appear to be the case in *Xenopus* oocytes: RNAs that are completely deadenylated during maturation retain their caps in a methylated form (Gillian-Daniel et al 1998).

LOCALIZATION AND TRANSLATION

Macro-Localization and Translational Activity

mRNAs are sometimes localized in order to produce protein in only one region of the cell. Mechanisms exist to repress mRNAs that have not yet reached their proper destination or are not properly anchored there. Although this form of repression has been conclusively demonstrated only in the fly embryo, circumstantial evidence suggests it may be more general.

oskar and *nanos* mRNAs are required for formation of the posterior region of *Drosophila*. Both are localized to the presumptive posterior of the oocyte and early embryo (St Johnston 1995, Macdonald & Smibert 1996). To reach that destination, the mRNAs must move across the oocyte, since they enter the anterior end of the oocyte from nurse cells. Translational repression of *oskar* mRNA during its transit is mediated by a protein, Bruno, which binds to Bruno responsive elements (BRE) in the *oskar* 3′UTR (Kim-Ha et al 1995, Webster et al 1997). Repression by Bruno may involve deadenylation, as a rapid deadenylation signal in Eg2 mRNA of *Xenopus* contains consensus BRE sequence that may interact with a *Xenopus* orthologue of Bruno Etr, (Bouvet et al 1994, Webster et al 1997). However, regulation of *oskar* mRNA does not appear to be accompanied by changes in its poly(A) length (Webster et al 1997). Bruno may have other mRNA targets, as suggested by the *bruno* mutant phenotype (Schupbach & Wieschaus 1991, Webster et al 1997).

nanos mRNA also contains signals within its 3′UTR that direct it to the posterior and control its translation (Gavis & Lehmann 1994). Unlike the BREs in *oskar*, the regulatory elements in *nanos* do not inhibit translation during transit of the mRNA; rather ectopic Nanos protein in the developing oocyte may be rapidly degraded (Smibert et al 1996, Wang et al 1994). The control elements do, however, prevent translation of mRNAs that remain unlocalized in the early embryo (Dahanukar & Wharton 1996, Gavis et al 1996, Smibert et al 1996). A 135-kDa protein, Smaug, has been identified that likely binds to these elements (Smibert et al 1996).

As the numbers of examples of localized mRNAs increases, it should become clear whether mRNAs that are mis-localized or still in transit are commonly less active. At this early stage, it appears this may be the case. For example, expression of *ASH1* mRNA appears to be more efficient once it is localized in budding yeast (Long et al 1997). The mechanisms responsible for such regulation are not known, but may include the formation of transport particles in which the mRNAs are trafficked but translation does not occur (reviewed by Bassell & Singer 1997).

Micro-Localization: The Role of the Cytoskeleton in Translational Control

The cytoskeleton may have several functions in the regulation of mRNA expression (reviewed in Bassell & Singer 1997). It may provide a surface for the interaction of cellular components, allow mRNAs to be spatially organized where their products are to be utilized, provide an opportunity for feedback regulation, and/or sequester mRNAs from the translational machinery until they reach their destination.

Links between translation and cytoskeletal association have been suggested from at least four lines of evidence. First, the majority of mRNAs and polyribosomes are found to be associated with the cytoskeleton after extraction with certain detergents (Lenk et al 1977, Fulton et al 1980, Zambetti et al 1985,

Ornelles et al 1986). Second, drugs that depolymerize the cytoskeleton result in a release of mRNAs and a decrease in general protein synthesis (Lenk et al 1977, Ornelles et al 1986, Taneja et al 1992). Moreover, efficient translation of *oskar* mRNA requires mRNA localization, which can be disrupted by mutations in the mRNA and by chemical or genetic disruptions of the cytoskeleton (Theurkauf et al 1993, Clark et al 1994, Theurkauf 1994, Erdelyi et al 1995, Kim-Ha et al 1995, Markussen et al 1995, Rongo et al 1995, Tetzlaff et al 1996). Third, in granules that contain cytoskeletally associated mRNAs, ribosomes, at least one tRNA and elongation factor eEF-1α (Yang et al 1990, Barabese et al 1995) have been described. Fourth, by electron micrographic in situ hybridization, the majority of polyadenylated RNA in fibroblasts is found in actin filament intersections that also contain eEF-1α and ribosomes (Bassell et al 1994).

Recently, proteins that may mediate the interaction of mRNAs with the cytoskeleton have been identified. For example, *Drosophila* Staufen appears to form a cytoskeletally associated complex with *oskar* mRNA that leads to its localization and translation (Ephrussi et al 1991, Kim-Ha et al 1991, St Johnston et al 1991, Ferrandon et al 1994, Manseau et al 1996). It appears to be involved in the maintenance (anchoring) of *oskar* mRNA at the posterior pole, a function that requires oskar protein itself (Ephrussi et al 1991, Kim-Ha et al 1991, Markussen et al 1995, Rongo et al 1995). Staufen is also required for the localization of *bicoid* and perhaps other mRNAs (St Johnston 1989, St Johnston et al 1991, Ferrandon et al 1994). A number of putative localization proteins in other species have also been identified. These include Spnr, a 71-kDa protein, located on cytoplasmic microtubules, which interacts with the 3'UTR of protamine-1 mRNA in mouse spermatids (Schumacher et al 1995), and a 70-kDa protein (ZBP-1) that binds to β-actin zipcodes (Ross et al 1997). A protein with homology to ZBP-1 has been implicated in Vg1 mRNA localization in *Xenopus* oocytes (L Havin, submitted).

The biochemical mechanism(s) by which the cytosketeton contributes to translation regulation is not understood. In one simple model, the role of the cytoskeleton is restricted to positioning the mRNA correctly. For example, Staufen, contributes to both the localization and translational activation of *oskar*: It may activate *oskar* translation by bringing and maintaining the mRNA in a region conducive to its translation.

NUCLEAR AND CYTOPLASMIC CROSS-TALK

Because translation occurs in the cytoplasm, nuclear events are often thought to be entirely unrelated to its control. Recently, a growing body of evidence has begun to suggest otherwise.

Two key features of mRNAs, the cap and poly(A) tail, are recognized in both the nucleus and cytoplasm. In the nucleus, the cap is recognized by CBC α complex of two proteins involved in pre-mRNA processing (Izaurralde et al 1994), while in the cytoplasm, a different cap binding complex, eIF-4F, is bound (Sonenberg 1996). The exchange between the two complexes, perhaps soon after or coincident with emergence of the mRNA from the nucleus, is a critical event in translation and could, in principle, be modulated. A significant fraction of eIF-4E is located in the nucleus, in both yeast and mammalian cells (Lejbkowicz et al 1992, Lang et al 1994). The function of this nuclear subpopulation is unclear. Similarly, PAB, which participates in cytoplasmic events including translation, also modulates the length of poly(A) added in the nucleus (Amrani et al 1997, Minvielle-Sebastia et al 1997). A second protein, PABII, is exclusively nuclear and participates in nuclear polyadenylation (Wahle 1991).

In some cases, sequence-specific translational repression may be established in the nucleus and carried to the cytoplasm. For example, hnRNP K, an abundant nuclear protein that can shuttle to and from the cytoplasm (Michael et al 1997), represses translation of LOX mRNA. Several other proteins that regulate translation may also have nuclear functions. These include *Drosophila* Sex Lethal (Green 1991) and Bicoid (Driever 1992), and the yeast ribosomal protein L32 (Dabeva & Warner 1993).

In Xenopus oocytes the translation of mRNAs originating from the nucleus can be repressed relative to that of the same mRNAs injected into the cytoplasm. The repressive effect of the "nuclear experience" may be from the binding of so-called FRGY proteins (Sommerville & Ladomery 1996, Wolffe & Meric 1996), which also are transcription factors.

NETWORKS: REGULATORS WITH MULTIPLE ROLES

An increasing number of complex regulatory networks involving translational control have appeared in the literature. In some, regulatory proteins respond to a variety of regulatory signals and/or control a number of mRNA targets. In others, the same proteins are used to control gene expression at different levels.

hnRNP E1 (αCP1) and hnRNP K

hnRNP E1 (αCP-1) and hnRNP K can repress the translation of LOX mRNA (Ostareck et al 1997). hnRNP E1 is also part of a complex (α-complex) that controls the stability of α-globin mRNA by binding to CU-rich sequences in its 3'UTR (Kiledjian et al 1995, Wang et al 1995). Interestingly, the CU-rich sequence of α-globin mRNA cannot substitute for the DICE element of LOX mRNA in mediating translational repression (Ostareck et al 1997). However, a second protein, E2 (αCP2), which is a close relative of E1, is also involved in globin stability (Kiledjian et al 1995) and may be able to mediate translational repression via DICE elements (Ostareck et al 1997). hnRNP K also appears to have a dual function. In addition to its role in translation repression it also functions in the transcriptional activation of c-myc, which contains a CT-rich promoter (Takiamoto et al 1993, Michelotti et al 1996). Thus these proteins seem to be involved in the regulation of transcription, translation, and mRNA stability. This raises the possibility that regulation of one protein, or its partners, could affect a network of genes at several levels of gene expression.

IRP

IRPs are at the hub of a complex network of metabolic circuits (Figure 6). IRP was first identified as a regulator of IRE-containing genes involved in the control of iron homeostatis (reviewed in Hentze & Kuhn 1996). The interaction of IRPs with IREs in the 5'UTR of a number of mRNAs leads to their translational repression. In contrast, transferrin receptor mRNA, which contains multiple IREs within its 3'UTR, is stabilized against endonucleolytic cleavage by the presence of IRP (Binder et al 1994). In addition, IRP-1 is also a cytoplasmic aconitase (reviewed in Hentze & Kuhn 1996), which catalyzes the conversion between citrate and iso-citrate. The regulatory and enzymatic functions of IRP-1 are mutually exclusive and depend on the status of an iron-sulfur cluster within the protein (reviewed in Hentze & Kuhn 1996).

The IRE-binding activity of IRP-1 is regulated in response to at least two additional signals, nitric oxide and oxidative stress (in the form of hydrogen peroxide) (Figure 6) (Hentze & Kuhn 1996). This has fueled speculation that iron metabolism and oxidative stress, which result in the production of harmful free radicals, may be coordinately regulated. This speculation is supported by the presence of functional IREs in two Krebs cycle enzymes (Kohler et al 1995, Gray et al 1996, Melefors 1996, Schalinske et al 1998), the pathway that fuels production of mitochondrial reactive oxygen intermediates. Also, IRP-1 has been suggested to be a target of protein kinase C (Schalinske et al 1997).

A second IRP, IRP-2, is regulated in response to iron and nitric oxide but not by oxidative stress (Figure 6) (Hentze & Kuhn 1996). In contrast to IRP-1, IRP-2 is not modulated by post-transcriptional changes in its iron-sulfur cluster but instead is regulated by changes in its stability (Hentze & Kuhn 1996).

Thus IRP-mediated regulation allows a network of mRNAs to be coordinately regulated in response to a variety of signals. The differential expression of IRP-1 and IRP-2 may have physiological consequences: Cells in which IRP-1 is the most abundant may be more responsive to oxidative stress. IRP-1 and IRP-2 bind to distinct but overlapping sets of RNA sequences (Henderson 1996). Thus different cellular mRNAs may be regulated differentially by these proteins.

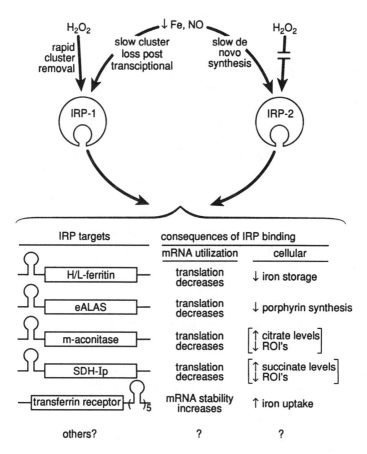

Figure 6 Regulation of gene expression by IRP-1 and IRP-2. The RNA-binding activities of IRP-1 and IRP-2 are activated in response to low cellular iron and nitric oxide. The activation of IRP-1 involves a slow post-transcriptional disassembly of its iron sulfur cluster, while activation of IRP-2 is also slow and involves synthesis of IRP-2 protein. IRP-1 binding activity is also activated by oxidative stress and involves a rapid disassembly of the iron-sulfur cluster. Binding of the IRPs results in translational repression of ferritin, erythroid 5-aminolevolinate synthase (eALAS), mitochondrial aconitase (m-aconitase), and succinate dehydrogenase iron protein (SDH-Ip) mRNA and in stabilization of transferrin receptor mRNA. The cellular consequences of IRP binding are indicated; however, the cellular consequences of IRP-regulation of aconitase and succinate dehydrogenase iron protein mRNAs are speculative. ROI, reactive oxygen intermediates. IREs do not function in the ORF (E Paraskeva, NK Gray, B Schlaeger, K Wehr, MW Hentze, submitted).

Sex Lethal

Sex lethal, a female-specific RNA-binding protein, regulates alternative splicing in the *Drosophila* sex determination hierarchy, determining splice-site choice for its own mRNA and transformer mRNA (Green 1991). Msl-2, part of a multi-subunit complex that functions in dosage compensation in male flies, is also regulated by Sex lethal. Sex lethal appears to act as a translational repressor of *msl-2* mRNA in females (Bashaw & Baker 1997, Kelly et al 1997) and is not present in male flies. The 5′UTR of *msl-2* mRNA contains two Sex lethal binding sites and the 3′UTR contains four (Bashaw & Baker 1997; Kelley et al 1997). Simultaneous interaction of Sex lethal with the 5′ and 3′ UTR binding sites appears to cause synergistic repression of *msl-2* (Bashaw & Baker 1997, Kelley et al 1997). The ability of Sex lethal to repress translation has recently been confirmed in vitro (Gebauer et al 1998). Thus this protein regulates both splicing in the nucleus and translation in the cytoplasm.

Sex lethal is not the only protein with a role in both regulated splicing and translation. Ribosomal protein L32 of *S. cerevisiae* regulates the splicing and translation of its own mRNA (Dabeva & Warner 1993). *Drosophila* Bicoid is a transcription factor but also represses the translation of *caudal* mRNA by binding to sites within its 3′UTR (Dubnau & Struhl 1996, Rivera-Pomar et al 1996).

GLOBAL CONTROL: REGULATION VIA INITIATION FACTORS

Changes in the rate or pattern of protein synthesis occur in response to such stimuli as heat shock, mitogenic stimulation, or growth. Such gross changes in translation are normally mediated by changes in the activity or abundance of the translation initiation factors. Modulation of the activity of the basal translation apparatus can preferentially affect the translation of specific mRNAs, as discussed below.

Numerous components of the translational machinery are phosphoproteins, including at least 13 initiation factors as well as 3 elongation factor subunits, 3 ribosomal proteins, and a number of amino-acyl tRNA synthases (Hershey 1991). Although the phosphorylation state of eIF-4B, eIF-4E, eIF-4G, eIF-2, and eIF-3 can all be modulated in vivo (reviewed by Merrick 1992, Morley 1994), a detailed understanding of the effect of these modifications is available only for eIF-2 and eIF-4E.

Analysis of the effects of initiation factor modifications in vivo is complicated by the multiplicity of responses that might in principle affect translation. For example, mitogen-stimulated T-cell activation leads to a two- to threefold increase in eIF-2 α and β subunits and eIF-4E levels, a similar increase in mRNA and ribosome levels (Cohen et al 1990, Boal et al 1993), and an increase in eIF-4E phosphorylation and utilization (Boal et al 1993, Morley et al 1993). Similarly, in reticulocytes stimulated with phorbol esters, eIF-3, eIF-4B, eIF-4E, and eIF-4G are all phosphorylated (Morley & Traugh 1989). The situation has become even more complex recently with the discovery of factors that sequester initiation factors; at least one of these factors is regulated by phosphorylation. Dissecting the individual contributions of any one event on cellular growth and metabolism is a serious and central challenge.

The signaling pathways that control initiation factor phosphorylation are discussed in recent reviews (Morley 1994, Clemens 1996, Pain 1996, Sonenberg 1996, Flynn et al 1997). We focus here on the mechanisms by which initiation appears to be modulated.

eIF-2

eIF-2 binds GTP and the initiator tRNA and delivers this complex to the small ribosomal subunit (Figure 2). The GTP is hydrolyzed at the initiator AUG, prior to joining of the large ribosomal subunit; eIF-2-GDP is released, leaving a charged initiator tRNA in place (Merrick 1992, Clemens 1996). In addition, eIF-2 appears to function in identification of the initiator codon (Donahue et al 1988, Cigan et al 1989). Phosphorylation of eIF-2, which consists of three subunits (α, β, and γ), results in an inhibition of translation and is a central control point in the initiation pathway (Clemens 1996). The α subunit of eIF-2 can be phosphorylated at serine 51 by a hemin-controlled repressor kinase (HCR) in response to heme deficiency in reticulocytes (Clemens 1996) or by yeast *GCN2* kinase in response to uncharged tRNA (Hinnebusch 1996). Finally, it can be phosphorylated by double-stranded RNA-regulated protein kinase (PKR) in response to double-stranded RNA (Clemens 1996, Clemens & Elia 1997). Phosphorylation of eIF-2 does not inhibit its activity per se but instead inhibits its recycling by the GDP/GTP exchange factor, eIF-2B (Clemens 1996). Recycling of eIF2-GDP to eIF2-GTP is required for the next round of initiation (Merrick 1992). The interaction of phosphorylated eIF-2 with the recycling factor eIF-2B forms a stable complex in which the bound GDP cannot be exchanged for GTP (Rowlands et al 1988, Dholakia & Wahba 1989, Kimball et al 1998). As eIF-2 is normally in excess of eIF-2B, this essentially sequesters the cellular eIF-2B activity and leads to a general inhibition of translation.

Regulation of eIF-2 activity by HCR and Gcn2p kinase are generally considered to represent specialized forms of regulation. However, several observations suggest that regulation by PKR may play a more generalized role in growth control. First, interleukin-3 stimulation of cell growth involves the dephosphorylation of PKR and eIF-2 (Ito et al 1994). Second, PKR activity is inhibited in ras-transformed cells (Mundschau & Faller 1992). Third, dominant-negative mutants of PKR, and mutants of eIF-2α that cannot be phosphorylated, cause transformation of transfected cells (Koromilas et al 1992b, Donze et al 1995). Fourth, these transformed cell lines can form tumors in nude mice (Meurs et al 1993). However, because PKR phosphorylates several transcription factors (Clemens & Elia 1997), only some of its effects may be through eIF-2α.

PKR is not essential in vivo. Homozygous knockout PKR mice display only a limited deficiency in their interferon response, not aberrant growth or high tumor incidence (Yang et al 1995). Similarly, a survey of human hematological malignancies suggest that PKR activity is not abnormally low (Basu et al 1997). These results may indicate that eIF-2 phosphorylation and PKR have little function in growth control in vivo. On the other hand, an alternative kinase pathway may exist, as may other modes for controlling the activity of eIF-2 in response to growth signals. Indeed, the levels and activity of the recycling factor eIF2B are regulated (Clemens 1996, Welsh et al 1998).

eIF-4E

The cytoplasmic cap-binding protein, eIF-4E, has been suggested to be limiting for translation in vivo and appears to be a critical regulator of cell growth, development, and differentiation (reviewed by Flynn & Proud 1996, Sonenberg 1996, Morley 1997). For example, eIF-4E overexpression induces aberrant cell growth, transformation of cells to form foci in soft agar, and tumors in nude mice (reviewed in Sonenberg 1996). Moreover, elevated eIF-4E levels are found in several transformed tumor cell lines (Miyagi et al 1995) and in virtually all breast carcinomas (Kerekatte et al 1995, Li et al 1997, Nathan et al 1997a) and may be a marker for predicting the recurrence of head and neck cancer (Nathan et al 1997b). Increased levels of eIF-4E phosphorylation correlate with an increased translation during oocyte maturation in starfish (Xu et al 1993), *Xenopus* (Morley & Pain 1995a), and mouse oocytes (Gavin & Schorderet-Slatkine 1997). Additionally, microinjection of eIF-4E into *Xenopus* embryos causes mesoderm induction (Klein & Melton 1994).

In vivo, phosphorylation of eIF-4E at serine 209 occurs in response to growth factors, hormones, and mitogens (reviewed by Sonenberg 1996). Conversely, dephosphorylation is triggered by serum deprivation, viral infection, and heat shock (reviewed by Sonenberg 1996). Phosphorylation at the same position can be achieved by a number of kinases; in vivo, protein kinase C and a kinase in the MAP-kinase cascade (possibly Mnk1) (Waskiewicz et al 1997) are likely candidates (Flynn & Proud 1996, Sonenberg 1996, Morley 1997). It should be noted that phosphatase activity may also contribute to eIF-4E regulation (Sonenberg 1996, Morley 1997).

Phosphorylation of eIF-4E appears to enhance its activity, because the phosphorylated form of eIF-4E is predominately found in 48S pre-initiation complexes (Joshi-Barve et al 1990). However, a large proportion of phosphorylated eIF-4E is not associated with mRNAs (Rau et al 1996). Phosphorylation has been reported to increase both its affinity to the cap (Minich et al 1994) and its association with eIF-4A and eIF-4G to form eIF-4F complexes (e.g. Lamphear & Panniers 1990, Bu et al 1993, Morley et al 1993, Morley & Pain 1995b). Since eIF-4F has been reported to have a greater affinity for the cap than eIF-4E alone (Bu et al 1993, Haghihat & Sonenberg 1997), effects of eIF-4E phosphorylation may result from a combination of an increase in the amount of eIF-4F and from enhanced cap-binding capacity.

Limiting eIF-4E levels may regulate translation of specific mRNAs by forcing all mRNAs to compete for the translation apparatus (Hiremath et al 1985, Duncan et al 1987). In this view, when eIF-4E (and therefore eIF-4F) is limiting, mRNAs that have structure-rich 5' UTRs will be most poorly translated. The increased availability of eIF-4F will result in an increased delivery of RNA helicase activity to the 5'UTR, disrupting the secondary structures. Indeed, in mammalian cells, overexpression of eIF-4E results in a more efficient translation of reporter mRNAs containing structured 5'UTRs (Koromilas et al 1992a).

The importance of eIF-4E in cell growth regulation is illustrated by its connections to ras. eIF-4E can substitute for ras in a two-oncogene transformation assay (Lazaris-Karatzas & Sonenberg 1992). A number of approaches suggest that ras is an upstream activator of eIF-4E (e.g. Frederickson et al 1992, Rinker-Schaeffer et al 1992). For example, overexpression of ras can elevate eIF-4E phosphorylation in the absence of extracellular stimuli (Rinker-Schaeffer et al 1992). Yet ras also appears to be downstream of eIF-4E; eIF-4E overexpression increases ras activity, and eIF-4E's transforming ability is prevented by blocking the activation of ras (Lazaris-Karatzas et al 1992). These data suggest a simple positive feedback loop: Ras activates eIF-4E phosphorylation, which leads to increased translation of growth factors that are then secreted, bind cell surface receptors, and thus induce further ras activation (reviewed by Rhoads 1991, Sonenberg 1996). A similar pathway may explain the induction of mesoderm caused by eIF-4E overexpression in *Xenopus* embryos, since that process can be inhibited by co-expression of a dominant-negative ras mutants (Klein & Melton 1994). In yeast, however, overexpression of eIF-4E is without pronounced effect and does not enhance translation of mRNAs with structured 5'UTRs (Lang et al 1994).

A prediction of the feedback models above is that overexpression of eIF-4E will lead to the activation of one or more mRNAs encoding growth factors and mitogenic proteins with structure-rich 5'UTRs. Indeed, the translation of a number of such cellular mRNAs in response to elevated eIF-4E levels has been observed. These include the growth-promoting proteins, cyclin D1 (Rosenwald et al 1993) and ornithine decarboxylase (Shantz & Pegg 1994), and the growth-related protein, P23 (Bommer et al 1994).

eIF-4EBP/PHAS-I

eIF-4E activity can be modulated by interaction with a regulatory protein, designated eIF-4EBP1 or PHAS-I (Lin et al 1994, Pause et al 1994a). This 118-amino acid phosphoprotein competes with eIF-4G for binding to eIF-4E and prevents formation of eIF-4F (Haghighat et al 1995). eIF-4EBP1 and eIF-4G share a motif involved in binding eIF-4E, which explains their competitive binding (Haghighat et al 1995, Mader et al 1995). Under conditions such as serum deprivation and heat shock, eIF-4EBP1 becomes dephosphorylated and sequesters eIF-4E, globally limiting cap-dependent translation (reviewed in Flynn & Proud 1996, Sonenberg 1996, Lawrence & Abraham 1997). The effects of eIF-4EBP1 may be most severe on specific subsets of mRNAs with secondary structure in their 5'UTR. Interestingly, the modulation of eIF-4E and eIF-4EBP1 activity does not always act in concert but may vary in their response to stimuli, for example during certain stages of adenovirus infection (Feigenblum & Schneider 1996) and heat shock in some cell types (Scheper et al 1997). Phosphorylation of eIF-4EBP1 by the mTOR/FRAP protein kinase pathway, indicated by sensitivity to the immunosuppressant rapamycin, leads to its dissociation from eIF-4E (reviewed in Lawrence & Abraham 1997). Recent evidence suggests that mTOR may directly phosphorylate eIF-4EBP1 (Brunn et al 1997). A second protein, eIF-4EBP2, appears to share many of the properties of eIF-4EBP1 (Pause et al 1994a) but exhibits a different pattern of expression (Tsukiyama-Kohara et al 1996).

A yeast homologue of eIF-4EBP, called *CAF20*, shares the common motif thought to be involved in eIF-4E binding (Altmann et al 1997). As expected, yeast strains deficient in Caf20p exhibit accelerated growth, whereas overexpression of Caf20p decreases growth rate (Altmann et al 1997).

Control of eIF-4E activity is exerted at two levels, via its phosphorylation status and by its sequestration via eIF-4EBP1. The cellular importance of the eIF-4EBP1 interaction is suggested by the finding that eIF-4EBP1 over-expression in eIF-4E transformed fibroblasts significantly inhibited proliferation and the ability of these cells to grow in soft agar (Rousseau et al 1996). However, even though rapamycin treatment results in rapid and complete dephosphorylation of eIF-4EBP1, its effect on protein synthesis and growth rates manifest more slowly and are reduced by at most 50% (Berretta et al 1996, Feigenblum & Schneider 1996). The importance of eIF-4EBP1 may vary in different cell types and conditions and may primarily act through specific subsets of mRNAs.

eIF-4G Decoys

eIF-4G is phosphorylated in response to many stimuli but the sites and consequences of phosphorylation are not yet well defined (reviewed by Morley et al 1997). eIF-4G, like eIF-4E, has been suggested to be limiting in cells, and amplification of its gene has been found in independent squamous cell lung carcinomas (Brass et al 1997). Moreover, levels of eIF-4G appear to be tightly regulated in cells with control occurring both at the level of synthesis and turnover (discussed in Morley et al 1997).

Levels of free eIF-4G may be regulated by proteins analogous to those that prevent the interaction of eIF-4E with its partners. A novel 97-kDa protein, referred to as NAT1, DAP-5, Eif4g2, or p97, has 30% homology to the C-terminal two thirds of eIF-4G (Morley et al 1997). This portion of eIF-4G does not interact with eIF-4E but can promote internal initiation and contains binding sites for eIF-3 and eIF-4A and has RNA-binding activity. This protein appears to act as a eIF-4G decoy through its affinity for eIF-3 and/or eIF-4A, both of which it can interact with in vitro (Imataka et al 1997). Thus the eIF-4G decoy suppresses both cap-dependent and IRES-mediated translation. In principle, eIF-4G decoys could also activate specific mRNAs (Hentze 1997). Overexpression of the eIF-4G decoy inhibits cell growth. Surprisingly, although the N-terminal part of the eIF-4G decoy is most homologous to eIF-4G, it is the C-terminal region that seems to result in growth inhibition (Levy-Strumpf et al 1997). As a result, it is unclear whether these proteins repress growth by titrating initiation factors or through another mechanism.

Ribosomal Protein S6

The activation of a number of mRNAs whose translation and function are closely correlated to cell growth is partially inhibited by rapamycin (Jefferies et al 1994b, Pedersen et al 1997), which prevents the activation of $p70^{S6k}$ and phosphorylation of eIF-4EBP1. These mRNAs are controlled through sequences in their 5'UTR, which typically contain short ($\approx$8 nt) polypyrimidine tracts (terminal oligopyrimidine tracts, TOP) (Meyuhas et al 1996) near their caps. TOP mRNAs include vertebrate ribosomal proteins and two translation elongation factors, eEF-1α and eEF-2 (Jefferies et al 1994a, Terada et al 1994, Meyuhas et al 1996). Although the absolute requirement for the TOP element to be cap proximal (Hammond et al 1991) suggested that eIF-4E may regulate these mRNAs, this does not appear to be the case; for example, overexpression of eIF-4E does not increase their translation (Shama et al 1995).

Studies of a number of ribosomal protein mRNAs suggest that proteins that bind to their 5'UTRs may control translation; however, binding does not correlate with translational regulation (Gray & Hentze 1994b, Amaldi et al 1995, Meyuhas et al 1996). Control may be achieved by regulated recruitment of repressor or activator proteins by these constitutively bound factors. Alternatively, sensitivity to rapamycin raises the possibility that modification of ribosomal protein S6 by $p70^{S6k}$ directly enhances TOP mRNA translation (Jefferies et al 1994b, Terada et al 1994). Mutants of $p70^{S6k}$ support the idea that rapamycin is acting through this and not another kinase in the mTOR pathway (Jefferies et al 1997). Modification of S6, which lies within the mRNA-binding site of the ribosome (Jefferies & Thomas 1996), increases the affinity of the small ribosomal subunits for poly(U) (Gressner & van de Leur 1980). This may indicate that S6 modification results in more efficient interactions with TOP mRNAs via the polypyrimidine tract. Regulation may be achieved by a combination of these mechanisms. For instance, modification of S6 may enable 40S ribosomal subunits to overcome putative repressors. Alternatively, putative repressors may be targets for p70^{S6k} phosphorylation, possibly inducing changes in protein-protein interactions that result in translation.

Non-Identical Twins

Each of the three subunits of eIF-4F has different iso-forms arising from different genes or alternative splicing, further enhancing the opportunities for translational regulation.

eIF-4A was first found to be encoded by two genes in mice and is also encoded by two genes in yeast (Nielsen & Trachsel 1988, Linder & Slonimski 1989); the two products may vary in abundance between cell types and growth states (Nielsen & Trachsel 1988, Williams-Hill et al 1997) and may form eIF-4F complexes with different cap affinities (Conroy et al 1990).

eIF-4G is encoded by two genes with nonidentical functions in *S. cerevisiae* (Goyer et al 1993, Tarun et al 1997). In yeast, the two genes have non-identical functions (Goyer et al 1993, Tarun et al 1997). Recently, a second eIF-4G gene, called eIF-4G$_{II}$, has been found in mammals (humans) (Gradi et al 1998). eIF-4G$_{II}$ shares many characteristics of the previously identified human eIF-4G factor but may be more resistant to cleavage during picornaviral infection (Gradi et al 1998), and the two forms differ in abundance among cell types (Gradi et al 1998).

Only one eIF-4E gene has been identified in yeast and flies. Recently, a second gene, *EIF4E2*, was described in humans (Gao et al 1998); however it is not clear whether the mRNA from this gene gives rise to protein. In *Drosophila*, alternative splicing generates two different iso-forms, called eIF-4E$_I$ and eIF-4E$_{II}$ (Lavoie et al 1996). Only eIF-4E$_I$ is detected in embryos, whereas both are detected in adults (Lavoie et al 1996).

IN CLOSING

We have tried to encompass many of the broad themes in the regulation of translation initiation, with special emphasis on its pertinence to the control of development and cell growth. We have highlighted important unresolved issues and likely upcoming developments, as have other recent reviews in specific areas of consideration.

The enormous biological breadth of translational regulation and its emergence as a central means by which genes are controlled has led to an enhanced appreciation of its complexities. The effort to consolidate the rich biology with detailed understanding of the underlying biochemical mechanisms promises an exciting and surprising future.

ACKNOWLEDGMENTS

Unfortuntately, we have not been able to cite all of the relevant literature. To those authors we have omitted, we apologize. We also are painfully aware of the common review writer's frailty noted by Merrick (1992) and apologize for any myopia.

We thank the following members of the Wickens laboratory for their critical reading of the manuscript and their helpful advice: Aaron Barkoff, Jeff Coller, Lena Nielsen, and especially Scott Ballantyne and Kris Dickson. Matthias Hentze, Richard Jackson, Simon Morley, and Finn-Hugo Markussen are gratefully acknowledged for their extensive input into the manuscript and for quick responses on short notice. Judith Kimble, Steve Liebhaber, Rob Singer, Sid Strickland, and Robin Wharton provided critical comments that also were useful. Nicole Benkers, Bruce Brady, Adrienne Keith, and Alison La Pean are gratefully acknowleged for their assistance with references. Nancy Standart, Nahum Sonenberg, Betsy Goodwin, and Matthias Hentze are thanked for allowing us to cite data prior to publication. We are grateful to the University of Wisconsin Biochemistry Media Lab, particularly Adam Steinberg, for figure preparation and patience. NKG is funded by a Wellcome International Prize Travelling Research Fellowship. Work in the Wickens laboratory is supported by grants from the National Institutes of Health.

Visit the *Annual Reviews home page* at
http://www.AnnualReviews.org

Literature Cited

Acland P, Dixon M, Peters G, Dickson C. 1990. Subcellular fate of the Int-2 oncoprotein is determined by the choice of initiation codon. *Nature* 343:662–65

Altmann M, Schmitz N, Berset C, Trachsel H. 1997. A novel inhibitor of cap-dependent translation initiation in yeast: p20 competes with eIG-4G for binding to eIF-4E. *EMBO J.* 16:1114–21

Amaldi F, Camacho-Vanegas O, Cardinali B,

Cecconi F, Crosio C, et al. 1995. Structure and expression of ribosomal protein genes in *Xenopus laevis. Biochem. Cell Biol.* 73:969–77

Ambros V, Horvitz HR. 1987. The *lin*-14 locus of *Caenorhabditis elegans* controls the time of expression of specific post-embryonic developmental events. *Genes Dev.* 1:398–414

Amrani N, Minet M, Le Gouar M, Lacroute F, Wyers F. 1997. Yeast Pab1 interacts with

Rna15 and participates in the control of the poly(A) tail length in vitro. *Mol. Cell. Biol.* 17:3694–701

Aziz N, Munro HN. 1987. Iron regulates ferritin mRNA translation through a segment of its 5' untranslated region. *Proc. Natl. Acad. Sci. USA* 84:8478–82

Baer BW, Kornberg RD. 1983. The protein responsible for the repeating structure of cytoplasmic poly (A)-ribonucleoprotein. *J. Cell Biol.* 96:717–21

Baker EJ, Diener DR, Rosenbaum JL. 1989. Accelerated poly(A) loss on α-tubulin mRNAs during protein synthesis inhibition in *Chlamydomonas. J. Mol. Biol.* 207:771–81

Banerjee AK. 1980. 5'-Terminal cap structure in eucaryotic messenger ribonucleic acids. *Microbiol. Rev.* 44:175–205

Barabese E, Koppel DE, Deutscher MP, Smith CL, Ainger K, et al. 1995. Protein translation components are colocalized in granules in oligodendrocytes. *J. Cell Sci.* 108:2781–90

Barkoff A, Ballantyne S, Wickens M. 1998. Meiotic maturation in *Xenopus* requires polyadenylation of multiple mRNAs. *EMBO J.* 17:3168–75

Bashaw GJ, Baker BS. 1997. The regulation of the Drosophila *msl-2* gene reveals a function for Sex-lethal in translational control. *Cell* 89:789–98

Bassell G, Singer RH. 1997. mRNA and cytoskeletal filaments. *Curr. Opin. Cell Biol.* 9:109–15

Bassell GJ, Powers CM, Taneja KL, Singer RH. 1994. Single mRNAs visualised by ultrastructural in situ hybridisation are principally localized at actin filament intersections in fibroblasts. *J. Cell. Biol.* 126:863–76

Basu S, Panayioditidis P, Hart SM, He L-Z, Man A, et al. 1997. Role of double-stranded RNA-activated protein kinase in human hematological malignancies. *Cancer Res.* 57:943–47

Beelman CA, Parker R. 1995. Degradation of mRNA in eukaryotes. *Cell* 81:179–83

Bernstein J, Sella O, Le S-Y, Elroy-Stein O. 1997. PDGF2/c-*sis* mRNA leader contains a differentiation-linked internal ribosomal entry site (D-IRES). *J. Biol. Chem.* 272:9356–62

Bernstein J, Shefler I, Elroy-Stein O. 1995. The translational repression mediated by the platelet-derived growth factor 2/c-*sis* mRNA leader is relieved during megakaryocytic differentiation. *J. Biol. Chem.* 270:10559–65

Beretta L, Gingras A-C, Svitkin YV, Hall MN, Sonenberg N. 1996. Rapamycin blocks the phosphorylation of 4E-BP1 and inhibits cap-dependent initiation of translation. *EMBO J.* 15:658–64

Bhasker CR, Burgiel G, Neupert B, Emery-Goodman A, Kühn LC, May BK. 1993.

The putative iron-responsive element in the human erythroid 5-aminolevulinate synthase mRNA mediates translational control. *J. Biol. Chem.* 268:12699–705

Binder R, Horowitz JA, Basilion JP, Koeller DM, Klausner RD, Harford JB. 1994. Evidence that the pathway of transferrin receptor mRNA degradation involves an endonucleolytic cleavage within the 3' UTR and does not involve poly(A) tail shortening. *EMBO J.* 13:1969–80

Boal TR, Chiorini JA, Cohen RB, Miyamoto S, Fredrickson RM, et al. 1993. Regulation of eukaryotic translation initiation factor expression during T-cell activation. *Biochim. Biophys. Acta* 1176:257–64

Boeck R, Kolakofsky D. 1994. Positions +5 and +6 can be major determinants of the efficiency of non-AUG initiation codons for protein synthesis. *EMBO J.* 13:3608–17

Bommer U-A, Lazaris-Karatzas A, De Benedetti A, Nürnberg P, Benndorf R, et al. 1994. Translational regulation of the mammalian growth related protein P23: involvement of eIF-4E. *Cell. Mol. Biol. Res.* 40: 633–41

Bouvet P, Omilli F, Arlot-Bonnemains Y, Legagneux V, Roghi C, et al. 1994. The deadenylation conferred by the 3' untranslated region of a developmentally controlled mRNA in *Xenopus* embryos is switched to polyadenylation by deletion of a short sequence element. *Mol. Cell Biol.* 14:1893–900

Brass N, Heckel D, Sahin U, Pfreudschuh M, Sybrecht GW, Meese E. 1997. Translation initiation factor eIF-4γ is encoded by an amplified gene and induces an immune response in squamous cell lung carcinoma. *Hum. Mol. Gen.* 6:33–39

Brogna S, Ashburner M. 1997. The Adh-related gene of *Drosophila melanogaster* is expressed as a functional dicistronic messenger RNA: multigenic transcription in higher organisms. *EMBO J.* 16:2023–31

Brown PH, Daniels-McQueen S, Walden WE, Patino MM, Gaffield L, et al. 1989. Requirements for the translational repression of ferritin transcripts in wheat germ extracts by a 90-kDa protein for rabbit liver. *J. Biol. Chem.* 264:13383–86

Browning KS. 1996. The plant translational apparatus. *Plant Mol. Biol.* 32:107–44

Brunn GJ, Hudson CC, Sekulic A, Williams JM, Hosoi H, et al. 1997. Phosphorylation of the translational repressor PHAS-I by the mammalian target of rapamycin. *Science* 277:99–101

Bu X, Haas DW, Hagedorn CH. 1993. Novel phosphorylation sites of eukaryotic initiation factor-4F and evidence that phosphorylation stabilizes interactions of the p25 and p220 subunits. *J. Biol. Chem.* 268:4975–78

Buckley B, Ehrenfeld E. 1987. The cap-binding protein complex in uninfected and poliovirus-infected HeLa cells. *J. Biol. Chem.* 262: 13599–606

Caldwell DC, Emerson CP. 1985. The role of cap methylation in the translational activation of stored maternal histone mRNA in sea urchin embryos. *Cell* 42:691–700

Cao J, Geballe AP. 1994. Mutational analysis of the translational signal in the human cytomegalovirus gpUL4 (gp48) transcript leader by retroviral infection. *Virology* 205:151–60

Chen CY, Sarnow P. 1995. Initiation of protein synthesis by the eukaryotic translational apparatus on circular RNAs. *Science* 268: 415–17

Christensen AK, Kahn LE, Bourne CM. 1987. Circular polysomes predominate on the rough endoplasmic reticulum of somatotropes and mammotropes in the art anterior pituitary. *Am. J. Anat.* 178:1–10

Christerson LB, Mckearin DM. 1994. *orb* is required for anteroposterior and dorsoventral patterning during *Drosophila* oogenesis. *Genes Dev.* 8:614–28

Cigan AM, Pabich EK, Feng L, Donahue TF. 1989. Yeast translation initiation suppressor *sui*2 encodes the α subunit of eukaryotic initiation factor 2 and shares sequence identity with the human α subunit. *Proc. Natl. Acad. Sci. USA* 86:2784–88

Clark I, Giniger E, Ruohola-Baker H, Jan LY, Jan YN. 1994. Transient posterior localization of a kinesin fusion protein reflects anteroposterior polarity of the *Drosophila* oocyte. *Curr. Biol.* 4:289–300

Clemens MJ. 1996. Protein kinases that phosphorylate eIF-2 and eIF-2B, and their role in eukaryotic cell translational control. See Hershey et al 1996, pp. 139–72

Clemens MJ, Elia A. 1997. The double-stranded RNA-dependent protein kinase PKR: structure and function. *J. Interferon Cytokine Res.* 17:503–24

Cohen RB, Boal TR, Safer B. 1990. Increased eIF-2α expression in mitogen-activated primary T lymphocytes. *EMBO J.* 9:3831–37

Conroy SC, Dever TE, Owens CL, Merrick WC. 1990. Characterization of the 46,000 dalton subunit of eIF-4F. *Arch. Biochem. Biophys.* 282:363–71

Cox TC, Bawden MJ, Martin A, May BK. 1991. Human erythroid 5-aminolevulinate synthase: promoter analysis and identification of an iron-responsive element in the mRNA. *EMBO J.* 10:1891–902

Craig AWB, Haghighat A, Yu ATK, Sonenberg N. 1998. Interaction of polyadenylate-binding protein with the eIF-4G homologue Paip enhances translation. *Nature* 392:520–23

Culp PA, Musci TJ. 1998. Translational activation and cytoplasmic polyadenylation of FGF receptor-1 are independently regulated during *Xenopus* oocyte maturation. *Dev. Biol.* 193:63–76

Curtis D, Lehmann R, Zamore PD. 1995. Translational regulation in development. *Cell* 81:171–78

Curtis D, Treiber DK, Tao F, Zamore PD, Williamson JR, Lehmann R. 1997. A CCHC metal-binding domain in Nanos is essential for translational regulation. *EMBO J.* 16:834–43

Dabeva MD, Warner JR. 1993. Ribosomal protein L32 of *Saccharomyces cerevisiae* regulates both splicing and translation of its own transcript. *J. Biol. Chem.* 268:19669–74

Dahanukar A, Wharton RP. 1996. The Nanos gradient in *Drosophila* embryos is generated by translational regulation. *Genes Dev.* 10: 2610–20

Dandekar T, Stripecke R, Gray NK, Goossen B, Constable A, et al. 1991. Identification of a novel iron-responsive element in murine and human erythroid δ-aminolevulinic acid synthase mRNA. *EMBO J.* 10:1903–9

Danthinne X, Seurinck J, Muelwaeter F, van Montagu M, Cornelissen M. 1993. The 3′ untranslated region of satellite tobacco necrosis virus RNA stimulates translation in vitro. *Mol. Cell. Biol.* 13:3340–49

Dasso MC, Milburn SC, Hershey JWB, Jackson RJ. 1990. Selection of the 5′-proximal translation initiation site is influenced by mRNA and eIF-2 concentrations. *Eur. J. Biochem.* 187:361–71

Decker CJ, Parker R. 1995. Diversity of cytoplasmic functions for the 3′ untranslational region of eukaryotic transcripts. *Curr. Opin. Cell. Biol.* 7:386–92

Degnin CR, Schleiss MR, Cao J, Geballe AP. 1993. Translational inhibition mediated by a short upstream open reading frame in the human cytomegalovirus gpUL4 (gp48) transcript. *J. Virol.* 67:5514–21

Dehlin E, Von Gabin A, Alm G, Dingelmaier R, Resnekov O. 1996. Repression of beta interferon gene expression in virus-infected cells is correlated with a poly(A) tail elongation. *Mol. Cell. Biol.* 16:468–74

Delbecq P, Werner M, Feller A, Filipkowski RK, Messenguy F, Pierard A. 1994. A segment of mRNA encoding the leader peptide of the CPA1 gene confers repression by arginine on a heterologous yeast gene transcript. *Mol. Cell. Biol.* 14:2378–90

de Melo Neto OP, Standart N, Martins DeSa C. 1995. Autoregulation of poly(A)-binding protein synthesis in vitro. *Nucleic Acids Res.* 23:2198–205

Descombes P, Schibler U. 1991. A liver-enriched transcriptional activator protein, LAP, and a transcriptional inhibitory protein, LIP, are translated from the same mRNA. *Cell* 67:569–79

Dholakia JN, Wahba AJ. 1989. Mechanism of the nucleotide exchange reaction in eukaryotic polypeptide chain initiation. *J. Biol. Chem.* 264:546–50

Dominguez DI, Ryabova LA, Pooggin MM, Schmidtpuchta W, Fütterer J, Hohn T. 1998. Ribosome shunting in cauliflower mosaic virus—identification of an essential and sufficient structural element. *J. Biol. Chem.* 273:3669–78

Donahue TF, Cigan AM, Pabich EK, Valavicius BC. 1988. Mutations at a Zn(II) finger motif in the yeast eIF-2β gene alter ribosomal start-site selection during the scanning process. *Cell* 54:621–32

Donze O, Jagus R, Koromilas AE, Hershey JWB, Sonenberg N. 1995. Abrogation of translation initiation factor eIF-2 phosphorylation causes malignant transformation of NIH 3T3 cells. *EMBO J.* 14:3828–34

Draper BW, Mello CC, Bowerman B, Hardin J, Priess JR. 1996. MEX-3 is a KH domain protein that regulates blastomere identity in early C. elegans embryos. *Cell* 87:205–16

Driever W. 1992. The Bicoid morphogen: concentration-dependent transcriptional activation of zygotic target genes during early *Drosophila* development. In *Transcriptional Regulation*, ed. SL McKnight, KR Yamamoto, pp. 1221–50. Cold Spring Harbor, NY: Cold Spring Harbor Lab.

Dubnau J, Struhl G. 1996. RNA recognition and translational regulation by a homeodomain protein. *Nature* 379:694–99

Duncan R, Milburn SC, Hershey JWB. 1987. Regulated phosphorylation and low abundance of HeLa cell initiation factor eIF-4F suggests a role in translational control. *J. Biol. Chem.* 262:380–88

Ephrussi A, Dickinson LK, Lehmann R. 1991. *oskar* organises the germ plasm and directs localisation of the posterior determinant *nanos*. *Cell* 66:37–50

Erdelyi M, Michon A-M, Guichet A, Glotzer JB, Ephrussi A. 1995. Requirement for *Drosophila* cytoplasmic tropomyosin in *oskar* mRNA localization. *Nature* 377:524–27

Evans TC, Crittenden SL, Kodoyianni V, Kimble J. 1994. Translational control of maternal *glp-1* mRNA establishes an asymmetry in the C. elegans embryo. *Cell* 77:183–94

Feigenblum D, Schneider RJ. 1996. Cap-binding protein (eukaryotic initiation factor 4E) and 4E-inactivating protein BP-1 independently regulate cap-dependent translation. *Mol. Cell. Biol.* 16:5450–57

Ferrandon D, Elphick L, Nüsslein-Volhard C, St Johnston D. 1994. Staufen protein associates with the 3′UTR of *bicoid* mRNA to form particles that move in a microtubule-dependent manner. *Cell* 79:1221–32

Florkiewicz RZ, Sommer A. 1989. Human basic fibroblast growth factor gene encodes four polypeptides: three initiate translation from non-AUG codons. *Proc. Natl. Acad. Sci. USA* 86:3978–81

Flynn A, Proud CG. 1996. The role of eIF4 in cell proliferation. *Cancer Surv.* 27:293–310

Flynn A, Vries RGJ, Proud CG. 1997. Signalling pathways which regulate eIF4E. *Biochem. Soc. Trans.* 25:192

Fox CA, Sheets MD, Wickens MP. 1989. Poly (A) addition during maturation of frog oocytes: distinct nuclear and cytoplasmic activities and regulation by the sequence UUUUUAU. *Genes Dev.* 3:2151–62

Frederickson RM, Mushynski WE, Sonenberg N, Rozen R. 1992. Phosphorylation of translation initiation factor eIF-4E is induced in a ras-dependent manner during nerve growth factor-mediated PC12 cell differentiation. *Mol. Cell. Biol.* 12:1239–47

Fulton AB, Wan KM, Penman S. 1980. The spatial distribution of polyribosomes in 3T3 cells and the associated assembly of proteins into the skeletal framework. *Cell* 20:849–57

Fütterer J, Kiss-Laszlo Z, Hohn T. 1993. Nonlinear ribosome migration on cauliflower mosaic virus 35S RNA. *Cell* 73:789–802

Galili G, Kawata EE, Smith LD, Larkins BA. 1988. Role of the 3′-poly(A) sequence in translational regulation of mRNAs in *Xenopus laevis* oocytes. *J. Biol. Chem.* 263:5764–70

Gallie DR. 1991. The cap and the poly (A) tail function synergistically to regulate mRNA translational efficiency. *Genes Dev.* 5:2108–16

Gallie DR, Walbot V. 1990. RNA pseudoknot domain of tobacco mosaic virus can functionally substitute for a poly(A) tail in plant and animal cells. *Genes Dev.* 4:1149–57

Gao M, Rychlik W, Rhoads RE. 1998. Cloning and characterization of human eIF-4E genes. *J. Biol. Chem.* 273:4622–28

Gavin AC, Schorderet-Slatkine S. 1997. Ribosomal S6 kinase p90^{rsk} and mRNA cap-binding protein eIF-4E phosphorylations correlate with MAP kinase activation during meiotic reinitiation of mouse oocytes. *Mol. Reprod. Dev.* 46:383–91

Gavis ER, Lehmann R. 1994. Translational regulation of *nanos* by RNA localization. *Nature* 369:315–18

Gavis ER, Lunsford L, Bergsten SE, Lehmann R. 1996. A conserved 90 nucleotide element mediates translational repression of *nanos* RNA. *Development* 122:2791–800

Geballe AP, Morris DR. 1994. Initiation codons within 5'-leaders of mRNAs as regulators of translation. *Trends Biochem. Sci.* 19:159–64

Gebauer F, Merendino L, Hentze MW, Valcarcel J. 1998. The *Drosophila* splicing regulator Sex-lethal directly inhibits translation of *male-specific-lethal 2* mRNA. *RNA* 4:142–50

Gebauer F, Richter JD. 1996. Mouse cytoplasmic polyadenylation element binding protein: an evolutionarily conserved protein that interacts with the cytoplasmic polyadenylation elements of c-*mos* mRNA. *Proc. Natl. Acad. Sci. USA* 93:14602–7

Gebauer F, Richter JD. 1997. Synthesis and function of Mos: the control switch of vertebrate oocyte meiosis. *BioEssays* 19:23–28

Gebauer F, Xu W, Cooper GM, Richter JD. 1994. Translational control by cytoplasmic polyadenylation of c-*mos* mRNA is necessary for oocyte maturation in the mouse. *EMBO J.* 13:5712–20

Gillian-Daniel DL, Gray NK, Åström J, Barkoff A, Wickens M. 1998. Modifications of the 5' cap of mRNAs during *Xenopus* oocyte maturation: independence from changes in poly (A) length and impact on translation. *Mol. Cell Biol.* In press

Goossen B, Caughman SW, Harford JB, Klausner RD, Hentze MW. 1990. Translational repression by a complex between the iron-responsive element of ferritin mRNA and its specific cytoplasmic binding protein is position-dependent in vivo. *EMBO J.* 9:4127–33

Goossen B, Hentze MW. 1992. Position is the critical determinant for function of iron-responsive elements as translational regulators. *Mol. Cell. Biol.* 12:1959–66

Goyer C, Altmann M, Lee HS, Blanc A, Deshmukh M, et al. 1993. *TIF4631* and *TIF4632*: Two yeast genes encoding the high-molecular-weight subunits of the cap-binding protein complex (eukaryotic initiation factor 4F) contain an RNA recognition motif-like sequence and carry out an essential function. *Mol. Cell. Biol.* 13:4860–74

Gradi A, Imataka H, Svitkin YV, Rom E, Raught B, et al. 1998. A novel functional human eukaryotic translation initiation factor 4G. *Mol. Cell. Biol.* 18:334–42

Gray NK, Hentze MW. 1994a. Iron regulatory protein prevents binding of the 43S translation pre-initiation complex to ferritin and eALAS mRNAs. *EMBO J.* 13:3882–91

Gray NK, Hentze MW. 1994b. Regulation of protein synthesis by mRNA structure. *Mol. Biol. Rep.* 19:195–200

Gray NK, Pantopoulos K, Dandekar T, Ackrell BAC, Hentze MW. 1996. Translational regulation of mammalian and *Drosophila* Krebs cycle enzymes via iron-responsive elements. *Proc. Natl. Acad. Sci. USA* 93:4925–30

Gray NK, Quick S, Goossen B, Constable A, Hirling H, et al. 1993. Recombinant iron regulatory factor functions as an iron-responsive element-binding protein, a translational repressor and an aconitase. A functional assay for translational repression and direct demonstration of the iron switch. *Eur. J. Biochem.* 218:657–67

Green MR. 1991. Biochemical mechanisms of constitutive and regulated pre-mRNA splicing. *Annu. Rev. Cell. Biol.* 7:559–99

Grens A, Scheffler IE. 1990. The 5'- and 3'-untranslated regions of ornithine decarboxylase mRNA affect the translational efficiency. *J. Biol. Chem.* 265:11810–16

Gressner AM, van de Leur E. 1980. Interactions of synthetic polynucleotides with small rat liver ribosomal subunits possessing low and highly phosphorylated protein S6. *Biochim. Biophys. Acta* 608:459–68

Grünert S, Jackson RJ. 1994. The immediate downstream codon strongly influences the efficiency of utilization of eukaryotic translation initiation codons. *EMBO J.* 13:3618–30

Gu W, Hecht NB. 1996. Translation of a testes-specific Cu/Zn superoxide dismutase (SOD-1) mRNA is regulated by a 65-kilodalton protein which binds to its 5'-untranslated region. *Mol. Cell. Biol.* 16:4535–43

Ha I, Wightman B, Ruvkun G. 1996. A bulged LIN-4/LIN-14 RNA duplex is sufficient for *Caenorhabditis elegans* LIN-14 temporal gradient formation. *Genes Dev.* 10:3041–50

Haghighat A, Mader S, Pause A, Sonenberg N. 1995. Repression of cap-dependent translation by 4E-binding protein 1: competition with p220 for binding to eukaryotic initiation factor-4E. *EMBO J.* 14:5701–9

Haghighat A, Sonenberg N. 1997. eIF4G dramatically enhances the binding of eIF4E to the mRNA 5'-cap structure. *J. Biol. Chem.* 272:21677–80

Hake LE, Mendez R, Richter JD. 1998. Specificity of RNA binding by CPEB: requirement for RNA recognition motifs and a novel zinc finger. *Mol. Cell. Biol.* 18:685–93

Hake LE, Richter JD. 1994. CPEB is a specificity factor that mediates cytoplasmic polyadenylation during Xenopus oocyte maturation. *Cell* 79:617–27

Hammond ML, Merrick W, Bowman LH. 1991. Sequences mediating the translation of mouse S16 ribosomal protein mRNA during myoblast differentiation and in vitro and possible control points for the in vitro translation. *Genes Dev.* 5:1723–36

Hann LE, Webb AC, Cai J-M, Gehrke L. 1997.

Identification of a competitive translation determinant in the 3'-untranslated region of alfalfa mosaic virus coat protein mRNA. *Mol. Cell Biol.* 17:2005–13

Hann SR, King MW, Bentley DL, Anderson CW, Eisenman RN. 1988. A non-AUG translational initiation in *c-myc* exon 1 generates a N-terminally distinct protein whose synthesis is disrupted in Burkitt's lymphoma. *Cell* 52:185–95

Hann SR, Sloan-Brown K, Spotts GD. 1992. Translational activation of the non-AUG-initiated *c-myc* 1 protein at high cell densities due to methionine deprivation. *Genes Dev.* 6: 1229–40

Hay B, Jan LY, Jan YN. 1988. A protein component of the Drosophila polar granules is encoded by *vasa* and has extensive sequence similarity to ATP-dependent helicases. *Cell* 55:577–87

Hellen CUT, Witherell GW, Schmid M, Shin SH, Pestova TV, et al. 1993. A cytoplasmic 57-kDa protein that is required for translation of picornavirus RNA by internal ribosome entry is identical to the nuclear pyrimidine tract-binding protein. *Proc. Natl. Acad. Sci. USA* 90:7642–46

Hemmings-Mieszczak M, Steger G, Hohn T. 1998. Regulation of CaMV 35S RNA translation is mediated by a stable hairpin in the leader. *RNA* 4:101–11

Henderson BR. 1996. Iron regulatory proteins 1 and 2. *BioEssays* 18:739–46

Hentze MW. 1997. eIF4G:A multipurpose ribosome adapter? *Science* 275:500–1

Hentze MW, Caughman SW, Rouault TA, Barriocanal JG, Dancis A, et al. 1987. Identification of the iron-responsive element for the translational regulation of human ferritin mRNA. *Science* 238:1570–73

Hentze MW, Kühn LC. 1996. Molecular control of vertebrate iron metabolism: mRNA-based regulatory circuits operated by iron, nitric oxide, and oxidative stress. *Proc. Natl. Acad. Sci. USA* 93:8175–82

Hershey JWB. 1991. Translational control in mammalian cells. *Annu. Rev. Biochem.* 60: 717–55

Hershey JWB, Mathews MB, Sonenberg N, eds. 1996. *Translational Control.* Cold Spring Harbor, NY: Cold Spring Harbor Lab.

Hill JR, Morris DR. 1993. Cell-specific translational regulation of S-adenosylmethionine decarboxylase mRNA. *J. Biol. Chem.* 268: 726–31

Hinnebusch AG. 1996. Translational control of GCN4: gene-specific regulation by phosphorylation of eIF2. See Hershey et al 1996, pp. 199–244

Hiremath LS, Webb NR, Rhoads RE. 1985. Immunological detection of the messenger RNA cap-binding protein. *J. Biol. Chem.* 260: 7843–49

Huarte J, Stutz A, O'Connell ML, Gubler P, Belin D, et al. 1992. Transient translational silencing by reversible mRNA deadenylation. *Cell* 69:1021–30

Hunter CP, Kenyon C. 1997. Spatial and temporal controls target pal-1 blastomere-specification activity to a single blastomere lineage in C. elegans embryos. *Cell* 87:217–26

Iizuka N, Najita L, Franzusoff A, Sarnow P. 1994. Cap-dependent and cap-independent translation by internal initiation of mRNAs in cell extracts prepared from *Saccharomyces cerevisiae. Mol. Cell. Biol.* 14:7322–30

Imataka H, Nakayama K, Yasumoto K-I, Mizuno A, Fujii-Kuriyami Y, Hayami M. 1994. Cell-specific translational control of transcription factor BTEB expression. *J. Biol. Chem.* 269:20668–73

Imataka H, Oslen HS, Sonenberg N. 1997. A new translational regulator with homology to eukaryotic translation initiation factor 4G. *EMBO J.* 16:817–25

Ito T, Jagus R, May WS. 1994. Interleukin 3 stimulates protein synthesis by regulating double-stranded RNA-dependent protein kinase. *Proc. Natl. Acad. Sci. USA* 91:7455–59

Izaurralde E, Lewis J, McGuigan C, Jankowska M, Darzynkiewicz E, Mattaj IW. 1994. A nuclear cap-binding complex involved in pre-mRNA splicing. *Cell* 78:657–68

Jackson RJ. 1996. A comparative view of initiation site selection mechanisms. See Hershey et al 1996, pp. 71–112

Jackson RJ, Kaminski A. 1995. Internal initiation of translation in eukaryotes: the picornavirus paradigm and beyond. *RNA* 1:985–1000

Jacobson A. 1996. Poly(A) metabolism and translation: the closed-loop model. See Hershey et al 1996, pp. 451–80

Jang SK, Kraüsslich HG, Nicklin MJH, Duke GM, Palmenberg AC, Wimmer E. 1988. A segment of the 5' non-translated region of encephalomyocarditis virus RNA directs internal entry of ribosomes during in vitro translation. *J. Virol.* 62:2636–43

Jefferies HBJ, Fumagalli S, Dennis PB, Reinhard C, Pearson RB, Thomas G. 1997. Rapamcin suppresses 5'TOP mRNA translation through inhibition of p70^{s6k}. *EMBO J.* 16:3693–704

Jefferies HBJ, Reinhard C, Kozma SC, Thomas G. 1994a. Rapamycin selectively represses translation of the "polypyrimidine tract" mRNA family. *Proc. Natl. Acad. Sci. USA* 91:4441–45

Jefferies HBJ, Thomas G. 1996. Ribosomal protein S6 phosphorylation and signal transduction. See Hershey et al 1996, pp. 389–409

Jefferies HBJ, Thomas G, Thomas G. 1994b. Elongation factor 1-α mRNA is selectively translated following mitogenic stimulation. *J. Biol. Chem.* 269:4367–72

Johannes G, Berger FG. 1992. Alterations in mRNA translation as a mechanism for the modification of enzyme synthesis during evolution: the ornithine decarboxylase model. *J. Biol. Chem.* 267:10108–15

Jones A, Schedl T. 1995. Mutations in *gld-1*, a female germ cell-specific tumor suppressor gene in *Caenorhabditis elegans* affected a conserved domain also found in Src-associated protein Sam68. *Genes Dev.* 9: 1491–504

Jones PM, Burrin JM, Ghatei MA, O'Halloran DO, Legon S, Bloom SR. 1990. The influence of thyroid hormone status on the hypothalamo-hypophyseal growth hormone axis. *Endocrinology* 126:1374–79

Joshi-Barve S, Rychlik W, Rhoads RE. 1990. Alteration of the major phosphorylation site of eukaryotic protein synthesis initiation factor 4E prevents its association with the 48S initiation complex. *J. Biol. Chem.* 265:2979–83

Kaminski A, Hunt SL, Patton JG, Jackson RJ. 1995. Direct evidence that polypyrimidine tract binding protein (PTB) is essential for internal initiation of translation of encephalomyocarditis virus RNA. *RNA* 1:924– 38

Kastern WH, Berry SJ. 1976. Non-methylated guanosine as the 5′ terminus of capped mRNA from insect oocytes. *Biochem. Biophys. Res. Commun.* 71:37–44

Kastern WH, Swindlehurst M, Aaron C, Hooper J, Berry SJ. 1982. Control of mRNA translation in oocytes and developing embryos of gaint moths. *Dev. Biol.* 89:437–49

Kaufman RJ, Murtha P, Davies MV. 1987. Translational efficiency of polycistronic mRNAs and their utilization to express heterologous genes in mammalian cells. *EMBO J.* 6:187–93

Kelley RL, Wang J, Bell L, Kuroda MI. 1997. *Sex-lethal* controls dosage compensation in *Drosophila* by a non-splicing mechanism. *Nature* 387:195–99

Kempe E, Muhs B, Schäfer M. 1993. Gene regulation in *Drosophila* spermatogenesis: analysis of protein binding at the translational control element TCE. *Dev. Genet.* 14:449–59

Kerekatte V, Smiley K, Hu B, Smith A, Gelder F, De Benedetti A. 1995. The proto-oncogene/translation factor eIF4E: a survey of its expression in breast carcinomas. *Int. J. Cancer* 64:27–31

Kiledjian M, Wang X, Leibhaber SA. 1995. Identification of two KH domain proteins

in the α-globin mRNP stability complex. *EMBO J.* 14:4357–64

Kimball SR, Heinzinger NK, Horetsky RL, Jefferson LS. 1998. Identification of interprotein interactions between the subunits of eukaryotic initiation factors eIF2 and eIF2B. *J. Biol. Chem.* 273:3039–44

Kim-Ha J, Kerr K, Macdonald PM. 1995. Translational regulation of *oskar* mRNA by Bruno, an ovarian RNA-binding protein, is essential. *Cell* 81:403–12

Kim-Ha J, Smith JL, Macdonald PM. 1991. *oskar* mRNA is localized to the posterior pole of the Drosophila oocyte. *Cell* 66:23–35

Klein PS, Melton DA. 1994. Induction of mesoderm in *Xenopus laevis* embryo by translation initiation factor 4E. *Science* 265:803–6

Kohler SA, Henderson BR, Kühn LC. 1995. Succinate-dehydrogenase-b mRNA of *Drosophila melanogaster* has a functional iron-responsive element in its 5′-untranslated region. *J. Biol. Chem.* 270:30781–86

Koloteva N, Mueller PP, McCarthy JEG. 1997. The position dependence of translational regulation via RNA-RNA and RNA-protein interactions in the 5′-untranslated region of eukaryotic mRNA is a function of thermodynamic competence of 40S ribosomes in translational initiation. *J. Biol. Chem.* 272:16531–39

Koromilas AE, Lazaris-Karatzas A, Sonenberg N. 1992a. mRNAs containing extensive secondary structure in their 5′ non-coding region translate efficiently in cells overexpressing initiation factor eIF-4E. *EMBO J.* 11:4153–58

Koromilas AE, Roy S, Barber GN, Katze MG, Sonenberg N. 1992b. Malignant transformation by a mutant of the IFN-inducible dsRNA-dependent protein kinase. *Science* 257:1685–89

Kozak M. 1983. Translation of insulin-related polypeptides from messenger RNAs with tandemly reiterated copies of the ribosome binding site. *Cell* 34:971–78

Kozak M. 1984a. Point mutations close to the AUG initiator codon affect the efficiency of translation of rat preproinsulin in vivo. *Nature* 308:241–46

Kozak M. 1984b. Selection of initiation sites by eucaryotic ribosomes: effect of inserting AUG triplets upstream from the coding sequence for preproinsulin. *Nucleic Acids Res.* 12:3873–93

Kozak M. 1986a. Influences of mRNA secondary structure on initiation by eukaryotic ribosomes. *Proc. Natl. Acad. Sci. USA* 83:2850–54

Kozak M. 1986b. Point mutations define a sequence flanking the AUG initiator codon that modulates translation by eukaryotic ribosomes. *Cell* 44:283–92

Kozak M. 1987a. An analysis of 5'-noncoding sequences from 699 vertebrate messenger RNAs. *Nucleic Acids Res.* 15:8125–48

Kozak M. 1987b. Effects of intercistronic length on the efficiency of reinitiation by eucaryotic ribosomes. *Mol. Cell. Biol.* 7:3438–45

Kozak M. 1988. Leader length and secondary structure modulate mRNA function under conditions of stress. *Mol. Cell Biol.* 8:2737–44

Kozak M. 1989a. Circumstances and mechanisms of inhibition of translation by secondary structure in eucaryotic mRNAs. *Mol. Cell. Biol.* 9:5134–42

Kozak M. 1989b. Context effects and inefficient initiation at non-AUG codons in eucaryotic cell-free translation systems. *Mol. Cell. Biol.* 9:5073–80

Kozak M. 1990. Downstream secondary structure facilitates recognition of initiator codons by eukaryotic ribosomes. *Proc. Natl. Acad. Sci. USA* 87:8301–5

Kozak M. 1991a. An analysis of vertebrate mRNA sequences: intimations of translational control. *J. Cell Biol.* 115:887–903

Kozak M. 1991b. Effects of long 5' leader sequences on initiation by eukaryotic ribosomes in vitro. *Gene Expr.* 1:117–25

Kozak M. 1991c. A short leader sequence impairs the fidelity of initiation by eukaryotic ribosomes. *Gene Expr.* 1:111–15

Kozak M. 1997. Recognition of AUG and alternative initiator codons is augmented by G in position +4 but is not generally affected by the nucleotides in positions +5 and +6. *EMBO J.* 16:2482–92

Kuge H, Richter JD. 1995. Cytoplasmic 3' poly(A) addition induces 5' cap ribose methylation: implications for translational control of maternal mRNA. *EMBO J.* 14:6301–10

Kuhn R, Kuhn C, Börsch D, Glätzer KH, Schäfer U, Schäfer M. 1991. A cluster of four genes selectively expressed in the male germ line of *Drosophilia melanogaster*. *Mech. Dev.* 35:143–51

Lamphear BJ, Kirchweger R, Skern T, Rhoads RE. 1995. Mapping functional domains in eukaryotic protein synthesis initiation factor 4G (eIF4G) with picornaviral proteases. *J. Biol. Chem.* 270:21975–83

Lamphear BJ, Panniers R. 1990. Cap binding protein complex that restores protein synthesis in heat-shocked Ehrlich cell lysates contains highly phosphorylated eIF-4E. *J. Biol. Chem.* 265:5333–36

Lang V, Zanchin NIT, Lünsdorf H, Tuite M, McCarthy JEG. 1994. Initiation factor eIF-4E of *Saccharomyces cerevisiae*: distribution within the cell, binding to mRNA, and consequences of its overproduction. *J. Biol. Chem.* 269:6117–23

Lantz V, Ambrosio L, Schedl P. 1992. The *Drosophila orb* gene is predicted to encode sex-specific germline RNA-binding proteins and has localized transcripts in ovaries and early embryos. *Development* 115:75–88

Lantz V, Chang JS, Horabin JI, Bopp D, Schedl P. 1994. The *Drosophila orb* RNA-binding protein is required for the formation of the egg chamber and establishment of polarity. *Genes Dev.* 8:598–613

Laskey RA, Mills AD, Gurdon JB, Partington GA. 1977. Protein synthesis in oocytes of Xenopus laevis is not regulated by the supply of messenger RNA. *Cell* 11:345–51

Lasko PF, Ashburner M. 1988. The product of *Drosophila* gene *vasa* is very similar to eukaryotic initiation factor-4A. *Nature* 335:611–17

Lavoie CA, Lachance PED, Sonenberg N, Lasko P. 1996. Alternatively spliced transcripts from the *Drosophila eIF4E* gene produce two different cap-binding proteins. *J. Biol. Chem.* 271:16393–98

Lawrence JC Jr, Abraham RT. 1997. PHAS/4E-BPs as regulators of mRNA translation and cell proliferation. *Trends Biochem. Sci.* 22:345–49

Lawson TG, Ray BK, Dodds JT, Grifo JA, Abramson RD, et al. 1986. Influence of 5' proximal secondary structure on the translational efficiency of eukaryotic mRNAs and on their interaction with initiation factors. *J. Biol. Chem.* 261:13979–89

Lazaris-Karatzas A, Smith MR, Frederickson RM, Jaramillo ML, Liu Y, et al. 1992. Ras mediates translation initiation factor 4E-induced malignant transformation. *Genes Dev.* 6:1631–42

Lazaris-Karatzas A, Sonenberg N. 1992. The mRNA 5' cap-binding protein, eIF-4E, cooperates with *v-myc* or E1A in the transformation of primary rodent fibroblasts. *Mol. Cell. Biol.* 12:1234–38

Le H, Tanquay RL, Balasta ML, Wei C-C, Browning KS, et al. 1997. Translation initiation factors eIF-iso4G and eIF-4B interact with the poly(A)-binding protein and increase its RNA binding activity. *J. Biol. Chem.* 272:16247–55

Lee RC, Feinbaum RL, Ambros V. 1993. The C. elegans heterochronic gene *lin-4* encodes small RNAs with antisense complementarity to *lin-14*. *Cell* 75:843–54

Lejbkowicz F, Goyer C, Darveau A, Neron S, Lemieux R, Sonenberg N. 1992. A fraction of the mRNA 5' cap-binding protein, eukaryotic initation factor 4E localizes to the nucleus. *Proc. Natl. Acad. Sci. USA* 89:9612–16

Lenk R, Ransom L, Kaufmann Y, Penman S. 1977. A cytoskeletal structure with associated polyribosomes obtained from HeLa cells. *Cell* 10:67–78

Levy-Strumpf N, Deiss LP, Berissi H, Kimichi A. 1997. DAP-5, a novel homolog of eukaryotic translation initiation factor 4G isolated as a putatitive modulator of gamma interferon-induced programmed cell death. *Mol. Cell. Biol.* 17:1615–25

Li DDL, Liu L, Dawson M, De Benedetti A. 1997. Overexpression of eukaryotic initiation factor 4E (eIF-4E) in breast carcinoma. *Cancer* 79:2385–90

Liang L, Diehl-Jones W, Lasko P. 1994. Localization of Vasa protein to the *Drosophila* pole plasm is independent of its RNA-binding and helicase activities. *Development* 120:1201–11

Lieberfarb ME, Chu T, Wreden C, Theurkauf W, Gergen JP, Strickland S. 1996. Mutations that perturb poly (A)-dependent maternal mRNA activation block the initiation of development. *Development* 122:579–88

Liebig HD, Ziegler E, Yan R, Hartmuth K, Klump H, et al. 1993. Purification of two picornaviral proteinases: interaction with eIF-4γ and influence on in vitro translation. *Biochemistry* 32:7581–88

Lin FT, MacDougald OA, Diehl AM, Lane MD. 1993. A 30-kDa alternative translation product of the CCAAT/enchancer binding protein α message: transcriptional activator lacking antimitotic activity. *Proc. Natl. Acad. Sci. USA* 90:9606–10

Lin TA, Kong X, Haystead TAJ, Pause A, Belsham G, et al. 1994. PHAS-I as a link between mitogen-activated protein kinase and translation initiation. *Science* 266:653–56

Linder P, Slonimski PP. 1989. An essential yeast protein, encoded by duplicate genes *TIF1* and *TIF2* and homologous to the mammalian initiation factor eIF-4A, can suppress a mitochondrial missense mutation. *Proc. Natl. Acad. Sci. USA* 86:2286–90

Liu C-C, Simonsen CC, Levinson AD. 1984. Initiation of translation at internal AUG codons in mammalian cells. *Nature* 309:82–85

Long RM, Singer RH, Meng X, Gonzalez I, Nasmyth K, Jansen R-P. 1997. Mating type switching in yeast controlled by asymmetric localization of ASH-1 mRNA. *Science* 277:383–87

Macdonald PM, Smibert CA. 1996. Translational regulation of maternal mRNAs. *Curr. Opin. Genet. Dev.* 6:403–7

Macejak DG, Sarnow P. 1991. Internal initiation of translation mediated by the 5′ leader of a cellular mRNA. *Nature* 353:90–94

Mader S, Lee H, Pause A, Sonenberg N. 1995.

The translation initiation factor eIF-4E binds to a common motif shared by the translation factor eIF4γ and the translation repressors 4E-binding proteins. *Mol. Cell. Biol.* 15:4990–97

Manseau L, Calley J, Phan H. 1996. Profilin is required for posterior patterning of the *Drosophila* oocyte. *Development* 122:2109–16

Manzella JM, Blackshear PJ. 1990. Regulation of rat ornithine decarboxylase mRNA translation by its 5′-untranslated region. *J. Biol. Chem.* 265:11817–22

Manzella JM, Rychlik W, Rhoads RE, Hershey JWB, Blackshear PJ. 1991. Insulin induction of ornithine decarboxylase: importance of mRNA secondary structure and phosphorylation of eucaryotic initiation factors eIF-4B and eIF-4E. *J. Biol. Chem.* 266:3383–89

Markussen F-H, Michon A-M, Breitwieser W, Ephrussi A. 1995. Translational control of *oskar* generates short OSK, the isoform that induces pole plasm assembly. *Development* 121:3723–32

McCarthy JEG, Brimacombe R. 1994. Prokaryotic translation: the interactive pathway leading the initiation. *Trends Genet.* 10:402–7

McGrew LL, Dworkin-Rastl E, Dworkin MB, Richter JD. 1989. Poly (A) elongation during *Xenopus* oocyte maturation is required for translational recruitment and is mediated by a short sequence element. *Genes Dev.* 3:803–15

Meerovitch K, Svitkin YV, Lee HS, Lejbkowicz F, Kenan DJ, et al. 1993. La autoantigen enhances and corrects aberrant translation of poliovirus RNA in reticulocyte lysate. *J. Virol.* 67:3798–807

Melefors Ö. 1996. Translational regulation in vivo of the *Drosophila melanogaster* mRNA encoding succinate dehydrogenase iron protein via iron responsive elements. *Biochem. Biophys. Res. Commun.* 221:437–41

Melefors Ö, Goossen B, Johansson HE, Stripecke R, Gray NK, Hentze MW. 1993. Translational control of 5-aminolevulinate synthase mRNA by iron-responsive elements in erythroid cells. *J. Biol. Chem.* 268:5974–78

Merrick WC, Hershey JWB. 1996. The pathway and mechanism of eukaryotic protein synthesis. See Hershey et al 1996, pp. 31–69

Merrick WC. 1992. Mechanism and regulation of eukaryotic protein synthesis. *Microbiol. Rev.* 56:291–315

Meurs EF, Galabru J, Barber GN, Katze MG, Hovanessian AG. 1993. Tumor suppressor function of the interferon-induced double-stranded RNA-activated protein kinase. *Proc. Natl. Acad. Sci. USA* 90:232–36

Meyuhas O, Avni D, Shama S. 1996. Translational control of ribosomal protein mRNAs in eukaryotes. See Hershey et al 1996, pp. 363–88

Michael WM, Eder PS, Dreyfuss G. 1997. The K nuclear shuttling domain: a novel signal for nuclear import and nuclear export in the hnRNP K protein. *EMBO J.* 16:3587–98

Michelotti EF, Michelotti GA, Aronsohn AI, Levens D. 1996. Heterogeneous nuclear ribonucleoprotein K is a translation factor. *Mol. Cell. Biol.* 16:2350–60

Miller PF, Hinnebusch AG. 1989. Sequences that surround the stop codons or upstream open reading frames in GCN4 mRNA determine their distinct functions in translational control. *Genes Dev.* 3:1217–25

Minich WB, Balasta ML, Goss DJ, Rhoads RE. 1994. Chromatographic resolution of the in vivo phosphorylated and nonphosphorylated eukaryotic translation initiation factor eIF-4E: increased cap affinity of the phosphorylated form. *Proc. Natl. Acad. Sci. USA* 91:7668–72

Minvielle-Sebastia L, Preker PJ, Wiederkehr T, Strahm Y, Keller W. 1997. The major yeast poly(A)-binding protein is associated with cleavage factor IA and functions in premessenger RNA 3'-end formation. *Proc. Natl. Acad. Sci. USA* 94:7897–902

Miyagi Y, Sugiyama A, Asai A, Okazaki T, Kuchino Y, Kerr SJ. 1995. Elevated levels of eukaryotic translation initiation factor eIF-4E, mRNA in a broad spectrum of transformed cell lines. *Cancer Lett.* 91:247–52

Morley SJ. 1994. Signal transduction mechanisms in the regulation of protein synthesis. *Mol. Biol. Rep.* 19:221–31

Morley SJ. 1997. Intracellular signalling pathways regulating initiation factor eIF-4E phosphorylation during the activation of cell growth. *Biochem. Soc. Trans.* 25:503–9

Morley SJ, Curtis PS, Pain VM. 1997. eIF4G: Translation's mystery factor begins to yield its secrets. *RNA* 3:1085–104

Morley SJ, Pain VM. 1995a. Hormone-induced meiotic maturation in *Xenopus* oocytes occurs independently of p70^{s6k} activation and is associated with enhanced initiation factor (eIF-4F) phosphorylation and complex formation. *J. Cell Sci.* 108:1751–60

Morley SJ, Pain VM. 1995b. Translational regulation during activation of porcine peripheral blood lymphocytes: association and phosphorylation of the α and γ subunits of the initiation factor complex eIF-4F. *Biochem. J.* 312:627–35

Morley SJ, Rau M, Kay JE, Pain VM. 1993. Increased phosphorylation of eukaryotic initiation factor 4α during early activation of T lymphocytes correlates with increased initiation factor 4F complex formation. *Eur. J. Biochem.* 218:39–48

Morley SJ, Traugh JA. 1989. Phorbol esters stimulate phosphorylation of eukaryotic initiation factors 3, 4B, and 4F. *J. Biol. Chem.* 264:2401–4

Moss EG, Lee RC, Ambros V. 1997. The cold shock domain protein LIN-28 controls developmental timing in C. elegans and is regulated by the *lin-4* RNA. *Cell* 88:637–46

Muckenthaler M, Gray NK, Hentze MW. 1998. IRP-1 binding to ferritin mRNA disrupts the bridging interaction between cap-binding complex and the small ribosomal subunit. *Mol. Cell.* In press

Muckenthaler M, Gunkel N, Stripecke R, Hentze MW. 1997. Regulated poly(A) tail shortening in somatic cells mediated by cap-proximal translational repressor proteins and ribosomal association. *RNA* 3:983–95

Muhlrad D, Decker CJ, Parker R. 1994. Deadenylation of the unstable mRNA encoded by the yeast MFA2 gene leads to decapping followed by 5'-3' digestion of the transcript. *Genes Dev.* 8:855–66

Mundschau LJ, Faller DV. 1992. Oncogenic *ras* induces an inhibitor of double-stranded RNA-dependent eukaryotic initiation factor 2α-kinase activation. *J. Biol. Chem.* 267:23092–98

Munroe D, Jacobson A. 1990. mRNA poly (A) tail, a 3' enhancer of translational initiation. *Mol. Cell. Biol.* 10:3441–55

Murata Y, Wharton RP. 1995. Binding of pumilio to maternal *hunchback* mRNA is required for posterior patterning in Drosophila embryos. *Cell* 80:747–56

Murphy D, Pardy K, Seah V, Carter D. 1992. Posttranscriptional regulation of rat growth hormone gene expression: increased message stability and nuclear polyadenylation accompany thyroid hormone depletion. *Mol. Cell. Biol.* 12:2624–32

Muschel R, Khoury G, Reid LM. 1986. Regulation of insulin mRNA abundance and adenylation: dependence on hormones and matrix substrata. *Mol. Cell. Biol.* 6:337–41

Muthukrishnan S, Moss B, Cooper JA, Maxwell ES. 1978. Influence of 5'-terminal cap structure on the initiation of translation of vaccinia virus mRNA. *J. Biol. Chem.* 253:1710–15

Nathan C-A, Carter P, Liu L, Li BDL, Abreo F, et al. 1997a. Elevated expressions of eIF4E and FGF-2 isoforms during vascularization of breast carcinomas. *Oncogene* 15:1087–94

Nathan C-AO, Liu L, Li BD, Abreo FW, Nandy I, De Benedetti A. 1997b. Detection of the proto-oncogene eIF4E in surgical margins may predict recurrence in head and neck cancer. *Oncogene* 15:579–84

Nelson EM, Winkler MM. 1987. Regulation of mRNA entry into polysomes: parameters affecting polysome size and the fraction of mRNA in polysomes. *J. Biol. Chem.* 262:11501–6

Nielsen PJ, Trachsel H. 1988. The mouse protein synthesis initiation factor 4A gene family includes two related functional genes which are differentially expressed. *EMBO J.* 7:2097–105

OH SK, Sarnow P. 1993. Gene regulation: translational initiation by internal ribosome binding. *Curr. Opin. Genet. Dev.* 3:295–300

OH SK, Scott MP, Sarnow P. 1992. Homeotic gene *antennapedia* mRNA contains 5'-noncoding sequences that confer translational initiation by internal ribosome binding. *Genes Dev.* 6:1643–53

Ohlmann T, Rau M, Pain VM, Morley SJ. 1996. The C-terminal domain of eukaryotic protein synthesis initiation factor (eIF) 4G is sufficient to support cap-independent translation in the absence of eIF-4E. *EMBO J.* 15:1371–82

Ornelles DA, Fey EG, Penman S. 1986. Cytochalasin releases mRNA from the cytoskeletal framework and inhibits protein synthesis. *Mol. Cell. Biol.* 6:1650–62

Ostareck DH, Ostareck-Lederer A, Wilm M, Thiele BJ, Mann M, Hentze MW. 1997. mRNA silencing in erythroid differentiation: hnRNP K and hnRNP E1 regulate 15-lipoxygenase translation from the 3' end. *Cell* 89:597–606

Ostareck-Lederer A, Ostareck DH, Standart N, Thiele B-J. 1994. Translation of 15-lipoxygenase mRNA is inhibited by a protein that binds to a repeated sequence in the 3' untranslated region. *EMBO J.* 13:1476–81

Paek I, Axel R. 1987. Glucocorticoids enchance stability of human growth hormone mRNA. *Mol. Cell. Biol.* 7:1496–507

Pain VM. 1996. Initiation of protein synthesis in eukaryotic cells. *Eur. J. Biochem.* 236:747–71

Paris J, Swenson K, Piwnica-Worms H, Richter JD. 1991. Maturation-specific polyadenylation: in vitro activation by $p34^{cdc2}$ and phosphorylation of a 58-kDa CPE-binding protein. *Genes Dev.* 5:1697–708

Parola AL, Kobilka BK. 1994. The peptide product of a 5' leader cistron in a β_2 adrenergic receptor mRNA inhibits receptor synthesis. *J. Biol. Chem.* 269:4497–505

Pause A, Belsham GJ, Gingras A-C, Donze O, Lin T-A, et al. 1994a. Insulin-dependent stimulant of protein synthesis by phosphorylation of a regulator of 5'-cap function. *Nature* 371:762–67

Pause A, Méthot N, Svitkin Y, Merrick WC, Sonenberg N. 1994b. Dominant negative mutants of mammalian translation initiation factor eIF-4A define a critical role for eIF-4F in cap-dependent and cap-independent initiation of translation. *EMBO J.* 13:1205–15

Peabody DS, Berg P. 1986. Termination-reinitiation occurs in the translation of mammalian cell mRNAs. *Mol. Cell. Biol.* 6:2695–703

Pedersen S, Celis JE, Nielsen J, Christiansen J, Nielsen FC. 1997. Distinct repression of translation by wortmannin and rapamycin. *Eur. J. Biochem.* 247:449–56

Pelletier J, Sonenberg N. 1985a. Insertion mutagenesis to increase secondary structure within the 5' noncoding region of a eukaryotic mRNA reduces translational efficiency. *Cell* 40:515–26

Pelletier J, Sonenberg N. 1985b. Photochemical cross-linking of cap binding proteins to eukaryotic mRNAs: effect of mRNA 5' secondary structure. *Mol. Cell. Biol.* 5:3222–30

Pelletier J, Sonenberg N. 1988. Internal initiation of translation of eukaryotic mRNA directed by a sequence derived from poliovirus RNA. *Nature* 334:320–25

Pestova TV, Shatsky IN, Fletcher SP, Jackson RJ, Hellen CUT. 1998. A prokaryotic-like mode of cytoplasmic eukaryotic ribosome binding to the initiation codon during internal translation initiation of hepatitis C and classical swine fever virus RNAs. *Genes Dev.* 12:67–83

Pestova TV, Shatsky IN, Hellen CUT. 1996. Functional dissection of eukaryotic initiation factor 4F: The 4A subunit and the central domain of the 4G subunit are sufficient to mediate internal entry of 43S preinitiation complexes. *Mol. Cell. Biol.* 16:6870–78

Prats H, Kaghad M, Prats AC, Klagsbrun M, Lelias JM, et al. 1989. High molecular mass forms of basic fibroblast growth factor are initiated by alternative CUG codons. *Proc. Natl. Acad. Sci. USA* 86:1836–40

Preiss T, Hentze MW. 1998. Dual function of the messenger RNA cap structure in poly (A)-tail-promoted translation in yeast. *Nature* 392:516–20

Proud CG. 1994. Peptide-chain elongation in eukaryotes. *Mol. Biol. Rep.* 19:161–70

Proweller A, Butler JS. 1997. Ribosome concentration contributes to discrimination against poly(A) mRNA during translation initiation in *Saccharomyces cerevisiae*. *J. Biol. Chem.* 272:6004–10

Proweller A, Butler S. 1994. Efficient translation of poly (A)-deficient mRNAs in *Saccharomyces cerevisiae*. *Genes Dev.* 8:2629–40

Puoti A, Gallegos M, Zhang B, Wickens MP, Kimble J. 1997. Controls of cell fate and pattern by 3' untranslated regions: the *Caenorhabditis elegans* sperm/oocyte decision. *Cold Spring Harbor Symp. Quant. Biol.* 62:19–24

Rao CD, Pech M, Robbins KC, Aaronson SA. 1988. The 5' untranslated sequence of the c-sis/platelet-derived growth factor 2 transcript is a potent translational inhibitor. *Mol. Cell. Biol.* 8:284–92

Rapoport SM, Schewe T. 1986. The maturational breakdown of mitochondria in reticulocytes. *Biochim. Biophys. Acta* 864:471–95

Rau M, Ohlmann T, Morley SJ, Pain VM. 1996. A reevaluation of the cap-binding protein, eIF4E as a rate-limiting factor for initiation of translation in reticuloyte lysate. *J. Biol. Chem.* 271:8983–90

Reynolds K, Zimmer AM, Zimmer A. 1996. Regulation of RARβ2 mRNA expression: evidence for an inhibitory peptide encoded in the 5'-untranslated region. *J. Cell Biol.* 134: 827–35

Rhoads RE. 1991. Protein synthesis, cell growth and oncogenesis. *Curr. Opin. Cell Biol.* 3: 1019–24

Richter JD. 1996. Dynamics of poly (A) addition and removal during development. See Hershey et al 1996, pp. 481–503

Rinker-Schaeffer CW, Austin V, Zimmer S, Rhoads RE. 1992. *ras* transformation of cloned rat embryo fibroblasts results in increased rates of protein synthesis and phosphorylation of eukaryotic initiation factor 4E. *J. Biol. Chem.* 267:10659–64

Rivera-Pomar R, Niessing D, Schmidt-Ott U, Gehring WJ, Jäckle H. 1996. RNA binding and translational suppression in bicoid. *Nature* 379:746–49

Rongo C, Gavis ER, Lehmann R. 1995. Localization of *oskar* RNA regulates oskar translation and requires Oskar protein. *Development* 121:2737–46

Rosenwald IB, Lazaris-Karatzas A, Sonenberg N, Schmidt EV. 1993. Elevated levels of cyclin D1 protein in response to increased expression of eucaryotic initiation factor 4E. *Mol. Cell. Biol.* 13:7358–63

Ross AF, Oleynikov Y, Kislauskis EH, Taneja KL, Singer RH. 1997. Characterization of a β-actin mRNA zipcode-binding protein. *Mol. Cell. Biol.* 17:2158–65

Rousseau D, Gingras A-C, Pause A, Sonenberg N. 1996. The eIF4E-binding proteins 1 and 2 are negative regulators of cell growth. *Oncogene* 13:2415–20

Rowlands AG, Panniers R, Henshaw EC. 1988. The catalytic mechanism of guanine nucleotide exchange factor action and competitive inhibition by phosphorylated eukaryotic initiation factor 2. *J. Biol. Chem.* 263:5526–33

Ruan H, Shantz LM, Pegg AE, Morris DR. 1996. The upstream open reading frame of the mRNA encoding S-adenosylmethionine decarboxylase is a polyamine-responsive translational control element. *J. Biol. Chem.* 271: 29576–82

Sachs A, Buratowski S. 1997. Common themes in translational and transcription regulation. *Trends Biochem. Sci.* 22:189–92

Sachs AB, Davis RW. 1989. The poly(A) binding protein is required for poly(A) shortening and 60S ribosomal subunit-dependent translation initiation. *Cell* 58:857–67

Sachs AB, Davis RW. 1990. Translation initiation and ribosome biogenesis: involvement of a putative RNA helicase and RPL46. *Science* 247:1077–79

Sachs AB, Davis RW, Kornberg RD. 1987. A single domain of yeast poly(A)-binding protein is necessary and sufficient for RNA binding and cell viability. *Mol. Cell. Biol.* 7:3268–76

Sachs AB, Sarnow P, Hentze MW. 1997. Starting at the beginning, middle and end: translation initiation in eukaryotes. *Cell* 89:831–38

Sagata N. 1997. What does Mos do in oocytes and somatic cells. *BioEssays* 19:13–21

Salles FJ, Lieberfarb ME, Wreden C, Gergen JP, Strickland S. 1994. Regulated polyadenylation of maternal mRNAs allows coordinate initiation of *Drosophila* development. *Science* 266:1996–99

Saris CJM, Domen J, Berns A. 1991. The *pim*-1 oncogene encodes two related protein-serine/threonine kinases by alternative initiation at AUG and CUG. *EMBO J.* 10:655–64

Schäfer M, Kuhn R, Bosse F, Schäfer U. 1990. A conserved element in the leader mediates post-meiotic translation as well as cytoplasmic polyadenylation of a *Drosophila* spermatocyte mRNA. *EMBO J.* 9:4519–25

Schalinske KL, Anderson SA, Tuazon PT, Chen OS, Kennedy MC, Eisenstein RS. 1997. The iron-sulfur cluster of iron regulatory protein 1 modulates the accessibility of RNA binding and phosphorylation sites. *Biochemistry* 36:3950–58

Schalinske KL, Chen OS, Eisenstein RS. 1998. Iron differentially stimulates translation of mitochondrial aconitase and ferritin mRNAs in mammalian cells—implications for iron regulatory proteins as regulators of mitochondrial citrate utilization. *J. Biol. Chem.* 273: 3740–46

Scheper GC, Mulder J, Kleijn M, Voorma HO, Thomas AAM, van Wijk R. 1997. Inactivation of eIF2B and phosphorylation of PHAS-I in heat-shocked rat hepatoma cells. *J. Biol. Chem.* 272:26850–56

Schleiss MR, Degnin CR, Geballe AP. 1991. Translational control of human cytomegalovirus gp48 expression. *J. Virol.* 65:6782–89

Schnabel R, Priess JR. 1997. Specification of cell fates in the early embryo. In *C. elegans II*, ed. DL Riddle, T Blumenthal, BJ Meyer,

JR Priess, pp. 361–82. Cold Spring Harbor, NY: Cold Spring Harbor Press

Schnierle BS, Gershon PD, Moss B. 1992. Cap-specific mRNA (nucleotide-$O^{2'}$-)-methyltransferase and poly(A) polymerase stimulatory activities of vaccinia virus are mediated by a single protein. *Proc. Natl. Acad. Sci. USA* 89:2897–901

Schumacher JM, Lee K, Edelhoff S, Braun RE. 1995. Spnr, a murine RNA-binding protein that is localized to cytoplasmic microtubules. *J. Cell. Biol.* 129:1023–32

Schupbach T, Wieschaus E. 1991. Female sterile mutations on the second chromosome of *Drosophila melanogaster*. II. Mutations blocking oogenesis or altering egg morphology. *Genetics* 129:1119–36

Sedman SA, Gelembiuk GW, Mertz JE. 1990. Translation initiation at a downstream AUG occurs with increased efficiency when the upstream AUG is located very close to the 5′ cap. *J. Virol.* 64:453–57

Shama S, Avni D, Fredrickson RM, Sonenberg N, Meyuhas O. 1995. Over-expression of initiation factor eIF-4E does not relieve the translational repression of ribosomal protein mRNAs. *Gene Expr.* 4:241–52

Shantz LM, Pegg AE. 1994. Overproduction of ornithine decarboxylase caused by relief of translational repression is associated with neoplastic transformation. *Cancer Res.* 54: 2313–16

Sheets MD, Fox CA, Hunt T, van Woude G, Wickens M. 1994. The 3′-untranslated regions of c-*mos* and cyclin mRNAs stimulate translation by regulating cytoplasmic polyadenylation. *Genes Dev.* 8:926–38

Sheets MD, Wu M, Wickens MP. 1995. Polyadenylation of c-*mos* as a control point in *Xenopus* meiotic maturation. *Nature* 374: 511–16

Simon R, Tassan JP, Richter JD. 1992. Translational control by poly (A) elongation during *Xenopus* development: differential repression and enhancement by a novel cytoplasmic polyadenylation element. *Genes Dev.* 6:2580–91

Simon R, Wu L, Richter JD. 1996. Cytoplasmic polyadenylation of activin receptor mRNA and the control of pattern formation of *Xenopus* development. *Dev. Biol.* 179:239–50

Smibert CA, Wilson JE, Kerr K, Macdonald PM. 1996. Smaug protein represses translation of unlocalized *nanos* mRNA in the *Drosophila* embryo. *Genes Dev.* 10:2600–9

Sommerville J, Ladomery M. 1996. Transcription and masking of mRNA in germ cells: involvement of Y-box proteins. *Chromosoma* 104:469–78

Sonenberg N. 1994. mRNA translation: influ-

ence of the 5′ and 3′ untranslated regions. *Curr. Opin. Genet. Dev.* 4:310–15

Sonenberg N. 1996. mRNA 5′ cap-binding protein eIF4E and control of cell growth. See Hershey et al 1996, pp. 245–69

Spradling A, Penman S, Pardue ML. 1975. Analysis of *Drosophila* mRNA by in situ hybridization: sequences transcribed in normal and heat shocked cultured cells. *Cell* 4:395–404

Standart N. 1992. Masking and unmasking of maternal mRNA. *Semin. Dev. Biol.* 3:367–79

Standart N, Dale M, Stewart E, Hunt T. 1990. Maternal mRNA from clam oocytes can be specifically unmasked in vitro by antisense RNA complementary to the 3′-untranslated region. *Genes Dev.* 4:2157–68

Standart N, Jackson RJ. 1994. Regulation of translation by specific protein/mRNA interactions. *Biochimie* 76:867–79

Stebbins-Boaz B, Hake LE, Richter JD. 1996. CPEB controls the cytoplasmic polyadenylation of cyclin, Cdk2 and c-*mos* mRNAs and is necessary for oocyte maturation in *Xenopus*. *EMBO J.* 15:2582–92

St Johnston D. 1995. The intracellular localization of messenger RNAs. *Cell* 81:161–70

St Johnston D, Beuchle D, Nüsslein-Volhard C. 1991. *staufen*, a gene required to localise maternal mRNAs in the Drosophila egg. *Cell* 66: 51–63

St Johnston D, Brown NH, Gall JG, Jantsch M. 1992. A conserved double-stranded RNA-binding domain. *Proc. Natl. Acad. Sci. USA* 89:10979–83

St Johnston D, Driever W, Berleth T, Richstein S, Nüsslein-Volhard C. 1989. Multiple steps in the localization of *bicoid* mRNA to the anterior pole of the *Drosophila* oocyte. *Development* 107(Suppl.):13–19

St Johnston D, Nüsslein-Volhard C. 1992. The origin of pattern and polarity in the Drosophila embryo. *Cell* 68:201–19

Stoneley M, Paulin FEM, Le Quesne JPC, Chappell SA, Willis AE. 1998. c-*myc* 5′ untranslated region contains an internal ribosome entry segment. *Oncogene* 16:423–28

Storti RV, Scott MP, Rich A, Pardue ML. 1980. Translational control of protein synthesis in response to heat shock in D. melanogaster cells. *Cell* 22:825–34

Stripecke R, Hentze MW. 1992. Bacteriophage and spliceosomal proteins function as position-dependent *cis/trans* repressors of mRNA translation in vitro. *Nucleic Acids Res.* 20:5555–64

Stripecke R, Oliveira CC, McCarthy JEG, Hentze MW. 1994. Proteins binding to 5′ untranslated region sites: a general mechanism for translational regulation of mRNAs in human and yeast cells. *Mol. Cell. Biol.* 14:5898–909

Svitkin YV, Meerovitch K, Lee HS, Dholakia JN, Kenan DJ, et al. 1994a. Internal translation initiation on poliovirus RNA: further characterization of La function in poliovirus translation in vitro. *J. Virol.* 68:1544–50

Svitkin YV, Ovchinnikov LP, Dreyfuss G, Sonenberg N. 1996. General RNA binding proteins render translation cap dependent. *EMBO J.* 15:7147–55

Svitkin YV, Pause A, Sonenberg N. 1994b. La autoantigen alleviates translational repression by the 5′ leader sequence of the human immunodeficieny virus type 1 mRNA. *J. Virol.* 68:7001–7

Tafuri SR, Wolffe AP. 1993. Selective recruitment of masked maternal mRNA from messenger ribonucleoprotein particles containing FRGY2 (mRNP4). *J. Biol. Chem.* 268:24255–61

Takimoto M, Tomonaga T, Matunis M, Avigan M, Krutzsch H, et al. 1993. Specific binding of heterogeneous ribonucleoprotein particle protein K to the human c-*myc* promoter in vitro. *J. Biol. Chem.* 268:18249–58

Taneja KL, Lifshitz LM, Fay FS, Singer RH. 1992. Poly(A) RNA codistribution with microfilaments: evaluation by in situ hybridization and quantitative digital imaging microscopy. *J. Cell. Biol.* 119:1245–60

Tarun SZ, Sachs AB. 1995. A common function for mRNA 5′ and 3′ ends in translation initiation in yeast. *Genes Dev.* 9:2997–3007

Tarun SZ, Sachs AB. 1996. Association of the yeast poly(A) tail binding protein with translation initiation factor eIF-4G. *EMBO J.* 15:7168–77

Tarun SZ, Wells SE, Deardorff JA, Sachs AB. 1997. Translation initiation factor eIF4G mediates in vitro poly(A) tail-dependent translation. *Proc. Natl. Acad. Sci. USA* 94:9046–51

Tautz D, Pfeifle C. 1989. A non-radioactive in situ hybridization method for the localization of specific RNAs in *Drosophila* embryos reveals translational control of the segmentation gene *hunchback*. *Chromosoma* 98:81–85

Teerink H, Voorma HO, Thomas AAM. 1995. The human insulin-like growth factor II leader 1 contains an internal ribosome entry site. *Biochim. Biophys. Acta* 1264:403–8

Terada N, Patel HR, Takase K, Kohno K, Nairn AC, Gelfand EW. 1994. Rapamycin selectively inhibits translation of mRNAs encoding elongation factors and ribosomal proteins. *Proc. Natl. Acad. Sci. USA* 91:11477–81

Tetzlaff MT, Jäckle H, Pankratz MJ. 1996. Lack of *Drosophila* cytoskeletal tropomyosin affects morphogenesis and the accumulation of *oskar* mRNA required for germ cell formation. *EMBO J.* 15:1247–54

Theurkauf WE. 1994. Premature microtubule-dependent cytoplasmic streaming in *cappucino* and *spire* mutant oocytes. *Science* 265:2093–96

Theurkauf WE, Alberts BM, Jan YN, Jongens TA. 1993. A central role for microtubules in the differentiation of *Drosophila* oocytes. *Development* 118:1169–80

Timmer RT, Benkowski LA, Schodin D, Lax SR, Metz AM, et al. 1993. The 5′ and 3′ untranslated regions of satellite tobacco necrosis virus RNA affect translational efficiency and dependence on a 5′ cap structure. *J. Biol. Chem.* 268:9504–10

Tsukiyama-Kohara K, Vidal SM, Gingras A-C, Glover TW, Hanash SM, et al. 1996. Tissue distribution, genomic structure, and chromosome mapping of mouse and human eukaryotic initiation factor 4E-binding proteins 1 and 2. *Genomics* 38:353–63

Tuite MF, Stansfield I. 1994. Termination of protein synthesis. *Mol. Biol. Rep.* 19:171–81

Vagner S, Gensac M-C, Maret A, Bayard F, Amalric F, et al. 1995. Alternative translation of human fibroblast growth factor 2 mRNA occurs by internal entry of ribosomes. *Mol. Cell. Biol.* 15:35–44

Vagner S, Touriol C, Galy B, Audigier S, Gensac M-C, et al. 1996. Translation of CUG- but not AUG-initiated forms of human fibroblast growth factor 2 is activated in transformed and stressed cells. *J. Cell. Biol.* 135:1391–402

Vernet C, Artzt K. 1997. A gene family involved in signal transduction and activation of RNA. *Trends Genet. Sci.* 13:479–84

Wahle E. 1991. A novel poly(A)-binding protein acts as a specificity factor in the second phase of messenger RNA polyadenylation. *Cell* 66:759–68

Walden WE, Daniels-McQueen S, Brown PH, Gaffield L, Russell DA, et al. 1988. Translational repression in eukaryotes: partial purification and characterization of a repressor of ferritin mRNA translation. *Proc. Natl. Acad. Sci. USA* 85:9503–7

Walker J, Dale M, Standart N. 1996. Unmasking mRNA in clam oocytes: role of phosphorylation of a 3′ UTR masking element-binding protein at fertilization. *Dev. Biol.* 173:292–305

Wang C, Dickinson LK, Lehmann R. 1994. Genetics of *nanos* localization in *Drosophila*. *Dev. Dyn.* 199:103–15

Wang S, Browning KS, Miller WA. 1997. A

viral sequence in the 3'-untranslated region mimics a 5' cap in facilitating translation of uncapped mRNA. *EMBO J.* 16:4107–16

Wang S, Miller WA. 1995. A sequence located 4.5 to 5 kilobases from the 5' end of the barley yellow dwarf virus (PAV) genome strongly stimulates translation of uncapped mRNA. *J. Biol. Chem.* 270:13446–52

Wang Z, Sachs MS. 1997. Arginine-specific regulation mediated by the *Neurospora crassa arg*-2 upstream open reading frame in a homologous, cell-free in vitro translation system. *J. Biol. Chem.* 272:255–61

Waskiewicz AJ, Flynn A, Proud CG, Cooper JA. 1997. Mitogen-activated protein kinases activate the serine/threonine kinases Mnk1 and Mnk2. *EMBO J.* 16:1909–20

Webster PJ, Liang L, Berg CA, Lasko P, Macdonald PM. 1997. Translational repressor *bruno* plays multiple roles in development and is widely conserved. *Genes Dev.* 11:2510–21

Wei C-C, Balasta ML, Ren J, Goss DJ. 1998. Wheat germ poly (A) binding protein enhances the binding affinity of eukaryotic initiation factor 4F and (iso)4F for cap analogue. *Biochemistry* 37:1910–16

Welsh GI, Miller CM, Loughlin AJ, Price NT, Proud CG. 1998. Regulation of eukaryotic initiation factor eIF2B: Glycogen synthase kinase-3 phosphorylates a conserved serine which undergoes dephosphorylation in response to insulin. *FEBS Lett.* 421:125–30

Werner M, Feller A, Messenguy F, Piérard A. 1987. The leader peptide of yeast gene *CPA*1 is essential for the translational repression of its expression. *Cell* 49:805–13

Wharton RP. 1992. Regulated expression from maternal mRNAs in *Drosophila. Semin. Dev. Biol.* 3:391–97

Wharton RP, Struhl G. 1991. RNA regulatory elements mediate control of Drosophila body pattern by the posterior morphogen *nanos. Cell* 67:955–67

Wickens M, Anderson P, Jackson RJ. 1997. Life and death in the cytoplasm: messages from the 3' end. *Curr. Opin. Genet. Dev.* 7:220–32

Wickens M, Kimble J, Strickland S. 1996. Translational control of developmental decisions. See Hershey et al 1996, pp. 411–50

Wightman B, Bürglin TR, Gatto J, Arasu P, Ruvkun G. 1991. Negative regulatory sequences in the *lin*-14 3'-untranslated region are necessary to generate a temporal switch during *Caenorhabditis elegans* development. *Genes Dev.* 5:1813–24

Wightman B, Ha I, Ruvkun G. 1993. Posttranscriptional regulation of the heterochronic gene *lin*-14 by *lin*-4 mediates temporal pattern formation in C. elegans. *Cell* 75:855–62

Williams-Hill DM, Duncan RF, Nielsen PJ, Tahara SM. 1997. Differential expression of the murine eukaryotic translation initiation factor isogenes eIF4A$_1$ and eIF4A$_{11}$ is dependent upon cellular growth status. *Arch. Biochem. Biophys.* 338:111–20

Wolffe AP, Meric F. 1996. Coupling transcription to translation: a novel site for the regulation of eukayotic gene expression. *Int. J. Biochem. Cell Biol.* 28:247–57

Wormington M, Searfoss AM, Hurney CA. 1996. Overexpression of poly(A) binding protein prevents maturation-specific deadenylation and translational inactivation in *Xenopus* oocytes. *EMBO J.* 15:900–9

Wreden C, Verotti AC, Schisa JA, Lieberfarb ME, Strickland S. 1997. *Nanos* and *pumilio* establish embryonic polarity in *Drosophila* by promoting posterior deadenylation of *hunchback* mRNA. *Development* 124:3015–23

Xu Z, Dholakia JN, Hille MB. 1993. Maturation hormone induced an increase in the translational activity of starfish oocytes coincident with the phosphorylation of the mRNA cap binding protein, eIF-4E, and the activation of several kinases. *Dev. Genet.* 14:424–39

Yang F, Demma M, Warren V, Dharmawardhane S, Condeelis J. 1990. Identification of an actin-binding protein from *Dictyostelium* as elongation factor 1α. *Nature* 347:494–96

Yang Q, Sarnow P. 1997. Location of the internal ribosome entry site in the 5' noncoding region of the immunoglobulin heavy-chain binding protein (BIP) mRNA: evidence for specific RNA-proten interactions. *Nucleic Acids Res.* 25:2800–7

Yang Y, Reis LFL, Pavlovic J, Aguzzi A, Schäfer R, et al. 1995. Deficient signaling in mice deviod of double-stranded RNA-dependent protein kinase. *EMBO J.* 14:6095–106

Yeuh A, Schneider RJ. 1996. Selective translation initiation by ribosome jumping in adenovirus-infected and heat-shocked cells. *Genes Dev.* 10:1557–67

Zambetti G, Schmidt W, Stein G, Stein J. 1985. Subcellular localization of histone messenger RNAs on cytoskeleton-associated free polysomes in HeLa S$_3$ cells. *J. Cell. Physiol.* 125:345–53

Zelus BD, Giebelhaus DH, Eib DW, Kenner KA, Moon RT. 1989. Expression of the poly (A)-binding protein during development of *Xenopus laevis. Mol. Cell. Biol.* 9:2756–60

Zhang B, Gallegos M, Puoti A, Durkin E, Fields
S, et al. 1997. A conserved RNA binding protein that regulates sexual fates in the *C. elegans* hermaphrodite germ line. *Nature* 390:
477–84

Ziegler E, Borman AM, Kirchweger R, Skern
T, Kean KM. 1995. Foot-and-mouth disease
virus Lb proteinase can stimulate rhinovirus

and enterovirus IRES-driven translation and
cleave several proteins of cellular and viral
origin. *J. Virol.* 69:3465–74

Zimmer A, Zimmer AM, Reynolds K. 1994.
Tissue specific expression of the retinoic acid
receptor-β2: regulation by short open reading frames in the 5'-noncoding region. *J. Cell.
Biol.* 127:1111–19

Annu. Rev. Cell Dev. Biol. 1998. 14:459–85

INTRACELLULAR SIGNALING FROM THE ENDOPLASMIC RETICULUM TO THE NUCLEUS

Rowan Chapman, Carmela Sidrauski, and Peter Walter

Howard Hughes Medical Institute and Department of Biochemistry
and Biophysics, University of California, San Francisco, California 94143-0448;
e-mail: walter@cgl.ucsf.edu

KEY WORDS: mRNA splicing, tRNA ligase, transmembrane kinase, transcriptional regulation, translation regulation

ABSTRACT

Cells respond to an accumulation of unfolded proteins in the endoplasmic reticulum (ER) by increasing transcription of genes encoding ER resident proteins. The information is transmitted from the ER lumen to the nucleus by an intracellular signaling pathway called the unfolded protein response (UPR). Recent work has shown that this signaling pathway utilizes several novel mechanisms, including translational attenuation and a regulated mRNA splicing step. In this review we aim to integrate these recent advances with current knowledge about maintenance of ER composition and abundance.

CONTENTS

459

OVERVIEW

Cells respond to an accumulation of unfolded proteins in the endoplasmic reticulum (ER) by increasing transcription of genes encoding ER resident proteins. Thus the folding capacity of the ER is adjusted according to need. The information that the capacity of the ER chaperones has been exceeded originates in the ER lumen and is transmitted to the nucleus by an intracellular signaling pathway, the unfolded protein response (UPR). In addition to ER resident proteins, transcription of some key enzymes of phospholipid biosynthesis is also upregulated when the UPR is induced. Thus the UPR may not be strictly a stress response to the accumulation of unfolded proteins in the ER lumen but may play a more general role in homeostasis of the ER compartment.

To date, three genes, *HAC1*, *IRE1*, and *RLG1* in *Saccharomyces cerevisiae* have been identified that collaborate in a unique signaling pathway (Figure 1). *HAC1* encodes a bZIP transcription factor that regulates transcription of genes controlled by the UPR. Intriguingly, the activity of Hac1p is controlled through the regulated splicing of its mRNA. Removal of the intron from the *HAC1* mRNA is a prerequisite for its translation and results in the production of the active transcription factor. The *HAC1* mRNA splicing reaction occurs by an unprecedented mechanism that does not involve spliceosomes, which mediate standard mRNA splicing. Rather, splicing occurs by the sequential action of two enzymes, Ire1p and Rlg1p. Ire1p is a transmembrane kinase that transmits the signal across the ER or inner nuclear membrane. In a similar fashion to growth factor receptors in the plasma membrane of higher eukaryotic cells, Ire1p is activated by phosphorylation and oligomerization. Ire1p, however, is a bifunctional enzyme that, in addition to being a kinase, also displays a specific endoribonuclease activity that cleaves *HAC1* mRNA at both splice junctions. tRNA ligase (encoded by *RLG1*), an essential enzyme previously known exclusively for its role in pre-tRNA splicing, then joins the two exons. The UPR thus reveals a novel mechanism by which eukaryotic gene expression can be

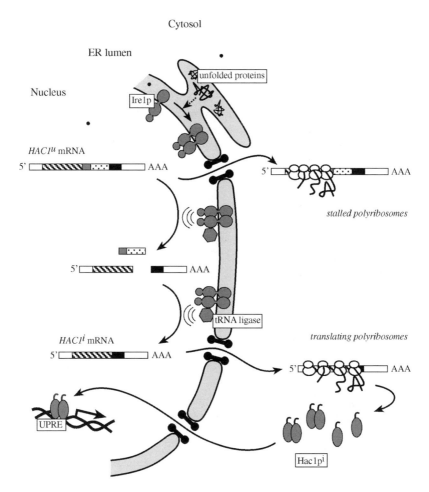

Figure 1 Model of the UPR signaling pathway. Accumulation of unfolded proteins in the endo-plasmic reticulum (ER) lumen triggers activation of Ire1p, which cleaves *HAC1*^{u} mRNA at both splice junctions. tRNA ligase then joins the two exons to produce spliced *HAC1*^{i} mRNA. Both forms of *HAC1* mRNA exit the nucleus and associate with polyribosomes. However, only the spliced form gives rise to protein Hac1p^i, which then enters the nucleus and upregulates UPRE-containing genes. Whether Ire1p is a resident protein in the inner nuclear membrane, as depicted in this model, has not been determined experimentally and remains a speculation.

controlled. The existence of a human homologue of Ire1p strongly suggests that the mechanism of signaling by the UPR is evolutionarily conserved.

PROTEIN FOLDING IN AND PROLIFERATION OF THE ER

Functions of the ER

The endoplasmic reticulum is the first compartment of the secretory pathway through which newly synthesized proteins pass. After entry into the ER lumen, proteins become folded and modified by ER resident chaperones and enzymes (Table 1). Subunits of multimeric proteins are then assembled in the ER.

As a distinct cellular compartment, the ER lumen provides a unique protein folding enviroment. The oxidizing conditions allow the formation of disulfide bonds, a protein modification that is generally disfavored in the reducing environment of the cytosol. In addition, the ER is a major store for Ca^{2+} ions, with concentrations reaching 1 mM, compared with 100 nM in the cytosol.

Protein folding in the ER relies primarily on homologues of the large cytoplasmic heat shock proteins (Hsps) (BiP/GRP78 and GRP94) and their accessory proteins (reviewed in Gething & Sambrook 1992). No ER homologues of the small Hsps or the GroEL/GroES chaperonin system have been identified. N-linked carbohydrates are added to secretory and membrane proteins as they enter the ER. In many cases, carbohydrate addition and subsequent modification help proteins achieve their correct conformation (reviewed in Helenius 1994). The ER contains a unique class of lectin-like chaperones, calnexin and calreticulin, that interact with incompletely modified carbohydrate chains found on protein-folding intermediates.

Membrane or secretory proteins accumulate in the ER lumen if they are not properly folded or assembled. Such proteins are thought to be retained in the

Table 1   ER chaperones regulated by the UPR

Mammalian	Yeast	Function
BiP (GRP78)	KAR2	hsp70 homologue
PDI (Erp59)	PDI	protein disulfide isomerase
GRP170		hsp70-like
GRP94		hsp90-like
ERP72		PDI-like
GRP58		PDI-like
	FKBP12	prolyl-*cis-trans*-isomerase
	LHS1	BiP-like
	EUG1	PDI-like
	ERO1	oxidoreductase

compartment by interactions with chaperones. Eventually, if the defect cannot be corrected, misfolded proteins are degraded after retro-translocation across the ER membrane back into the cytosol where, after deglycosylation and ubiquitination, they are digested by proteasomes (Kopito 1997). The mechanism of retro-translocation is not yet understood and may involve the same protein translocation pore, the Sec61 complex, that mediates protein translocation into the ER. Together, the selective retention and degradation of aberrantly folded proteins in the ER act as a quality control mechanism ensuring that only properly folded and assembled proteins leave the ER and move on to the cell surface (Hammond & Helenius 1995).

Regulation of ER Abundance and Composition

The ER differs in abundance and composition between different cell types. For example, cells that specialize in protein secretion, such as hepatocytes, are packed with rough ER, which has secretory protein biosynthetic functions. In contrast, cells that specialize in steroid biosynthesis, such as Leydig cells, are packed with smooth ER, which has lipid biosynthetic functions. Cells that secrete few proteins, e.g. fibroblasts, have far fewer ER membranes than active secretors. Thus the abundance and particular subspecialization of the ER varies according to need.

The abundance of the ER is adjusted as cells differentiate. A classic example is the differentiation of immature B-lymphocytes to plasma cells during the immune response (Wiest et al 1990). Plasma cells secrete large amounts of antibodies and accordingly have a vastly increased volume of rough ER compared with the precursor cells. Another example is the induction of the smooth ER in hepatocytes by drugs such as phenobarbital (Kanai et al 1986). In this case, large quantities of cytochrome P450, an ER-resident integral membrane protein, are induced to detoxify the drugs, which leads to a proliferation of the smooth ER.

Proliferation of membranes in response to overexpression of mammalian cytochrome P450 also occurs in the yeast *S. cerevisiae* (Schnuck et al 1989, Kargel et al 1996), suggesting that it is the overproduction of ER membrane proteins rather than an independent signal that triggers this type of ER expansion. In yeast, induced ER membranes (called karmellae) often form characteristic multilayered structures that surround the nucleus. Karmellae are continuous with the ER and nuclear envelope and can be induced by overexpression of a variety of integral membrane proteins (Wright 1993).

Changes in the composition or abundance of an organelle in response to need must involve intracellular communication pathways that control gene expression programs according to conditions in, and requirement for, the particular organelle (Nunnari & Walter 1996). Most often this is achieved by controlling transcription of genes encoding specific organelle proteins that carry out the particular function that is needed. Thus information originating in the organelle has to be transmitted to the cell nucleus.

One ER-to-nucleus signaling pathway known to control synthesis of ER components is the UPR. In this pathway, the presence of unfolded proteins is detected in the ER, and a signal is sent to the nucleus that results in an increased expression of ER chaperones. This makes sense—folding in the ER is compromised; therefore, more chaperones are needed. In addition to upregulating synthesis of ER chaperones, the UPR also upregulates transcription of some of the key enzymes involved in phospholipid biosynthesis. This coordinated regulation of ER lumenal and membrane lipid components suggests that the UPR is intimately involved in general aspects of ER biosynthesis (Cox et al 1997).

Two additional ER to nucleus signaling pathways have been described in mammalian cells: The first responds to changes in sterol abundance in the ER membrane and the second to changes in the amount of ER membrane proteins. Depletion of sterols in the ER membrane leads to upregulation of transcription of genes containing sterol-regulatory elements (SRE) in their promoters (Smith et al 1990). Such genes encode enzymes involved in cholesterol and fatty acid biosynthesis; their coregulation thus coordinates different facets of membrane biogenesis (Brown & Goldstein 1997, Pahl & Baeuerle 1997a).

The ER overload response, or EOR, is an ER to nucleus signaling pathway that is activated by the accumulation of ER integral membrane proteins (Pahl & Baeuerle 1995, Pahl et al 1996, Pahl & Baeuerle 1997b). Some conditions that lead to activation of the EOR also induce the UPR; however, these two pathways have distinct downstream effects. The EOR activates NF-κB, a factor that upregulates transcription of genes encoding interferons and cytokines during immune and inflammatory responses. It does not affect transcription of genes encoding ER components. The EOR, therefore, does not appear to be important for ER biogenesis. The reason for its activation by conditions that perturb ER function is thought to relate to cellular infection by viruses. Viral proteins are often synthesized in large amounts in the ER membrane, where they are assembled into coats for newly produced virions. Accordingly, mammalian cells may react to an overproduction of ER membrane proteins with an anti-viral response.

TRANSCRIPTIONAL REGULATION OF THE TARGETS OF THE UPR

Targets of the UPR

The UPR pathway controls transcription of a set of genes encoding ER resident proteins that catalyze folding, assembly, and modification of proteins in the ER lumen (Table 1) (McMillan et al 1994, Shamu et al 1994). These proteins were first identified as polypeptides that were highly induced in mammalian cells upon glucose starvation (which impairs protein glycosylation and hence causes protein misfolding in the ER) and, accordingly, were called glucose-regulated proteins or GRPs (Lee 1987). GRP78 encodes BiP, a member of the HSP70 family of molecular chaperones. BiP constitutes 5 to 10% of the lumenal protein of the ER. GRP94, also known as endoplasmin, is a member of the HSP90 family of molecular chaperones. Both BiP and GRP94 are the major molecular chaperones implicated in folding and oligomeric assembly in the ER lumen (Gething & Sambrook 1992). In addition, GRP170 (a hsp70-like ER lumenal glycoprotein) (Chen et al 1996), protein disulfide isomerase (PDI) (catalyzing disulfide-bond formation), and two PDI-related ER proteins (Erp72 and GRP58), are also upregulated (Mazarella et al 1990).

In *S. cerevisiae*, the accumulation of unfolded proteins in the ER induces a similar set of target genes (Table 1). The ER resident proteins induced in yeast include BiP (encoded by *KAR2*) (Normington et al 1989), yeast PDI (LaMantia et al 1991), Eug1p (a Pdi1p-like protein) (Tachibana & Stevens 1992), peptidyl-prolyl *cis-trans* isomerase Fkbp2 (Partadelis & Berlin 1993), Lhs1p (a hsp70-like protein) (Craven et al 1996), and Ero1p (required for maintenance of the ER redox potential) (Pollard et al 1998, Frand & Kaiser 1998). It is likely that additional targets of the response remain to be identified in both yeast and mammals.

The Unfolded Protein Response Element (UPRE)

The coordinate transcriptional induction of the GRPs in mammalian cells suggests that they may be regulated by a common transcription factor. In vitro footprinting has shown that multiple protein factors interact with various regions in the promoters (Resendez et al 1988, Wooden et al 1991, Li et al 1994). The presence of a 28-bp conserved sequence in multiple promoters suggests a candidate-binding site for a common transcription factor or factors that afford regulation (Chang et al 1989). However, the transcriptional activator that regulates the expression of these genes in response to the conditions inside the ER lumen has not yet been identified.

In *S. cerevisiae*, the promoter element responsible for transactivation of target genes is more streamlined than in mammalian cells. A single 22-bp element, which is conserved among the targets of the UPR, termed the UPRE (unfolded protein response element), is necessary for activation of ER resident proteins upon accumulation of unfolded proteins (Mori et al 1992, Kohno et al 1993). The UPRE is also sufficient to confer induction by the UPR to a heterologous promoter. UPREs from different genes encoding ER resident proteins are characterized by short E box-like palindromic sequences separated by a single nucleotide (CANCNTG) (Mori et al 1996, 1998). The exact spacing of nucleotides in the palindromic sequence is essential for UPRE activity.

Hac1p As the UPR-Specific Transcription Factor

Regulation of transcription from UPRE-containing promoters is mediated by the transcription factor Hac1p. The gene encoding Hac1p was identified independently by three different genetic approaches (Mori et al 1996, Cox & Walter 1996, Nikawa et al 1996). Cells that lack *HAC1* are viable but unable to mount a UPR. As they cannot respond to the accumulation of unfolded proteins, they are supersensitive to agents that induce the UPR and die at normally sublethal doses (Mori et al 1996).

HAC1 was initially identified as a homologue of the ATF/CREB family of bZIP transcription factors. This similarity led to the gene being named *HAC1* (homology to ATF and CREB) (Nojima et al 1994), and Hac1p was proposed to bind to cAMP regulatory elements (CRE). However, recent gel shift analyses showed that the major specific DNA-binding activity of Hac1p is to functional UPRE-elements and not to CRE-elements (Cox & Walter 1996, Mori et al 1996). The *HAC1* ORF predicts that it encodes a 230 amino acid protein, with a DNA-binding domain and leucine zipper in the N-terminal portion. The C terminus contains a PEST-region rich in the amino acids Pro, Glu, Asp, Ser, and Thr that destabilizes proteins by targeting them to the ubiquitin-dependent proteolysis pathway. As predicted from the presence of such sequences, Hac1p is an unstable protein with a half-life of 2 min (Cox & Walter 1996, Chapman & Walter 1997, Cox et al 1997, Kawahara et al 1997).

bZIP transcription factors bind to DNA as homo- or heterodimers. The symmetrical nature of the UPRE and the ability of Hac1p to homodimerize (shown using a two hybrid approach; Nikawa et al 1996) suggest that Hac1p binds to the UPRE as a homodimer.

An additional region in the UPRE, upstream of the Hac1p-binding site, is also required for its function (Mori et al 1996). This region is likely to provide binding sites for constitutive transcription factors that collaborate with Hac1p. It has been suggested that the yeast Gcn5p/Ada2p/Ada3p/Ada5p complex of general factors plays a role in transcription from the UPRE (Welihinda et al 1997), although binding of these to the UPRE or their association with Hac1p remain to be demonstrated directly.

REGULATION OF Hac1p EXPRESSION

UPRE-dependent transcription is regulated by the abundance of Hac1p. In the absence of unfolded proteins, no Hac1p is detected in yeast cells (Cox & Walter 1996, Kawahara et al 1997). Transcription of *HAC1* is independent of UPR activity, and remains constant throughout the cell cycle (Nojima et al 1994, Cox & Walter 1996, Kawahara et al 1997), indicating that the appearance of Hac1p under UPR-inducing conditions is because of post-transcriptional regulation. This regulation involves two unprecedented mechanisms: *HAC1* mRNA splicing and translational attenuation of unspliced *HAC1* mRNA.

Splicing of HAC1 mRNA

In the absence of unfolded proteins, $HAC1^u$ mRNA (u for uninduced) is present as a single, stable species in yeast cells. When the UPR is activated, an additional, smaller mRNA species is produced, called $HAC1^i$ mRNA (i for induced), in which a 252 nucleotide intron located toward the 3' end of the *HAC1* open reading frame is removed (Figure 2) (Cox & Walter 1996, Sidrauski et al 1996, Kawahara et al 1997). Splicing of $HAC1^u$ mRNA is tightly regulated; processing occurs only when misfolded proteins accumulate in the ER lumen and when Ire1p (see NON-CONVENTIONAL SPLICING OF *HAC1* mRNA) is present in cells. Expression of the spliced form is sufficient to fully activate the UPR (Cox & Walter 1996, Kawahara et al 1997). To our knowledge, this is the only

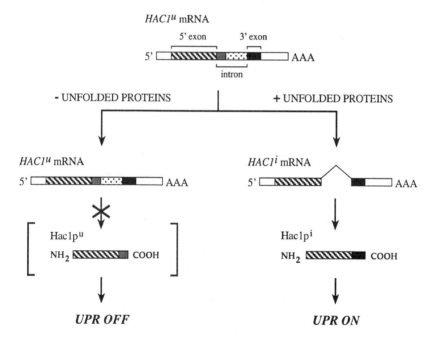

Figure 2   Splicing of $HAC1^u$ mRNA. Removal of the intron alters the open reading frame of Hac1p. Thus the unspliced $HAC1^u$ mRNA encodes Hac1p^u that contains a 10-amino acid tail encoded by intron sequences (*gray boxes*), which upon splicing is replaced by a different 18-amino acid tail encoded by 3' exon sequences (*black boxes*). No detectable amounts of Hac1p^u are produced in cells because $HAC1^u$ mRNA is not translated.

example of a regulated mRNA splicing event controlling the activity of a signal transduction pathway.

The unspliced $HAC1^u$ mRNA predicts a 230–amino acid protein called Hac1p^u. Splicing removes the nucleotide sequence encoding the last 10 C-terminal amino acids of the predicted Hac1p^u and replaces them with a new nucleotide sequence present in the second exon of $HAC1$ mRNA, which encodes a different 18-amino acid tail (Figure 2) (Cox & Walter 1996, Kawahara et al 1997). Tail-specific antibodies have shown that the 238-amino acid protein, Hac1p^i, encoded by the spliced mRNA, is the only form of Hac1p that can be detected in UPR-induced cells (Cox & Walter 1996). Activation of the UPR results in splicing of $HAC1$ mRNA and rapid accumulation of Hac1p^i. The short half-life of Hac1p^i ensures that UPRE-dependent transcription is rapidly downregulated when the UPR is no longer induced.

Translational Attenuation of $HAC1^u$ mRNA

Unlike other pre-mRNAs, $HAC1^u$ mRNA is stable in yeast cells. In addition, it exits from the nucleus, escaping controls that retain other pre-mRNAs in this compartment (Chapman & Walter 1997). The translation of $HAC1^u$ mRNA is initiated in the cytosol. Evidence for this comes from the observation that $HAC1^u$ mRNA co-fractionates with polyribosomes in sucrose gradients (Cox & Walter 1996). Furthermore, nascent Hac1p chains can be co-immunoprecipitated with polyribosomes. This excludes the possibility that $HAC1^u$ mRNA is present in another ribonucleoprotein complex that fortuitously co-sediments with polyribosomes (Chapman & Walter 1997). Despite the functional association of $HAC1^u$ mRNA with polyribosomes, no full-length Hac1p^u is produced. This suggests that translation elongation is blocked.

It was initially suggested that full-length Hac1p^u could be produced constitutively when the UPR is turned off but then be degraded significantly faster than Hac1p^i (Cox & Walter 1996). However, if intron sequences beyond the Hac1p^u stop codon are removed experimentally, Hac1p^u is expressed in cells and, with a half-life of 2 min, has a stability similar to that of Hac1p^i (Chapman & Walter 1997, Kawahara et al 1997). Hac1p^u thus produced migrates with a mobility different from that of Hac1p^i in SDS-PAGE because it is differently phosphorylated and activates UPRE-dependent transcription, albeit at a reduced level. These results further support the notion that the $HAC1^u$ mRNA intron prevents translation of $HAC1^u$ mRNA.

The mechanism by which the $HAC1^u$ mRNA intron inhibits translation is unknown. When transplanted into the 3′ untranslated region (3′ UTR) of $HAC1^u$ mRNA or an unrelated mRNA, the $HAC1^u$ mRNA intron still functions as an efficient translational attenuator (Chapman & Walter 1997, Kawahara et al 1997). In each case, mRNAs become recruited into polyribosomes, but no full-length products can be detected. The ability of the intron to block translation when transplanted into the 3′ UTR of an mRNA rules out the simplest model whereby translating ribosomes stall because they cannot traverse some structural block imposed by the intron sequences. It is not known whether all ribosomes dissociate from a mRNA upon termination of protein synthesis. Therefore, it is possible that some or all ribosomes could continue to traverse the 3′ UTR and stall when encountering the intron (Figure 3, Direct model). This would cause a domino effect, with other ribosomes stalling behind. As a result the stop codon would be covered up, preventing production of further full-length proteins beyond the initial few molecules. Alternatively, the intron may fold back and contact ribosomes traversing the preceding open reading frame to block translation (Figure 3, Indirect model).

It is surprising that cells attenuate production of Hac1p^u at the level of translational elongation, prompting speculation whether this particular mechanism affords an additional level of control. Cells could, for example, have some mechanism for temporarily overcoming the translation block, enabling them to quickly produce a burst of Hac1p^u from already partially synthesized chains. This could provide a fast, alternative pathway for induction of the UPR that is independent of *HAC1* mRNA splicing. While this remains an interesting possibility, there is at the present time no experimental evidence that Hac1p^u is ever produced under physiological conditions.

NON-CONVENTIONAL SPLICING OF *HAC1* mRNA

The change in Hac1p abundance upon induction of the UPR is the result of regulated splicing of *HAC1* mRNA. Remarkably, splicing of *HAC1* mRNA is not catalyzed by the spliceosome but uses a unique splicing machinery composed of two proteins: the bifunctional Ire1p transmembrane kinase/endonuclease

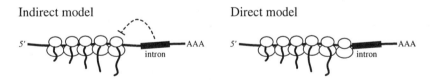

Figure 3   Model for translation attenuation by the *HAC1*^{u} mRNA intron. The Indirect model predicts that ribosomes and their associated nascent chains stall upstream of the intron. Consequently, no full-length protein is produced. According to the Direct model, the first ribosome stalls upon directly encountering the intron, presumably at a region of tight secondary structure. Further ribosomes and associated nascent chains stack behind it. If the intron is localized in the 3′ untranslated region (UTR) of a mRNA, this mechanism could work only if ribosomes continue moving down the 3′ UTR after protein synthesis has terminated.

(encoded by the *IRE1* gene) and tRNA ligase (encoded by the *RLG1* gene). Mutations in both *IRE1* and *RLG1* were isolated in mutant hunts for components of the UPR.

Ire1p, a Transmembrane Kinase Required for the UPR

IRE1 (high inositol-requiring mutant) was first described as a gene required for inositol prototrophy (see COORDINATE REGULATION OF THE UPR AND LIPID SYNTHESIS) (Nikawa & Yamashita 1992). In genetic screens using UPRE-driven lacZ reporters, two independent groups isolated mutations in *IRE1* (also called *ERN1*) that prevent induction of β-galactosidase expression in the presence of agents causing accumulation of unfolded proteins in the ER (Cox et al 1993, Mori et al 1993). Like cells lacking *HAC1*, cells lacking the function of the *IRE1* gene are viable under normal growth conditions but are supersensitive to treatments that induce accumulation of unfolded protein in the ER lumen.

IRE1 encodes a 1115-amino acid polypeptide (Ire1p) with an N-terminal signal sequence and a single transmembrane domain (Figure 4). The C-terminal half contains a domain that has all the sequence characteristics of a serine/threonine protein kinase followed by C-terminal domain that has homology to the putative ribonucleolytic domain of mammalian RNase L. In contrast, the N-terminal half of Ire1p has no sequence homology to other known proteins. The domain organization of *IRE1* resembles that of mammalian growth factor kinase receptors. Based on its glycosylation and fractionation behavior, Ire1p is an integral membrane protein with its N-terminal domain in the ER lumen

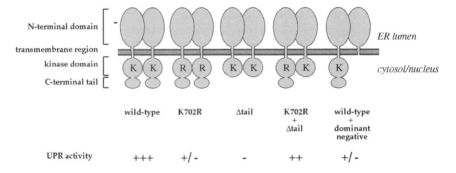

Figure 4 Activation of Ire1p by oligomerization. Ire1p oligomerizes and auto-trans-phosphorylates upon activation by unfolded protein accumulation in the ER lumen. Evidence to support this model comes from interallelic complementation of Ire1p(K702R) and Δtail mutants and is consistent with the dominant-negative phenotype of an Ire1p mutant that lacks the cytosolic kinase and tail domains.

(Mori et al 1993). This topology suggests that the N-terminal portion of Ire1p serves as a sensor domain detecting the accumulation of unfolded proteins in the ER lumen. Ire1p could lie in the ER or inner nuclear membrane (with which the ER membrane is continuous around the nuclear pores) with its C-terminal half facing the cytoplasm or the nucleus. It is not known whether Ire1p localizes to the nuclear membrane, the ER membrane, or both, or whether its localization changes upon activation of the pathway.

Immunoprecipitation experiments showed that, in vivo, Ire1p is phosphorylated predominantly on serine residues (Shamu & Walter 1996). Phosphorylation of Ire1p increases on activation of the UPR, suggesting a regulatory role for this modification. Consistent with this, point mutations in the lysine residue that lies in the catalytic site of the kinase domain of Ire1p (K702A or K702R) abolish or diminish the UPR (Mori et al 1993, Shamu & Walter 1996). Furthermore, the K702A mutant of Ire1p is not phosphorylated either in vivo or in vitro (Shamu & Walter 1996, Welihinda & Kaufman 1996). Taken together, these data indicate that Ire1p's activation leads to induction of its kinase activity, which in turn results in its autophosphorylation. In addition, overexpression of Ptc2p, a phosphatase responsible for dephosphorylation of Ire1p, turns off the pathway (Welihinda et al 1998).

Molecular genetic and biochemical data strongly suggest that upon induction of the pathway, Ire1p oligomerizes and is *trans*-autophosphorylated by neighboring Ire1p molecules. Interallelic complementation between a full-length Ire1p (K702R) mutant and a mutant Ire1p lacking the C-terminal 133-amino acid domain (Δtail) indicates that *trans*-autophosphorylation occurs in vivo (Figure 4) (Shamu & Walter 1996). Consistent with this oligomerization model, antibodies directed toward the C-terminal tail domain of Ire1p co-immunoprecipitate co-expressed Ire1p-Δtail. Furthermore, C-terminally truncated forms and kinase-inactivated forms of Ire1p are dominant negative (Figure 4). Activation of Ire1p, therefore, resembles that of well-characterized growth factor receptors in the plasma membrane of mammalian cells.

Ire1p Is an Endoribonuclease that Cleaves HAC1[u] mRNA at Both Splice Junctions

Historically, several lines of evidence indicated that *HAC1* mRNA splicing does not utilize the conventional pre-mRNA processing machinery or spliceosome (Sidrauski et al 1996). First, the splice junctions of *HAC1* mRNA do not resemble the consensus sequences found in other pre-mRNAs. These sequences are recognized by direct base-pairing with snRNAs in the spliceosome, and this considerable divergence makes *HAC1* mRNA an unlikely substrate for the spliceosome. Second, *HAC1* mRNA splicing is not affected by mutations that inhibit spliceosome function. Third, a mutation that blocks splicing of the

5' splice junction of *HAC1* mRNA does not abolish cleavage at the 3' splice junction (Sidrauski & Walter 1997). This result is incompatible with the chemistry of a spliceosome-catalyzed reaction, where cleavage of the 5' splice junction is required for cleavage at the 3' splice junction.

Conclusive evidence for a non-conventional mechanism of *HAC1* mRNA splicing came from the characterization of the components that carry out the reaction. The similarity in domain structure and sequence between Ire1p and a mammalian nuclease, RNase L, led to the proposal that Ire1p may have both kinase and nuclease activities (Bork & Sander 1993). RNase L, or 2'-5'A-dependent RNase, is a soluble nonspecific nuclease that is activated by the 2'-5'-linked oligoadenylates (2-5A) produced upon treatment of animal cells with interferon (Zhou et al 1993, Dong et al 1994). Although RNase L is a soluble nuclease, it has a number of features that are similar to Ire1p. RNase L, like Ire1p, contains a kinase domain followed by a C-terminal domain (Figure 5). The C-terminal tail domain of RNase L has 29% sequence identity to the C-terminal domain of Ire1p. The C-terminal tail of RNase L has been proposed to be the nuclease domain, as deletion of this domain abolishes nuclease activity

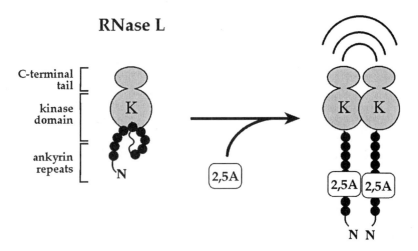

Figure 5   Similarities between Ire1p and RNase. Both RNase L, a soluble enzyme, and Ire1p, a transmembrane protein, contain a kinase domain followed by a C-terminal tail domain that is required for ribonuclease activity. The kinase (K) and the C-terminal tail domains show amino acid sequence similarity. The N-terminal regions of both molecules function to sense the upstream signal in their respective pathways, but show no homology. Binding of 2'-5'-linked oligoadenylates (2-5A) to two of the N-terminal ankyrin repeats of RNase L allows oligomerization and activation of the nuclease. Similarly, accumulation of unfolded proteins leads to oligomerization and activation of the kinase and nuclease activities of Ire1p.

in vitro (Dong & Silverman 1997). For Ire1p, the C-terminal domain is essential for transmitting the unfolded protein signal (Shamu & Walter 1996) (Figure 4). The N-terminal domains of RNase L and Ire1p are involved in sensing signals that lead to oligomerization and activation of the nuclease domain (Dong & Silverman 1995). These striking similarities in sequence domain structure and mechanism of activation strongly suggest that Ire1p is the nuclease responsible for cleavage of $HAC1^u$ mRNA.

The nuclease activity of Ire1p was directly demonstrated by assaying the activity of a recombinantly expressed fusion protein of the C-terminal half of Ire1p, which contains both the kinase (k) and C-terminal tail domain (t) and glutathione transferase (GST). This GST-Ire1p(k+t) fusion autophosphorylates in vitro and thus contains an active kinase domain (Welihinda & Kaufman 1996). GST-Ire1p(k+t) specifically cleaves in vitro transcribed $HAC1^u$ RNA at both its 5′ and 3′ splice junctions (Sidrauski & Walter 1997). Moreover, GST-Ire1p(k+t)-mediated in vitro cleavage of $HAC1^u$ RNA has substrate requirements indistinguishable from $HAC1^u$ mRNA cleavage in vivo: Point mutations that change a conserved G residue at either the 5′ or 3′ splice junction to a C abolish cleavage at the mutated junction both in vivo and in vitro (Sidrauski & Walter 1997, Kawahara et al 1997). Thus Ire1p(k+t) contains kinase activity and endoribonuclease activity that is highly specific for $HAC1^u$ RNA. In contrast, RNaseL is a nonspecific endoribonuclease, and it will be of interest in comparative studies to decipher the determinants in Ire1p that confer substrate specificity.

tRNA Ligase Completes Splicing of HAC1 mRNA

The involvement of *RLG1* in $HAC1^u$ mRNA splicing was demonstrated genetically (Sidrauski et al 1996). *RLG1* encodes tRNA ligase, an essential enzyme involved in pre-tRNA splicing. tRNA ligase is involved in the second step of splicing, that is the ligation of tRNA halves generated by tRNA endonuclease. tRNA ligase is a multidomain protein with four distinct enzymatic activities required for ligation of tRNA substrates: a polynucleotide kinase activity, a cyclic phosphodiesterase activity, an adenylate synthetase activity, and an RNA ligase activity. The identified UPR-inactivating allele in tRNA ligase, *rlg1-100*, encodes a mutant protein that contains a histidine-to-tyrosine substitution at position 148. This mutation does not map to any of the identified catalytic domains.

Induction of the UPR in *rlg1-100* mutants results in an Ire1p-dependent degradation of $HAC1^u$ mRNA; no spliced $HAC1^i$ mRNA product is detected. This observation is consistent with the idea that the first step in the splicing reaction (Ire1p-dependent cleavage of $HAC1^u$ mRNA) takes place in the mutant strain but that ligation of the mRNA halves does not occur. The *HAC1* mRNA fragments produced are rapidly degraded. Although the *rlg1-100* allele blocks *HAC1* mRNA splicing, splicing of pre-tRNAs is not affected in the mutant strain. If pre-tRNA splicing is blocked, cells accumulate tRNA splicing intermediates and die because they lack the necessary complement of tRNAs. This suggests that the enzymatic activities of the mutant protein required for pre-tRNA splicing are intact (Figure 6). Thus the *rlg1-100* allele is a pathway-specific mutation that explicitly impairs splicing of *HAC1* mRNA. The mutant phenotype could arise either because the mutant tRNA ligase cannot efficiently recognize its substrates (the *HAC1* mRNA exons) or because the mutant protein is not properly localized.

Identification of tRNA ligase as the component required for the second step in *HAC1* mRNA splicing allowed reconstitution of the splicing reaction in vitro. Addition of purified tRNA ligase to the Ire1p(k+t) in vitro cleavage reaction results in the correct processing of *HAC1* mRNA. Thus in contrast to spliceosome-mediated pre-mRNA splicing, which requires more than 100 components, processing of *HAC1* mRNA is surprisingly simple, requiring the sequential action of only two enzymes: the bifunctional kinase/endonuclease Ire1p and tRNA ligase.

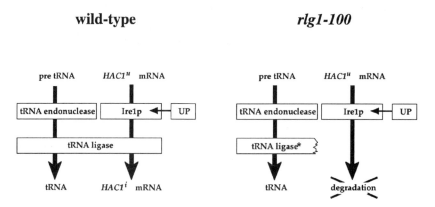

Figure 6 *rlg1-100* encodes a UPR pathway-specific loss-of-function mutant of tRNA ligase. tRNA ligase functions in two RNA processing pathways: the constitutive splicing of pre-tRNAs and the regulated splicing of *HAC1*^{u} mRNA. In cells bearing the *rlg1-100* allele, *HAC1*^{u} mRNA becomes selectively degraded when Ire1p is activated. Ire1p presumably initiates *HAC1*^{u} mRNA processing by cleaving at either or both splice junctions. The resulting fragments are unstable if their re-ligation is impaired. In contrast, pre-tRNA splicing is unaffected in the mutant strain, suggesting that the enzymatic functions of the mutant protein are intact. The *rlg1-100* mutation might therefore confer an inability to use *HAC1* mRNA fragments as substrates, or it could impair an interaction between Ire1p and tRNA ligase required for efficient processing. (UP, unfolded proteins).

The involvement of tRNA ligase in processing of *HAC1* mRNA suggests parallel processing machineries for splicing of pre-tRNAs and *HAC1* mRNA. They share tRNA ligase as a common component but utilize different endoribonucleases. Both Ire1p and tRNA endonuclease cleave the splice sites in their respective substrates independently and in no obligate order. Here the similarity ends, as they differ significantly with respect to their subunit composition and substrate recognition. tRNA endonuclease is composed of four subunits (Trotta et al 1997), whereas Ire1p is composed of only one known subunit. tRNA endonuclease recognizes the folded tertiary structure of the pre-tRNA and pays little attention to the nucleotide sequence at the junctions or within the intron. In contrast, Ire1p appears to recognize nucleotide sequence at the intron-exon junction of *HAC1*[u] mRNA since single G-to-C mutations at either junction abolish cleavage.

Secondary structure predictions reveal strikingly similar stem-loop structures at both junctions of *HAC1* mRNA (Figure 7) (Sidrauski & Walter 1997). At both junctions, Ire1p cleaves adjacent to the conserved G located in the third position in the seven-membered loop. Other nucleotides conserved within the predicted loops are required for splicing in vivo (Mori et al 1998), confirming the role of the nucleotide sequence in the junctions of *HAC1* mRNA for Ire1p-mediated cleavage. The predicted structural symmetry of the substrate may reflect binding of Ire1p as a dimer to *HAC1*[u] mRNA with each monomer of Ire1p containing an active site that recognizes one stem-loop. A similar mechanism has been postulated for archeal pre-tRNAs, which display internal twofold symmetry and are cleaved by a homodimeric archeal tRNA endonuclease (Kleman-Leyer et al 1997).

In yeast, tRNA ligase localizes to the nucleus where it interacts with the tightly membrane-associated tRNA endonuclease. As tRNA ligase is localized in the nuclear compartment it is likely that at least a portion of the cellular Ire1p molecules is localized to the inner nuclear membrane to catalyze *HAC1*[u] mRNA splicing. This would place the kinase and the C-terminal putative nuclease domain of Ire1p in the nucleus where it could collaborate with tRNA ligase in splicing of *HAC1*[u] mRNA before or during transport to the cytosol. Indeed, pulse-chase experiments show that cytosolic *HAC1*[u] mRNA, which is engaged on translating polyribosomes, is not converted to *HAC1*[i] mRNA upon induction of the UPR (R Chapman & P Walter, unpublished results). Thus the UPR pathway may indeed take the direct route from the ER lumen to the nucleus across the inner nuclear membrane, as depicted in Figure 1.

The discovery of the endonuclease activity of Ire1p suggests a role for its kinase activity. To date, the only known substrate that is phosphorylated by Ire1p is Ire1p itself. Thus it is possible that the kinase domain is required to activate the nuclease function to initiate splicing. There are many possible models to

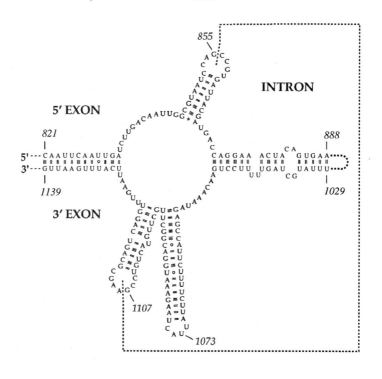

HACI^u mRNA
5' splice junction

HACI^u mRNA
3' splice junction

explain how Ire1p kinase activity could be instrumental in turning on its nuclease activity. Phosphorylation of Ire1p, for example, could enhance the affinity of Ire1p molecules for one another, which would result in activation if endonuclease activity requires oligomerization. Alternatively, the Ire1p nuclease may normally be inhibited by a negative regulator; phosphorylation could lead to the release of this putative inhibitor, unmasking the nuclease function. A third model would assume that phosphorylation is required to relocalize Ire1p in the cell, e.g. to the proximity of nuclear pores, so that it can interact efficiently with *HAC1*[u] mRNA in transit from its site of transcription to the cytosol. Deciphering the role of the Ire1p kinase domain remains an exciting open question.

INDUCTION OF THE UPR

Activators

The UPR is induced by a variety of cellular insults that perturb the function of the ER. Some of these treatments—such as inhibition of disulfide bonding with reducing agents, inhibition of ER glycosylation with drugs such as tunicamycin, or expression of aberrant proteins that do not fold properly—directly cause an increase in the concentration of unfolded proteins in the ER (Shamu et al 1994). In yeast, for example, a thermosensitve mutation in *SEC11*, a gene that encodes signal peptidase, acts as an inducer of the UPR. At the nonpermissive temperature, *sec11* ts mutants presumably accumulate secretory proteins that do not fold properly due to the presence of the uncleaved signal sequence (Bohni et al 1988).

In addition to these treatments, a variety of stresses that affect ER function, but may not result directly in accumulation of misfolded proteins, are inducers of the UPR. For example, blocking ER-to-Golgi transport (Liu et al 1992), depleting the ER of Ca^{2+} (Drummond et al 1987, Li et al 1993), and inhibiting protein degradation (Bush et al 1997) all activate the UPR. In addition, overproduction of normal secretory or membrane proteins also induces the UPR. It is clear that accumulation of unfolded proteins is not sufficient for induction of the

← ———————————————————————————————

Figure 7   Secondary structure predictions of the *HAC1*[u] mRNA splice junctions. The 5′ and 3′ splice junctions are predicted to form similar stem-loop structures. At each junction cleavage occurs at the 3′ side [and not at the 5′ side, as previously assigned (Sidrauski & Walter 1997)] of the conserved G residue that is localized in the third position of a seven-membered loop (Kawahara et al 1997; T Gonzales & P Walter, unpublished data). It is likely that sequences in the intron contain an extensive secondary structure that allows the intron to fold back onto itself. This would bring both splice sites into proximity, possibly positioning them for concerted processing by an oligomeric Ire1p complex.

UPR. When an improperly folded mutant of the simian virus 5 hemagglutinin-neuraminidase glycoprotein that does not bind BiP accumulates in the ER, no induction of the UPR is detected. In contrast, when other misfolded mutants of this glycoprotein that bind BiP accumulate in the ER the UPR is induced. This observation led to the proposal that the sensing mechanism detects changes in either the concentration of complexes formed between BiP and unfolded proteins or in the concentration of free BiP itself (Ng et al 1992).

Several other indirect observations also suggest that the cell may be monitoring the levels of free BiP in the ER. Overexpression of mammalian BiP down-regulates the UPR in CHO cells (Dorner et al 1990). Similarly, overexpression of BiP in yeast cells suppresses induction of UPR target genes (Kohno et al 1993). Conversely, if BiP levels are artificially lowered by expressing a mutant in BiP that is not retained in the ER lumen, cells induce transcription of ER resident protein genes (Hardwick et al 1990, Beh & Rose 1995, Sidrauski et al 1996). The identification of the mechanism that activates Ire1p, which is the most upstream UPR component identified to date, will be a key step in understanding the signal that leads to induction of the UPR.

Activation of Ire1p

How activation of Ire1p is induced by accumulation of unfolded proteins in the ER lumen is not known. Oligomerization may be positively regulated in response to binding of a ligand to the ER lumenal domain of Ire1p. The ligand could be unfolded proteins themselves, a complex of unfolded proteins bound to ER-chaperones, or an as yet unidentified ligand generated by the increased activity of chaperones in the ER compartment. In this model, activation of Ire1p would resemble that of mammalian growth factor receptor kinases. An alternative possibility (a negative regulatory model) is that a chaperone, such as BiP, binds to Ire1p when there are few unfolded proteins in the ER preventing its oligomerization and thus maintaining it in an inactive monomeric state. When the concentration of unfolded proteins increases, the chaperone is titrated from Ire1p, allowing oligomerization driven by an intrinsic affinity of Ire1p molecules for one another.

Interestingly, a similar mechanism has been proposed for the regulation of HSF1 (heat shock factor 1) by cytosolic hsp70 in animal cells (Morimoto et al 1994). Under nonstressful conditions, HSF1 is maintained in an inactive monomeric state through transient interactions with hsp70. When heat shock causes the accumulation of misfolded proteins in the cytosol, hsp70 binds to the increased pool of substrates, permitting HSF1 oligomerization into the active trimeric form. Thus it is possible that parallels exist between these two stress response pathways: Chaperones such as hsp70 or its ER lumenal counterpart BiP may function as the ultimate sensors that monitor protein folding.

COORDINATE REGULATION OF THE UPR
AND LIPID SYNTHESIS

IRE1 was originally identified as a gene required for inositol prototrophy (Nikawa & Yamashita 1992). Thus when *IRE1* was demonstrated to play a key role in the UPR, it was proposed that the UPR and ER membrane biogenesis were linked (Cox et al 1993, Shamu et al 1994). Indeed, all subsequently isolated mutants that block the UPR (mutants in *HAC1* and *RLG1*) are also inositol auxotrophs. The ER is the major site of cellular lipid synthesis and membrane production. In yeast, transcription of genes encoding enzymes required for phospholipid biosynthesis is controlled primarily by the levels of available inositol, which is a precursor of the major structural phospholipids in yeast (Greenberg & Lopes 1996, Henry & Patton-Vogt 1998). Taken together, these facts suggest that the UPR and lipid biogenesis are intimately linked.

Control of Transcription by the Inositol Response

A highly conserved 10-bp element (5'-CATGTGAAAT-3'), termed the UAS_{ino}, is found in promoters of genes encoding key regulatory enzymes involved in phospholipid biosynthesis (Carman & Henry 1989). This element is both necessary and sufficient for regulation by the concentration of inositol. When inositol is plentiful, transcription from promoters containing this element is repressed, and when inositol is depleted from the growth medium, transcription is highly induced.

Transcriptional regulation by the inositol response acts via control of a transcriptional repressor encoded by *OPI1* (White et al 1991). The sequence of Opi1p shows that it is a member of the leucine zipper family of transcription factors. Δ*opi1* mutant cells are insensitive to inositol deprivation and express UAS_{ino}-regulated genes constitutively. A pair of bZIP transcription activators, Ino2p and Ino4p, bind as a heterodimer to the UAS_{ino} and are also required for inositol-dependent transcription of downstream target genes (Hirsch & Henry 1986).

Coordinate Regulation of the UPR and the Inositol Response

The inositol response is coordinately regulated with the unfolded protein response (Cox et al 1997). Changes in the concentration of inositol, or in levels of unfolded proteins, induce transcription of both UPRE- and UAS_{ino}-controlled genes. These transcriptional responses have different kinetics but are both dependent on *IRE1* and *HAC1*. Δ*ire1* or Δ*hac1* cells are blocked in UPRE-dependent transcription and cannot maintain high levels of transcription of UAS_{ino}-controlled genes, thereby explaining why UPR-impaired cells are inositol auxotrophs. If a *upr* mutant is combined with an *opi1* deletion, the double mutant cells constitutively express UAS$_{ino}$-controlled but not UPRE-controlled genes (Cox et al 1997). These data suggest that the components of the UPR act upstream of the Opi1p/Ino2p/Ino4p transcriptional apparatus in a branched pathway. One branch, dependent on only *IRE1*, *HAC1*, and *RLG1* controls UPRE-dependent transcription, the other also requires *INO2*, *INO4*, and *OPI1* and controls transcription from UAS$_{ino}$-containing promoters (Figure 8).

It is currently not known how Ire1p is activated by the divergent signals of a decrease in inositol concentration and an increase in the levels of unfolded proteins. These signals are distinct; a decrease in inositol does not appear to increase the levels of unfolded proteins in the ER and vice versa. It is possible that changes in either signal result in modulation of a common Ire1p ligand. Alternatively different parts of the Ire1p molecule may have the ability to respond to changes in the state of the ER lumen and ER membrane.

Control of the Inositol Response by UPR Components

Both biochemical and genetic data show that activation of Ire1p by either depletion of inositol or an increase in unfolded proteins results in the appearance of Hac1p^i (Cox et al 1997). How might Hac1p^i affect transcription of the UAS$_{ino}$-controlled promoters? It is formally possible that Hac1p^i binds directly to both types of promoter to direct transcription. However, several lines of evidence make this unlikely. Hac1p^i has been shown to bind specifically to the UPRE sequence (Cox & Walter 1996, Mori et al 1996) and does not have a significant

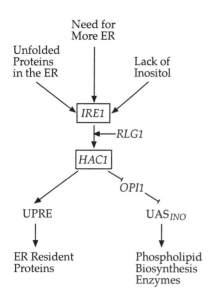

Figure 8 Ire1p and Hac1p coordinate the UPR and inositol starvation response. Ire1p is activated by the different signals of unfolded proteins, inositol starvation, and also by overexpression of ER membrane proteins. The resulting Hac1p transcription activator can either bind directly to UPRE sequences, thereby activating transcription of genes encoding ER resident proteins, or antagonize the function of the transcriptional repressor Opi1p, thereby activating transcription of genes encoding some of the key regulatory enzymes of phospholipid biosynthesis. These latter genes contain a regulatory element, termed UAS$_{ino}$, in their promoters that is required for repression by Opi1p.

affinity for the UAS_{ino}. Furthermore, in the absence of Opi1p, Hac1p^i is not required for transcription from the UAS_{ino} (Cox et al 1997). Thus one likely possibility is that Hac1p^i antagonizes Opi1p repressor activity. This could be directly via a physical association of the two proteins or indirectly by Hac1p-induced transcription of some, as yet unknown, UPRE-controlled gene that is capable of antagonizing Opi1p.

Why Are the UPR and the Inositol Response Linked?

At a first glance, one might wonder why the cell coordinates the UPR and the inositol response. However, it does makes sense for a cell to coordinate production of ER lumenal and membrane components. The UPR controls production of ER resident chaperones, whose function it is to help fold accumulated proteins in the lumen of an organelle. The inositol response controls synthesis of ER membrane proteins involved in lipid synthesis. These proteins and the products of their enzymatic activity form some of the known protein and lipid components of the ER membrane. If either the lumenal contents of the ER increase or the membranous components increase, the cell must compensate by coordinately increasing production of the remaining part of the organelle. Thus when unfolded proteins accumulate, chaperones are induced, and the membranes to house the extra contents are also increased. Conversely, when more lipid synthesis is needed, the ER membrane must expand, which in turn increases the lumenal volume and chaperone content of the ER.

CONCLUSIONS

The characterization of the UPR pathway has revealed many surprises, both in its physiological complexities and the novel mechanistic aspects of signal transduction. Work in yeast has allowed rapid progress because both genetic and biochemical avenues could be readily combined. Based on the unusual nature of the reactions uncovered, however, it remains valid to ask whether the knowledge obtained in yeast could be generalized to other eukaryotic cells. It now seems likely that the mammalian UPR uses similar, if not identical, steps. In particular, recent experiments show that yeast $HAC1^u$ mRNA becomes accurately spliced in HeLa cells when the UPR is induced by tunicamycin treatment (M Niwa & P Walter, unpublished results). Moreover, cDNA clones encoding mammalian homologues of Ire1p have been isolated and characterized, suggesting that not only the mechanism but also the components of the pathway are conserved from yeast to mammalian cells (Tirasophon et al 1998; M Niwa & P Walter, unpublished results). Thus it will be exciting to determine what, if any, role the UPR plays in ER proliferation in cells that have to expand their secretory capacity as part of their normal developmental program.

ACKNOWLEDGMENTS

We thank Guy Cavet, Ted Powers, and Vladimir Denic for helpful discussions and comments on the manuscript. CS is the recipient of a Chancellor's predoctoral fellowship from the University of California at San Francisco. This work was also supported by a postdoctoral fellowship from the American Heart Association to RC and by grants from the National Institutes of Health and the American Cancer Society. PW is an Investigator of the Howard Hughes Medical Institute.

> **Visit the *Annual Reviews home page* at**
> **http://www.AnnualReviews.org**

Literature Cited

Beh CT, Rose MD. 1995. Two redundant systems maintain levels of resident proteins within the yeast endoplasmic reticulum. *Proc. Natl. Acad. Sci. USA* 92:9820–43

Bohni PC, Deshaies RI, Schekman RW. 1988. SEC11 is required for signal peptide processing and yeast cell growth. *J. Cell Biol.* 106:1035–46

Bork P, Sander C. 1993. A hybrid protein kinase-RNase in an interferon-induced pathway? *FEBS Lett.* 334:149–52

Brown MS, Goldstein JL. 1997. The SREBP pathway: regulation of cholesterol metabolism by proteolysis of a membrane-bound transcription factor. *Cell* 89:331–40

Bush DT, Goldberg AL, Nigam SK. 1997. Proteasome inhibition leads to a heat-shock response, induction of endoplasmic reticulum chaperones, and thermotolerance. *J. Cell Biol.* 272:9086–92

Carman GM, Henry SA. 1989. Phospholipid biosynthesis in yeast. *Annu. Rev. Biochem.* 58:635–69

Chang SC, Erwin AE, Lee AS. 1989. Glucose-regulated protein (GRP94 and GRP78) genes share common regulatory domains and are coordinately regulated by common *trans*-acting factors. *Mol. Cell. Biol.* 9:2153–62

Chapman RE, Walter P. 1997. Translational attenuation mediated by an mRNA intron. *Curr. Biol.* 7:850–59

Chen X, Easton D, Oh H, Lee-Yoon D, Liu X, Subjeck J. 1996. The 170 kDa glucose regulated stress protein is a large HSP-70-HSP110-like protein of the endoplasmic reticulum. *FEBS Lett.* 380:68–72

Cox JS, Chapman RE, Walter P. 1997. The unfolded protein response coordinates the production of ER protein and ER membrane. *Mol. Biol. Cell* 8:1905–14

Cox JS, Shamu CE, Walter P. 1993. Transcriptional induction of genes encoding endoplasmic reticulum resident proteins requires a transmembrane protein kinase. *Cell* 73:1197–206

Cox JS, Walter P. 1996. A novel mechanism for regulating activity of a transcription factor that controls the unfolded protein response. *Cell* 87:391–404

Craven RA, Egerton M, Stirling CJ. 1996. A novel Hsp70 of the yeast ER lumen is required for the efficient translocation of a number of protein precursors. *EMBO J.* 15:2640–50

Dong B, Silverman RH. 1995. 2-5A-dependent RNase molecules dimerize during activation by 2-5A*. *J. Biol. Chem.* 270:4133–37

Dong B, Silverman RH. 1997. A bipartite model of 2-5A-dependent RNase. *J. Biol. Chem* 272:22236–42

Dong B, Xu L, Zhou A, Hassel BA, Lee X, et al. 1994. Intrinsic molecular activities of the interferon-induced 2-5A-dependent RNase. *J. Biol. Chem.* 269:14153–58

Dorner AJ, Wasley LC, Raney P, Haugejorden S, Green M, Kaufman RJ. 1990. The stress response in Chinese hamster ovary cells. *J. Biol. Chem.* 265:22029–34

Drummond IAS, Lee AS, Resendez E, Steinhardt RA. 1987. Depletion of intracellular calcium stores by calcium ionophore A23187 induces the genes for glucose-regulated proteins in hamster fibroblasts. *J. Biol. Chem.* 262:12081–85

Frand AR, Kaiser CS. 1998. The *ERO1* gene of yeast is required for oxidation of protein dithiols in the endoplasmic reticulum. *Mol. Cell* 1:161–70

Gething M-J, Sambrook J. 1992. Protein folding in the cell. *Nature* 355:33–45

Greenberg ML, Lopes JM. 1996. Genetic regulation of phospholipid biosynthesis in *Saccharomyces cerevisiae*. *Microbiol. Rev.* 60:1–20

Hammond C, Helenius A. 1995. Quality control in the secretory pathway. *Curr. Opin. Cell Biol.* 7:523–29

Hardwick KG, Lewis MJ, Semenza J, Dean N, Pelham HRB. 1990. *ERD1*, a yeast gene required for the retention of luminal endoplasmic reticulum proteins, affects glycoprotein processing in the Golgi apparatus. *EMBO J.* 9:623–30

Helenius A. 1994. How N-linked oligosaccharides affect glycoprotein folding in the endoplasmic reticulum. *Mol. Biol. Cell* 5:253–65

Henry SA, Patton-Vogt JL. 1999. Genetic regulation of phospholipid metabolism: yeast as a model eukaryote. *Prog. Nucleic Acids Res. Mol. Biol.* In press

Hirsch JP, Henry SA. 1986. Expression of *Saccharomyces cerevisiae* inositol-1-phosphate synthase (*INO1*) gene is regulated by factors that affect phospholipid synthesis. *Mol. Cell. Biol.* 6:3320–28

Kanai K, Watanabe J, Kanamura S. 1986. Quantitative analysis of smooth and rough endoplasmic reticulum proliferation in differentiating hepatocytes of midpostnatal mice treated with phenobarbital. *J. Ultrastruct. Mol. Struct. Res.* 97:64–72

Kargel E, Menzel R, Honeck H, Vogel F, Bohmer A, Schunck WH. 1996. *Candida maltosa* NADPH-cytochrome P450 reductase: cloning of a full-length cDNA, heterologous expression in *Saccharomyces cerevisiae* and function of the N-terminal region for membrane anchoring and proliferation of the endoplasmic reticulum. *Yeast* 12:333–48

Kawahara T, Yanagi H, Yura T, Mori K. 1997. Endoplasmic reticulum stress-induced mRNA splicing permits synthesis of transcription factor Hac1p/Ern4p that activates the unfolded protein response. *Mol. Biol. Cell* 8:1845–62

Kleman-Leyer K, Ambruster DW, Daniels CJ. 1997. Properties of *H. volcanii* tRNA intron endonuclease reveal a relationship between the archeal and eucaryal intron processing systems. *Cell* 89:839–47

Kohno K, Normington K, Sambrook J, Gething MJ, Mori K. 1993. The promoter region of the yeast *KAR2* (BiP) gene contains a regulatory domain that responds to the presence of unfolded proteins in the endoplasmic reticulum. *Mol. Cell. Biol.* 13:877–90

Kopito RR. 1997. ER quality control: the cytoplasmic connection. *Cell* 88:427–30

LaMantia M, Miura T, Tachikawa H, Kaplan HA, Lennarz WJ, Mizunaga T. 1991. Glycosylation site binding protein and protein disulfide isomerase are identical and essential for cell viability in yeast. *Proc. Natl. Acad. Sci. USA* 88:4453–57

Lee AS. 1987. Coordinated regulation of a set of genes by glucose and calcium ionophores in mammalian cells. *Trends Biochem. Sci.* 12:20–23

Li WW, Alexander S, Cao X, Lee AS. 1993. Transactivation of the grp78 promoter by Ca^{2+} depletion. A comparative analysis with A23187 and the endoplasmic reticulum Ca^{2+}-ATPase inhibitor thapsigargin. *J. Biol. Chem.* 268:12003–9

Li WW, Sistonen L, Morimoto RI, Lee AS. 1994. Stress induction of the mammalian GRP78/BiP protein gene: in vivo genomic footprinting and identification of p70CORE from human nuclear extract as a DNA-binding component specific to the stress regulatory element. *Mol. Cell. Biol.* 14:5533–46

Liu ES, Ou JH, Lee AS. 1992. Brefeldin A as a regulator of *grp78* gene expression in mammalian cells. *J. Biol. Chem.* 267:7128–33

Mazarella RA, Srinivasan M, Haugejordan SM, Green M. 1990. Erp72, an abundant lumenal endoplasmic reticulum protein, contains three copies of the active site sequences of protein disulfide isomerase. *J. Biol. Chem.* 265:1094–101

McMillan DR, Gething M-J, Sambrook J. 1994. The cellular response to unfolded proteins: intercompartamental signaling. *Curr. Opin. Biotechnol.* 5:540–45

Mori K, Kawahara T, Yoshida H, Yanagi H, Yura T. 1996. Signalling from endoplasmic reticulum to nucleus: transcription factor with a basic-leucine zipper motif is required for the unfolded protein-response pathway. *Genes Cells* 1:803–17

Mori K, Ma W, Gething M-J, Sambrook J. 1993. A transmembrane protein with a $cdc2^+$/CDC28-related kinase activity is required for signaling from the ER to the nucleus. *Cell* 74:743–56

Mori K, Ogawa N, Kawahara T, Yanagi H, Yura T. 1998. Palindrome with spacer of one nucleotide is characteristic of the *cis*-acting unfolded protein response element in *Saccharomyces cerevisiae*. *J. Biol. Chem.* 273:9912–20

Mori K, Sant A, Kohno K, Normington K, Gething MJ, Sambrook JF. 1992. A 22 bp *cis*-acting element is necessary and sufficient for the induction of the yeast *KAR2* (BiP) gene by unfolded proteins. *EMBO J.* 11:2583–93

Morimoto RI, Jurivich DA, Kroeger PE, Mathur SK, Murphy SP, et al. 1994. Regulation of heat shock gene transcription by a family of heat shock factors. In *The Biology of Heat Shock Proteins and Molecular Chaperones*, ed. RI Morimoto, A Tissieres, C Georgopoulos, pp. 417–55. New York: Cold Spring Harbor Press

Ng DTW, Watowich SS, Lamb RA. 1992. Analysis in vivo of GRP78-BiP/substrate interactions and their role in induction of the GRP78-BiP gene. *Mol. Biol. Cell* 3:143–55

Nikawa J, Akiyoshi M, Hirata S, Fukuda T. 1996. *Saccharomyces cerevisiae IRE2/HAC1* is involved in *IRE1*-mediated *KAR2* expression. *Nucleic Acids Res.* 24:4222–26

Nikawa JI, Yamashita S. 1992. *IRE1* encodes a putative protein kinase containing a membrane-spanning domain and is required for inositol prototrophy in *Saccharomyces cerevisiae. Mol. Microbiol.* 6:1441–46

Nojima H, Sun-Hee L, Araki H, Sakai A, Nakashima N, et al. 1994. Hac1: A novel yeast bZIP protein binding to the CRE motif is a multicopy suppressor for *cdc10* mutant of *Schizosaccharomyces pombe. Nucleic Acids Res.* 22:5279–88

Normington K, Kohno K, Kozutsumi Y, Gething MJ, Sambrook J. 1989. S. cerevisiae encodes an essential protein homologous in sequence and function to mammalian BiP. *Cell* 57:1223–36

Nunnari J, Walter P. 1996. Regulation of organelle biogenesis. *Cell* 84:389–94

Pahl HL, Baeuerle PA. 1995. A novel signal transduction pathway from the endoplasmic reticulum to the nucleus is mediated by transcription factor NF-κB. *EMBO J.* 14:2580–88

Pahl HL, Baeuerle PA. 1997a. Endoplasmic-reticulum-induced signal transduction and gene expression. *Trends Cell Biol.* 7:50–55

Pahl HL, Baeuerle PA. 1997b. The ER-overload response: activation of NF-κB. *Trends Biochem. Sci.* 22:63–67

Pahl HL, Sester M, Burgert HG, Baeuerle PA. 1996. Activation of transcription factor NF-κB by the adenovirus E3/19K protein requires its ER retention. *J. Cell Biol.* 132:511–22

Partadelis JA, Berlin V. 1993. The *FKB2* gene of *Saccharomyces cerevisiae*, endoding the immunosuppresssant-binding protein FKBP-13, is regulated in response to accumulation of unfolded proteins in the endoplasmic reticulum. *Proc. Natl. Acad. Sci. USA* 90:5450–54

Pollard MG, Travers KJ, Weissman JS. 1998. Ero1p: a novel and ubiquitous protein with an essential role in oxidative protein folding in the endoplasmic reticulum. *Mol. Cell* 1:171–82

Resendez E Jr, Wooden SK, Lee AS. 1988. Identification of highly conserved regulatory domains and protein-binding sites in the promoters of the rat and human genes encoding

the stress-inducible 78-kilodalton glucose-regulated protein. *Mol. Cell. Biol.* 8:4579–84

Schnuck W-H, Kargel E, Gross B, Wiedmann B, Mauersberger S, et al. 1989. Molecular cloning and characterization of the primary structure of the alkane hydroxylating cytochrome P-450 from the yeast *Candida maltosa. Biochem. Biophys. Res. Com.* 161:843–50

Shamu CE, Cox JS, Walter P. 1994. The unfolded-protein-response pathway in yeast. *Trends Cell Biol.* 4:56–60

Shamu CE, Walter P. 1996. Oligomerization and phosphorylation of the Ire1p kinase during intracellular signaling from the endoplasmic reticulum to the nucleus. *EMBO J.* 15:3028–39

Sidrauski C, Cox JS, Walter P. 1996. tRNA ligase is required for regulated mRNA splicing in the unfolded protein response. *Cell* 87:405–13

Sidrauski C, Walter P. 1997. The transmembrane kinase Ire1p is a site-specific endonuclease that initiates mRNA splicing in the unfolded protein response. *Cell* 90:1–20

Smith JR, Osborne TF, Goldstein JL, Brown MS. 1990. Identification of nucleotides responsible for enhancer activity of sterol regulatory element in low density lipoprotein receptor gene. *J. Biol. Chem.* 265:2306–10

Tachibana C, Stevens TH. 1992. The yeast *EUG1* gene encodes an endoplasmic reticulum protein that is functionally related to protein disulfide isomerase. *Mol. Cell. Biol.* 12:4601–11

Tirasophon W, Welihinda AA, Kaufman RJ. 1998. A stress response pathway from the endoplasmic reticulum to the nucleus requires a novel bifunctional protein kinase/endonuclease (Ire1p) in mammalian cells. *Genes. Dev.* 12:1812–24

Trotta CR, Miao F, Arn EA, Stevens SW, Ho CK, et al. 1997. The yeast tRNA splicing endonuclease: a tetrameric enzyme with two active site subunits homologous to the archeal tRNA endonucleases. *Cell* 89:849–58

Welihinda AA, Kaufman RJ. 1996. The unfolded protein response pathway in *Saccharomyces cerevisiae*. Oligomerization and trans-autophosphorylation of Ire1p (Ern1p) are required for kinase activation. *J. Biol. Chem.* 271:18181–87

Welihinda AA, Tirasophon W, Green SR, Kaufman RJ. 1997. Gene induction in response to unfolded protein in the endoplasmic reticulum is mediated through Ire1p kinase interaction with a transcriptional coactivator complex containing Ada5p. *Proc. Natl. Acad. Sci. USA* 94:4289–94

Welihinda AA, Tirasophon W, Green SR, Kaufman RJ. 1998. Protein serine/threonine phosphatase Ptc2p negatively regulates the unfolded-protein response by dephosphorylating Ire1p kinase. *Mol. Cell. Biol.* 18:1967–77

White JJ, Hirsch JP, Henry SA. 1991. The *OPI1* gene of *Saccharomyces cerevisiae*, a negative regulator of phospholipid biosynthesis, encodes a protein containing polyglutamine tracts and a leucine zipper. *J. Biol. Chem.* 266:863–72

Wiest DL, Burkhardt JK, Hester S, Hortsch M, Meyer DI, Argon Y. 1990. Membrane biogenesis during B cell differentiation: most endoplasmic reticulum proteins are expressed coordinately. *J. Cell Biol.* 110:1501–11

Wooden SK, Li LJ, Navarro D, Qadri I, Pereira L, Lee AS. 1991. Transactivation of the *grp78* promoter by malfolded proteins, glycosylation block, and calcium ionophore is mediated through a proximal region containing a CCAAT motif which interacts with CTF/NF-I. *Mol. Cell. Biol.* 11:5612–23

Wright R. 1993. Insights from inducible membranes. *Curr. Biol.* 3:870–73

Zhou A, Hassel BA, Silverman RH. 1993. Expression cloning of 2-5A-dependent RNAse: a uniquely regulated mediator of interferon action. *Cell* 72:753–65

Annu. Rev. Cell Dev. Biol. 1998. 14:487–525

DEFINING ACTIN FILAMENT LENGTH IN STRIATED MUSCLE:
Rulers and Caps or Dynamic Stability?

R. Littlefield and V. M. Fowler

Department of Cell Biology, The Scripps Research Institute, La Jolla, California
92037; e-mail: velia@scripps.edu

KEY WORDS: myofibril, nebulin, tropomyosin, tropomodulin, myosin, capZ, titin

---

ABSTRACT

Actin filaments (thin filaments) are polymerized to strikingly uniform lengths
in striated muscle sarcomeres. Yet, actin monomers can exchange dynamically
into thin filaments in vivo, indicating that actin monomer association and dissociation at filament ends must be highly regulated to maintain the uniformity of
filament lengths. We propose several hypothetical mechanisms that could generate uniform actin filament length distributions and discuss their application to
the determination of thin filament length in vivo. At the Z line, titin may determine the minimum extent and tropomyosin the maximum extent of thin filament
overlap by regulating α-actinin binding to actin, while a unique Z filament may
bind to capZ and regulate barbed end capping. For the free portion of the thin
filament, we evaluate possibilities that thin filament components (e.g. nebulin or
the tropomyosin/troponin polymer) determine thin filament lengths by binding
directly to tropomodulin and regulating pointed end capping, or alternatively, that
myosin thick filaments, together with titin, determine filament length by indirectly
regulating tropomodulin's capping activity.

CONTENTS

487

1081-0706/98/1115-0487$08.00

INTRODUCTION

It is well established that actin polymerization dynamics underly many events in motile cells, including the extension of the leading lamella, cytokinesis, protrusion of filopodia, and formation of stress fibers (Carlier 1998). Actin filaments also form the basis of specialized architectural or contractile structures in a variety of differentiated cells, including the long bundles of actin filaments in microvilli of the intestinal brush border, the short actin filaments in the erythrocyte membrane skeleton, and the long actin filaments (thin filaments) in striated muscle sarcomeres (Fowler 1996, 1997). Although the length of the actin filaments differs from structure to structure, the length distribution of the filaments in each structure is strikingly uniform (Fowler 1997). This is in marked contrast to the wide variations in actin filament lengths in vitro (Oosawa & Asakura 1975) and in labile actin structures such as the leading lamella (Podolski & Steck 1990, Cano et al 1991, Small et al 1995, Cramer et al 1997).

The persistence of the characteristic actin filament lengths over the lifetime of these cellular structures has led to the notion that the actin filaments are relatively static (Fowler 1996). However, the in vivo characteristics of striated muscle actin filaments suggest that actin dynamics are important not only to assemble the filaments into sarcomeres but also to maintain their precise lengths over the lifetime of the sarcomere. Specification of actin filament lengths in striated muscle sarcomeres is unlikely to be a one-time event; that is, continuing monomer exchange into apparently stable filaments indicates that filaments do not simply polymerize to the appropriate length and then become tightly capped at their ends after assembly. Instead, actin polymerization dynamics are likely to be important for the initial determination of filament length and for the maintenance of length in the final structure.

We have chosen the thin filaments in striated muscle sarcomeres to develop this thesis, but it is likely that our ideas will be applicable, at least in part, to explain actin filament length regulation in other cell types. Among all the differentiated cell types with regulated actin filament length distributions, striated muscle is unique in that considerable information is available about actin filament dynamics, actin filament structural and biochemical organization, and molecular genetic analysis of protein function in vivo. Furthermore, muscle is an excellent experimental system for studying actin filament length regulation because the repetitive and practically crystalline organization of sarcomeres in striated muscle means that even subtle changes or defects are readily apparent (Huxley 1960, Fyrberg & Beall 1990, Bernstein et al 1993). In addition, the parallel arrangement and relatively long lengths of muscle thin filaments make it possible to evaluate actin filament dynamics and structure relatively easily. The organization of the actin filaments in striated muscle sarcomeres and their key interactions with the principal actin-binding proteins of the sarcomere are depicted in Figure 1.

Understanding how actin filament lengths are regulated in striated muscle is important because defects in specific components of the sarcomere and/or alterations in their structural organization are the molecular basis for several debilitating muscle diseases, including familial hypertrophic cardiomyopathy (Vikstrom & Leinwand 1996) and nemaline myopathy (Gyure et al 1997). In addition, variations in thin filament lengths in different muscle types correlate with physiological properties of the muscle and indicate that thin filament lengths are likely to be important for the characteristic mechanical properties of different muscles (Huxley 1960, Vigoreaux 1994, Simpson et al 1994).

Herein we discuss how the stochastic characteristics of actin polymerization observed in vitro can be controlled to generate the uniform and precisely regulated length distributions such as observed in muscle and other cells. Several simple models are proposed for how actin filament lengths might be specified. Next, we discuss actin dynamics in the thin filaments of muscle sarcomeres because any mechanistic models must take in vivo actin dynamics into account. Finally, we discuss the particular structural components of the sarcomere and how they may contribute to the molecular mechanisms that influence the lengths of the cross-linked (Z line) or free portions of the thin filaments.

ACTIN POLYMERIZATION AND FILAMENT LENGTH DISTRIBUTIONS

To understand how a uniform distribution of actin filament lengths is specified and maintained it is necessary to review the multiple equilibria involved in actin filament formation. The equilibrium between monomers and nuclei, and that between monomers and filaments, is well understood within the context of the nucleation-elongation mechanism of actin polymerization (Oosawa & Asakura 1975, Pollard & Cooper 1986, Carlier et al 1994) and is not covered in detail here. Briefly, nucleation involves the association of three to four monomers into a stable oligomer (nucleus) from which filament elongation may occur by the stochastic addition of monomers to the filament ends. Filament elongation continues until the equilibrium between monomer and polymer is reached, i.e. when the available actin monomer reaches the critical concentration. At this point, the rate of monomer addition and loss are equal, and the average filament length is determined by the ratio of the polymer mass to the filament number. It is not generally appreciated, however, that a third equilibrium, involving the stochastic exchange of monomers between filaments of different lengths, results in a redistribution of filament lengths at the end of the elongation phase (Oosawa & Asakura 1975). Because individual monomers exchange with equal rates from filaments of different lengths, the steady-state filament length distribution satisfying each monomer-binding reaction is exponential (Figure 2) (Oosawa

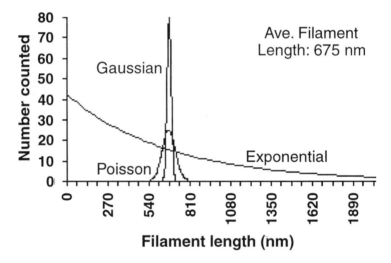

Figure 2   Three models of actin filament length distributions chosen with the same average length, m = 250 monomers (675 nm), predict different probabilities (i.e. relative frequency) of finding filaments shorter and longer than the average length. The expected number of filaments, p(x), is plotted as a function of length, assuming 2.7 nm per subunit, x. The exponential distribution, $p(x) = (1/m)e^{-x/m}$, has filaments of many different lengths with a large variance, $\sigma^2 = m^2 = 62500$ monomers. This type of distribution results after monomers exchange within the filaments. The Poisson distribution, $p(x) = e^{-m}m^x/x!$, describes the distribution of filaments efficiently elongated from nuclei. The distribution is much more uniform compared with the exponential distribution because the variance equals the average length, $\sigma^2 = m = 250$ monomers. In contrast, the Gaussian distribution, $p(x) = (\sigma^2 2\phi)^{-1/2}e^{-1/2(x-m)2/\sigma^2}$, describes an extremely uniform population of filament lengths, with a variance, σ^2, determined independently of the average length (set here to 25 monomers). The distribution of thin filament lengths in vertebrate skeletal muscle is described by a Gaussian distribution because the variance is often much less than the average length. The distributions are calculated assuming that filaments differing in length by one monomer are distinguishable. For the purpose of illustration, the exponential, Poisson, and Gaussian distributions are scaled by 1000, 1000, and 10000, respectively.

1970, Kawamura & Maruyama 1972, Oosawa & Asakura 1975, Janmey et al 1986, Burlacu et al 1992, Dufort & Lumdsen 1995). Although ATP hydrolysis by actin affects the thermodynamic equilibria for nucleation and growth of filaments (Oosawa & Asakura 1975, Pollard & Cooper 1986, Carlier et al 1994), this is unlikely to affect the filament length distribution at steady state. This is because the nucleotide state of subunits at the filament ends is independent of filament length.

Polymer mass and filament number are controlled by mechanisms that regulate nucleation and elongation of actin filaments. For example, the total polymer mass can be increased by the desequestration of actin monomers from monomer-binding proteins, followed by polymerization of the monomers until the critical concentration is reached. Reduction of the critical concentration by uncapping barbed ends or activation of monomer by specific proteins (e.g. profilin) may also lead to dramatic increases in polymer mass. Filament number may be increased through the activation of nuclei or by activation of filament-severing proteins. Total polymer amount may be increased by uncapping of filament ends and elongation or by interaction with filament side-binding proteins such as tropomyosin (Broschat 1990) or bundling proteins (Zigmond et al 1992), which can prevent depolymerization by reducing the monomer off rate. Thus average filament length may be controlled by mechanisms that vary the critical concentration and the number of filaments.

Can regulation of polymer number and mass in itself generate or maintain a uniform population of filament lengths? Coordination of regulatory mechanisms for nucleation and elongation may induce efficient and synchronous filament elongation (Theriot 1994a, Carlier 1998), which is predicted to result in a Poisson filament length distribution (Figure 2) (Oosawa 1970, Oosawa & Asakura 1975). However, the filament lengths will redistribute with a rate depending primarily on the rate of monomer exchange and the average filament length (Oosawa 1970, Oosawa & Asakura 1975). The average filament length, but not the polymer mass, determines the exponential distribution, i.e. the relative number of short and long filaments (Kawamura & Maruyama 1972, Janmey et al 1986). While monomer exchange can be reduced by capping proteins, monomer-binding proteins, and/or filament side-binding proteins, this will slow but not prevent the redistribution of filament lengths because the binding reactions cannot be driven to completion; uncapped ends and free monomers will always be present. Thus nucleation and elongation itself cannot generate the extremely uniform (Gaussian) filament length distributions (Figure 2) observed in muscle (Huxley 1960, Fowler 1997); and, although the regulation of filament elongation and nucleation is sufficient to regulate the average filament length, it is insufficient to prevent the redistribution of filament lengths. Unless there are specific mechanisms that regulate the rate of monomer exchange differently for filaments of different lengths, the distribution of filament lengths will become exponential over time.

Length-Dependent Regulation

In some cases, it has been demonstrated that non-equivalent contacts of identical subunits within the polymer (quasi-equivalence) regulate polymer length. This is the basis for the accumulated strain mechanism proposed to regulate the lengths of the bipolar myosin thick filaments in striated muscle (Higuchi et al 1986, Davis 1986). Because actin can polymerize to indeterminate lengths, there is little evidence for this type of non-equivalence in actin filaments themselves; however, that does not preclude the induction of non-equivalence by filament-binding proteins. It is possible that capping at one filament end could result in a cooperative conformational change in the actin filament that is propagated along a number of subunits. For example, capping of the barbed end by gelsolin has been shown to lead to long range (> 100 subunits) conformational changes in the actin subunits throughout the polymer (Orlova et al 1995, Prochniewicz et al 1996, Khaitlina & Hinssen 1997). However, the length dependence of this conformational change is unknown.

Another possibility is that a separate component or template could determine actin filament length, as previously proposed for striated muscle (Spudich et al 1972, Ishiwata & Funatsu 1985, Fyrberg & Beall 1990, Fowler 1996). A template protein (gpH) has been shown to regulate the extent of bacteriophage tail protein polymerization (Katsura & Hendrix 1984). The general idea is that templates regulate monomer exchange in a way that provides additional stability to filaments that are the length of the template, thereby generating a uniform filament length distribution and preventing length redistribution from taking place.

We have divided template mechanisms into three subcategories: rulers, verniers, and scaffolds, each of which differs in its mechanism for determining length (Figure 3). Additional models of greater complexity combine or share aspects of these three types of mechanisms. It should be noted that these mechanisms can regulate the length of either an entire filament by spanning from one end to the other or a portion of a filament by binding to some side-binding protein in the middle of a filament and extending to only one end. Furthermore, the ruler and the vernier mechanisms can regulate the length of isolated or individual filaments because each length-sensing component is intrinsic to and binds directly to the filament. This would potentially allow filaments of the appropriate length to be recognized or specified by the template prior to assembly into a filament array. In contrast, the scaffold mechanism relies on the assembly of filaments into the scaffold structure before they can be regulated in length.

The Ruler Mechanism

The molecular ruler mechanism is intuitively simple. It consists of an individual molecule that has many actin-binding sites and extends along the length of an individual filament or portion of a filament (Figure 3A). One end of the molecular ruler binds to another filament-associated component (e.g. a capping protein) to target the molecular ruler to the correct filament or portion of the filament. At the other end, the molecular ruler binds to a capping protein and stabilizes its association with the end to further prevent monomer addition or loss [Figure 3A(i)]. Alternatively, a capping protein may not be needed at one end because the ruler itself reduces the off rate of the terminal monomer and directly stabilizes the filament [Figure 3A(ii)]. Additional filament elongation would not occur appreciably if the free monomer concentration were below the monomer affinity for that end (Cooper & Pollard 1986, Carlier 1998). In addition, the ruler molecule should bind equivalently to all subunits along the entire length of the filament. Otherwise shorter filaments can be mis-specified if a loop is formed by the ruler molecule along the filament [Figure 3A(iii)]. Thus in order to consistently determine a unique filament length, we would expect some other mechanism to reliably fix the position of the ruler in an extended conformation.

The Vernier Mechanism

The vernier mechanism relies on the copolymerization of another molecule along the length of the actin filament (Figure 3B) and is very similar to a ruler mechanism in that it requires an additional component at one end that targets the copolymer and aligns the first subunit in a precise position with respect to the actin monomers at the filament end. However, the key difference from a ruler is that a vernier determines filament lengths much longer than the length of an individual copolymer subunit. Unlike a molecular ruler, each vernier molecule binds a nonintegral number of actin subunits in non-equivalent positions along the filament. This requires that the binding to each actin subunit is not stereo specific and allows each sucessive vernier subunit to be in a slightly different position with respect to the actin subunits in the filament. The copolymerization of the vernier molecule and actin is terminated (i.e. the filament is capped) when the terminal vernier subunit and the terminal actin monomer simultaneously bind to a capping protein and stabilize the association of the capping protein with the filament end (Spudich et al 1972, Ishiwata & Funatsu 1985).

A) Ruler

i)

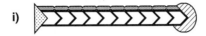

ii)

iii)

B) Vernier

C) Scaffold

i)

ii)

iii)

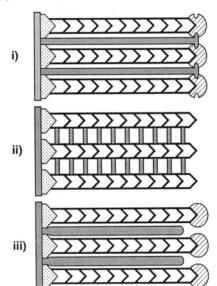

The Scaffold Mechanism

A scaffold is a more general type of template and may have many more subcomponents than depicted here (Figure 3C). The scaffold mechanism is unique with respect to rulers and verniers in that it does not determine filament lengths by counting the number of monomers along the length of the individual filaments. Instead, it aligns the opposite ends of the filaments a particular distance from each other. The scaffold may directly align one end of a filament to a bridging or cross-linking structure and extend it to the other end where the scaffold binds a capping protein [Figure 3C(i)]. Alternatively, an internal scaffold may form by saturating the filaments with a high concentration of cross-linkers [Figure 3C(ii)], reducing the off rate of cross-linked monomers. This would maximally stabilize the filaments (i.e. form the most cross-links) in the same bundle when they are all the same length. The total amount of polymer could be regulated to give a particular average length for a filament bundle produced this way; however, this would normally not be sufficient to generate uniform lengths between many different bundles (Stokes & DeRosier 1991, Furukawa & Fecheimer 1996). Another possible type of scaffold [Figure 3C(iii)] would indirectly determine filament lengths by sterically blocking filament capping at lengths shorter than the extent of the scaffold. Filaments would be prevented from growing any further by maintaining a high concentration of capping protein, which would tend to immediately bind to the end of the filament when its length exceeded that of the scaffold structure.

Figure 3 Examples of molecular template mechanisms for actin filament length regulation. Actin monomers are indicated by *chevrons* (10 or fewer are shown for clarity in each example). (A) Ruler. A barbed end capping protein (*stippled triangle*) aligns one end of the molecular ruler (*shaded*) at the barbed filament end, and actin monomers polymerize to the other end of the ruler. (i) A pointed end capping protein (*striped*) only caps filaments that are the length of the ruler. (ii) The molecular ruler may also stabilize the association of a specific number of actin monomers along its length without requiring a pointed end cap. (iii) If the ruler molecule does not adopt a fully extended conformation, filament length may be mis-specified by inappropriate capping. (B) Vernier. A copolymer may form between the actin and the vernier molecule (*shaded*). Note that each vernier molecule makes non-equivalent contact with an actin monomer. Filaments are capped at both ends only when the copolymers are correctly aligned. (C) Scaffold. Components of the scaffold are *shaded dark gray*. Filaments may be aligned in the scaffold at the barbed end through the attatchment of capping proteins (*stippled triangles*) to the scaffold. (i) A component of the scaffold that extends alongside the actin filaments may specify the filament length by directly binding to pointed end capping proteins (*striped*). Alternatively, (ii) cross-linking proteins (*lightly shaded rectangles*) may bind to filament monomers to stabilize filaments of uniform lengths by preventing monomer exchange, or (iii) filament lengths may be specified if the scaffold sterically restricts the ability of the pointed end capping protein (*striped*) to bind at actin filament lengths shorter than the scaffold.

ACTIN FILAMENT STABILITY AND DYNAMICS IN THIN FILAMENTS

Isolated myofibrils are remarkably stable contractile units that retain their structural organization and contractile function for weeks in vitro (Huxley 1960). The thin filaments in striated muscle myofibrils are capped by capZ at their barbed ends and by tropomodulin at their pointed ends (Figure 1). Several classic experiments have demonstrated that exogenous actin cannot exchange into thin filaments of isolated myofibrils unless the caps have been extracted. Fluorescently labeled G-actin does not incorporate at the thin filament pointed ends unless the myofibrils are first extracted with 0.6 M salt to remove tropomodulin (Sanger et al 1984, Ishiwata & Funatsu 1985, Fowler et al 1993). Similarily, incorporation of fluorescent actin at the Z line was observed only after pretreatment of myofibrils with Triton X-100 (Peng & Fischman 1991), which is likely to have extracted capZ from the barbed end (A Almenar-Queralt & V Fowler, unpublished observations). Myofibrillar proteins are also very stable, with half-lives on the order of days. For example, actin has a half-life of $\approx$5 days in myofibrils of embryonic chick or neonatal rat cardiac myocytes (Clark & Zak 1981, Sussman et al 1998a) and $\approx$7 days in adult rat heart (Zak et al 1977). In contrast, in intestinal epithelial cells the actin turnover rate is on the order of a few hours (Stidwell et al 1984).

The apparently static nature of thin filaments in isolated myofibrils in vitro, together with the protein stability in vivo, has led to the misconception that thin filaments are static structures that do not exchange their components. However, microinjection experiments demonstrate directly that actin monomers and other thin filament components can exchange into thin filaments in vivo. Fluorescently labeled G-actin rapidly incorporates into myofibrils after microinjection into living skeletal and cardiac muscle cells, resulting in the appearance within $\approx$5–30 min of a pattern of narrow striations along myofibrils (Glacy 1983, McKenna et al 1985, Dome et al 1988, Hayakawa et al 1996). After longer times the fluorescence spreads throughout the entire thin filament (Dome et al 1988, Hayakawa et al 1996). Fluorescently labeled tropomyosin or α-actinin are also incorporated in about the same time into the thin filaments in the I band region or at the Z lines, respectively, of cardiac myocytes or skeletal myotubes (McKenna et al 1986, Sanger et al 1986, Dome et al 1988). Determination of subunit exchange rates from these studies is complicated by potential polymerization of new filaments and the possibility of low-affinity binding sites.

The half time of fluorescent recovery after photobleaching (FRAP) for rhodamine-labeled muscle actin in thin filaments of striated myofibrils in cultured chick cardiac myocytes was recently determined to be $\approx$1 h (Shimada et al 1997), which is relatively slow in comparison with other actin structures, such as stress fibers ($\approx$5–10 min) (Kreis et al 1979, Theriot & Mitchison 1991, Shimada et al 1997), *Listeria monocytogenes* tails ($\approx$30 s) (Theriot 1994b), and lamellae in migrating cells (30–180 s) (Theriot 1994b, Theriot & Mitchison 1991). However, in one instance, initial actin incorporation into cardiac myofibrils was observed to occur within 5 s; detection of this weak signal was possible only after fixation and extraction of the cells to remove the high background fluorescence of unincorporated monomer in the cytoplasm of the living cells (Imanaka-Yoshida et al 1993). Although it is commonly believed that the initial site of actin incorporation is at the barbed ends in the Z line (McKenna et al 1985, Dome et al 1988, Shimada et al 1997), this has not been rigorously verified by colocalization with other sarcomeric components. Additionally, the distance between fluorescent bands in some studies indicates that actin may incorporate at both thin filament ends (Glacy 1983; R Littlefield & VM Fowler, unpublished observations). These experiments suggest that actin filament ends are not tighly capped all of the time.

One possible way to maintain constant thin filament lengths while allowing monomer exchange would be for the rate of monomer addition at the barbed end to be balanced by the rate of monomer loss at the pointed end (i.e. treadmilling) (Wanger et al 1984). However, this does not appear to be the case because thin filaments in cultured chick skeletal myotubes do not disassemble in the presence of cytochalasin D or B, which binds and caps the barbed end of actin filaments and prevents monomer addition (Sanger et al 1971, Miranda & Godman 1973, Holtzer et al 1975). Other observations indicate that maintenance of thin filament length in muscle cells, unlike in many other cell types, does not rely on input of monomer from a substantial monomer pool. Thin filaments do not disassemble when excess monomer-binding protein (either DNase I or vitamin D-binding protein) is microinjected into cultured chick skeletal myotubes or cardiac myocytes (Sanger et al 1990). In contrast, microinjection of these monomer-binding proteins into PtK2 cells causes stress fibers to disassemble within 30 min. Thin filaments in mature striated myofibrils are also resistant to depolymerization by gelsolin (Huckriede et al 1988) or by cofilin (Nagaoka et al 1995). Finally, although the total amount of actin increases dramatically during muscle differentiation, the amount of G-actin drops from 25 μM ($\approx$40% of the total actin) in 10-day chick embryos to 3.5 μM ($\approx$0.4% of the total actin) at 2 months post-hatching (Shimuzu & Obinata 1986, Nagaoka et al 1996). Along with this drop in G-actin, there is a substantial decrease of monomer-binding proteins [profilin, cofilin, actin depolymerizing factor (ADF), and thymosin β4] (Bamburg & Bray 1987, Nagaoka et al 1996, Obinata et al 1997).

Because the exchange of actin monomers in and out of thin filaments in living muscle cells is relatively quick in comparison to protein turnover rates, an individual actin monomer may exist in many different thin filaments during its lifetime. A comparison between the actin incorporation half time (1 h; Shimada et al 1997) and the actin turnover half time ($\approx$5 days; see above) for cardiac myocytes suggests that actin monomers go in and out of a cardiac thin filament >100 times on average! Yet, despite this exchange, the lengths of all the thin filaments remain the same and do not revert to an exponential length distribution (Figure 2). We cannot exclude the possibility that the microinjection of concentrated actin may have increased the incorporation rate or that different actin pools turnover at extremely different rates; however, it is reasonably clear that thin filaments are in a dynamic equilibrium with a monomer pool and that the mechanism specifying and maintaining thin filament length must be tolerant of subunit exchange.

Exchange of actin in and out of the thin filament in vivo occurs despite the presence of the thin filament capping proteins, tropomodulin and capZ, at the thin filament ends. Therefore, it seems likely that any length-regulating mechanism(s) must specifically regulate tropomodulin and capZ activity to allow actin subunit exchange without leading to redistribution of filament lengths. The inability of actin to incorporate into thin filaments in isolated myofibrils further indicates that regulated actin exchange in vivo is likely to require an active process that has not been reconstituted in vitro. In conclusion, any mechanism that accounts for determination of thin filament length must be capable of directly or indirectly regulating the capping proteins, thereby regulating actin dynamics at the filament ends.

LENGTH REGULATION AT THE BARBED END: THE Z LINE PORTION

At the Z line, the thin filament barbed ends of apposing sarcomeres are cross-linked by α-actinin (Z filaments) into a precisely aligned antiparallel bundle capable of transmitting and distributing force (Squire 1981, Vigoreaux 1994). The thin filaments extend through the Z line just to the opposite side and no farther, where their barbed ends are capped by capZ, which indicates that the Z line portion of the thin filament is precisely regulated in length (Figure 1) (Vigoreaux 1994). The width of the Z line can vary in length from only $\approx$30 nm in fish skeletal muscle (Franzini-Armstrong 1973) up to $\approx$160 nm in vertebrate cardiac muscle (Goldstein et al 1979). Regulation of the amount of thin filament overlap in the Z line is likely to be physiologically important because Z line width tends to be inversely correlated to the shortening speed of the muscle; fast and slow twitch fibers have narrow and wide Z lines, respectively (Rowe 1973, Vigoreaux 1994). Furthermore, in some debilitating muscle diseases such as nemaline myopathy, Z line widths can be greater than 1 μm (Yamaguchi et al 1983, 1985; Vigoreaux 1994).

We focus herein on the potential roles of the Z line actin-binding proteins, α-actinin and capZ, in determining the extent of thin filament overlap in the Z line. Key factors are expected to include (*a*) positioning capZ and the barbed filament ends from adjacent sarcomeres at the two opposite sides of the Z line, (*b*) regulating capZ activity to prevent inappropriate filament elongation at the barbed end, and (*c*) determining the number and spacings of Z filament (α-actinin) cross-links along the thin filament.

CapZ

CapZ is a high-affinity barbed end capping protein ($K_d \approx 1$ nM) that can also nucleate actin filament assembly from the barbed filament end in vitro (Schafer & Cooper 1995, Fowler 1996). CapZ has been proposed to target and align the barbed ends of the thin filaments at the opposite sides of the Z line based on the following observations: First, in skeletal myotubes, capZ assembles at nascent Z bodies before mature actin striations have developed, i.e. prior to the alignment of thin filament pointed ends and formation of the H zone (Schafer et al 1993). Second, when the actin capping activity of capZ is inhibited in embryonic chick skeletal myotubes, the organization of α-actinin into periodic Z lines and the appearance of actin striations is delayed during assembly (Schafer et al 1995). It is also worth noting that disruption of capZ function in chick myotubes has no effect on either titin or thick filament organization, suggesting that assembly of myosin and titin into myofibrillar arrays is independent of barbed end targeting to Z lines (Schafer et al 1995). Third, capZ appears to bind to a component at the Z line independently of its ability to cap actin filament barbed ends; i.e. low levels of anti-capZ antibody, which disrupt capZ's actin-capping activity, fail to dissociate capZ from the Z line (Schafer et al 1995). Together, these observations are consistent with the idea that capZ functions to target and align the barbed ends at the Z line through an additional binding activity.

What structural components of the Z line might capZ bind to other than actin filament barbed ends? Evidence for a capZ-binding Z filament is provided by three-dimensional reconstructions of the complex Z lines of honeybee flight muscle (Deatherage et al 1989) and of simple Z lines in fish muscle (Luther 1991), which showed Z filaments linking directly to the thin filament tips where capZ is located. Indeed, a preliminary report indicates that capZ may interact directly with α-actinin (Papa et al 1997). Other possible binding partners are the C-terminal domain of nebulin, which is proposed to cross the Z line based on its size (Labeit & Kolmerer 1995a, Wang et al 1996); the extreme N-terminal end of titin, which has been shown to extend to the opposite side of the Z line (Figure 1) (Young et al 1998); or a novel 19 kDa protein (T-cap), which binds to the two Ig repeats at the extreme N-terminal end of titin (CC Gregorio, K Trombitas, B Kolmerer, G Stier, H Granzier et al, submitted).

In addition to providing an anchoring site for capZ and actin filament barbed ends, one of these components, or another component, might also regulate capZ activity to allow for balanced monomer exchange at the barbed filament end while preserving the uniformity of filament overlaps (i.e. lengths) in the Z line. One possible regulatory molecule is phosphatidylinositol 4,5-bisphosphate (PIP_2), which causes rapid dissociation of capZ from actin filament barbed ends in vitro (Schafer et al 1996). Another regulatory candidate is the Z line-associated S100 protein, which binds to capZ in a calcium-dependent manner (Ivanenkov et al 1995). While binding of S100 protein to capZ does not affect capZ's actin-capping activity directly (Schafer et al 1996), S100 protein may modulate the interaction of capZ with other Z line components and regulate barbed end alignments in the Z line.

α-Actinin

The width of the Z line (i.e. the length of thin filament overlap in the Z line) is determined by the number of repeating layers of Z filaments, which vary from 1 in a simple Z line of fish white muscle (Luther 1991) to ≈3–4 layers in rat soleus (Schroeter et al 1996) to 10 or more in nemaline myopathies (Yamaguchi et al 1985, Morris et al 1990, Vigoreaux 1994). The cross-connecting Z filaments are believed to consist primarily of α-actinin dimers linking the antiparallel thin filaments from adjacent sarcomeres (Vigoreaux 1994). Interestingly, spacings between Z filaments observed in three-dimensional reconstructions of some Z lines are only ≈18 nm (Morris et al 1990, Schroeter et al 1996), in contrast to ≈36–38 nm spacings observed for α-actinin cross-links in bundles of actin filaments assembled in vitro (Podlubnaya et al 1975, Meyer & Aebi 1990). This suggests that other components must modulate the stoichiometry of α-actinin binding to actin in the Z line.

The N-terminal portion of titin, which extends across the Z line, has been proposed to interact directly with α-actinin, possibly strengthening α-actinin binding to actin and targeting α-actinin to the portion of the thin filament near the barbed end, thereby determining the number of Z filament layers (Sorimachi et al 1997, Young et al 1998). This N-terminal region of titin encodes several Ig-like domains as well as a series of 2 to 7 alternately spliced, 45-residue Z-repeats that bind to the extreme C-terminal end of α-actinin in vitro (Labeit & Kolmerer 1995b; Ohtsuka et al 1997a,b; Sorimachi et al 1997; Young et al 1998). The number of Z repeats expressed in titins from different muscle types correlates to some extent with the width of the Z line and has led to the idea that the number of Z repeats may determine the number of α-actinin cross-links along the thin filament (Gautel et al 1996, Ohtsuka et al 1997b, Sorimachi

Muscle Sarcomere

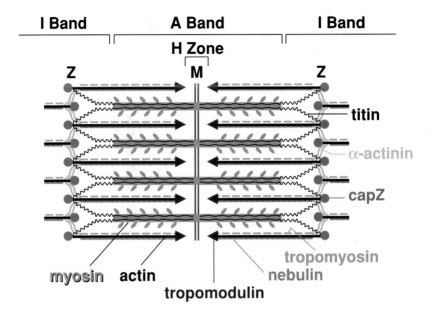

Figure 1   A schematic diagram of a sarcomere. The actin (thin) filament array (*thick black lines*) is centered at the Z line, which forms the boundaries of the sarcomere, whereas the center of the myosin bipolar thick filament array (*gray*) is at the M line in the middle of the sarcomere. Giant titin (connectin) molecules (*thin black squiggly lines*) extend from the M line all the way to the opposite side of the Z line and provide an elastic connection between the thick filaments and the Z line, centering the thick filaments in the middle of the sarcomere. At the Z line, the barbed ends of the thin actin filaments are capped by capZ (*blue circles*) and cross-linked by α-actinin (*yellow squiggles*) into a narrow antiparallel lattice that contributes to force transmission between adjacent sarcomeres. The free portion of the thin filament extends a uniform distance from the Z line into the middle of the sarcomere where it is capped by tropomodulin (*red triangles*) and interdigitates with the thick filaments. A giant nebulin molecule (*orange line*) and a head-to-tail tropomyosin/troponin polymer (*green dashes*) are associated with each strand of the thin filament and extend along its entire length toward the middle of the sarcomere. For clarity, only one strand of the thin filament is depicted along with one nebulin molecule and one tropomyosin/troponin strand. There are also three to six titin molecules associated with each thick filament in each half-sarcomere and six thin filaments associated with each thick filament in a hexagonal lattice in vertebrate muscle. For reviews on sarcomere components and organization see Huxley (1960), Squire (1981, 1997), Fowler (1996), Trinick (1994), Vigoreaux (1994), and Labeit et al (1997).

et al 1997, Young et al 1998). However, there may not be a simple one-to-one correspondence between the number of titin Z repeats and the number of α-actinins at the Z line (Ohtsuka et al 1997b, Sorimachi et al 1997). The effects of titin on α-actinin binding to actin are likely to be complex as another 70 amino acid region in the Z line portion of titin has been reported to interact with the central spectrin-like repeats of the α-actinin rod (Young et al 1998).

Interaction of α-actinin with the titin Z repeats is likely to be functionally important because expression of a truncated α-actinin missing the C-terminal EF-hand/titin-binding region leads to hypertrophy of Z lines in cultured chick myotubes (Schulthiess et al 1992; Z Lin, T Hijikata, Z Zhang, J Choi, S Holtzer et al, submitted). This suggests that the inability of α-actinin to bind to titin and/or improper regulation of α-actinin binding to actin at the Z line can result in the misregulation of the Z line width. Different α-actinin isoforms are associated with naturally wider Z lines (Schachat et al 1985), also supporting the possibility that differences in α-actinin binding to titin or actin may normally generate variations in the length of the Z line portion of the thin filaments.

Additionally, it is possible that interaction of the C-terminal portion of nebulin with α-actinin may also influence its binding to actin (Nave et al 1990, Wang et al 1996). Clearly, the Z line portions of titin or nebulin would be unable to extend across the full length of the massively enlarged Z lines in nemaline rods; yet the organization of individual Z filaments within the lattice is the same as in normal Z lines (Yamaguchi et al 1985, Morris et al 1990). This indicates that interactions of α-actinin with titin (or nebulin) do not control the spacings between α-actinins on the Z line portion of thin filaments. Instead, titin (or nebulin) may set the minimum number of Z filaments in the Z line, through a scaffold-like mechanism (Figure 3C).

The determination of the extent of thin filament overlap in the Z line also may include complementary mechanisms that prevent α-actinin from binding elsewhere along the thin filament and target α-actinin to the portion of the thin filament near the barbed end, thereby determining the number of Z filament layers. It is very likely that tropomyosin prevents α-actinin from binding to the free portion of the thin filament. Tropomyosin inhibits α-actinin binding to actin filaments in vitro (Goll et al 1972, Blanchard et al 1989, Lin et al 1997), and a three-dimensional reconstruction of actin filaments decorated with the actin-binding domain of α-actinin shows that tropomyosin would likely sterically block α-actinin binding to actin (McGough et al 1994). Furthermore, on a tropomyosin-actin filament, the most likely place where tropomyosin would be absent is at a filament end because of cooperativity of tropomyosin binding along the thin filament (Wegner 1979, Hitchcock-DeGregori 1994, Tobacman 1996). Consistent with this idea, an autosomal dominant nemaline myopathy with grossly enlarged Z lines (i.e. longer lengths of thin filaments in the Z line) has been linked to a tropomyosin point mutation, Met9→Arg (Laing et al 1995). This mutation is in the 'a' position of the tropomyosin heptad repeat and is predicted to destabilize coiled-coil formation, possibly weakening cooperative tropomyosin head-to-tail associations and/or tropomyosin binding to actin (Hitchcock-DeGregori 1994, Reinach et al 1995). A weaker binding tropomyosin might allow more α-actinin to bind, thereby promoting an increase in the extent of thin filament overlap. Abnormally wide Z lines are also observed in *Drosophila* indirect flight muscle (IFM) mutants lacking tropomyosin and/or troponins I or T (Fyrberg et al 1990b, Beall & Fyrberg 1991).

The phenotypes of α-actinin mutants in *Drosophila* IFM raise the possibility that α-actinin cross-links may determine not only Z line width (i.e. extent of thin filament overlap in the Z line), but may also have a mechanical function. For example, *fliA*[3] and *fliA*[4] α-actinin mutants fail to accumulate normal levels of α-actinin, yet assemble thin filaments into surprisingly normal-looking sarcomeres; however, the Z lines are somewhat discontinuous or perforated in places, and the muscles are paralyzed and degenerate after pupation (Fyrberg et al 1990b, Roulier et al 1992). Assembly of thin filaments into a functional Z line in *Drosophila* IFM may be a highly cooperative process; thus a partial deficiency of α-actinin would lead to fewer thin filaments being cross-linked into Z lines rather than narrower Z lines. Cooperativity in Z line assembly may play a role in determining the uniformity of Z line widths.

Strikingly, Z line formation in *Drosophila* IFM is completely prevented by an actin mutation (E93K) (Sparrow et al 1991), which is in the α-actinin binding site on actin and could prevent α-actinin binding to actin (McGough et al 1994). In these mutants, Z lines as well as α-actinin and other high-molecular weight Z line proteins are absent, and the thin and thick filaments are randomly misaligned in pseudo-myofibrillar bundles (Sparrow et al 1991). Thus thin filament cross-linking at Z lines appears to be required for thin and thick filament alignments into periodic sarcomeres in IFM. However, it may be that in addition to impaired α-actinin-binding ability for the mutant actin, filament capping, interactions with myosin, titin and/or other components might also be defective.

In conclusion, multiple mechanisms are likely to act cooperatively to specify the number of Z filament layers and to ensure that Z line width is properly regulated. The Z repeats in the N-terminal region of titin may determine the minimal number of Z filaments by stabilizing α-actinin binding to actin along the actin filaments, whereas tropomyosin may limit the extent of the Z line by restricting the sites along the thin filament available for α-actinin binding. CapZ may function to target and align thin filament barbed ends to their proper position at the edge of the Z line, perhaps by binding directly or indirectly to the N-terminal end of titin at the edge of the Z line. Finally, the integrity of the Z line is critical for organizing both thick and thin filaments into periodic sarcomeric arrays, i.e. myofibrils.

LENGTH REGULATION AT THE POINTED END: THE FREE PORTION

The free portions of the thin filaments extend from the edge of the Z line toward the middle of the sarcomere where they terminate at the bare zone of the myosin thick filaments and are capped by tropomodulin (Fowler 1996) (Figure 1). Whereas the uniform length distribution of the free portions of the thin filaments is generally preserved in most muscles, their particular lengths in various muscles are diverse. For example, the length of the free portion of the thin filament is 1.1 μm in rabbit psoas skeletal muscle (Sosa et al 1994), 0.94 μm for fast twitch and 1.24 μm for slow twitch fibers of perch muscle (Granzier et al 1991), and 1.5 μm in *Drosophila* IFM (Reedy & Beall 1993). An exception to the uniformity of thin filament lengths appears to be cardiac muscle, which has a somewhat wider variation in the thin filament length distribution, e.g. from 0.9 to 1.1 μm for rat papillary muscle (Robinson & Winegrad 1979). A wider variation in thin filament length distribution has also been reported for several rat skeletal muscles (Traeger & Goldstein 1983).

The length of the free portion of the thin filament appears to be distinctly regulated apart from the extent of thin filament overlap in the Z line. Thus wider Z lines in slow skeletal muscle fibers do not appear to be correlated with shorter free portions of the thin filament (Rowe 1973, Granzier et al 1991). Particularly striking examples are nemaline rods in skeletal and cardiac muscle, where extremely wide Z lines often form the boundaries of amazingly normal-looking sarcomeres in which the free portions of the thin filaments are unchanged in length (e.g. Cotè et al 1970, Fawcett 1968, Hudgson et al 1967, Roy & Morin 1971, Yamaguchi et al 1983). The increase in total thin filament length in sarcomeres that are adjacent to abnormally wide Z lines in nemaline rod diseases implies that compensatory polymerization at the pointed ends of the thin filaments has occurred, thereby maintaining the lengths of the free portions of the thin filaments.

Herein we discuss possible molecules that can determine the lengths of the free portions of the thin filaments, together with mechanisms that may regulate actin polymerization and preserve the uniformity of filament length distributions. We focus on actin-binding proteins, which are intrinsic to and co-extensive with the thin filament (the tropomyosin/troponin polymer or nebulin), and on a potential role for actomyosin interactions in conjunction with a stretch-sensitive titin scaffold. A key component of any potential mechanism for regulation of the free portion of the thin filament is expected to include a direct or indirect interaction of the length-sensing protein(s) with tropomodulin to regulate actin monomer association and dissociation from the pointed filament end (Figure 3).

Tropomodulin

Tropomodulin is unlike other actin filament capping proteins in that it completely inhibits actin elongation only from the pointed ends of tropomyosin-actin copolymers in vitro (K_d < 1 nM) (Weber et al 1994). In the absence of tropomyosin, tropomodulin caps the pointed ends of pure actin filaments much more weakly ($K_d \approx$ 0.1–0.4 μM). Similarly, in the absence of actin, tropomodulin also binds more weakly to tropomyosin ($K_d \approx$ 0.2 μM) (Babcock & Fowler 1994). Thus the tight capping activity of tropomodulin for the tropomyosin-actin copolymer is likely a consequence of tropomodulin binding directly to both tropomyosin and actin (for reviews on tropomodulin, see Fowler 1996, Fowler & Conley 1998). Based on these characteristics, tropomodulin has been proposed to be a critical component of a length-regulating mechanism involving tropomyosin (Figure 3) (Fowler 1996).

Tropomodulin function in vivo has been studied using a variety of approaches including antibody microinjection and molecular genetic approaches to alter tropomodulin expression levels. In the first of these experiments, a monoclonal antibody, which inhibits tropomodulin's actin filament capping, but not tropomyosin binding, activity in vitro, was microinjected into beating embryonic chick cardiac myocytes (Gregorio et al 1995). This resulted in elongation of actin, but not tropomyosin, from the thin filament pointed ends across the H zone, while tropomodulin remained associated with the terminal tropomyosin molecules at the former thin filament pointed ends. This demonstrates that tropomodulin's actin filament capping activity is important to maintain thin filament length in vivo. Furthermore, tropomodulin may also cap the tropomyosin polymer, preventing its cooperative assembly along the new portions of the actin filaments (Fowler 1990, Wegner 1979).

In addition to inappropriate elongation of actin filaments, inhibition of tropomodulin's actin capping activity in the microinjected cells also led to a dramatic reduction in the number of beating cells. This could be a consequence of the absence of tropomyosin on the newly polymerized actin filament extensions (i.e. their unregulated character) rather than the result of increased length of the actin filaments per se (Gregorio & Fowler 1996, Fowler 1996). Alternatively, selective inhibition of tropomodulin's actin, but not tropomyosin-binding activity, may have influenced the position of the tropomyosin-troponin polymer on the existing portion of the thin filament, possibly leading to misregulation of myosin activity (see below).

In another study, tropomodulin levels were increased or decreased in neonatal rat cardiac myocytes using sense or antisense adenoviral expression vectors (Sussman et al 1998a). Reduction of tropomodulin levels results in loss of actin striations in the myofibrils in the peripheral regions of beating rat cardiomyocytes within 48 h. These nonstriated portions of myofibrils resemble the nonstriated, stress fiber-like structures (SFLSs) in the peripheral regions of cardiac myocytes that are thought to be precusors of myofibrils (Dlugosz et al 1984, Schultheiss et al 1990, Gregorio & Fowler 1995). This suggests that tropomodulin may play a role in stabilizing the transition from SFLSs to striated myofibrils, which may involve changes in length and/or filament realignments. However, based on results with chick cardiac myocytes, tropomodulin does not appear to be essential for this transition because tropomodulin assembles onto cardiac thin filaments after the appearance of actin striations and formation of an H zone (Gregorio & Fowler 1995). This implies that tropomodulin is not required for the initial determination of thin filament lengths but rather is required to maintain thin filament lengths once they have been assembled, presumably by reducing actin dynamics at the pointed filament end.

Unexpectedly, increasing tropomodulin levels results in a dramatic disarray of thin and thick filaments and sarcomere disassembly in cultured neonatal rat cardiac myocytes (Sussman et al 1998a). Furthermore, postnatal overexpression of tropomodulin in transgenic mice under control of the α-MHC promoter also produces sarcomeric degeneration and leads to dilated cardiomyopathy in vivo (Sussman et al 1998b). The sarcomeric disarray and degeneration is not a nonspecific effect on myofibril protein stability because the turnover rates for actin and myosin are the same in tropomodulin-overexpressing and control cardiac myocytes (Sussman et al 1998a). However, effects on the levels of other sarcomeric components cannot be ruled out. In areas where myofibrils are not completely disrupted, I band width is significantly reduced, and sarcomeres appear hypercontracted. In addition, closely spaced, periodic arrays of electron-dense structures with short filaments (referred to as leptomeres) between them are often observed (Sussman et al 1998a,b). These structures may represent strings of abnormal Z lines with very short remnant thin filament free portions between them and are reminiscent of the periodic arrays of abnormal Z lines observed in the tropomyosin/troponin-deficient mutants in *Drosophila* IFM (discussed below) (Fyrberg et al 1990a, Beall & Fyrberg 1991). It is possible that high levels of tropomodulin might interfere with normal assembly of tropomyosin into thin filaments, leading to destabilization and shortening of the free portion of the thin filaments, followed by myofibril degeneration and assembly of abnormal Z line arrays. This is consistent with in vitro observations that high levels of tropomodulin can inhibit tropomyosin binding to actin filaments by blocking tropomyosin head-to-tail association along filaments (Fowler 1990).

Another possibility is that the interaction of tropomodulin with tropomyosin and actin at the pointed end is dynamic and sensitive to tropomodulin concentrations in the cell. Normally, ≈40% of the tropomodulin is present in a soluble pool in embryonic chick cardiac myocytes (Gregorio & Fowler 1995); this has not been investigated for rat cardiac myocytes or mice hearts. Excess cytosolic tropomodulin might change the fraction of time that tropmodulin is bound to the pointed end, thereby affecting normal regulation of actin monomer dynamics and maintenance of thin filament length.

As expected from tropomodulin's ability to cap the pointed ends of tropomyosin-actin filaments in vitro, these experiments indicate that tropomodulin maintains the length of the free portion of the thin filament by preventing actin filament elongation from the pointed end. However, it is surprising that pointed end capping by tropomodulin is not required for the initial determination of thin filament length. Furthermore, it would seem that tropomodulin-capping activity is somehow regulated so that actin monomer can exchange into thin filaments without leading to changes in their length.

Tropomyosin/Troponin

It was proposed some years ago that the tropomyosin/troponin polymer might directly specify the length of the free portion of the thin filament through a vernier-like mechanism (Figure 3B) with the actin polymer (Spudich et al 1972, Ishiwata & Funatsu, 1985). In this vernier model, each tropomyosin/troponin polymer is predicted to be anchored by one end to a component at the edge of the Z line, and a stereospecific-binding site for a hypothetical terminator molecule at the pointed filament end is predicted to exist only at a filament length of 1.08 μm when the repeat of the actin long pitch helix (36 nm) and the repeat of the tropomyosin/troponin polymer (38.5 nm) are in register. This idea was revived recently based on tropomodulin's requirement for tropomyosin for tight capping of actin filament pointed ends (Fowler 1996).

The first requirement of the vernier model, that the tropomyosin/troponin polymer be anchored at the face of the Z line, appears to be satisfied because antibody labeling indicates that individual tropomyosin/troponin complexes are all in register with one another on all of the thin filaments with respect to the Z line (Ohtsuki 1974, Obinata et al 1979). However, the second requirement of a simple vernier model, that a stereospecific, tight tropomodulin-binding site always exists at the pointed ends of thin filaments, is difficult to reconcile with the substantial shifts in the position of the tropomyosin/troponin polymer during the muscle contraction cycle (Vibert et al 1997, Squire 1997).

The vernier mechanism also requires that a non-integral number of actin monomers are spanned by each rod-like tropomyosin molecule, i.e. that the seven actin-binding sites along tropomyosin make varying contacts with each actin monomer (Fowler 1996). However, based on three-dimensional reconstructions of electron micrographs of negatively stained native thin filaments (Vibert et al 1997 and references therein), or of frozen synthetic thin filaments (Milligan et al 1990), and on X-ray fiber diffraction data of tropomyosin-actin filaments (Lorenz et al 1995), it seems likely that each tropomyosin molecule makes uniform contacts with the actin subunits along the long pitch helix. These studies all demonstrate that the two tropomyosin/troponin polymers follow the same helical pitch as the two long pitch helices of the actin polymer. The resolution of the X-ray fiber diffraction data was not sufficient to resolve the amino acid side chains nor the position of the tropomyosin head-to-tail overlap. Furthermore, while the troponin complex was visible in the negatively stained images of the native thin filaments used for image analysis (Vibert et al 1997), the exact longitudinal (axial) position of the troponin complex and individual tropomyosin molecules along the actin strands in the three-dimensional reconstructions could not be determined because the helical repeat of the actin polymer rather than the tropomyosin/troponin polymer was used to reconstruct the structure from the electron microscopic images. Further studies will be required to establish definitively whether each tropomyosin molecule binds equivalently to the actin subunits along the filament.

The effects of tropomyosin levels on thin filament lengths in *Drosophila* IFM are also inconsistent with a vernier mechanism and suggest that thin filament lengths are not uniquely specified by the concerted action of tropomyosin with tropomodulin. Reductions in the amount of tropomyosin (TmI) in two different mutants *Ifm(3)3* and *TmI*[C10] lead to impairment in flight, decreases in myofibril width, and disorganization of thin and thick filament packing at the periphery of the myofibrils due to insufficient numbers of thin filaments. Strikingly, the sarcomeres in severely affected flies are shorter ($\approx$2.7 μm versus $\approx$3.4 μm for wild-type), as well as being thinner and more fragile (Tansey et al 1991, Kreuz et al 1996). The effects of tropomyosin expression levels on sarcomere size (length and width) indicate that the degree of sarcomeric assembly may be limited by the amount of available tropomyosin with respect to other thin filament proteins. Interestingly, myofibril width (i.e. number of thin filaments) was most sensitive to reduction in TmI levels, followed by sarcomere length. It is likely that the overall length of the sarcomere reflects that of the thin filaments, since thin filament lengths increase coordinately with sarcomere length during sarcomere assembly in normal *Drosophila* IFM development (Reedy & Beall 1993). Thus when tropomyosin is limiting, thin filaments cannot elongate past a given length, nor can additional filaments be stabilized for assembly into sarcomeres. Significantly, in the TmI-deficient mutants with shorter sarcomeres, the mechanism that controls the distribution of filament lengths still appears to be operative, i.e. all the thin filaments have about the same length. These results suggest that the mechanism controlling the uniformity of thin filament lengths in IFM is independent of tropomyosin levels; the absolute lengths are not.

More severe phenotypes are observed in *upheld*[2] mutant flies, which are homozygous null for troponin T and are also completely missing both TmI and a larger tropomyosin-related protein, TmH (Fyrberg et al 1990a). In these flies, sarcomeres do not assemble, and the muscle is filled with loosely packed, misaligned thick filaments along with irregular strings of abnormally wide Z lines connected by short thin filaments. Troponin I deficiency in *heldup*[3,4,5] mutants also leads to a reduction in thin filaments and grossly abnormal thin and thick filament organization in IFM (Beall & Fyrberg 1991). The greater severity of these phenotypes compared with those of the *Ifm3(3)* and *TmI*[C10] mutants may indicate that in the presence of troponins I and T, the related TmH proteins might compensate for the absence of TmI in the *Ifm3(3)* and *TmI*[C10] mutants (Bernstein et al 1993, Kreuz et al 1996).

The effects of altered tropomyosin levels on thin filament length in *Drosophila* IFM may be partly a consequence of the ability of tropomyosin to stabilize actin filaments by reducing monomer off rates and depolymerization from the pointed filament ends (Broschat 1990, Weber et al 1994). Tropomyosin does not appear to influence the rate of actin filament elongation at the pointed end, probably because the binding of additional tropomyosin molecules along the filament lags behind actin monomer addition (Broschat 1990, Weber et al 1994; A Weber & VM Fowler, unpublished data). Actin filament stabilization by tropomyosin may require a minimum filament length because of the cooperative binding of tropomyosin to actin filaments and also a sufficient tropomyosin concentration for the terminal tropomyosin molecule to bind to the end of the tropomyosin polymer (Wegner 1979, Hitchcock-DeGregori 1994, Tobacman 1996). The function of troponins I and T in this context may be to promote tropomyosin binding to actin leading to thin filament stabilization (Tobacman 1996).

In mammals, the amount of tropomyosin also appears to be critical for normal myofibril assembly, based on the tight regulation of tropomyosin levels. In mouse α-tropomyosin knockout heterozygotes in which mRNA levels are reduced by 50%, normal amounts of tropomyosin are synthesized and myofibril organization is normal (Blanchard et al 1997, Rethinasamy et al 1998). (Mice homozygous for the α-tropomyosin knockout die early in embryogenesis.) Ectopic expression of β-tropomyosin in a transgenic mouse heart at a 34-fold excess over normal levels is compensated by down-regulation of α-tropomyosin expression so that normal levels of total tropomyosin with respect to actin are maintained and myofibril organization is unaffected (Muthuchamy et al 1995).

In conclusion, levels of tropomyosin appear to be important to determine the total amount of actin polymer in sarcomeres (i.e. average thin filament length and number), but are unlikely to specify thin filament length via a vernier mechanism with tropomodulin. In addition, while changes in tropomyosin levels can influence particular lengths, they do not appear to influence the uniformity of length distributions. Nevertheless, binding of tropomodulin to the tropomyosin-actin copolymer at the pointed end may restrict the possible lengths of tropomyosin-actin filaments in an incremental fashion so that filament lengths can vary only in steps that are the length of one tropomyosin rod. In this case, a tropomodulin-binding site is expected to appear every 14 monomers as the actin filament polymerizes a distance of a tropomyosin rod; the tropomyosin can be thought of as a very short ruler [Figure 3A(i)]. This ruler mechanism has been suggested to account for the short lengths of the erythrocyte actin filaments, which contain tropomodulin and a nonmuscle tropomyosin isoform ≈34 nm long (Fowler 1996). It may also be significant that occasional thin filaments in the IFM of the giant water bug *Lethocerus* are longer or shorter than the majority uniform length population by the length of one tropomyosin molecule (Reedy et al 1993).

Nebulin

Nebulin is a leading candidate for a molecular ruler (Figure 3A) for the free portion of the thin filament in skeletal muscle based on the following observations: (*a*) Individual nebulin molecules are associated with skeletal muscle thin filaments and extend along the entire length of the thin filament with their C-terminal domains anchored at the Z line and their N-terminal domains at the pointed filament end (Figure 1). (*b*) The length of the free portion of the thin filament is correlated with the size of nebulin in different skeletal muscles. (*c*) Nebulin sequence organization correlates with the molecular organization of the thin filament and consists of almost 200 individual 35 amino acid α-helical repeats, which are further grouped into 22 seven-module super-repeats, corresponding to the actin subunit and tropomyosin/troponin repeats of the thin filament, respectively. (*d*) Individual nebulin repeat modules and sets of modules can bind to and stabilize actin filaments. Many of the individual observations supporting the proposed function of nebulin as a molecular ruler have been discussed recently (Trinick 1994, Keller 1995, Labeit & Kolmerer 1995a, Fowler 1996, Wang et al 1996) and are not the focus of this section. Instead, we focus on the mechanistic requirements nebulin must fulfill if it is to determine thin filament length by a ruler mechanism. Additionally, we describe properties of nebulin and smaller, nebulin-related proteins that have been recently identified, suggesting that nebulin is likely to have other, nonruler functions in muscle.

For nebulin to function as a molecular ruler (Figure 3A) and determine a unique length, there must be some mechanism to assure that it will adopt a fully extended conformation that is fixed with respect to the length of the thin filament. In solution, nebulin repeat modules appear to adopt a partially un-folded, transient helical conformation (Chen & Wang 1994; Pfuhl et al 1994, 1996). Nebulin has been proposed to adopt a stable, extended conformation along the actin thin filament by means of a zipper-like actin-binding mechanism (Chen et al 1993, Pfuhl et al 1996). Comparison of actin-binding affinity of individual, recombinant 35 amino acid nebulin modules indicates that higher-affinity actin-binding modules tend to be located more proximal to the Z line than lower-affinity actin-binding modules, which are located distal to the Z line (Pfuhl et al 1996). Additionally, an increasing trend in α-helical propen-sity for modules toward the C terminus has been identified by computational algorithms; it was suggested that a more α-helical conformation of a nebulin module would stabilize its binding to actin (Pfuhl et al 1994, 1996). This graded actin-binding affinity for the modules could provide directionality to nebulin binding and effectively zip the nebulin molecule along the free portion of the thin filament from the Z line to the pointed end in a completely extended con-formation, thus ensuring that the N-terminal domain of nebulin would be at the pointed end of the thin filament.

This model for nebulin binding to actin is supported by results from several other experimental approaches. First, immunofluorescence staining of assem-bling myofibrils in differentiating chick skeletal myotubes shows that nebulin epitopes first appear in association with nascent Z bodies. Later, nebulin stain-ing extends farther along the thin filament into the A band (Komiyama et al 1992, Moncman & Wang 1996). Second, the presence of nebulin normally restricts rhodamine-phalloidin staining to portions of the thin filament near the barbed and pointed ends in isolated skeletal myofibrils (Ao & Lehrer 1995, Zhukarev et al 1997). However, at longer incubation times of rhodamine-phalloidin, the width of the rhodamine-phalloidin-stained band progressively expands from the pointed end toward the Z line, while nebulin is progressively displaced from the pointed end of the thin filament (Ao & Lehrer 1995). This is consistent with lower-affinity actin-binding modules being located at greater distances from the Z line.

However, recombinant nebulin fragments show unexpected variability in their actin-binding properties and are inconsistent with nebulin functioning as a simple molecular ruler. For example, some repeats stabilize actin filaments, whereas others depolymerize actin and appear to increase the critical concen-tration (Chen et al 1993, Root & Wang 1994, Pfuhl et al 1996, Wang et al

1996, Zhang et al 1998). In addition, the actin-binding affinities of different repeats are not always correlated with their distance from the Z line (Wang et al 1996); some repeats may cross-link actin filaments (Pfuhl et al 1996), and the stoichiometry of binding for individual modules or super-repeats to actin filaments is extremely variable, ranging from 0.5 modules per actin subunit up to 8–12 modules (expressed as one fragment) per actin subunit (Chen et al 1993, Root & Wang 1994, Pfuhl et al 1996, Zhang et al 1998). Some of these differences may result from improper folding and aggregation of recombinant nebulin fragments with incorrect phasing of the repeat (Zhang et al 1998). It is also possible that not all modules in a given repeat bind equally well to actin; i.e. that the association of nebulin with actin may be floppy rather than tight, as would be expected for a simple molecular ruler.

Interactions of nebulin modules or super-repeats with tropomyosin/troponin, myosin, and calmodulin also suggest a more complex, regulatory role for nebulin along the thin filament, as proposed by Wang et al (1996). For example, several recombinant nebulin fragments consisting of about seven to eight modules (i.e. one super-repeat) can bind actin, tropomyosin, and myosin with high affinity and inhibit actomyosin ATPase and filament sliding in a motility assay (Root & Wang 1994). In addition, chemical cross-linking studies have localized the nebulin-binding site on actin to the N-terminal region of actin where tropomyosin and myosin also bind (Shih et al 1997). This location is inconsistent with modeling data that nebulin occupies the phalloidin-binding groove on the actin filament (Pfuhl et al 1994); perhaps nebulin can shift position on the actin filament analogously to the tropomyosin/troponin polymer (Wang et al 1996). Of course, a molecular ruler function for nebulin is not necessarily ruled out by an additional regulatory function on the thin filament.

A second requirement for nebulin to function as a molecular ruler is that it would be expected to provide a unique binding site for tropomodulin at its N-terminal end to target tropomodulin to the pointed ends of thin filaments of the appropriate length. Additionally, the interaction of nebulin with tropomodulin at the filament end would still permit monomer exchange at the thin filament pointed end, as discussed above. Consistent with this notion, tropomodulin can bind nebulin on blot overlays (CC Gregorio & VM Fowler, unpublished data), but it has not been conclusively determined if tropomodulin binds specifically to the unique region at the extreme N-terminal end of nebulin. If nebulin were to target tropomodulin to the thin filament pointed ends, as in a simple ruler mechanism, it is likely that tropomodulin would not assemble onto thin filament pointed ends until after they had polymerized to their correct lengths in association with nebulin during myofibril assembly. Although it is difficult to directly measure thin filament lengths during myofibril assembly, tropomodulin is associated with the earliest appearing nonstriated premyofibrils in chick skeletal myotubes, well before formation of actin striations (Almenar-Queralt et al 1996). Since nebulin association along the entire length of the thin filament appears to be a relatively late event in myofibril assembly (Komiyama et al 1992), these observations are again inconsistent with the simple idea that nebulin targets tropomodulin to the thin filament pointed end.

High molecular weight nebulins ($M_r \approx 600$–900) have been found only in vertebrate skeletal muscle so far, yet thin filament lengths are also regulated in other muscles. For example, a nebulin isoform has not been found in arthropods, where thin filament lengths increase gradually and uniformly from ≈ 0.8 to ≈ 1.5 μm during development of *Drosophila* IFM (Reedy & Beall 1993). It is difficult to imagine that this increase in length is accomplished by a molecular ruler, which would have to extend gradually and synchronously on all thin filaments to accomodate the precise and coordinated filament growth. In vertebrate cardiac muscle, a much smaller isoform of nebulin, nebulette (107 kDa), is associated with the Z line and is predicted to extend only ≈ 0.2 μm along the thin filament based on the number of 35 amino acid repeat modules in its sequence (Moncman & Wang 1995). Another 133-kDa nebulin-related protein (N-RAP, nebulin-related anchoring protein), which contains two full nebulin super-repeats and a LIM domain, has been localized to the myotendenous junction in skeletal muscle and intercalated discs in cardiac muscle (Luo et al 1997). The absence of a long nebulin molecule is proposed to account for the wider distribution of thin filament lengths in cardiac muscle (0.9–1.1 μm) (Robinson & Winegrad 1979, but see Yasuda et al 1994). Nevertheless, the length distribution of cardiac thin filaments is not exponential, demonstrating that they are regulated in length, but not by a mechanism involving nebulin.

In conclusion, nebulin is properly positioned to directly determine thin filament length in skeletal muscle, but direct evidence for this is lacking and will require a better understanding of how nebulin interacts with actin, tropomyosin, and tropomodulin. Furthermore, recent studies showing that nebulin modules may regulate actomyosin interactions, perhaps by interaction with myosin directly and/or by forming a copolymer with tropomyosin/troponin along the free portion of the thin filament, suggest that nebulin and other nebulin-related proteins (nebulette, N-RAP) contribute to sarcomere function through a regulatory mechanism.

Myosin Thick Filaments and Titin

A critical feature of both the proposed nebulin (ruler) and tropomyosin/troponin (vernier) mechanisms is that intrinsic components of the free portion of the thin filament regulate its length. However, there are a number of important experiments suggesting that the length of the free portion is not only specified by intrinsic components of the thin filament, but also by extrinsic components:

namely, the myosin thick filaments together with titin. Myosin thick filaments are organized into A bands and connected to Z lines by giant titin molecules (Figure 1) (Maruyama 1997, Labeit et al 1997). The spring-like portions of the titin molecules that extend between the thick filaments and the Z lines maintain the A band in the center of mature sarcomeres and also position each Z line equidistant from the ends of the thick filaments, thus generating regular Z line spacing (i.e. sarcomere lengths) (Goulding et al 1997). There is considerable evidence that the myosin/titin array acts as a scaffold, which directly determines the position of the thin filament pointed ends relative to the Z line, thereby regulating thin filament length. Clearly though, the activity of a myosin/titin scaffold would have to adjust for the movement of the thin filaments relative to the thick filament, yet still maintain the thin filament length. Several molecular mechanisms are considered below by which a myosin/titin scaffold could (*a*) regulate both actin dynamics and tropomodulin capping in resting sarcomeres to generate uniform thin filament lengths and yet (*b*) allow tropomodulin to tightly cap and fix thin filament length in response to sarcomere length changes during contraction and/or stretching.

A MYOSIN/TITIN SCAFFOLD DETERMINES THIN FILAMENT LENGTH   Probably the best evidence that thin filament length regulation is dependent on inter-actions with myosin thick filaments comes from ultrastructural analysis of *Drosophila* IFM-specific myosin [*Ifm(2)2*] and actin (*KM88*) null alleles (Karlik et al 1984, Chun & Falkenthal 1988, Beall et al 1989; reviewed by Fyrberg & Beall 1990). In the complete absence of myosin [in *Ifm(2)2* homozygotes], aberrant thin filament arrays assemble in which wavy and disorganized thin filaments extend between Z lines that are spaced ≈0.1 μm to >1 μm apart (Chun & Falkenthal 1988). The variability in Z line spacings suggests that thin filament lengths are not specified to a unique length in the absence of thick filaments. Thin filaments also appear disorganized in the larval intersegmental muscles of *Drosophila* muscle myosin null heterozygotes (Bernstein et al 1993).

A reduction of myosin content in IFM to ≈50% of wild-type in *Ifm(2)2* het-erozygotes (and in other myosin mutants, see Bernstein et al 1993) results in flightlessness; thin myofibrils assemble with fragmented M lines and a reduced thick-to-thin filament ratio compared with wild-type (Chun & Falkenthal 1988, Bernstein et al 1993). Thin filaments are organized with thick filaments into pe-riodic sarcomeric arrays; however, the free portions of many thin filaments are either absent or appear to extend past the mid-point of the sarcomere, indicating that length regulation of the free portion of the thin filament is defective (Chun & Falkenthal 1988, Beall et al 1989). Interestingly, mutants with both actin and myosin levels reduced to 50% of wild-type [in *Ifm(2)2/KM88* double het-erozygotes] have a normal thin-to-thick filament ratio and their sarcomeres are much more organized (and functional) compared with the single heterozygotes (Beall et al 1989). Together, these results suggest that interactions between thin and thick filaments directly influence the length of the free portion of the thin filament and that thin filaments, which are not properly interdigitated with thick filaments, are not regulated precisely in length.

Several lines of evidence suggest that thick filaments may be organized into a periodic, myofibrillar array independently of the free portion of the thin filament and therefore could be capable of directly specifying its length. First, bipolar thick filaments of uniform lengths can co-assemble from myosin and other thick filament components both in vitro and in vivo in the absence of thin filaments (Huxley 1963, Vikstrom et al 1997, Liu et al 1997). Second, the formation of aligned thick filament arrays containing M lines (A bands) is observed in *Drosophila* IFM-specific actin (*KM88*) null mutants (Karlik et al 1984, Beall et al 1989) and in a myosarcoma cell line (BC3H1), which does not assemble thin filaments apparently due to the absence of α-actinin (Holtzer et al 1997). Third, in cultured chick skeletal myoblasts grown in Taxol, thick filaments assemble into A bands, which associate with titin and Z line remnants into periodic sarcomeric arrays in the absence of the free portions of thin filaments (Hill et al 1986, Moncman & Wang 1996). A similar myosin/titin scaffold is observed in myotubes after treatment with phorbol esters (Lin et al 1989) or activation of v-src (Castellani et al 1995). The assembly of myosin and titin into myofibrillar thick filament arrays would have the potential to direct the assembly of actin into filaments of uniform lengths during myofibrillogenesis.

Further evidence that a thick filament/titin scaffold is stable in the absence of the free portions of the thin filaments, and may therefore regulate actin filament lengths, comes from experiments using isolated myofibrils. Treatment of isolated myofibrils with gelsolin (Funatsu et al 1990, 1994; Granzier et al 1997) or DNase I (Taylor et al 1997) removes the free portions of the thin filaments, yet preserves the organization of the myosin/titin scaffold. This is a commonly used technique to visualize the titin strands connecting thick filaments to the Z lines (Funatsu 1990, Granzier et al 1997, Linke et al 1997).

Interestingly, when exogenous actin (and tropomyosin/troponin) was added to gelsolin-treated cardiac or skeletal myofibrils, actin filaments polymerized extensively from the pointed ends, extending into and interdigitating with the thick filament array, and achieving a length distribution similar to the native thin filaments (Funatsu et al 1994, Fujita et al 1996). Since many new actin filaments did not cross the thick filament bare zone, this suggests that the thick filament scaffold determines thin filament length. Indeed, in the asymmetric sarcomeres of the crab *Portunus depurator*, the M line is displaced off-center in the A band, resulting in two half-sarcomeres with asymmetric thick filament portions; the thin filament lengths are also asymmetric such that both sets of pointed ends are positioned at the edge of the bare zone of the asymmetric thick filament array (Franzini-Armstrong 1970). Similarly, in the terminal thin filament array at cardiac intercalated discs, which follow a tortuous path, the pointed ends are in register at the bare zone, although the filament lengths vary (Severs 1985). In a recent study, replacement of *Drosophila* IFM myosin with a headless myosin mutant (i.e. rod and neck domains only), resulted in variable sarcomere lengths, consistant with mis-specification of thin filament lengths (RM Cripps, JA Suggs, SI Bernstein, submitted). These experiments suggest that the interaction of myosin heads with actin may directly regulate the polymerization of actin at the pointed end to influence the length of the free portion of the thin filament.

How could a thick filament scaffold determine thin filament length? Because the length of the thin filaments does not change when they move relative to the thick filaments during stretch or contraction (Huxley 1960, Sosa et al 1994), one might expect that a thick filament scaffold would actively specify thin filament length only at a particular sarcomere length (e.g. resting length) and would be inactive during sarcomere length changes. We propose a hypothetical molecular mechanism in which (*a*) at resting sarcomere length, tropomodulin capping may be down-regulated by structural changes at the thin filament pointed end, allowing myosin heads to control the extent of actin polymerization and specify thin filament length, and (*b*) stretch or contraction changes the structure of the thin filament pointed end and up-regulates tropomodulin capping to maintain thin filament length during sarcomere length changes (Figure 4). The separation of the mechanisms for thin filament length specification and maintenance into two states based on tropomodulin capping could reconcile the apparently contradictory observations of actin dynamics and the stable, uniform length distribution of muscle thin filaments.

RESTING LENGTH SARCOMERES   We hypothesize that tropomodulin capping is down-regulated in relaxed, resting length sarcomeres via an allosteric mechanism involving structural changes at the pointed end of the thin filament. For example, tropomodulin may bind weakly to thin filament pointed ends when the tropomyosin/troponin strand is in the off position in the absence of calcium (Vibert et al 1997). In the absence of tropomodulin capping, the thick filament scaffold could specify the length of the thin filament directly if myosin heads control the extent of actin polymerization. Myosin heads could induce actin polymerization by reducing the off-rate of actin monomers at the pointed end much like cross-linking molecules (Zigmond et al 1992) and/or by increasing the monomer on-rate by directly accelerating actin polymerization through conformational changes in the actin (Eto et al 1991). Myosin head binding to G-actin does accelerate actin polymerization in vitro (Yagi et al

Resting Length   **Stretched/Contracted**

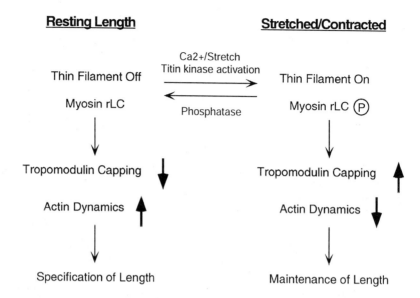

Figure 4 Hypothetical scheme by which thin filament and/or myosin linked regulation can modulate tropomodulin capping and actin dynamics at the thin filament pointed end, thereby determining thin filament lengths.

1965, Shimuzu & Obinata 1986, Ballweber et al 1994, Fievez et al 1997), possibly by a sub-critical condensation of actomyosin oligomers rather than a nucleation-elongation mechanism (Fievez et al 1997). Thus myosin crossbridges could influence the dynamics of monomer addition and loss such that thin filaments that are too short are induced to elongate to the bare zone because their pointed ends are located within the myosin head region of the thick filament. On the other hand, the absence of myosin crossbridges on thin filament pointed ends located in the bare zone region of the thick filaments could lead to net depolymerization of thin filaments that are too long if the available (i.e. non-sequestered) actin is near or below the critical concentration of the pointed end. The effects of myosin heads on actin polymerization could be prevented if tropomodulin capping were up-regulated during stretch or contraction, thus maintaining the thin filament length determined at resting length (Figure 4).

CONTRACTED OR STRETCHED SARCOMERES   We hypothesize that tropomodulin capping is up-regulated via stretch and calcium-dependent structural changes of the pointed end of the thin filament to maintain thin filament length during sarcomere length changes. For example, during calcium-activated contraction, the $\approx 25°$ azimuthal movement of the tropomyosin/troponin strand across the actin filament (Vibert et al 1997) could mediate tight tropomodulin capping. It may be significant that the position of tropomyosin on unregulated thin filaments, which are capped tightly by tropomodulin (Weber et al 1994), is the same as the position on regulated thin filaments in the presence of calcium (Lorenz et al 1995). Myosin binding may also contribute to regulation of tropomodulin capping since strong, myosin rigor crossbridges move the calcium-activated tropomyosin/troponin strand $10°$ farther toward the center of the actin filament (Milligan et al 1990, Al-Khayat et al 1995, Geeves & Conibear 1995, Vibert et al 1997). Furthermore, the interaction of myosin heads with the thin filament during contraction is also believed to induce cooperative and allosteric conformational changes in the actin subunits themselves, as well as in the position of the tropomyosin/troponin strand (Taylor et al 1989, Al-Khayat et al 1995, Egelman & Orlova 1995, Vibert et al 1997, Prochniewicz & Thomas 1997). Experiments measuring the pointed end capping activity of tropomodulin for regulated thin filaments in EGTA and Ca^{2+}, and in the presence and absence of myosin, will be one way to test this hypothesis.

In stretched sarcomeres, phosphorylation of myosin regulatory light chains (rLC) (Tohtong et al 1995) in response to titin kinase activation (Heierhorst et al 1995) may modulate the myosin crossbridges and their effect at the thin filament pointed end. Titin is an excellent candidate for a stretch-activated mechanism to regulate myosin because it contains an elastic portion in the I band that is responsible for the majority of passive tension in stretched sarcomeres (Trombitas et al 1998 and references therein). It is conceivable that as sarcomeres are stretched, passive tension from titin may propagate a conformational change through the thick filament, i.e. induce strain in the thick filament, as suggested by Tohtong et al (1995). This could result in dissociation of the adjacent autoinhibitory titin domain from the kinase, activation of the titin kinase domain (Kobe et al 1996), and phosphorylation of myosin rLC (Heierhorst et al 1995). A similar stretch-dependent enzymatic mechanism has been proposed to act at the kinetochore to control the metaphase-anaphase checkpoint in mitosis (Nicklas et al 1995). Calcium release during contraction may also activate the titin kinase, since a calmodulin-like EF-hand protein, S100AI2, binds to the autoinhibitory domain of twitchin (titin) and activates the kinase domain in a Ca^{2+}-dependent manner in vitro (Heierhorst et al 1996). This could provide a common mechanism for both calcium and stretch regulation of thin filament structure via myosin rLC phosphorylation (Figure 4). In addition to titin, other molecules (e.g. myosin light chain kinase) might also fulfill a stretch and/or a Ca^{2+}-activated role in some muscles. Significantly, in vertebrates, the single kinase domain in titin is located in the thick filament bare zone (Obermann et al 1996).

We believe that any mechanistic model for specification of the free portion of the thin filament length must account for its dependence on myosin thick filament organization. A thick filament scaffold model is not as simple as the nebulin ruler and tropomyosin/troponin vernier models, but can more readily account for the dynamic exchange of actin monomers in and out of the thin filament. Furthermore, a myosin/titin scaffold can explain how cardiac thin filaments are regulated in length in the absence of full-length nebulin and how thin filament lengths are determined before assembly of tropomodulin on the pointed end (Gregorio & Fowler 1996). We suggest the scaffold model to directly explain the dependence of thin filament length on thick filament organization; however, it is also possible that myosin activity could be indirectly involved in length regulation via effects on nebulin or tropomyosin. For instance, myosin may be necessary to promote the full extension (zippering) of nebulin along the length of the thin filament or to limit the number of tropomyosin subunits along the thin filament free portion through some accumulated strain mechanism.

CONCLUSIONS

Striated muscle is an extreme example of cytoskeletal architecture in which actin filament lengths and their structural organization are critical for a physiological function, contraction. Determination of actin filament lengths in myofibrils relies on a coordinated and regulated transition between dynamic and stable states and is likely to be highly tuned to the activity and regulation of muscle myosin motors (Figure 4). We have presented several testable hypotheses to account for the dynamic stability of thin filament lengths and hope that this will stimulate novel experiments to study the assembly and regulation of actin polymerization within the context of a molecular machine. For example, both capZ (Hopmann et al 1996) and tropomodulin (*sanpodo*) (Dye et al 1998) have been identified in *Drosophila*; direct tests of the importance of filament capping for thin filament length regulation and muscle function will now be possible. Real-time fluorescence imaging techniques in combination with ultrastuctural analysis and mechanical approaches in isolated myofibrils and living muscle cells will also provide a powerful approach to study the relationship of motor activity to actin filament dynamics and determination of thin filament lengths. We anticipate that the dynamic stability observed for thin filaments of striated muscle may also prove to be the basis for regulation of actin filament lengths in other specialized cellular architectures.

ACKNOWLEDGMENTS

We are particularly grateful to A Weber and CC Gregorio for critical reading of the manuscript and for their helpful editorial suggestions. We thank our many colleagues in the muscle research field whose ideas and unpublished work contributed greatly to this article. We also thank R Fischer for many helpful discussions and P Meyer for preparation of Figures 1 and 3. R Littlefield is a predoctoral fellow of the California Affiliate of the American Heart Association. This work was supported by grants to V Fowler from the National Institutes of Health (GM34225 and EY10814).

Visit the *Annual Reviews home page* at
http://www.AnnualReviews.org

Literature Cited

Al-Khayat HA, Yagi N, Squire JM. 1995. Structural changes in actin-tropomyosin during muscle regulation: computer modelling of low-angle x-ray diffraction data. *J. Mol. Biol.* 252:611–32

Almenar-Queralt A, Gregorio CC, Fowler VM. 1996. Assembly of tropomodulin into myofibrils: implications for regulation of actin filament length. *Mol. Biol. Cell Suppl.* 7:546a (Abstr.)

Ao X, Leher SS. 1995. Phalloidin unzips nebulin from thin filaments in skeletal myofibrils. *J. Cell Sci.* 108:3397–403

Babcock GG, Fowler VM. 1994. Isoform-specific interaction of tropomodulin with skeletal muscle and erythrocyte tropomyosins. *J. Biol. Chem.* 269:27510–18

Ballweber E, Hannappel E, Niggemeyer B, Mannherz HG. 1994. Induction of the polymerization of actin from the actin:thymosin β4 complex by phalloidin, skeletal myosin subfragment 1, chicken intestinal myosin I and free ends of filamentous actin. *Eur. J. Biochem.* 223:419–26

Bamburg JR, Bray D. 1987. Distribution and cellular localization of actin depolymerizing factor. *J. Cell Biol.* 105:2817–25

Beall CJ, Fyrberg E. 1991. Muscle abnormalities in *Drosophila melanogaster heldup* mutants are caused by missing or aberrant troponin-I isoforms. *J. Cell Biol.* 114:941–51

Beall CJ, Sepanski MA, Fyrberg EA. 1989. Genetic dissection of *Drosophila* myofibril formation: effects of actin and myosin heavy chain null alleles. *Genes Dev.* 3:131–40

Bernstein SI, O'Donnell PT, Cripps RM. 1993. Molecular genetic analysis of muscle development, structure, and function in *Drosophila*. *Int. Rev. Cytol.* 143:63–152

Blanchard A, Ohanian V, Critchley D. 1989. The structure and function of α-actinin. *J. Muscle Res. Cell Motil.* 10:280–89

Blanchard EM, Lizuka K, Christe M, Conner DA, Geisterfer-Lowrance A, et al. 1997. Targeted ablation of the murine α-tropomyosin gene. *Circ. Res.* 81:1005–10

Broschat KO. 1990. Tropomyosin prevents depolymerization of actin filaments from the pointed end. *J. Biol. Chem.* 265:21323–29

Burlacu S, Janmey PA, Borejdo J. 1992. Distribution of actin filament lengths measured by fluorescence microscopy. *Am. J. Physiol.* 262:C569–77

Cano ML, Lauffenburger DA, Zigmond SH. 1991. Kinetic analysis of F-actin depolymerization in poly-morphonuclear leukocyte lysates indicates that chemoattractant stimulation increases actin filament number without altering the filament length distribution. *J. Cell Biol.* 115:677–87

Carlier M-F. 1998. Control of actin dynamics. *Curr. Opin. Cell Biol.* 10:45–51

Carlier M-F, Valentin-Ranc C, Combeau, Fievez S, Pantoloni D. 1994. Actin polymerization: regulation by divalent metal ion and nucleotide binding, ATP hydrolysis and binding of myosin. *Adv. Exp. Med. Biol.* 358:71–81

Castellani L, Reedy MC, Gauzzi MC, Provenzano C, Alemà S, Falcone G. 1995. Maintenance of the differentiated state in skeletal muscle: activation of v-src disrupts sarcomeres in quail myotubes. *J. Cell Biol.* 130:871–85

Chen M-JG, Shih C-L, Wang K. 1993. Nebulin as an actin zipper. A two-module nebulin fragment promotes actin nucleation and stabilizes actin filaments. *J. Biol. Chem.* 268:20327–34

Chen M-JG, Wang K. 1994. Conformational studies of a two-module fragment of nebulin and implications for actin association. *Arch. Biochem. Biophys.* 310:310–17

Chun M, Falkenthal S. 1988. *Ifm(2)2* is a myosin heavy chain allele that disrupts myofibrillar assembly only in the indirect flight muscle of *Drosophila melanogaster*. *J. Cell Biol.* 107:2613–21

Clark WA Jr, Zak R. 1981. Assessment of

fractional rates of protein synthesis in cardiac muscle cultures after equilibrium labeling. *J. Biol. Chem.* 256:4863–70

Cotè G, Mohiuddin SM, Roy PE. 1970. Occurrence of Z-band widening in human atrial cells. *Exp. Mol. Pathol.* 13:307–18

Cramer LP, Siebert M, Mitchison T. 1997. Identification of novel graded polarity actin filament bundles in locomoting heart fibroblasts: implications for the generation of motile force. *J. Cell Biol.* 136:1287–1305

Davis JS. 1986. A model for length-regulation in thick filaments of vertebrate skeletal myosin. *Biophys. J.* 50:417–22

Deatherage DF, Cheng N, Bullard B. 1989. Arrangement of filaments and cross-links in the bee flight muscle Z disk by image analysis of oblique sections. *J. Cell Biol.* 108:1775–82

Dlugosz AA, Antin PB, Nachmias VT, Holtzer H. 1984. The relationship between stress fiber-like structures and nascent myofibrils in cultured cardiac myocytes. *J. Cell Biol.* 99:2268–78

Dome JS, Mittal B, Pochapin MB, Sanger JM, Sanger JW. 1988. Incorporation of fluorescently labeled actin and tropomyosin into muscle cells. *Cell Diff.* 23:37–52

Dufort PA, Lumsden CJ. 1995. A mathematical model of the actin filament length distribution predicts only one unique steady state. *Biophys. J.* (2 part 2)68:A284 (Abstr.)

Dye CA, Lee J-K, Atkinson RC, Brewster R, Han P-L, Bellen HJ. 1998. The *Drosophila sanpodo* gene controls sibling cell fate and encodes a tropomodulin homolog, an actin/tropomyosin associated protein. *Development* 125:1845–56

Egelman EH, Orlova A. 1995. New insights into actin filament dynamics. *Curr. Opin. Struct. Biol.* 5:172–80

Eto M, Morita F, Nishi N, Tokura S, Ito T, Takahashi K. 1991. Actin polymerization promoted by a heptapeptide, an analog of the actin-binding S site on myosin head. *J. Biol. Chem.* 266:18233–36

Fawcett DW. 1968. The sporadic occurrence in cardiac muscle of anomalous Z bands exhibiting a periodic structure suggestive of tropomyosin. *J. Cell Biol.* 36:266–70

Fievez S, Carlier M-F, Pantaloni D. 1997. Mechanism of myosin subfragment-1-induced assembly of Ca G-actin and Mg G-actin into F-actin-S1-decorated filaments. *Biochemistry* 36:11843–50

Fowler VM. 1990. Tropomodulin: a cytoskeletal protein that binds to the end of erythrocyte tropomyosin and inhibits tropomyosin binding to actin. *J. Cell Biol.* 111:471–82

Fowler VM. 1996. Regulation of actin filament length in erythrocytes and striated muscle. *Curr. Opin. Cell Biol.* 8:86–96

Fowler VM. 1997. Capping actin filament growth: tropomodulin in muscle and non-muscle cells. *52nd Symp. Soc. Gen. Physiol.: Cytoskeletal Regulation of Membrane Function,* 52:79–89

Fowler VM, Conley CA. 1998. Tropomodulin. In *Guidebook to the Cytoskeletal and Motor Proteins,* ed. TE Kreis, RD Vale. Oxford: Oxford Univ. Press. In press

Fowler VM, Sussman MA, Miller PG, Flucher BE, Daniels MP. 1993. Tropomodulin is associated with the free (pointed) ends of the thin filaments in rat skeletal muscle. *J. Cell Biol.* 120:411–20

Franzini-Armstrong C. 1970. Natural variability in the length of thin and thick filaments in single fibres from a crab, *Portunus depurator*. *J. Cell Sci.* 6:559–92

Franzini-Armstrong C. 1973. The structure of a simple Z line. *J. Cell Biol.* 58:630–42

Fujita H, Yasuda K, Niitsu S, Funatsu T, Ishiwata S. 1996. Structural and functional reconstitution of thin filaments in the contractile apparatus of cardiac muscle. *Biophys. J.* 71:2307–18

Funatsu T, Anazawa T, Ishiwata S. 1994. Structural and functional reconstitution of thin filaments in skeletal muscle. *J. Muscle Res. Cell Motil.* 15:158–71

Funatsu T, Higuchi H, Ishiwata S. 1990. Elastic filaments in skeletal muscle revealed by selective removal of thin filaments with plasma gelsolin. *J. Cell Biol.* 110:53–62

Furukawa R, Fechheimer M. 1996. Role of the *Dictyostelium* 30 kDa protein in actin bundle formation. *Biochemistry* 35:7224–32

Fyrberg E, Beall C. 1990. Genetic approaches to myofibril form and function in *Drosophila*. *Trends Genet.* 6:126–31

Fyrberg E, Fyrberg CC, Beall C, Saville DL. 1990a. *Drosophila melanogaster* troponin-T mutations engender three distinct syndromes of myofibrillar abnormalities. *J. Mol. Biol.* 216:657–75

Fyrberg E, Kelly M, Ball E, Fyrberg C, Reedy MC. 1990b. Molecular genetics of *Drosophila* alpha-actinin mutant alleles disrupt Z disc integrity and muscle insertions. *J. Cell Biol.* 110:1999–2011

Gautel M, Goulding D, Bullard B, Weber K, Fürst DO. 1996. The central Z-disk region of titin is assembled from a novel repeat in variable copy numbers. *J. Cell Sci.* 109:2747–54

Geeves MA, Conibear PB. 1995. The role of three-state docking of myosin S1 with actin in force generation. *Biophys. J.* 68:194-201s

Glacy SD. 1983. Pattern and time course of rhodamine-actin incorporation in cardiac myocytes. *J. Cell Biol.* 96:1164–67

Goldstein MA, Schroeter JP, Sass RL. 1979.

The Z lattice in canine cardiac muscle. *J. Cell Biol.* 83:187–204

Goll DE, Suzuki A, Temple J, Holmes GR. 1972. Studies on purified α-actinin. I. Effect of temperature and tropomyosin on the α-actinin/F-actin interaction. *J. Mol. Biol.* 67: 469–88

Goulding D, Bullard B, Gautel M. 1997. A survey of in situ sarcomere extension in mouse skeletal muscle. *J. Muscle Res. Cell Motil.* 18:465–72

Granzier H, Kellermayer M, Helmes M, Trombitás K. 1997. Titin elasticity and mechanism of passive force development in rat cardiac myocytes probed by thin-filament extraction. *Biophys. J.* 73:2043–53

Granzier HLM, Akster HA, Ter Keurs HEDJ. 1991. Effect of thin filament length on the force-sarcomere length relation of skeletal muscle. *Am. J. Phys.* 260:C1060–70

Gregorio CC, Fowler VM. 1995. Mechanisms of thin filament assembly in embryonic chick cardiac myocytes: Tropomodulin requires tropomyosin for assembly. *J. Cell Biol.* 129:683–95

Gregorio CC, Fowler VM. 1996. Tropomodulin function and thin filament assembly in cardiac myocytes. *Trends Cardiovasc. Med.* 6:136–41

Gregorio CC, Weber A, Bondad M, Pennise CR, Fowler VM. 1995. Requirement of pointed-end capping by tropomodulin to maintain actin filament length in embryonic chick cardiac myocytes. *Nature* 377:83–86

Gyure KA, Prayson RA, Estes ML. 1997. Adult-onset nemaline myopathy. A case report and review of the literature. *Arch. Pathol. Lab. Med.* 121:1210–13

Hayakawa K, Ono S, Nagaoka R, Saitoh O, Obinata T. 1996. Differential assembly of cytoskeletal and sarcomeric actins in developing skeletal muscle cells in vitro. *Zool. Sci.* 13:509–17

Heierhorst J, Kobe B, Feil SC, Parker MW, Benian GM, et al. 1996. Ca^{2+}/S100 regulation of giant protein kinases. *Nature* 380:636–39

Heierhorst J, Probst WC, Kohanski RA, Buku A, Weiss KR. 1995. Phosphorylation of myosin regulatory light chains by the molluscan twitchin kinase. *Eur. J. Biochem.* 233: 426–31

Higuchi H, Funatsu T, Ishijima A, Okamura N, Ishiwata S. 1986. Accumulated strain mechanism for length determination of thick filaments in skeletal muscle. I. Experimental bases. *J. Muscle Res. Cell Motil.* 7:491–500

Hill CS, Duran S, Lin Z, Weber K, Holtzer H. 1986. Titin and myosin, but not desmin, are linked during myofibrillogenesis in postmitotic mononucleated myoblasts. *J. Cell Biol.* 103:2185–96

Hitchcock-DeGregori SE. 1994. Structural requirements of tropomyosin for binding to filamentous actin. *Adv. Exp. Med. Biol.* 358:85–96

Holtzer H, Croop J, Dienstman S, Ishikawa H, Somlyo AP. 1975. Effects of cytochalasin B and colcemide on myogenic cultures. *Proc. Natl. Acad. Sci. USA* 72:513–17

Holtzer H, Hijikata T, Lin ZX, Zhang ZQ, Holtzer S, et al. 1997. Independent assembly of 1.6 μm long bipolar MHC filaments and I-Z-I bodies. *Cell Struct. Funct.* 22:83–93

Hopmann R, Cooper JA, Miller KG. 1996. Actin organization, bristle morphology, and viability are affected by actin capping protein mutations in *Drosophila. J. Cell Biol.* 133:1293–305

Huckriede A, Hinssen H, Jockusch BM, Lazarides E. 1988. Gelsolin sensitivity of microfilaments as a marker for muscle differentiation. *Eur. J. Cell Biol.* 46:506–12

Hudson P, Gardner-Medwin D, Fulthorpe JJ, Walton JN. 1967. Nemaline myopathy. *Neurology* 17:1125–42

Huxley HE. 1960. Muscle cells. In *The Cell (Biochemistry, Physiology, Morphology)*, ed. J Brachet, AE Mirsky, 4:365–481. New York: Academic

Huxley HE. 1963. Electron microscope studies on the structure of natural and synthetic protein filaments from striated muscle. *J. Mol. Biol.* 7:281–308

Imanaka-Yoshida K, Sanger JM, Sanger JW. 1993. Contractile protein dynamics of myofibrils in paired adult rat cardiomyocytes. *Cell Motil. Cytoskelet.* 26:301–12

Ishiwata S, Funatsu T. 1985. Does actin bind to the ends of thin filaments in skeletal muscle? *J. Cell Biol.* 100:282–91

Ivanenkov VV, Jamieson GA Jr, Gruenstein E, Dimlich RVW. 1995. Characterization of S-100b binding epitopes. Identification of a novel target, the actin capping protein, CapZ. *J. Biol. Chem.* 270:14651–58

Janmey PA, Peetermans J, Zaner KS, Stossel TP, Tanaka T. 1986. Structure and mobility of actin filaments as measured by quasielastic light scattering, viscometry, and electron microscopy. *J. Biol. Chem.* 261:8357–62

Karlik CC, Coutu MD, Fyrberg EA. 1984. A nonsense mutation within the act88F actin gene disrupts myofibril formation in Drosophila indirect flight muscles. *Cell* 38: 711–19

Katsura I, Hendrix RW. 1984. Length determination in bacteriophage lambda tails. *Cell* 39:691–98

Kawamura M, Maruyama K. 1972. A further study of electron microscopic particle length of F-actin polymerized in vitro. *J. Biochem.* 72:179–88

Keller TCS III. 1995. Structure and function of titin and nebulin. *Curr. Opin. Cell Biol.* 7:32–38

Khaitlina S, Hinssen H. 1997. Conformational changes in actin induced by its interaction with gelsolin. *Biophys. J.* 73:929–37

Kobe B, Heierhorst J, Feil SC, Parker MW, Benian GM, et al. 1996. Giant protein kinases: domain interactions and structural basis of autoregulation. *EMBO J.* 15:6810–21

Komiyama M, Zhou Z-H, Maruyama K, Shimada Y. 1992. Spatial relationship of nebulin relative to other myofibrillar proteins during myogenesis in embryonic chick skeletal muscle in vitro. *J. Muscle Res. Cell Motil.* 13:48–54

Kreis TE, Winterhalter KH, Birchmeier W. 1979. In vivo distribution and turnover of fluorescently labeled actin microinjected into human fibroblasts. *Proc. Natl. Acad. Sci. USA* 76:3814–18

Kreuz AJ, Simcox A, Maughan D. 1996. Alterations in flight muscle ultrastructure and function in *Drosophila* tropomyosin mutants. *J. Cell Biol.* 135:673–87

Labeit S, Kolmerer B. 1995a. The complete primary structure of human nebulin and its correlation to muscle structure. *J. Mol. Biol.* 248:308–15

Labeit S, Kolmerer B. 1995b. Titins: giant proteins in charge of muscle ultrastructure and elasticity. *Science* 270:293–96

Labeit S, Kolmerer B, Linke WA. 1997. The giant protein titin. Emerging roles in physiology and pathophysiology. *Circ. Res.* 80:290–94

Laing NG, Wilton SD, Akkari PA, Dorosz S, Boundy K, et al. 1995. A mutation in the α tropomyosin gene TPM3 associated with autosomal dominant nemaline myopathy. *Nat. Genet.* 9:75–79

Lin J-C, Warren KS, Wamboldt DD, Wang T, Lin JL-C. 1997. Tropomyosin isoforms in nonmuscle cells. *Int. Rev. Cytol.* 170:1–38

Lin Z, Eshelman J, Grund C, Fischman DA, Masaki T, et al. 1989. Differential response of myofibrillar and cytoskeletal proteins in cells treated with phorbol myristate acetate. *J. Cell Biol.* 108:1079–91

Linke WA, Ivemeyer M, Labeit S, Hinssen H, Rüegg JC, Gautel M. 1997. Actin-titin interaction in cardiac myofibrils: probing a physiological role. *Biophys. J.* 73:905–19

Liu F, Barral JM, Bauer CC, Ortiz I, Cook RG, et al. 1997. Assemblases and coupling proteins in thick filament assembly. *Cell Struct. Funct.* 22:155–62

Lorenz M, Poole KJV, Popp D, Rosenbaum G, Holmes KC. 1995. An atomic model of the unregulated thin filament obtained by X-ray fiber diffraction on oriented actin-tropomyosin gels. *J. Mol. Biol.* 246:108–19

Luo G, Zhang JQ, Nguyen T-P, Herrera AH, Paterson B, Horowits R. 1997. Complete cDNA sequence and tissue localization of N-RAP, a novel nebulin-related protein of striated muscle. *Cell Motil. Cytoskelet.* 38:75–90

Luther PK. 1991. Three-dimensional reconstruction of a simple Z-band in fish muscle. *J. Cell Biol.* 113:1043–55

Maruyama K. 1997. Connectin/titin, giant elastic protein of muscle. *FASEB J.* 11:341–45

McGough A, Way M, DeRosier D. 1994. Determination of the α-actinin-binding site on actin filaments by cryoelectron microscopy and image analysis. *J. Cell Biol.* 126:433–43

McKenna N, Meigs JB, Wang Y-L. 1985. Identical distribution of fluorescently labeled brain and muscle actins in living cardiac fibroblasts and myocytes. *J. Cell Biol.* 100:292–96

McKenna NM, Johnson CS, Wang Y-L. 1986. Formation and alignment of Z lines in living chick myotubes microinjected with rhodamine-labeled alpha-actinin. *J. Cell Biol.* 103:2163–71

Meyer RK, Aebi U. 1990. Bundling of actin filaments by α-actinin depends on its molecular length. *J. Cell Biol.* 110:2013–24

Milligan RA, Whittaker M, Safer D. 1990. Molecular structure of F-actin and location of surface binding sites. *Nature* 348:217–21

Miranda AF, Godman GC. 1973. The effects of cytochalasin D on differentiating muscle in culture. *Tissue Cell* 5:1–22

Moncman CL, Wang K. 1995. Nebulette: a 107 kD nebulin-like protein in cardiac muscle. *Cell Motil. Cytoskelet.* 32:205–25

Moncman CL, Wang K. 1996. Assembly of nebulin into the sarcomeres of avian skeletal muscle. *Cell Motil. Cytoskelet.* 34:167–84

Morris EP, Nneji G, Squire JM. 1990. The three-dimensional structure of the nemaline rod Z-band. *J. Cell Biol.* 111:2961–78

Muthuchamy M, Grupp IL, Grupp G, O'Toole BA, Kier AB, et al. 1995. Molecular and physiological effects of overexpressing striated muscle β-tropomyosin in the adult murine heart. *J. Biol. Chem.* 270:30593–603

Nagaoka R, Kusano K, Abe H, Obinata T. 1995. Effects of cofilin on actin filamentous structures in cultured muscle cells. Intracellular regulation of cofilin action. *J. Cell Sci.* 108:581–93

Nagaoka R, Minami N, Hayakawa K, Abe H, Obinata T. 1996. Quantitative analysis of low molecular weight G-actin-binding proteins, cofilin, ADF and profilin, expressed in developing and degenerating chicken skeletal muscles. *J. Muscle Res. Cell Motil.* 17:463–73

Nave R, Fürst DO, Weber K. 1990. Interaction of α-actinin and nebulin in vitro. Support for the existence of a fourth filament system in skeletal muscle. *FEBS Lett.* 269:163–66

Nicklas RB, Ward SC, Gorbsky GJ. 1995. Kinetochore chemistry is sensitive to tension and may link mitotic forces to a cell cycle checkpoint. *J. Cell Biol.* 139:929–39

Obermann WMJ, Gautel M, Steiner F, van der Ven PFM, Weber K, Fürst DO. 1996. The structure of the sarcomeric M band: localization of defined domains of myomesin, M-protein, and the 250-kD carboxy-terminal region of titin by immunoelectron microscopy. *J. Cell Biol.* 134:1441–53

Obinata T, Nagaoka-Yasuda R, Ono S, Kusano K, Mohri K, et al. 1997. Low molecular-weight G-actin binding proteins involved in the regulation of actin assembly during myofibrillogenesis. *Cell Struct. Funct.* 22:181–89

Obinata T, Shimada Y, Matsuda R. 1979. Troponin in embryonic chick skeletal muscle cells in vitro. An immunoelectron microscope study. *J. Cell Biol.* 81:59–66

Ohtsuka H, Yajima H, Maruyama K, Kimura S. 1997a. The N-terminal Z repeat 5 of connectin/titin binds to the C-terminal region of α-actinin. *Biochem. Biophys. Res. Commun.* 235:1–3

Ohtsuka H, Yajima H, Maruyama K, Kimura S. 1997b. Binding of the N-terminal 63 kDa portion of connectin/titin to α-actinin as revealed by the yeast two-hybrid system. *FEBS Lett.* 401:65–67

Ohtsuki I. 1974. Localization of troponin in thin filament and tropomyosin paracrystal. *J. Biochem.* 75:753–65

Oosawa F. 1970. Size distribution of protein polymers. *J. Theor. Biol.* 27:69–86

Oosawa F, Asakura S. 1975. *Thermodynamics of the Polymerization of Protein*, ed. B Horecker, NO Kaplan, J Marmur, HA Scheraga, pp 1–194. New York: Academic

Orlova A, Prochniewicz E, Egelman EH. 1995. Structural dynamics of F-actin: II. Cooperativity in structural transitions. *J. Mol. Biol.* 245:598–607

Papa I, Kwiatek O, Astier C, Roustan C, Benyamin Y. 1997. Purification, properties and regulation of CapZ from fish white muscle: interaction with alpha-actinin. *J. Muscle Res. Cell Motil.* 18:244 (Abstr.)

Peng I, Fischman DA. 1991. Post-translational incorporation of actin into myofibrils in vitro: evidence for isoform specificity. *Cell Motil. Cytoskelet.* 20:158–68

Pfuhl M, Winder SJ, Castiglione Morelli MA, Labeit S, Pastore A. 1996. Correlation between conformational and binding properties of nebulin repeats. *J. Mol. Biol.* 257:367–84

Pfuhl M, Winder SJ, Pastore A. 1994. Nebulin, a helical actin binding protein. *EMBO J.* 13:1782–89

Podlubnaya ZA, Tskhovrebova LA, Zaalishtsbvili MM, Stefanenko GA. 1975. Electron microscopic study of α-actinin. *J. Mol. Biol.* 92:357–59

Podolski JL, Steck TL. 1990. Length distribution of F-actin in *Dictyostelium discoideum*. *J. Biol. Chem.* 265:1312–18

Pollard TD, Cooper JA. 1986. Actin and actin-binding proteins. A critical evaluation of mechanisms and functions. *Annu. Rev. Biochem.* 55:987–1035

Prochniewicz E, Thomas DD. 1997. Perturbations of functional interactions with myosin induce long-range allosteric and cooperative structural changes in actin. *Biochemistry* 36:12845–53

Prochniewicz E, Zhang Q, Janmey PA, Thomas DD. 1996. Cooperativity in F-actin: binding of gelsolin at the barbed end affects structure and dynamics of the whole filament. *J. Mol. Biol.* 260:756–66

Reedy MC, Beall C. 1993. Ultrastructure of developing flight muscle in *Drosophila*. I. Assembly of myofibrils. *Dev. Biol.* 160:443–65

Reedy MK, Lucaveche C, Reedy MC, Somasundaram B. 1993. Experiments on rigor crossbridge action and filament sliding in insect flight muscle. In *Mechanism of Myofilament Sliding in Muscle Contraction*, ed. H Sugi, GH Pollack, pp. 33–46. New York: Plenum

Reinach FC. 1995. Nemaline myopathy mechanisms. *Nat. Genet.* 10:8

Rethinasamy P, Muthuchamy M, Hewett T, Boivin G, Wolska BM, et al. 1998. Molecular and physiological effects of α-tropomyosin ablation in the mouse. *Circ. Res.* 82:116–23

Robinson TF, Winegrad S. 1979. The measurement and dynamic implications of thin filament lengths in heart muscle. *J. Physiol.* 286:607–19

Root DD, Wang K. 1994. Calmodulin-sensitive interaction of human nebulin fragments with actin and myosin. *Biochemistry* 33:12581–91

Roulier EM, Fyrberg C, Fyrberg E. 1992. Perturbations of *Drosophila* α-actinin cause muscle paralysis, weakness, and atrophy but do not confer obvious nonmuscle phenotypes. *J. Cell Biol.* 116:911–22

Rowe RWD. 1973. The ultrastructure of Z disks from white, intermediate, and red fibers of mammalian striated muscles. *J. Cell Biol.* 57:261–77

Roy P-E, Morin PJ. 1971. Variations of the Z-band in human auricular appendages. *Lab. Invest.* 25:422–26

Sanger JM, Dabiri G, Mittal B, Kowalski MA, Haddad JG, Sanger JW. 1990. Disruption of microfilament organization in living nonmuscle cells by microinjection of plasma vitamin D-binding protein or DNase I. *Proc. Natl. Acad. Sci. USA* 87:5474–78

Sanger JM, Mittal B, Pochapin MB, Sanger JW. 1986. Myofibrillogenesis in living cells microinjected with fluorescently labeled alpha-actinin. *J. Cell Biol.* 102:2053–66

Sanger JW, Holtzer S, Holtzer H. 1971. Effects of cytochalasin B on muscle cells in tissue culture. *Nat. New Biol.* 229:121–23

Sanger JW, Mittal B, Sanger JM. 1984. Analysis of myofibrillar structure and assembly using fluorescently labeled contractile proteins. *J. Cell Biol.* 98:825–33

Schachat FH, Canine AC, Briggs MM, Reedy MC. 1985. The presence of two skeletal muscle α-actinins correlates with troponin-tropomyosin expression and Z-line width. *J. Cell Biol.* 101:1001–8

Schafer DA, Cooper JA. 1995. Control of actin assembly at filament ends. *Annu. Rev. Cell Dev. Biol.* 11:497–518

Schafer DA, Hug C, Cooper JA. 1995. Inhibition of CapZ during myofibrillogenesis alters assembly of actin filaments. *J. Cell Biol.* 128: 61–70

Schafer DA, Jennings PB, Cooper JA. 1996. Dynamics of capping protein and actin assembly in vitro: uncapping barbed ends by phosphoinositides. *J. Cell Biol.* 135:169–79

Schafer DA, Waddle JA, Cooper JA. 1993. Localization of CapZ during myofibrillogenesis in cultured chicken muscle. *Cell Motil. Cytoskelet.* 25:217–35

Schroeter JP, Bretaudiere J-P, Sass RL, Goldstein RA. 1996. Three-dimensional structure of the Z band in normal mammalian skeletal muscle. *J. Cell Biol.* 133:571–83

Schultheiss T, Choi J, Lin ZX, DiLullo C, Cohen-Gould L, et al. 1992. A sarcomeric α-actinin truncated at the carboxyl end induces the breakdown of stress fibers in PtK2 cells and the formation of nemaline-like bodies and breakdown of myofibrils in myotubes. *Proc. Natl. Acad. Sci. USA* 89:9282–86

Schultheiss T, Lin Z, Lu M-H, Murray J, Fischman DA, et al. 1990. Differential distribution of subsets of myofibrillar proteins in cardiac nonstriated and striated myofibrils. *J. Cell Biol.* 110:1159–72

Severs NJ. 1985. Intercellular junctions and the cardiac intercalated disk. In *Advances in Myocardiology*, ed. P Harris, PA Poole-Wilson, 5:223–42. New York: Plenum

Shih C-L, Chen M-JG, Linse K, Wang K. 1997. Molecular contacts between nebulin and actin: cross-linking of nebulin module to the N-terminus of actin. *Biochemistry* 36: 1814–25

Shimada Y, Suzuki H, Konno A. 1997. Dynamics of actin in cardiac myofibrils and fibroblast stress fibers. *Cell Struct. Funct.* 22:59–64

Shimizu N, Obinata T. 1986. Actin concentration and monomer-polymer ratio in developing chicken skeletal muscle. *J. Biochem.* 99: 751–59

Simpson DG, Carver W, Borg TK, Terracio L. 1994. Role of mechanical stimulation in the establishment and maintenance of muscle cell differentiation. *Int. Rev. Cytol.* 150:69–94

Small JV, Herzog M, Anderson K. 1995. Actin filament organization in fish keratocyte lamellipodium. *J. Cell Biol.* 129:1275–86

Sorimachi S, Freiburg A, Kolmerer B, Ishiura S, Stier G, et al. 1997. Tissue-specific expression and α-actinin binding properties of the Z-disc titin: implications for the nature of vertebrate Z-discs. *J. Mol. Biol.* 270:688–95

Sosa H, Popp D, Ouyang G, Huxley HE. 1994. Ultrastructure of skeletal muscle fibers studied by a plunge quick freezing method: myofilament lengths. *Biophys. J.* 67:283–92

Sparrow J, Reedy M, Ball E, Kyrtatas V, Molloy J, et al. 1991. Functional and ultrastructural effects of a missense mutation in the indirect flight muscle-specific actin gene of *Drosophila melanogaster*. *J. Mol. Biol.* 222: 963–82

Spudich JA, Huxley HE, Finch JT. 1972. Regulation of skeletal muscle contraction. II. Structural studies of the interaction of the tropomyosin-troponin complex with actin. *J. Mol. Biol.* 72:619–32

Squire J. 1981. *The Structural Basis of Muscular Contraction*. New York: Academic

Squire JM. 1997. Architecture and function in the muscle sarcomere. *Curr. Opin. Struct. Biol.* 7:247–57

Stidwill RP, Wysolmerski T, Burgess DR. 1984. The brush border cytoskeleton is not static: in vivo turnover of proteins. *J. Cell Biol.* 98: 641–45

Stokes DL, DeRosier DJ. 1991. Growth conditions control the size and order of actin bundles in vitro. *Biophys. J.* 59:456–65

Sussman MA, Baquè, Uhm C-S, Daniels MP, Price RL, et al. 1998a. Altered expression of tropomodulin in cardiomyocytes disrupts the sarcomeric structure of myofibrils. *Circ. Res.* 82:94–105

Sussman MA, Welch S, Cambon N, Klevitsky R, Hewett TE, et al. 1998b. Myofibril degeneration caused by tropomodulin overexpression leads to dilated cardiomyopathy in juvenile mice. *J. Clin. Invest.* 101:56–61

Tansey T, Schultz JR, Miller RC, Storti RV. 1991. Small differences in *Drosophila* tropomyosin expression have significant effects on muscle function. *Mol. Cell. Biol.* 11: 6337–42

Taylor KA, Reedy MC, Córdova L, Reedy MK. 1989. Three-dimensional image reconstruction of insect flight muscle I. The rigor myac layer. *J. Cell Biol.* 109:1085–102

Taylor RG, Papa I, Astier C, Ventre F, Benyamin Y, Ahmed O. 1997. Fish muscle cytoskeleton integrity is not dependent on intact thin filaments. *J. Muscle Res. Cell Motil.* 18:285–94

Theriot JA. 1994a. Regulation of the actin cytoskeleton in living cells. *Sem. Cell Biol.* 5:193–99

Theriot JA. 1994b. Actin filament dynamics in cell motility. *Adv. Exp. Med. Biol.* 358:133–45

Theriot JA, Mitchison TJ. 1991. Actin microfilament dynamics in locomoting cells. *Nature* 352:126–31

Tobacman LS. 1996. Thin filament-mediated regulation of cardiac contraction. *Annu. Rev. Physiol.* 58:447–81

Tohtong R, Yamashita H, Graham M, Haeberle J, Simcox A, Maughan D. 1995. Impairment of muscle function caused by mutations of phosphorylation sites in myosin regulatory light chain. *Nature* 374:650–53

Traeger L, Goldstein MA. 1983. Thin filaments are not of uniform length in rat skeletal muscle. *J. Cell Biol.* 96:100–3

Trinick J. 1994. Titin and nebulin: protein rulers in muscle? *Trends Biochem. Sci.* 19:405–9

Trombitás K, Greaser M, Labeit S, Jin J-P, Kellermayer M, et al. 1998. Titin extensibility in situ: entropic elasticity of permanently folded and permanently unfolded molecular segments. *J. Cell Biol.* 140:853–59

Vibert P, Craig R, Lehman W. 1997. Steric-model for activation of muscle thin filaments. *J. Mol. Biol.* 266:8–14

Vigoreaux JO. 1994. The muscle Z band: lessons in stress management. *J. Muscle Res. Cell Motil.* 15:237–55

Vikstrom KL, Leinwand LA. 1996. Contractile protein mutations and heart disease. *Curr. Opin. Cell Biol.* 8:97–105

Vikstrom KL, Seiler SH, Sohn RL, Strauss M, Weiss A, et al. 1997. The vertebrate myosin heavy chain: genetics and assembly properties. *Cell Struct. Funct.* 22:123–29

Wang K, Knipfer M, Huang Q-Q, van Heerden A, Hsu LC-L, et al. 1996. Human skeletal muscle nebulin sequence encodes a blueprint for thin filament architecture. Sequence motifs and affinity profiles of tandem repeats and terminal SH3. *J. Biol. Chem.* 271:4304–14

Wanger M, Keiser T, Neuhaus J-M, Wegner A. 1984. The actin treadmill. *Can. J. Biochem. Cell Biol.* 63:414–21

Weber A, Pennise CR, Babcock GG, Fowler VM. 1994. Tropomodulin caps the pointed ends of actin filaments. *J. Cell Biol.* 127:1627–35

Wegner A. 1979. Equilibrium of the actin-tropomyosin interaction. *J. Mol. Biol.* 131:839–53

Yagi K, Mase R, Sakakibara I, Asai H. 1965. Function of heavy meromyosin in the acceleration of actin polymerization. *J. Biol. Chem.* 240:2448–54

Yamaguchi M, Izumimoto M, Robson RM, Stromer MH. 1985. Fine structure of wide and narrow vertebrate muscle Z-lines. A proposed model and computer simulation of Z-line architecture. *J. Mol. Biol.* 184:621–44

Yamaguchi M, Robson RM, Stromer MH. 1983. Evidence for actin involvement in cardiac Z-lines and Z-line analogues. *J. Cell Biol.* 96:435–42

Yasuda K, Fujita H, Fujiki Y, Ishiwata S. 1994. Length regulation of thin filaments without nebulin. *Proc. Jpn. Acad. Sci.* 70:B151–56

Young P, Ferguson C, Bañuelos, Gautel M. 1998. Molecular structure of the sarcomeric Z-disk: two types of titin interactions lead to an asymmetrical sorting of α-actinin. *EMBO J.* 17:1614–24

Zak R, Martin AF, Prior G, Rabinowitz M. 1977. Comparison of turnover of several myofibrillar proteins and critical evaluation of double isotope method. *J. Biol. Chem.* 252:3430–35

Zhang JQ, Weisberg A, Horowits R. 1998. Expression and purification of large nebulin fragments and their interaction with actin. *Biophys. J.* 74:349–59

Zhukarev V, Sanger JM, Sanger JW, Goldman YE, Shuman H. 1997. Distribution and orientation of rhodamine-phalloidin bound to thin filaments in skeletal and cardiac myofibrils. *Cell Motil. Cytoskelet.* 37:363–77

Zigmond SH, Furukawa R, Feccheimer M. 1992. Inhibition of actin filament depolymerization by the *Dictyostelium* 30,000-D actin-bundling protein. *J. Cell Biol.* 119:559–67

SUBJECT INDEX

A

A bands
actin filament length in striated
muscle and, 514
ABC model
specification of leaf identity
during shoot development,
389–90, 393
ABF2 gene
mitochondrial dynamics in
yeast and, 290–91
Abscisic acid
specification of leaf identity
during shoot development,
380–81
systemin and, 2, 9–10
Acanthamoeba castellanii
pathogens and actin
cytoskeleton, 155
Accessory proteins
bioluminescence and, 197,
201
phosphoinositide signaling and,
238
Acid phosphatase
isoform sorting and intracellular
compartments, 346–47
Aconitase
translation initiation control in
animals and, 435
ACT1 gene
mitochondrial dynamics in
yeast and, 272, 276
actA gene
pathogens and actin
cytoskeleton, 150–54,
156–57
Actin cytoskeleton
bacterial entry into mammalian
cells
actA gene, 150–54, 156–57
bacterial factors, 150
Bartonella henselae, 148
cellular factors, 153–56
extracellular bacteria,
158–59
icsA gene, 153–54, 156–57
introduction, 138–39
Listeria monocytogenes,
150–54, 156–57
Listeria spp., 141–42
motility, 148–59
morphology, 149–50
Neisseria spp., 144–45

phosphoinositide signaling
and, 247
Salmonella spp., 145–46
Shigella flexneri, 153–54,
156–57
Shigella spp., 146–48
thermodynamics, 149–50
tight junction and, 101–2
trigger-type mechanism,
145–48
vaccinia virus, 156, 158
Yersinia spp., 142–44
zipper mechanism, 139,
141–45
isoform sorting and intracellular
compartments, 340,
342–49, 355, 357–60,
362–63, 365
mitochondrial dynamics in
yeast and, 275–78
signaling to
actin-binding proteins,
307–11
actin folding, 307
actin polymerization,
308
assembly control, 307–11
Cdc42 protein, 317–24
cell cycle in yeast, 311–13
cell proliferation, 321
functions, 306–7
future research, 327
introduction, 306
organization, 311–13
Rac proteins, 317–21
Rho GTPases, 314–17,
321–27
Rho proteins, 317–27
switching, 314–17
tight junction and, 102
translation initiation control in
animals and, 428, 432
Actin-binding proteins
isoform sorting and intracellular
compartments, 344–45
Actin-capping protein
isoform sorting and intracellular
compartments, 344
Actin-dependent motors
mitochondrial dynamics in
yeast and, 276–77
Actin depolymerizing factor
(ADF)
actin filament length in striated
muscle and, 497

signaling to actin cytoskeleton
and, 308–11
Actin filament length
in striated muscle
actin filament stability and
dynamics in thin filaments,
496–98
α-actinin, 500–3
actin polymerization and
length distributions,
489–95
barbed ends, 498–503
CapZ, 499–500
free portion, 503–18
introduction, 488–89
length-dependent regulation,
492–93
myosin, 512–18
nebulin, 509–12
pointed end, 503–18
resting length sarcomeres,
515–18
ruler mechanism, 493–95
scaffold mechanism, 494–95,
513–15
titin, 512–18
tropomodulin, 504–6
tropomyosin, 506–9
troponin, 506–9
vernier mechanism, 493–95
Z line, 498–503
α-Actinin
actin filament length in striated
muscle and, 487, 496,
498–503, 514
pathogens and actin
cytoskeleton, 140, 143,
146, 154–55
phosphoinositide signaling and,
240
Activation
muscle gene regulation by
myocyte enhancer factor-2,
182–83
translation initiation control in
animals and, 425–26
unfolded protein response and,
477–78
Wnt gene signaling and,
59
Acute-phase response
systemin and, 1, 12–13
Adaptors
phosphoinositide signaling and,
244–56

527

CUMULATIVE INDEXES

CONTRIBUTING AUTHORS, VOLUMES 10–14

CHAPTER TITLES, VOLUMES 10–14